Milankovitch and Climate

Understanding the Response to Astronomical Forcing

NATO ASI Series

Advanced Science Institutes Series

A series presenting the results of activities sponsored by the NATO Science Committee, which aims at the dissemination of advanced scientific and technological knowledge, with a view to strengthening links between scientific communities.

The series is published by an international board of publishers in conjunction with the NATO Scientific Affairs Division

A	Life Sciences	Plenum Publishing Corporation
B	Physics	London and New York
C	Mathematical and Physical Sciences	D. Reidel Publishing Company Dordrecht, Boston and Lancaster
D	Behavioural and Social Sciences	Martinus Nijhoff Publishers
E	Engineering and Materials Sciences	The Hague, Boston and Lancaster
F	Computer and Systems Sciences	Springer-Verlag
G	Ecological Sciences	Berlin, Heidelberg, New York and Tokyo

Series C: Mathematical and Physical Sciences Vol. 126 Part 1

Milankovitch and Climate

Understanding the Response to Astronomical Forcing

edited by

A. Berger

Institut d'Astronomie et de Géophysique Georges Lemaitre,
Université Catholique de Louvain-la-Neuve, Belgium

J. Imbrie

Department of Geological Sciences,
Brown University, Providence, Rhode Island, U.S.A.

J. Hays

Lamont-Doherty Geological Observatory,
Columbia University, Palisades, New York, U.S.A.

G. Kukla

Lamont-Doherty Geological Observatory,
Columbia University, Palisades, New York, U.S.A.

B. Saltzman

Department of Geology and Geophysics,
Yale University, New Haven, Connecticut, U.S.A.

D. Reidel Publishing Company

Dordrecht / Boston / Lancaster

Published in cooperation with NATO Scientific Affairs Division

Proceedings of the NATO Advanced Research Workshop on
Milankovitch and Climate
Palisades, New York, U.S.A.
November 30 – December 4, 1982

Library of Congress Cataloging in Publication Data

Milankovitch and climate.

(NATO ASI Series. Series C, Mathematical and physical sciences; 126)
"Proceedings of the NATO Advanced Research Workshop on Milankovitch and Climate, Lamont-Doherty Geological Observatory, Palisades, N.Y., November 30-December 4, 1982, CIP t.p. verso.
Includes index.
1. Paleoclimatology—Congresses. 2. Astrophysics—Congresses. 3. Milankovitch, Milutin. I. Berger, A. (André), 1942- . II. NATO Advanced Research Workshop on Milankovitch and Climate (1983 : Lamont-Doherty Geological Observatory) III. Series.
QC884.M55 1984 551.6 84-6805
ISBN 90-277-1777-X (Part 1)
ISBN 90-277-1778-8 (Part 2)
ISBN 90-277-1791-5 (Set)

Published by D. Reidel Publishing Company
P.O. Box 17, 3300 AA Dordrecht, Holland

Sold and distributed in the U.S.A. and Canada
by Kluwer Academic Publishers,
190 Old Derby Street, Hingham, MA 02043, U.S.A.

In all other countries, sold and distributed
by Kluwer Academic Publishers Group,
P.O. Box 322, 3300 AH Dordrecht, Holland

D. Reidel Publishing Company is a member of the Kluwer Academic Publishers Group

Printed in The Netherlands.

TABLE OF CONTENTS

INTRODUCTION.. ix
LIST OF PARTICIPANTS...................................... xvi
MILANKOVITCH V. - The Memory of my Father.............. xxiii

PART I - ORBITAL AND INSOLATION VARIATIONS

BERGER A. - Accuracy and frequency stability of the Earth's orbital elements during the Quaternary...... 3
BRETAGNON P. - Accuracy of long term planetary theory... 41
BUYS M. and M. GHIL - Mathematical methods of celestial mechanics illustrated by simple models of planetary motion.. 55
BERGER A. and P. PESTIAUX - Accuracy and stability of the Quaternary terrestrial insolation............... 83
TAYLOR K.E. - Fourier representations of orbitally induced perturbations in seasonal insolation.......... 113

PART II - GEOLOGICAL EVIDENCE FOR LONG-TERM CLIMATIC VARIATIONS AT ASTRONOMICAL FREQUENCIES

Section 1 - Pre-Pleistocene evidence of orbital forcing 127

OLSEN P.E. - Periodicity of lake-level cycles in the Late Triassic Lockatong formation of the Newark basin (Newark supergroup, New Jersey and Pennsylvania...... 129
ANDERSON R.Y. - Orbital forcing of evaporite sedimentation... 147
FISCHER A.G. and W. SCHWARZACHER - Cretaceous bedding rhythms under orbital control ? 163
de BOER P.L. and A.A.H. WONDERS - Astronomically induced rhythmic bedding in Cretaceous pelagic sediments near Moria (Italy)..................................... 177
ARTHUR M.A., W.E. DEAN, D. BOTTJER and P.A. SCHOLLE - Rhythmic bedding in Mesozoic-Cenozoic pelagic carbonate sequences : the primary and diagenetic origin of Milankovitch-like cycles........................... 191

FILLON R.H. - Ice-age Arctic ocean ice-sheets : a possible direct link with insolation 223
HERMAN Y. and J.K. OSMOND - Late Neogene Arctic paleoceanography : micropaleontology and chronology....... 241
PANTIĆ N. and D. STEFANOVIĆ - Complex interaction of cosmic and geological events that affect the variation of Earth climate through the geologic history.. 251
DEAN W.E. and J.V. GARDNER - Cyclic variations in calcium carbonate and organic carbon in Miocene to Holocene sediments, Walvis Ridge, South Atlantic ocean.. 265

Section 2 - Marine Pleistocene Records of Climatic Response.. 267

IMBRIE J., J.D. HAYS, D.G. MARTINSON, A. McINTYRE, A.C. MIX, J.J. MORLEY, N.G. PISIAS, W.L. PRELL and N.J. SHACKLETON - The orbital theory of Pleistocene climate : support from a revised chronology of the marine $\delta^{18}O$ record.................................. 269
PISIAS N.G. and M. LEINEN - Milankovitch forcing of the oceanic system : evidence from the northwest Pacific. 307
JANECEK T.R. and D.K. REA - Pleistocene fluctuations in northern hemisphere tradewinds and westerlies........ 331
PRELL W.L. - Monsoonal climate of the Arabian sea during the Late Quaternary : a response to changing solar radiation.. 349
ROSSIGNOL-STRICK M. - Immediate climate response to orbital insolation : Mediterranean sapropels and the African monsoon.................................. 367

Section 3 - Non-Marine Records of Pleistocene Climate... 369

HOOGHIEMSTRA H. - A Palynological registration of climatic change of the last 3.5 million years........... 371
AHARON P. - Implications of the coral-reef record from New Guinea concerning the astronomical theory of ice ages.. 379
MOLFINO B., L.H. HEUSSER and G.M. WOILLARD - Frequency components of a Grande Pile pollen record : evidence of precessional orbital forcing.................... 391
KANARI S., N. FUJI, and S. HORIE - The Paleoclimatological constituents of paleotemperature in lake Biwa.... 405

Section 4 - Estimation of Geologic Spectra.............. 415

PESTIAUX P. and A. BERGER - An optimal approach to the spectral characteristics of deep-sea climatic records.. 417

HERTERICH K. and M. SARNTHEIN - Brunhes time scale : tuning by rates of calcium-carbonate dissolution and cross spectral analyses with solar insolation........ 447

MORLEY J.J. and N.J. SHACKLETON - The effect of accumulation rate on the spectrum of geologic time series : evidence from two south atlantic sediment cores...... 467

DALFES H.N., S.H. SCHNEIDER and S.L. THOMPSON - Effects of bioturbation on climatic spectra inferred from deep-sea cores.................................... 481

PESTIAUX P. and A. BERGER - Impacts of deep-sea processes on paleoclimatic spectra........................ 493

INTRODUCTION

At an International Symposium held at Lamont-Doherty Geological Observatory, Palisades, N.Y., during the first week of December, over 100 scientists met to consider one of the classic, unsolved geophysical problems: the origin of the Pleistocene ice ages. The meeting was focused on the theory of ice-age climates proposed during the 1930's by the Yugoslav mathematician Milutin Milankovitch.

The Symposium was both a workshop sponsored by NATO and a symposium sponsored by the International Commission on Climate (ICCL) of the International Association of Meteorology and Atmospheric Physics (IAMAP), the U.S. National Science Foundation, and the Paleoclimatic Commission of the International Union for Quaternary Research (INQUA), and Lamont-Doherty Geological Observatory (L-DGO) of Columbia University.

The essence of the Milankovitch theory is that the major fluctuations in global climate associated with the ice-age cycle are caused by variations in the pattern of incoming solar radiation - variations that are, in turn, caused by slow changes in the geometry of the earth's orbit that occur in response to predictable changes in the gravitational field experienced by the Earth.

The special appeal of the astronomical climate theory consists of its ability to supply climate modelers with accurate data on time-related changes of the main climate forcing variable. However, until around 1970, this theory was controversial, in part, because discussions were based on incomplete and poorly dated geological records, and in part because they were based on insolation curves which were of uncertain accuracy and which represented only a limited range of latitudes and seasons (primarily summer, 65°N). Moreover, the theory was apparently in conflict with substantial geological evidence that the two hemispheres entered and left glacial states at approximately the same time.

Despite improvements in geologic dating and in interpreting the geological data in terms of paleoclimate, and despite the use of other insolation curves, only partial answers to many fundamental questions were obtained by the mid-70's. Among these questions are the following :

1) Do the calculations which describe insolation history give reliable results ?

A. L. Berger et al. (eds.), Milankovitch and Climate, Part 1, ix–xiii.

2) Are the quasi-periodicities of the Earth's orbital elements represented by significant concentrations of variance in climatic spectra ?
3) Is there significant correlation and phase coherency between insolation and geological curves ?
4) Can these insolation changes induce climatic changes of a magnitude similar to those which have been recorded in geological data ? If so, what physical mechanisms are involved?

Since the mid 1970s, attempts to approach these problems quantitatively have intensified, and much progress has been made. The main scientific objective of the meeting was to evaluate these efforts, in particular the rapid progress made in understanding and modelling the physical mechanisms by which the climate system responds to orbital variations. An additional objective was to honor the pioneer work of Milutin Milankovitch.

Some 38 papers and 15 posters were presented by an international group of experts which included 20 physical scientists from many of the major institutions of meteorology, climate dynamics, oceanography and glaciology. These papers include several which present original results obtained from numerical climate models. Such modelling experiments are important because they go beyond statistical correlations and deal directly with ideas about physical mechanisms.

One aim of the meeting was to review the geologic evidence that, during recent years, has made it clear that at least part of the observed variations in Pleistocene climate are driven in some way by the Milankovitch mechanism. One lecture session on the marine record and one poster session on the nonmarine record were devoted to this end. The oxygen isotopic record, which serves as a proxy for fluctuations in global ice volume, shows that 60±10 per cent of the total observed isotopic variance is coherent with calculated variations in the Earth's orbit over the past 800 000 years, this coherent behaviour being observed at four of the main forcing periods : 100 000 years, a period associated with variations in orbital eccentricity; 41 000 years, a period associated with variations in obliquity; and 23 000 and 19 000 years, periods associated with variations in the precession of the equinoxes. Micropaleontological and mineralogical record from deep-sea cores reveal also that the climatic response to orbital variations has a different spatial character, depending on the frequency band under investigation.

Evidence presented at the session devoted to the estimation of climatic spectra made it clear (i) that the coherency of orbital and climatic variables in the 100 000-yr (eccentricity) band is enhanced significantly when the geologic records are tuned precisely in the 41 000-yr (obliquity), and 23 000-yr and 19 000-yr (precession) bands; (ii) that the 100 000-yr cycle, so dominant a feature of the late Pleistocene record, does not exhibit a constant amplitude over the past 3 million years; and (iii) that improved methods of data analysis now make it possible to take variable sedimentation rates and step-wise variations of climate into account.

Another purpose was to review the geological evidence which now suggests to some investigators that orbitally-driven climatic variations occurred in pre-Pleistocene times. One day was devoted to this topic, with presentations based on data from Triassic red-bed sequences in New Jersey; Permian evaporite deposits in New Mexico; Cretaceous limestone sequences in Europe; and deep-sea Miocene and Pliocene deposits from the North Atlantic. That rhythmically bedded deposits occur in these pre-Pleistocene sequences is obvious from the data presented.

Another conference objective was to assess the accuracy of the astronomical part of the theory, particularly with regard to the dependability of calculations of orbital variations made for intervals of time many millions of years in the past. One lecture session was devoted to this topic. One conclusion was that the calculations made so far can be trusted back to several millions of years into the past. But for older epochs, the mathematical machinery employed (trigonometrical solutions of the Lagrangian equations of planetary motion) is not yet capable of producing reliable values. One approach is to develop a more general theory from which the frequencies and possibly the phases of key orbital variations could be deduced. Another is to use the geologic record to obtain estimates of past variation frequencies, and use these estimates to constrain the predictions made by celestial mechanics.

The main focus of the meeting was a review and an evaluation of the progress made in understanding and modelling the physical mechanisms by which the climate-system responds to the calculated changes in the pattern of incoming solar radiation. For it is in this area that recent progress by members of the numerical modeling community has been most rapid, and it is here that the need for interactions between geologists on the one hand, and theoreticians of climate on the other, is most needed.

One session was devoted to relatively simple energy balance models, i.e., models in which the atmospheric transport of energy is not explicitly resolved into cyclones and jets, but is parameterized by eddy diffusion coefficients. The results of one model were of particular interest, in that its response to varying the orbital boundary conditions simulated reasonably well the observed geographic distribution of Northern Hemisphere ice sheets during the last glacial maximum, 18 000 years ago. The key to this model's performance was the specification of a global field of heat-capacity values, a feature that made it possible to simulate realistically the modern (as well as ice-age) seasonal cycles.

One modelling session was devoted to models with an ice sheet, as well as an atmosphere and an ocean. The main focus of presentations was the problem of the observed 100 000-year ice--volume cycle, and how it might be derived by free-oscillation tendencies in a model that allowed a growing ice sheet to be isostatically compensated. One key question, it developed, is the time constant of that isostatic response, a parameter that in turn depends on mantle viscosity.

General circulation models of the atmosphere, and their application to the problem of the ice ages, was the subject of another session. One result of particular interest was that by changing the orbital configuration to a time of 9 000 years ago- a time of stronger northern hemisphere summer insolation - the model simulates a more energetic circulation of the Indian Monsoon. Such a feature of the geologic record is now well documented by a study of African lake levels, Indian Ocean sediment cores, and pollen records from India. Another important result was the first simulation of an abortive glaciation forced only by the astronomical change in the seasonal distribution of insolation between 125 000 and 115 000 yr BP.

One modelling session dealt with oscillator models of climate, i.e. models in which nests of negative and positive feedbacks produce limit cycles, or at least tendencies to self-oscillate at various frequencies. Using bifurcation and singular perturbation analysis, it was also shown that in the absence of systematic forcing, climatic fluctuations tend to deregulate the oscillatory behaviour. The presence of the forcing, on the other hand, allows the system to stabilize the oscillations and to amplify the response through resonance.

Another session dealt with conceptual models of the climatic response to orbital variation. One model showed that the geochemical responses of the ocean to changing sea level might yield changes in the atmospheric levels of carbon dioxide, and thus act to amplify variations in climate driven by Milankovitch or other mechanisms. Another was presented in which changes in the latitudinal gradient of insolation drive changes in poleward heat transport by the Atlantic Ocean.

A final chapter is devoted to summarizing the conference, drawing conclusions, and making recommendations for future work. This chapter is the result of a workshop in which 30 scientists participated.

Finally, a fitting tribute to Milutin Milankovitch was paid at the conference dinner, when Vasco Milankovitch, son of Milutin, gave an informal talk in which he recalled his childhood memories of life in Belgrade. These memories included scenes from the Milankovitch household, where much of his father's work was done. Many scientists present at this dinner were deeply moved by this opportunity to catch these glimpses of scholarly life as it was lived in Europe in the days before World War II, and to observed one of the great creative scientists of our age at work.

ACKNOWLEDGMENTS

In the early stage of the preparation of the symposium, the chairmen, A. Berger (UCL, Belgium) and J. Imbrie (Brown University, USA), received the strong support of an International Scientific Committee whose members were: J. Chappell (Australia), K. Hasselman (FRG), J.D. Hays (USA), A. Hecht (USA), Sir John Mason (U.K.), J.M. Mitchell,Jr. (USA), A. Monin (USSR), R. Newell (USA), P. Savis (Yugoslavia).

In addition to the co-chairmen, the Local Committee was comprised of R.M. Cline, J.D. Hays, G. Kukla and A. McIntyre. Warm thanks are due to all four, and to Dr. B. Raleigh, director of L-DGO, for providing us with the facilities of Lamont.

The financial support of NATO (Advanced Research Workshops Programme-ARW 20/82), U.S. NSF, ICCL, INQUA Paleo Cl3 and L-DGO is greatly acknowledged. Thanks also are due to the NATO Special Programme Panel on Air-Sea Interactions for having supported the idea of such a workshop.

We are grateful to our reviewers and to a number of people who were involved in the technical production of the book. Among them special thanks are due for the considerable work done by Mrs N. Materne-Depoorter, MM. Tchen Tse Viet, B. Saintes, M. Adami, Mrs L. Moens and all the members of the Institute of Astronomy and Geophysics G. Lemaître of the Catholic University in Louvain-la-Neuve.

The Editors, March 1984.

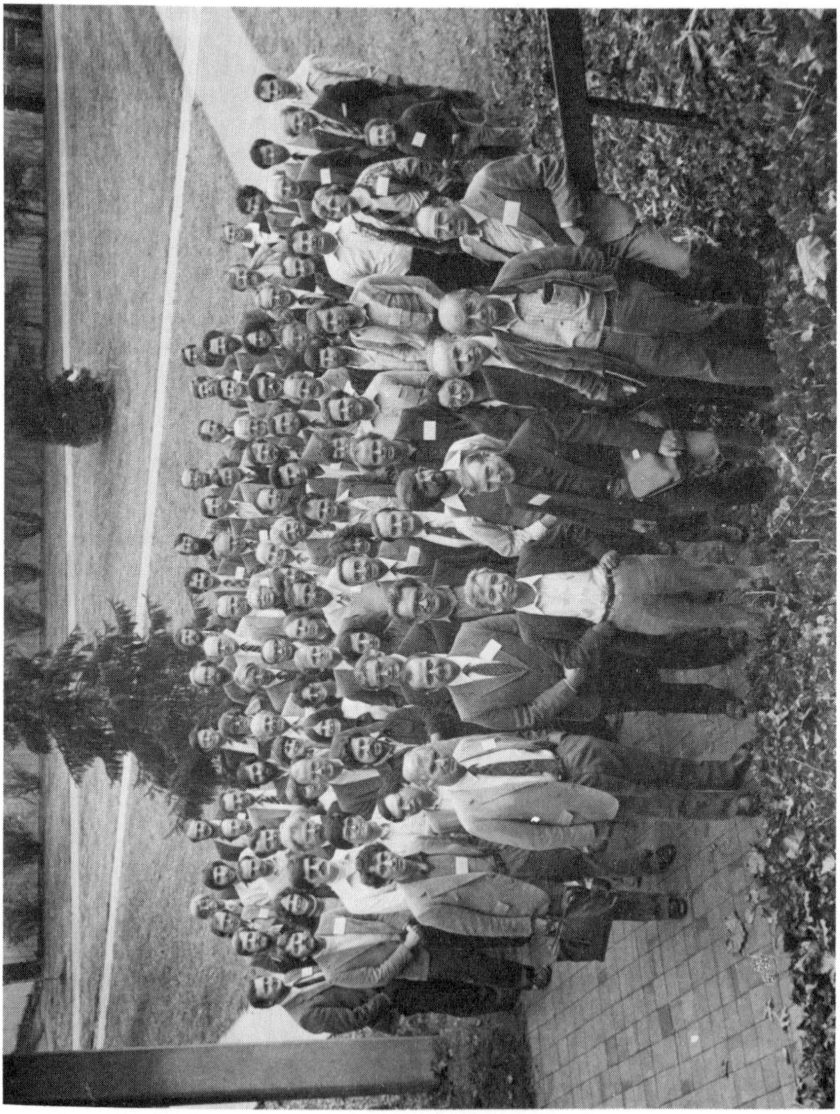

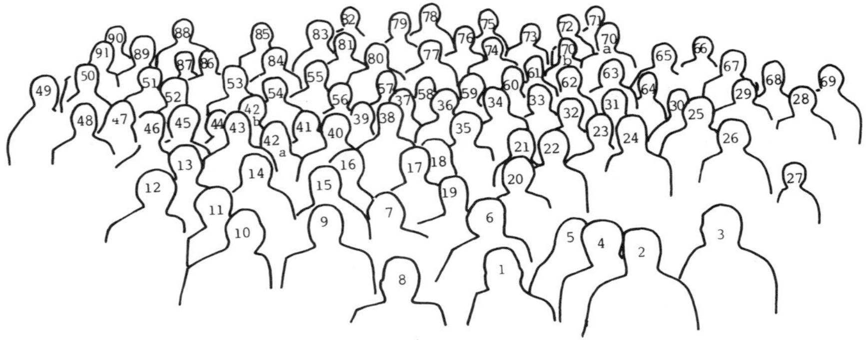

1. Imbrie J., 2. Milankovitch V., 3. Berger A., 4. McIntyre A., 5. Molfino B., 6. Jones G.,
7. Pantic N., 8. Manabe S., 9. Etkins R., 10. Fairbridge R., 11. Peltier W.R., 12. Schneider S.,
13. Streeter H., 14. Zimmerman H., 15. Crowley T.J., 16. Nicolis C., 17. Adem J., 18. Schramm C.T.,
19. Hutson W., 20. Ruddiman W.F., 21. Muzinski I., 22. Harvey D., 23. Pollard D.,
24. Hooghiemstra H., 25. Pisias N., 26. Mix A., 27. Herterich K., 28. Folland C., 29. Johnson R.G.,
30. Aharon P., 31. Kanari S.I., 32. Prell W., 33. Sarnthein M., 34. Schlesinger M.E., 35. Ghil M.,
36. North G.R., 37. Covey C., 38. MacCracken M., 39. Shackleton N.J., 40. Kerr R.A., 41. Herman Y.,
42a. Ledley T.S., 42b. Rossignol-Strick M., 43. Mitchell J.M., 44. Heusser L., 45. Hays J.D.,
46. Start G.G., 47. Leinen M., 48. Hodel M., 49. de Boer P.L., 50. Martinson D.G., 51. Sutera A.,
52. Rea D.K., 53. Dalfes N., 54. , 55. Deprit A., 56. Fong P., 57. Briskin M., 58. ,
59. Duplessy J.C., 60. Boyle E., 61. Eliasen E., 62. Pestiaux P., 63. Held I., 64. Bloom A.L.,
65. Birchfield E., 66. Weertman J., 67. Warren S., 68. , 69. Taylor K., 70a. Adam D.P.,
70b. Kutzbach J.E., 71. Laurmann J., 72. Schnitker D., 73. Fillon R.H., 74. Webb T., 75. Sellers W.D.,
76. , 77. Clark D.L., 78. Anderson R.Y., 79. Bowman K., 80. Guetter P., 81. James P.,
82. Arthur M.A., 83. , 84. Hansen T., 85. Watts R.G., 86. Saltzman B., 87. Royer J.F.,
88. Le Treut H., 89. Gaspar Ph., 90. Jouzel J., 91. van Ypersele J.P.

LIST OF PARTICIPANTS

ADAM D.
MAIL STOP 75
U.S. GEOLOGICAL SURVEY
345 MIDDLEFIELD ROAD
MENLO PARK CA 94025
U.S.A.

ADEM J.
CENTRO DE CIENCIAS DE LA
ATMOSFERA
CIRCUITO EXTERIOR
CIUDAD UNIVERSITARIA
MEXICO 20 D.F.
MEXICO

AHARON P.
DEPT. OF GEOLOGY
LOUISIANA STATE UNIVERSITY
BATON ROUGE, LA 70803
U.S.A.

ANDERSON R.Y
DEPARTMENT OF GEOLOGY
UNIVERSITY OF NEW MEXICO
ALBUQUERQUE
N.M. 87131
U.S.A

ARTHUR M.A.
GRADUATE SCHOOL
OF OCEANOGRAPHY
UNIV. OF RHODE ISLAND
NARRAGANSETT
R.I. 02882
U.S.A

BERGER A.
INSTITUT D'ASTRONOMIE ET
DE GEOPHYSIQUE
UNIVERSITE CATHOLIQUE DE LOUVAIN
2 CHEMIN DU CYCLOTRON
1348 LOUVAIN-LA-NEUVE
BELGIQUE

BIRCHFIELD G.E.
DEPARTMENT OF GEOLOGICAL SCIENCES,
LAY HALL
NORTHWESTERN UNIVERSITY- EVANSTON,
ILLINOIS 60201
U.S.A.

BLOOM A.L.
CORNELL UNIVERSITY
DEPARTMENT OF GEOLOGICAL SC.
211 KIMBALL HALL
ITHACA, N.Y. 14853
U.S.A.

BOWMAN K.P.
GEOPHYSICAL FLUID DYNAMICS PROGRAM
P.O. BOX 308
PRINCETON NJ 08540
U.S.A.

BOYLE E.
DEPARTMENT OF EARTH AND PLANETARY
SCIENCES
MASSACHUSETTS INSTITUTE OF TECHNOLOGY
CAMBRIDGE, MA 02139
U.S.A.

BRADLEY R.S.
DEPT. OF GEOLOGY GEOGRAPHY
MORRILL SCIENCE CENTER SO
UNIV. OF MASSACHUSETTS
AMHERST MASS 01003
U.S.A.

BRETAGNON P.
OBSERVATOIRE DU BUREAU DES LONGITUDES
77 AV. DEMFERT-ROCHEREAU
F- 75014 PARIS
FRANCE

BRISKIN M.
DEPT. OF GEOLOGY
UNIVERSITY OF CINCINNATI
CINCINNATI, OHIO 45221
U.S.A.

BROCCOLI A.J.
NOAA/GFDL
P.O. BOX 308
PRINCETON, NJ 08540
U.S.A.

BROECKER W.S.
LAMONT DOHERTY GEOLOGICAL OBSERVATORY
COLUMBIA UNIVERSITY
PALISADES NEW YORK 10964
U.S.A.

BUYS M.
DEPT. OF MATH. & STAT.
HUMANITIES BUILDING 419
THE UNIV. OF MEXICO
ALBUQUERQUE, NM 871331
U.S.A.

CLARK D.L.
DEPT. OF GEOLOGY & GEOPHYSICS
UNIV. OF WISCONSIN
MADISON, WI 53706
U.S.A.

COVEY C.C.
NCAR
P.O. BOX 3000
BOULDER, CO 80307
U.S.A.

CROWLEY T.
DEPT. OF PHYSICS
UNIVERSITY OF MISSOURI - ST. LOUIS
8001 NATURAL BRIDGE RD.
ST. LOUIS, MISSOURI 63121
U.S.A.

DALFES N.
NCAR
PO. BOX 3000
BOULDER COL 80307
U.S.A.

DEAN W.E.
U.S. DEPT.
U.S. GEOLOGICAL SURVEY
BOX 25046 M.S. 940
DENVER, CO 80225
U.S.A.

DE BOER P.L.
RIJKSUNIVERSITEIT UTRECHT
INSTITUUT VOOR AARDWETENSCHAPPEN
BUDAPESTLAAN 4
POSTBUS 80.021
3508 TA UTRECHT
NEDERLAND

DEPRIT A.
NATIONAL BUREAU OF STANDARDS
WASHINGTON, D.C. 20234
U.S.A.

DUPLESSY J.C.
CENTRE DES FAIBLES RADIOACTIVITES
LABORATOIRE MIXTE CNRS/CEA
GIF SUR YVETTE 91190
FRANCE

ELIASEN E.
UNIVERSITY OF COPENHAGEN
INST. OF THEORETICAL METEOROLOGY
HARALDSGADE 6
DK 2200 COPENHAGEN N
DANEMARK

ETKINS R.
NCPO/NOAA
6010 EXECUTIVE BLVD.
ROCKVILLE, MD 20852
U.S.A.

FAIRBANKS R.G.
LDGO
PALISADES, NY 10964
U.S.A.

FAIRBRIDGE R.
DEPT, OF GEOLOGICAL SCIENCE
SCHERMERHORN HALL 604
COLUMBIA UNIVERSITY IN THE CITY
OF NEW YORK
NEW YORK 10027
U.S.A.

FILLON R.H.
BELLE BARUCH INST.
AND DEPT. OF GEOLOGY
UNIVERSITY OF SOUTH CAROLINA
COLUMBIA, SC 29208
U.S.A.

FISCHER A.
DEPT. OF GEOLO. AND GEOPHY. SCIENCES
PRINCETON UNIVERSITY
PRINCETON, NEW JERSEY 08540
U.S.A.

FOLLAND C.K.
ROYAL METEOROLOGICAL SOCIETY
LONDON ROAD
BRACKNELL, BERKS, RG12 2SZ
U.K.

FONG P.
DEPARTMENT OF PHYSICS
EMORY UNIVERSITY
ATLANTA, GEORGIA 30322
U.S.A.

GASPAR P.
INSTITUT D'ASTRONOMIE ET
DE GEOPHYSIQUE
UNIVERSITE CATHOLIQUE DE LOUVAIN
2 CHEMIN DU CYCLOTRON
1348 LOUVAIN-LA-NEUVE
BELGIQUE

GHIL M.
NEW YORK UNIVERSITY
COURANT INST. OF MATHEMATICAL SC.
251 MERCER STR.
NEW YORK NY 10012
U.S.A.

GUADAGNINI J.
LDGO
PALISADES, NY 10964
U.S.A.

GUETTER P.J.
CENTER FOR CLIMATIC RESEARCH
INST. FOR ENVIRONMENTAL STUDIES
UNIV. OF WISCONSIN-MADISON
1225 WEST DAYTON STREET
MADISON, WI 53706
U.S.A.

HARVEY L.D.
N.C.A.R.
P.O. BOX 3000
BOULDER, CO 80307
U.S.A.

HAYDER M.D.
DEPT. OF AEROSPACE AND
MECHANICAL ENGINEERING
PRINCETON UNIVERSITY
PRINCETON, N.JERSEY
U.S.A.

HAYS J.
LAMONT DOHERTY GEOLOGICAL OBSERVATORY
COLUMBIA UNIVERSITY
PALISADES NEW YORK 10964
U.S.A.

HELD I.
GEOPHYSI. FLUID DYNA. LAB.
NOAA PRINCETON UNIVERSTITY
P.O. BOX 308
PRINCETON, NEW JERSEY 08540
U.S.A.

HERMAM Y.
DEPT. OF GEOLOGY
WASHINGTON STATE UN.
PULLMAN WASHINGTON 99163
U.S.A.

HERTERICH K.
MAX-PLANCK- INSTITUT FUR METEOROLOGIE
BUNDESSTRASSE 55
2000 HAMBURG 13
W-GERMANY

HEUSSER L.E.
LAMONT-DOHERTY GEOLOGICAL OBSERVATORY
OF COLUMBIA UNIVERSITY
PALISADES, N.Y. 10964
U.S.A.

HOOGHIEMSTRA H.
UNIVERSITEIT VAN AMSTERDAM
HUGO DE VRIES LABORATORIUM
SEKTIE PALYNOLOGIE & PALEOCOLOGIE
SARPHATISTRAAT 221
NL- 1018 EX AMSTERDAM
NEDERLAND

HORIE S.
INSTITUTE OF PALEOCLIMATOLOGY
AND PALEOENVIRONMENT ON LAKE BIWA
KYOTO UNIVERSITY
KYOTO
JAPAN

HUTSON W.
BELL LABS
WHIPPANY, NJ 07981
U.S.A.

HYDE W.
UNIVERSIY OF TORONTO
TORONTO,ONTARIO M5S 1A7
CANADA

IMBRIE J.
DEPT OF GEOLOGICAL SCIENCES
BROWN UNIVERSITY
PROVIDENCE
RHODE ISLAND 02912
U.S.A.

JACOBY G.
LDGO
PALISADES, NY 10964
U.S.A.

JAMES P.
PHYSICS DEPT.
UNIV. MISSOURI-ST. LOUIS
ST. LOUIS, MO 63121
U.S.A.

JANECEK T.R.
LAMONT-DOHERTY
GEOLOGICAL OBSERVATORY
OF COLUMBIA UNIVERSITY
PALISADES, NY 10964
U.S.A.

JOHNSON D.A.
WOODS HOLE OCEANOGRAPHIC INSTITUTION
WOODS HOLE, MA 02543
U.S.A.

JOHNSON R.G.
HONEYWELL CORPORATE TECHNOLOGY CENTER
10701 LYNDALE AVE. S.
BLOOMINGTON, MN 55420
U.S.A

JONES G.
LDGO
PALISADES, NY 10964
U.S.A.

JOUZEL J.
LABO. DE GEOCHIMIE ISOTOPIQUE
DPC/SP
CEN SACLAY
F-01191 GIF-SUR-YVETTE CEDEX
FRANCE

KANARI SEI-ICHI
DEPT OF GEOPHYSICS
HOKKAIDO UNIVERSITY
HOKKAIDO
JAPAN

KERR R.A.
SCIENCE MAGAZINE
1515 MASSACHUSETTS AVE.
WASHINGTON, DC 20005
U.S.A.

KUKLA G.
LAMONT DOHERTY GEOLOGICAL OBSERVATORY
COLUMBIA UNIVERSITY
PALISADES NEW YORK 10964
U.S.A.

KUTZBACH J.E.
UNIVERSITY OF WISCONSIN
CENTER FOR CLIMATIC RESEARCH
1225 WEST DAYTON STREET
MADISON, WISCONSIN 53706
U.S.A.

LAURMANN J.A.
GAS RESEARCH INST.
8600 W. BRYMAWR AVENUE
CHICAGO, IL 60631
U.S.A.

LAZARUS D.
LDGO
PALISADES, NY 10964
U.S.A.

LEDLEY T.S
RICE UNIVERSITY
DEPARTMENT OF SPACE PHYSICS
AND ASTRONOMY
P.O. BOX 1892
HOUSTON TEXAS 77251
U.S.A.

LEINEN M.
GSO
UNIV. OF RI
NARRAGANSETT, RI 02882
U.S.A.

LE TREUT H.
LAB. METEORO. DYN.
ECOLE NORMALE SUPERIEURE
RUE LHOMOND 24
F-75005 PARIS
FRANCE

MANABE S.
GEOPHYSICAL FLUID DYNAMICS LAB. NOAA
PRINCETON UNIVERSITY
P.O. BOX 308
PRINCETON NEW JERSEY 08540
U.S.A.

MARTISON D.G.
WHOI
WOODS HOLE, MA 02543
U.S.A.

MCCRACKEN M.C.
DEPUTY DIV. LEADER
ATM. S GEOPHYS. SC. DIVISION
PHYSICS DEPT. LAWRENCE LIVERMORE LAB.
UNIVERSITY OF CALIFORNIA
1470 DARWIN AVE. ,P.O. BOX 808
LIVERMORE, CA 94550
U.S.A.

MCINTYRE A.
LAMONT DOHERTY GEOLOGICAL OBS.
COLUMBIA UNIVERSITY
PALISADES
NY 10964
U.S.A.

MILANKOVIC V.
5 BURROUGHS RD.
BALWYN 3103 (VIC.)
AUSTRALIA

MITCHELL J.M. JR.
NOAA CODE R 32
GRAMAX BUILDING ROOM 625
8060 13 TH. STREET
SILVER SPRING
MARYLAND 20910
U.S.A.

MIX A.
LAMONT DOHERTY OBSERVATORY
COLUMBIA UNIVERSITY
PALISADES, N.Y. 10964
U.S.A.

MOLFINO B.
LDGO
PALISADES, NY 10964
U.S.A.

MORLEY J.
LAMONT-DOHERTY GEOLOGICAL OBSERVATORY
NEW CORE LAB.
PALISADES, N.Y. 10964
U.S.A.

NICOLIS C.
INSTITUT AERONOMIE SPACIALE
3 AV. CIRCULAIRE
1180 BRUXELLES

NORTH G.R.
NASA/GODDARD SPACE FLIGHT CENTER
GREENBELT, MARYLAND 20771
U.S.A.

OLSEN P.
DEPT. OF PALEONTOLOGY
UNIVERSITY OF CALIFORNIA
BERKELEY
CALIFORNIA 94720
U.S.A.

OLSON P.
YALE UNIVERSITY
NEW HAVEN, CT
U.S.A.

PANTIC N.
SERBIAN ACADEMY OF SCIENCES AND ARTS
35,KNEZ-MIHAILOVA
YU-11000 BEOGRAD
YUGOSLAVIA

PELTIER W.R.
DEPT. OF PHYSICS
UNIV. OF TORONTO
TORONTO, ONTARIO M5S 1A7
CANADA

PESTIAUX P.
INSTITUT D'ASTRONOMIE ET
DE GEOPHYSIQUE
UNIVERSITE CATHOLIQUE DE LOUVAIN
2 CHEMIN DU CYCLOTRON
1348 LOUVAIN-LA-NEUVE
BELGIQUE

PISIAS N.
OREGON STATE UNIVERSITY,
CORVALLIS, OREGON 97331
U.S.A.

POLLARD D.
3067 BATERMAN ST.
BERTELEY, CAL. 94705
U.S.A.

PRELL W.L.
DEPT. OF GEOLOGICAL SCIENCES
BROWN UNIVERSITY
PROVIDENCE, RHODE ISLAND 02912
U.S.A.

REA D.K.
OCEANOGRAPHY PROGRAM
DEPT. OF ATMOSPHERIC AND
OCEANIC SCIENCE
THE UNIVERSITY OF MICHIGAN
ANN ARBOR, MICHIGAN 48109
U.S.A.

ROSSIGNOL-STRICK
LAMONT-DOHERTY
GEOLOGICAL OBSERVATORY
OF COLUMBIA UNIVERSITY
PALISADE, WY10964
FRANCE

ROYER J.F.
DIRECTION DE LA METEOROLOGIE
CENTRE NATIONAL DE RECHERCHE METEO.
AV. EISENHOWER PROLONGEE
F-31057 TOULOUSE CEDEX
FRANCE

RUDDIMAN W.F.
LAMONT-DOHERTY GEOLOGICAL OBSERVATORY
COLUMBIA UNIVERSITY
PALISSADES, N.Y. 10964
U.S.A.

SALTZMAN B.
DEPT. OF GEOLOGY AND GEOPHYSICS
YALE UNIVERSITY
BOX 6666
NEW HAVEN CONN. 06511
U.S.A.

SARNTHEIN M.
GEOLOG. PALAEONT. INST. DER UNIVERSITAT
UND MUSEUM DER UNI. KIEL
OLSHANSENSTR. 40-60
D- 2300 KIEL
FEDERAL REPUBLIEK OF GERMANY

SCHLESINGER M.E.
DEPT. OF ATMOSPHERIE SCIENCES
OREGON STATE UNIVERSITY
CORVALLIS OREGON 97331
U.S.A.

SCHNEIDER S.H.
NATIONAL CENTER FOR ATMOSPHERIC
RESEARCH
P.O. BOX 3000
BOULDER, COLORADO 80307
U.S.A.

SCHNITKER D.
DEPT. OF GEOLOGY AND
OCEANOGRAPHY PROGRAM
UNIVERSITY OF MAINE
ORONO, MAINE 04469
U.S.A.

SCHRAMM C.T.
GSI
NARRAGANSETT, RI 02882
U.S.A.

SELLERS W.D.
ATMOSPHERIC PHYSICS DEPARTMENT
UNIVERSITY OF ARIZONA
TUCSON, ARIZONA 85721
U.S.A.

SHACKLETON N.J.
GODWIN LABORATORY
FREE SCHOOL LANE
CAMBRIDGE CB2 3RS
ENGLAND

START G.G.
DEPT. OF GEOLOGICAL SCI.
BROWN UNIVERSITY
PROVIDENCE, RI 02912
U.S.A.

STEFANOVIC D.
FACULTY OF MINES AND GEOLOGY
RUDARSKO
DJUSINA 7
YU-11000 BEOGRAD
YOUGOSLAVIA

STOUT M.
DEPT. OF GEOLOGY
UNIVERSITY OF NEBRASKA-LINCOLN
433 MORRILL HALL
LINCOLN, NE 68588-0340
U.S.A.

STREETER H.F.
DEPT. GEOLOGICAL SCI.
BROWN UNIVERSITY
PROVIDENCE, RI 02912
U.S.A.

SUTERA A.
THE CENTER FOR ENVIRONMENT AND MAN
275 WINDSOR STREET
HARTFORD CONNECTICUT 06120
U.S.A.

TAYLOR K.E
UNIVERSITY OF FLORIDA
DEPARTMENT OF PHYSICS
215 WILLIAMSON HALL
GAINESVILLE, FL 32611
U.S.A.

THALER J.
THALER J.S.
SOUTH LAKE BLVD.
MAHOPAC, NY 10541
U.S.A.

VAN YPERSELE
INSTITUT D'ASTRONOMIE ET
DE GEOPHYSIQUE
UNIVERSITE CATHOLIQUE DE LOUVAIN
2 CHEMIN DU CYCLOTRON
1348 LOUVAIN-LA-NEUVE
BELGIQUE

WARREN S.
UNIVERSITY OF WASHINGTON
DEPT. OF ATMOSPHERIC SCIENCES
GEOPHYSICS AK-50
SEATTLE, WA 98195
U.S.A.

WATTS R.G.
DEPT OF MECHANICAL ENGINEERING
TULANE UNIVERSITY
NEW ORLEANS, LA 70118
U.S.A.

WEBB THOMPSON
DEPT. OF GEOLOGICAL SCIENCES
BROWN UNIVERSITY
PROVIDENCE, RHODE ISLAND 02912
U.S.A.

WEERTMAN J.
MATERIALS SC. DEPT.
NORTHWESTERN UNIVERSITY
EVANSTON IL. 60201
U.S.A.

YOUNG M.
DEPT. OF GEOL. AND GEOGRAPHY
UNIVERSITY OF MASSACHUSETT
AMHERST, MA 01003
U.S.A.

ZIMMERMAN H.B.
DEPARTMENT OF CIVIL ENGINEERING
UNION COLLEGE
SCHENECTADI, NY 12308
U.S.A.

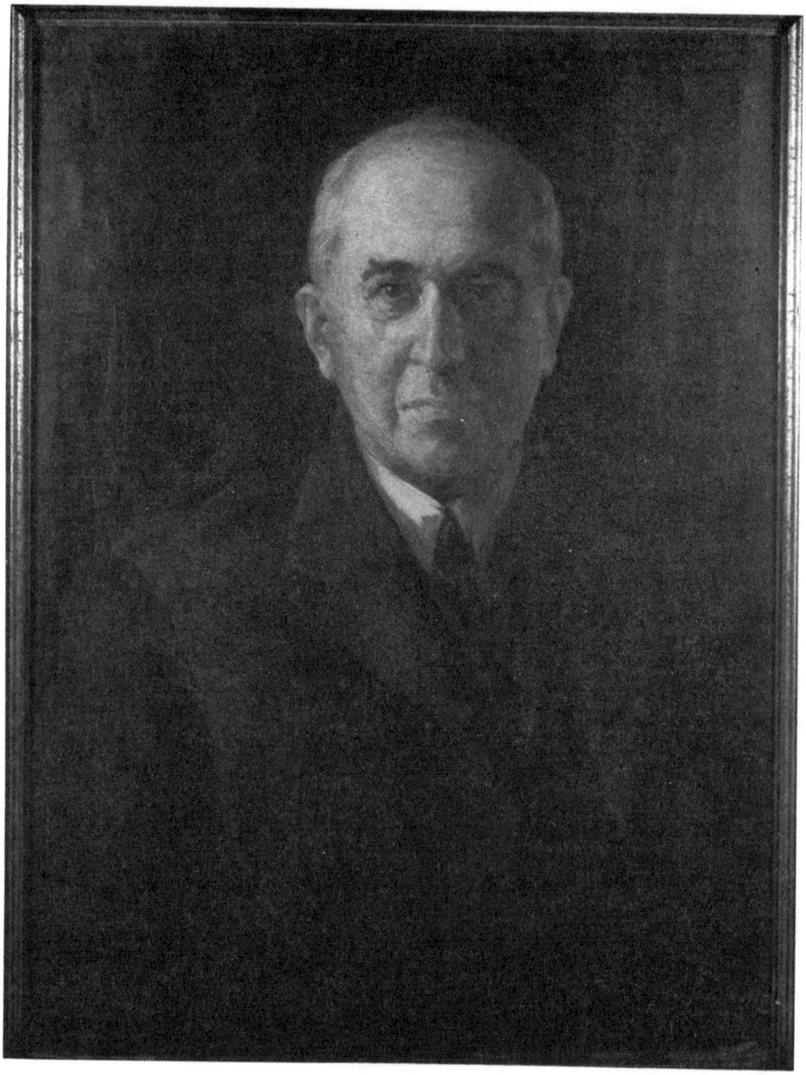

MILUTIN MILANKOVITCH

A portrait painted by Paja Jovanic in 1943
(Courtesy of Vasko Milankovitch)

THE MEMORY OF MY FATHER

V. Milankovitch

Burroughs Rd 5, Balwyn, Australia

In 1979, I went to Belgrade to attend a symposium organised by the Serbian Academy of Sciences, marking the 100th anniversary of the birth of Milutin Milankovitch, my father. There I had great pleasure in meeting for the first time John Imbrie and André Berger.

Two facts emerged from the symposium. Firstly, father's work is well known to the international scientific world, especially since the "Canon" was translated into English in 1969. And secondly, very little is known about his personality.

Father always shied away from publicity and, although he wrote lengthy memoirs published by the Serbian Academy of Sciences, they had a very restricted readership, because they were written in Serbian and printed in Cyrillic writing.

When André Berger and John Imbrie planned the present symposium, they invited me to talk about my father as I knew him through 32 years.

In the foreword to his memoirs, my father writes :

> I have not written these lengthy memoirs because I thought I was such an important person, but because I have lived in an historically interesting and turbulent period, and I described these events as a trustworthy witness. I have written about my personal experiences only so far as they were relevant to my scientific work. My

A. L. Berger et al. (eds.), Milankovitch and Climate, Part 1, xxiii–xxxiv.

> work, spanning some 30 years, has been closely connected with the work of other scientists who have used my results in their respective fields. The mutual collaboration and exchange of ideas has been documented with more than 600 letters and 100 publications. Therefore, these memoirs are, for a good part, the history of a branch of the sciences called "Astronomical Theory of Climatic Changes".

Gentlemen, I do not intend to translate the 872 pages of my father's memoirs. I have been taught by him that the quality of a talk is in inverse proportion to its length.

Among father's papers, I recently found a single page in his handwriting -untitled and undated (Fig. 1). You learned gentlemen, no doubt have been to beauty contests many times, where the young ladies are described by their "vital statistics". Well, this single sheet of paper written by my father gives the "vital statistics" of Milutin Milankovitch :

> Born of Serbian parents and into the Serbian orthodox religion on the 28th May, 1879, in Dalj, Slavonia (part of Austro-Hungary until 1919; and now a part of Jugoslavia. The 6000 inhabitants of the town on the banks of the Danube were, and still are, mostly farmers). Secondary school completed in Osijek (provincial city, garrison centre during Austro-Hungary, 15 kilometres from Dalj). Tertiary education : Technical High School of Vienna where, on 17th December 1904, became a doctor of technical sciences. Shortly afterwards, he was employed as chief engineer to some large construction companies specialising in reinforced concrete. He worked on complex projects and introduced new methods of construction which were patented. He wrote numerous papers relating to engineering mechanics. On the 1st October, 1909, he was elected professor at the University of Belgrade where he lectured on Rational Mechanics, Theoretical Physics, and Celestial Mechanics; until his retirement 46 years later. He was a member of the Serbian Academy of Sciences, Jugoslav Academy of Sciences and Arts, German Academy of naturalists : "Leopoldine" Halle, Italian Institute of Paleontology, and wrote some 70 books or papers, his major work being <u>Canon of Insolation of the Earth and its Application to the Problem of ice Ages</u> published by the Serbian Academy of

Милутин Миланковић рођен је у Даљу у Славонији 28 маја 1879. Реалку је учио у Осијеку, а Техничку високу школу у Бечу где је 17. децембра 1904 био промовисан за доктора техничких наука. Брзо иза тога ступио је [illegible] у инжењерску праксу у којој је био шеф-инжењер великих бечких грађевинских предузећа за армирани бетон. Ту се истакао својим пројектима, новим доцније патентираним конструкцијама, [illegible] и својим расправама из области инжењерске механике. Изабран позивом филозофског факултета Универзитета у Београду за професора рационалне механике, теоријске физике и небеске механике, дошао је 1 октобра 1909 године у Београд и ту остао, са прекидом првог светског рата који је провео у [illegible] заробљеништву, до сада. Прави је члан Српске Академије наука и немачке академије природњака „Леополдина" у Хале-у, а дописни члан Југословенске академије знаности и умјетности и Италијанског института за палеонтологију у Риму. Објавио је, који сам [illegible] дела, које претурају око седамдесет. Главно му је дело, Канон осунчавања Земље и његова примена у проблему ледених доба, које је објављено на немачком језику било заслужно издање Српске академије наука 1941 године.

Својим делом створио је, [illegible] небеске механике, сферне астрономије и теоријске физике, своју теорију о [illegible] и изградио своју теорију о [illegible], [illegible] о [illegible] ледених доба. Резултати његови [illegible] ушли су брзо у светску научну литературу и нашли своју широку примену.

О овом [illegible] [illegible] Миланковић [illegible], како у својој књизи „Кроз васиону и векове" која је доживела четири издања и два немачка издања и у својој „Успомени, доживљаји и сазнања" објављеним 1952 године као засебно издање Српске академије наука.

Figure 1 A single page in M. Milankovitch handwritting, untitled and undated from V. Milankovitch.

> sciences in 1941 in German. The theory of the Ice Ages based on Celestial Mechanics, Spheric Astronomy and Theoretical Physics, has since been widely used in science. About his own life, Milankovitch has written in detail in his book Through Space and Centuries (4 Serbian and 2 German editions) and in his memoirs.

I believe this single page, written at the time of his retirement from the university and two years before his death, was probably meant for entry in an encyclopaedia.

Father was barely 5'7" tall (1.70m) and of fine frame. He had a prominent forehead and bushy brows over brown eyes which were always alert and quietly smiling. His finely-cut lips had a barely noticeable twist giving a faint mocking expression to his face. He was not the bespectacled-professor-type of scien-

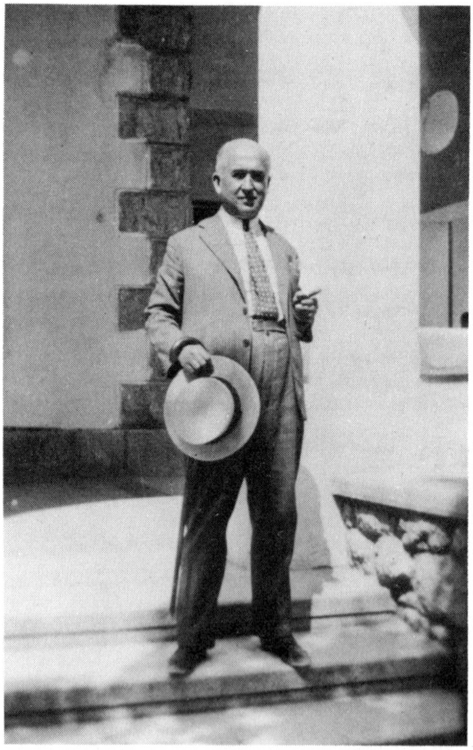

tist for he admired and enjoyed nature and loved all things aesthetically harmonious and maintained a constant interest in history, literature, painting and sculpture. Of all the arts, music was his favourite, and opera his first love. It dates back to his student days in Vienna where he spent many evenings in the "Staatsoper" which has been for over two centuries one of the greatest opera houses in the world. Although father did not play any musical instrument, my mother, who trained to be an opera singer, maintained that he had the finer ear. His love for abstract pleasures did not preclude him from earthy enjoyment. He enjoyed a glass of fine wine with his meals and would later relax with a favourite cigar. He often shared a good joke, and not necessarily a clean one either.

By nature he was a sentimentalist, perhaps even a dreamer, but certainly a born optimist. His easy-going nature was well known by his friends, who often inquired how he managed to remain so placid. He would reply : "Oh no, I do worry about everything, except for two things: the ones I cannot change ... and the ones I can!"

Although of excellent constitution, he was a gentle hypochondriac and would take note of any sneeze or cough, and the mildest fever would see him in bed. I recall in 1948: I had left the country and was living from day to day as a political refugee in Paris with my wife, not knowing from where our next meal would come, when an alarming letter came from home. Father had been to the dentist, and had had his first filling -just on his 69th birthday!

Amongst other faults, he was a slave of his habits. One thing repeated three times would continue as part of his routine for the rest of his life. Our dog Teddy was just the same; and the two loved each other dearly.

When father did not have to go to the university for his lecture, the two would retire to his study after breakfast. Father would smoke a pipe and work, while Teddy lay beneath the leather divan. The pipe generally lasted an hour. Once he finished smoking, father could not stand the smell of the tobacco hanging in the room. He would get up from behind his desk, the dog would crawl out from under the divan and the window would be flung open. The dog would jump on the window sill (he, too, probably did not like the smell) and father would leave the room. For an hour the lit pipe had been under his nose - that was all right - but once finished, you would think that the house were on fire! While waiting for the air to become clean and fresh, he would sit in my nearby study reading something totally unrelated to his work. Ten minutes later, he would close the window and return to work at his desk, with the dog once again under the divan.

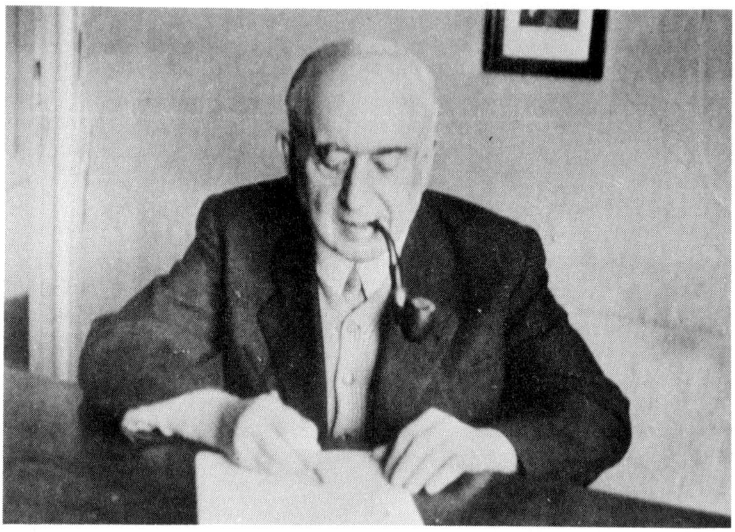

At ten o'clock, mother would bring black coffee. I would join them when I was at home. Ten minutes later, father's eyes would start twinkling and the shuffle of papers on his desk meant: "Well, coffee was excellent, but we can't sit all day long drinking coffee!" Mother promptly collected the cups and we would depart.

Lunch was at one o'clock sharp, either in the dining room or on the covered back terrace overlooking the garden. After lunch, father had a short "siesta", before smoking a cigar or another pipe. He then worked until six o'clock, at which time he would leave his desk for the day. He would then take a twenty minute stroll to his club, the "Nicola Tesla", and return home in plenty of time for dinner at eight o'clock.

When I look back for me, the most enjoyable part of the day was after the evening meal where we discussed various topics including the family, social events, politics and art. Mother might sing a few arias from a recently visited opera, accompagnying herself on the piano. If it were Sunday - mother's reception day - I would probably imitate some of her guests much to her dismay and father's great delight.

Father always retired to bed at ten o'clock to read books unrelated to his work for about an hour. Usually he remained awake and deep in thought for a considerable time.

I was always intrigued by his method of work -never rushing nor delegating anything, including even drawing and translating into French or German. He always made thorough preparations by outlining relevant points before precisely detailing the body of the article, then rewriting prior to typing the final copy himself. A simple reply to any correspondence would be treated in the same personal manner.

Yet, with all his slowness, he achieved a great deal. Apart from his university duties, his scientific work was interrupted by many other activities.

For over ten years he was actively engaged in civil engineering. The Jugoslav Air Force and Navy appointed him to supervise all their large projects in reinforced concrete. This work was very time consuming and required him to travel extensively throughout the country.

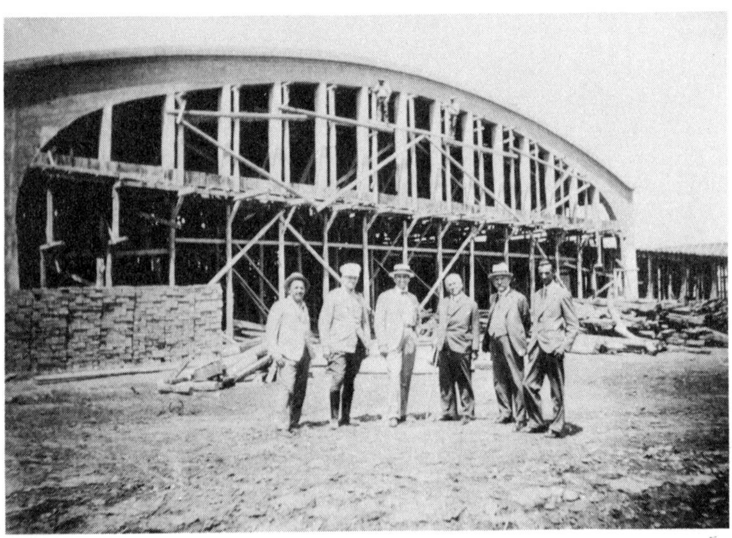

In 1923, he attended the All orthodox Churches Council in Constantinople for two months at the request of the Jugoslav government, to solve the discrepancy between the Gregorian and the Julian calendars.

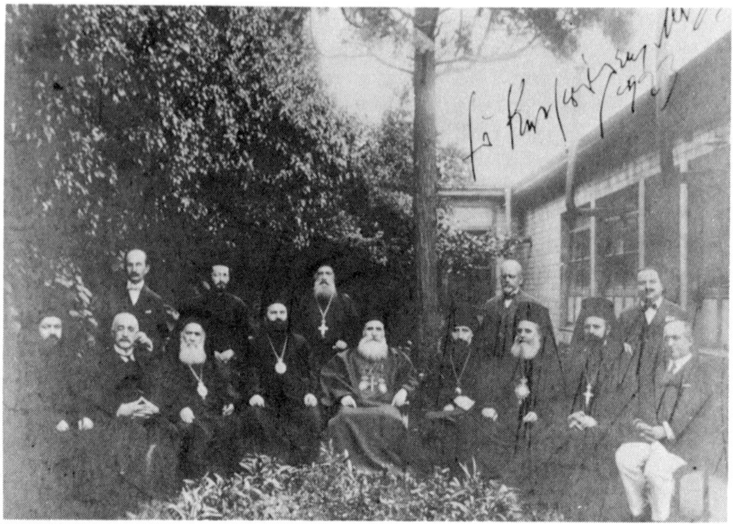

The Sultan of Tunisia required his services in 1930 for the calculation of important climatic data for their agriculture. He subsequently received a very elaborate and colourful decoration, which he gave to me for playing in my games of war and theatre.

In 1934, he had an idea from which he designed an anti-aircraft bomb!

He wrote several historical works about science as well as his known book on popular astronomy of some 320 pages, and translated it into German. Despite all these achievements, he used to say he "cooked on low fire".

He did not hold his good memory in high esteem -yet he drew on this source of knowledge frequently. He could recall in detail any item read once, especially if of some importance. When we visited Athens in 1937 - he was 58 years old - he showed us where every building used to be at the Acropolis. He gave us the name, year of erection, size, number of columns, their height, what sort of frieze it had and so on. When asked how he knew so much, his reply was simple : "As a student in Vienna, I had to know."

By way of contrast, one day on my way home from school, I met father leaving a menswear shop and complimented him on a tie just purchased. "I am glad you approve of it," he replied, gently pushing out his chest. "How much was it ?" I asked. He looked at me, paused for a second and said, rather apologetically, "I don't know".

Mother was the master of our family. Father would call her the "Home Secretary", and always showed her great respect. He was the well-looked-after guest with no household duties.

He was popular with the ladies due to his excellent manners and because he was a good raconteur. His widely read book of popular astronomy, written in the form of letters to a lady friend, added to his popularity with women. What those ladies never knew was that he really did not have a very high opinion of the fairer sex. Being physically different, he thought, they are not strong enough to compete with the male. He thought that they are less objective than men and with a nervous system more fragile. The real thread of larger problems would somehow escape them. He said there were no great scientists among women (and had a special opinion about Madame Curie) and that even in the culinary art, the great chefs were all men! in other words, he was a real male chauvinist!

Another idiosyncrasy was his opinion about pharmacists. He thought of them neither as professionals nor shopkeepers. I remember mother relating to me of a time before her first child was born. She was in high spirits, wondering what sex the baby would be, and what he or she would be in life. Father comforted her by saying, "If it is a girl and intelligent she might finish as a pharmacist. If it is a boy and, you know, not over-burdened with brains, he might become a pharmacist!". You know, gentlemen, he was right, the cunning old fox - I became the next best: a lawyer!

Father was a born individualist. He never belonged to any group, fraternity or political organisation. At the university he received criticism for his non-patriotic attitude. Following the First World War, many renowned Russian emigrant scientists were seeking university positions. Father wasted no time in obtaining chairs for them at Belgrade University. When some of his colleagues objected to the fact that local talents were not given first preference, father would reply, "Universities are not charitable organisations! Our criterion must be based on what he knows and not who he is." Looking back, it seems that the time between the two Wars was the "Golden Age" of the University of Belgrade.

Milutin Milankovitch was neither a fighter nor a hero, and of these shortcomings he was well aware I recall 1936 when the family was holidaying in Austria, and father went to Vienna to attend a congress of I.M.K.W.A. There the great Albrecht Penck told him that his Theory of the Ice Ages was all hogwash. Father made no attempt to defend himself against this criticism, but on returning to Belgrade, when we stopped in Graz, father spoke to Köppen and related Penck's comment. Unimpressed, Köppen summed up the situation by replying : "Penck thinks he can stop a swollen river by imposing his big body. That never succeeds. Facts cannot be disregarded." (I am quoting from the memoirs.)

As mentioned before, father shied away from publicity. He refused to give his photographs to the media. The few in existence are only the ones taken of him and printed without his consent.

In 1954, the technical High School of Vienna organised a ceremony to mark the 50th anniversary of father becoming a doctor of the famous school, and he was invited to come to Vienna to receive the golden diploma. At that time I was living in Australia and he write to me:

> I would love to go and sea Vienna again, but I could not stand to be the object of public celebration. Imagine, to sit and listen to other people praising you. I thanked the Chancellor for the invitation, but declined to attend. Our embassy will send somebody to accept the diploma.

Father did not believe that scientists and their work should be judged as soon as produced. "For an accurate assessment," he writes in his memoirs, "it is necessary to have some time lapse in order to judge or compare the importance of the work."

He was born in the same year as Albert Einstein, whom, incidentally, he greatly admired. On Einstein's Theory of Relativity he wrote an extensive paper, but felt that great injustice had been done to Einstein by his own compatriots by making so much publicity when he arrived in the States. Of course, they did this for their own advantage and not for his. He did not want it. Father thought that discoveries and new theories should be left alone until proven by others; and the less you or your supporters do, the better it is. When the Theorie Mathematique de la Radiation Solaire (his first major work) was published and received a lukewarm reception, he was unperturbed. In his memoirs he writes :

> "Although some sunshine shone on my workroom, I realised it was not the real thing. Many scientific discoveries, far greater than mine, lay unrecognised and unaccepted for many years. But, I know that if my work were to be a real contribution to science, it will find its way without anybody's help, recommendation or praise. With this conclusion, I turned to explore new fields."

I often recall an event of my youth that took place 50 years ago. Father and I were holidaying in Austria. One Sunday morning, I jumped into a swimming pool and fractured my collar bone. A doctor could not be located, so they drove me to the nearest hospital. I received pain-killing injections, and was put in a temporary axillary splint, made out of knitting wool, before returning to the hotel.

Later that afternoon and throughout dinner, father was very absent-minded which was most unusual for him. It would have been after ten o'clock when he finally settled me into bed in my room, connected to his large room where there was a writing desk. He left the door ajar in case I needed him. Instead of going to bed, he went to his desk, pulled some large sheets of paper from the centre drawer, lit the desk lamp and sat down. Something unusual must have happened, I thought. He never worked after dinner. He was facing the open door and I could clearly see what he was doing.

Father began writing fast, as I had never seen him before. The effect of my injection had worn off and the splint was cutting painfully into my shoulders and I could not sleep. He got up, put his foot on the chair and his elbow on his knee, took his glasses off and looked at me. He was not seeing me - he looked through me. A blue vein was clearly visible diagonally across his forehead. He sat down wrote again. Then he stopped. He put the paper away, took a new sheet and started writing again.

The woollen strap was hurting me. I called out for him to lift me and put some cotton wool under the strap, but I could see that he did not hear me.

He kept on writing and then he stopped and looked at the paper in front of him. He seemed to be revising all that he had written down, talking to himself, and dotting the "i's" as he read. Then he stopped. He then took another sheet of paper and started writing again, but slowly this time. The tension on his face gradually dispersed and his usual calm expression returned. Finally he slowed down and then stopped altogether.

He looked up and, recalling my presence, said, "Sorry, I forgot about you. Do you need anything?" He lifted me into a comfortable position on the pillows, put pads of cotton wool behind the strap and said, "I think I've got it." "You got what?" I asked. "The differential equation covering the movement of the Poles. This equation has eluded me for quite some time. I am right now." He patted me on my sound shoulder, went into his room and, a couple of minutes later, I could hear him gently snoring.

PART I

ORBITAL AND INSOLATION VARIATIONS

ACCURACY AND FREQUENCY STABILITY OF THE EARTH'S ORBITAL ELEMENTS DURING THE QUATERNARY

A. Berger

Institut d'Astronomie et de Géophysique Georges Lemaître, Université Catholique de Louvain, Louvain-la-Neuve, Belgium

ABSTRACT

Seven classical solutions of the planetary system are compared to test the accuracy of the long-term variations of the Earth's orbital elements used in astronomical theories of the Quaternary paleoclimates. After $3x10^6$ years, the most up-to-date solutions are getting out of phase by one fifth of a cycle for the obliquity, ε, one third of a cycle for the eccentricity, e, and one full cycle for the precession parameter, $e \sin \tilde{\omega}$. For testing the stability of the main frequencies of these elements, four time-spans were considered : 0-800, 800-1600, 1600-2400 and 2400-3100 kyr BP. Spectral analysis of these time series show that the main quasi-periods, 400, 100, 41, 23 and 19 kyr, do not deteriorate with time over the last 5 million years, but their relative importance is a function of the period considered.

INTRODUCTION

Modern research in astronomical theory of paleoclimates is now made of four consecutive chapters (1) which deal with : (i) the selection of the best long-term variations of the Earth's orbital parameters and related geometrical insolation; (ii) the build-up of climatic models (preferably time-dependent) transforming the insolation available at the Earth' surface for a completely transparent atmosphere into appropriate climate indices; (iii) the acquisition of reliable time-series of proxy climatic data; and (iv) the comparison of recorded proxy and

A. L. Berger et al. (eds.), Milankovitch and Climate, Part 1, 3–39.

simulated climates in the time and frequency domains or for some selected snapshots of the past.

As cumulative effect of computational approximation must be limited in order to allow input to the climatic models to be of real values, the detailed history of orbital variations is more and more recognized to play a basic role in understanding the climatic evolution of the planetary atmospheres. This is why it is of interest to focuss here on the accuracy of the long-term variations of those orbital elements which are fundamental in any astronomical theory of the Earth paleoclimates (2) : e the eccentricity of the Earth's orbit around the Sun, ε , its obliquity and $\tilde{\omega}$, the longitude of the perihelion measured from the moving vernal point[1]. The other two parameters are kept constant to their present-day values : a, the semi-major axis of the elliptical Earth's orbit and S_0, the so-called solar constant[2] (a measure of the solar energy at the mean Earth-sun distance), assumed to be 1358 Wm^{-2} or 1.95 cal $cm^{-2}day^{-1}$.

This accuracy will be investigated by comparing different classical long-term analytical solutions of the 10-body planetary system (9 planets and the sun). Some details will be given of why these solutions of the differential equations of the planetary motion are expressed in trigonometrical form and how their accuracy depends upon the accuracy and the number of terms kept in the perturbation function of the Lagrange and Laplace equations. As it is not possible to express analytically the influence upon the solution of the neglected terms nor the connection between the value of the constants used and the numerical values of the amplitude, the mean rate and the phase of each trigonometrical term in the solution, the present comparison will be made numerically.

Finally, spectral analysis will be computed for different sub-intervals of the whole time series generated over the past 3.2×10^6 years for each orbital elements, in order to test the stability in time of the different periods and of their relative importance (namely 23 kyr against 19 kyr in the precession term).

LAGRANGE EQUATION AND THE METHOD OF THE VARIATIONS OF ARBITRARY CONSTANTS

The basic concern of celestial mechanics is to study the motion of ten material points representing the sun, Mercury, Venus, Earth, Mars, Jupiter, Saturn, Uranus, Neptune and Pluto, assuming that this motion is influenced by their mutual attraction alone and that the attraction is computed according to Newton's Universal Law of Gravitation (5).

The inertial coordinate system to which we refer the motion of the 9 planets of the solar system is defined as follows (6): the origin is the center of inertia of the solar system; the fundamental plane is the instantaneous orbit of the Earth at a given epoch, such as 1950.0; the x-axis goes through the vernal equinox for the same epoch, the z-axis points to the north pole of the ecliptic and the y-axis is perpendicular to the x and z axis (Fig. 1).

In this system, the only forces present are due to mutual attraction. If the differential equations are written in any other coordinate system, additional terms appear which concern the non-inertial character of the system. For instance, for the investigation of the motion of the major planets, it is advisable to choose the heliocentric coordinate system as the fundamental system. Then, the differential equations of planetary motions can be formulated as :

$$\frac{d^2x_j}{dt^2} = \frac{\partial U_j}{\partial x_j} \qquad [1]$$

and similar equations for y_j, z_j $(1 \leq j \leq 9)$ where U_j is the force-function whose partial derivatives with respect to the planetary coordinates equal the components of the force acting on the planet j :

$$U_j = \frac{k^2(1+m_j)}{r_j} + R_j \qquad [2]$$

$$R_j = \sum_{\substack{i \neq j \\ i \neq sun}} k^2 m_i \left(\frac{1}{r_{ij}} - \frac{\vec{r}_i . \vec{r}_j}{r_i^3}\right) \qquad [3]$$

$\vec{r}_j(x_j,y_j,z_j)$ is the radius vector of a planet P_j, $\vec{r}_{ij}$ the interdistance between the planets, k^2 is the Gaussian gravitational constant derived from the third law of Kepler :
$\mu = k^2(1+m) = n^2 a^3$, n is the mean motion, a the semi-major axis of the osculating elliptical orbit and m_j the mass of P_j expressed in unit of solar mass.

The first term under the derivation in the right handside of this equation is corresponding to the two-body problem, whereas the second term is called the perturbating function with its principal part $(1/r_{ij})$ and its indirect portion $- \vec{r}_i . \vec{r}_j / r_i$ (this last arises, from our instance, on heliocentric coordinates and, it would vanish if we were willing to take the origin of coordinates at the center of mass of the solar system).

Unfortunately, only the two-body problem in the plane (such as the sun and one planet) is rigorously solvable because the two integrals of the differential equations of motion are sufficient to yield the two polar variables as functions of the time. As soon as the number of mass-points exceeds 2 the problem of describing their motion subject to their mutual gravitation becomes insolvable. This is due to the fact that the differential equations of motion for n mass-points, when $n > 2$, have no other integrals than those of the two-body problem; namely, the integrate stating the uniform motion of the centre of mass of the system, the integrals of area and the energy (or vis viva) integral (7).

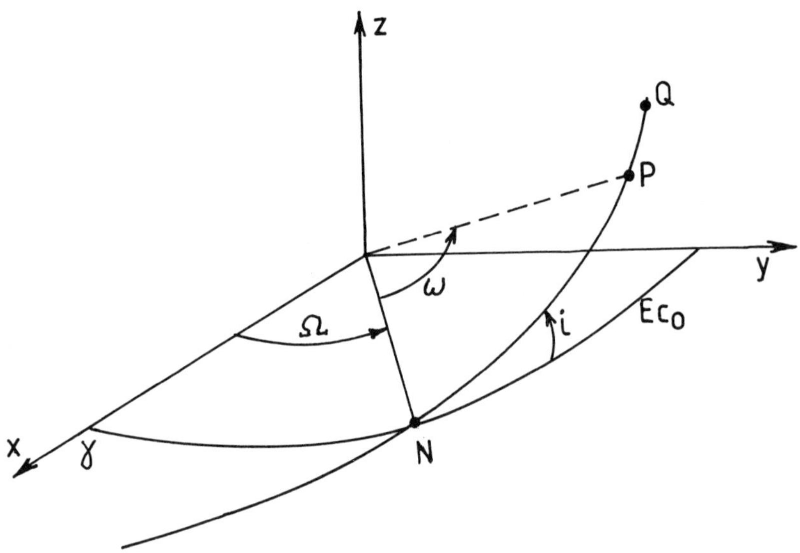

Figure 1 The planetary orbit in space. OX points to the vernal equinox, XOY is the fixed ecliptic of reference, OZ points towards the north ecliptic pole, N is the ascending node, P is the perihelion, Q is the planet, Ω is the longitude of the node, ω is the argument of the perihelion, $\pi = \Omega + \omega$, the sum of two angles lying usually in different planes, is the longitude of the perihelion relatively to the fixed equinox.

In the case of these planetary orbits, the acceleration caused by the principal attraction exerted by the sun is much greater than the "perturbing" accelerations produced by the other planets. It is therefore logical to consider the relative elliptic orbit described about the sun as a first approximation to the motion as if the sun alone determined the orbit of every planet, while the other planets merely produce small and slow changes of the elements of the Kepler orbits. As the motion progresses under the influence of the various attracting bodies, the coordinates and velocity components at any instant may be used to obtain a set of six orbital elements, as in the 2-body problem; the first three are : the semi-major axis, a, the eccentricity, e, and the inclination, i, of the orbit on the reference plane; the last three are (Fig. 1) : the longitude of the ascending node, Ω, the longitude of the perihelion, π, and the mean longitude recognized from the origin of time, ϵ (which often replaces the time of perihelion passage). These are precisely the elements of the ellipse that the planet would follow if from that particular instant on, the accelerations caused by all "perturbing" bodies ceased to exist.

Instead of obtaining the perturbed coordinates directly by the solutions of [1,2,3], it will thus be equally effective to first obtain the orbital elements as functions of the time, the coordinates being then found from the elements by the standard formulas of elliptic motion. This is the principle of the method of the variation of arbitrary constants which leads to the often called Lagrange equations (e.g.,(7) p. 204).

However, these equations possess some inconvenient features for application to orbits with small eccentricities or small inclinations : the appearance of the eccentricity and of sin i in the denominator of the expressions for $d\pi/dt$ and $d\Omega/dt$. As all planetary orbits lie almost exactly in the same plane and differ only slightly from circles, it is thus desirable to use a modified form of these equations by setting $h = e \sin \pi$, $k = e \cos \pi$, $p = \sin i \sin \Omega$ and $q = \sin i \cos \Omega$.

ANALYTICAL SOLUTIONS OF THE PLANETARY MOTIONS

These differential equations of the motion of 9 bodies (Pluto is not considered) are integrated in celestial mechanics in an approximate manner, either by series expansion (analytical methods leading to solutions called general perturbations), or by numerical integration (solution referred to as special perturbations). If the solution is given in the form of a series which progresses in powers of a small parameter, one usually chooses the planetary mass as this parameter, since even Jupiter's mass, the largest planetary mass in the solar system, is still 1047 times smaller than the solar mass. Such terms have the following form: At^m, $At^m \sin(\alpha t+B)$, $A \sin(\alpha t+B)$ where m=1,2,... . The terms of the first type are known as secular perturbations and the terms of the second type as mixed, whereas the third type represents periodic perturbations. The coefficients A contain the planetary mass raised to different positive powers and are thus small quantities.

This can be seen easily from the development of the disturbing function R in a suitable form of a series of periodic terms where a,e,i appear in the coefficients and Ω, π, ϵ in the arguments (e.g.,8). For two planets, for example, we have :

$$R = \sum F(a,a',e,e',i,i') \cos T$$
$$T = h(\epsilon+nt)+h'(\epsilon'+n't')+g\pi+g'\pi'+f\Omega+f'\Omega' \qquad [4]$$

where the osculating elements of the disturbed orbit are a, e, i, Ω, π, ϵ and those of the disturbing orbit are a', e', i', Ω', π', and ϵ'. The h's, g's and f's are integers whose values are negative, zero, or positive and, by their values, the various terms in the sum are characterized. The first three variational equations for a, e, i are clearly of the type

$$da/dt = \sum C_1 \sin T \qquad [5]$$

and the last three for Ω, π, ϵ of the type

$$d\Omega/dt = \sum C_4 \cos T \qquad [6]$$

The right-hand members of these equations, all contain m', the mass of the disturbing planet, as a factor. Since these perturbing masses are small in problems presented in the solar system, they are eminently suitable for a procedure of integration by successive approximations. Therefore, the <u>general perturbations of the first order in the masses</u> ($a_1, e_1, \ldots, \epsilon_1$) are obtained by integrating the right-hand members with respect to the time, where the elements are given their initial values : a_0, e_0, i_0, Ω_0, π_0, ϵ_0. These perturbations are for example :

$$a_1 = -\sum C_1 \cos T/(hn_0+h'n')$$
$$\Omega_1 = \sum C_4 \sin T/(hn_0+h'n') \qquad [7]$$

We notice that terms in R, for which h and h' are zero, are independent of the time, and therefore contribute terms of the type At, called secular perturbations, to the elements with the exception of a; so a_1 contains no secular perturbations of the first order in the masses. All other terms in R contribute to the elements periodic perturbations of the first order in the masses, of the type

$$[A \cos (hn + h'n')t + \text{const}]$$

The mean motion of any argument is therefore hn+h'n' and, in summary we have :

$$\begin{aligned} a &= a_0 + \delta_1 a \\ e &= e_0 + \dot{e}_1 t + \delta_1 e \\ i &= i_0 + \dot{i}_0 t + \delta_1 i \end{aligned} \qquad [8]$$

$$\Omega = \Omega_0 + \Omega_1 t + \delta_1 \Omega \quad \text{and similar for } \pi, \epsilon. \qquad [9]$$

The designation δ_1 is used for the periodic terms; the elements a, e, i will be expressed by cosine series, Ω, π, and ϵ by sine series.

The results obtained by integrating the derivatives of the elements by substituting constant values for the elements as they occur in the right-hand members of Eqs [5,6] are necessarily approximations. In many cases they are insufficient to yield values for the elements that will permit the calculation of the coordinates with an accuracy that corresponds to the accuracy of the observations. In principle, it is extremely simple to carry the process forward and consider perturbations of the second order, third order, etc., as far as may be desired. For example, for the next approximation, the right-hand members of the resulting expressions all have the second power of the disturbing mass as a factor. From the form of the expansion of R and the form of the perturbations of the first order, it is apparent that the right-hand members of the new equations will in general be of the form :

$A_0 + A_1 t$ + series of periodic terms (some of which contain t as a factor of the coefficients)

in which A_0 and A_1 have been contributed by the secular part of the disturbing function. The integration will give for the contributions of the second order the result : $A_0 t + 1/2 \ A_1 t^2$ + series of periodic terms some of which are factored by t. The appearance of t in the coefficients of periodic terms (mixed secular terms) is a new feature in the perturbations of the second order. It is possible, however, to show that, when the perturbations of the second order are included, the semi-major axis has no purely secular part; this is the theorem of Poisson (9).

This process of successive approximations is continued until the desired accuracy has been achieved. In practice the first one or two orders suffice for exceedingly accurate representations of the planetary motions, except for a few terms that are needed in higher orders because of the smallness of the associated hn+h'n'. Such terms can be appreciable because hn+h'n' appears as a divisor in the integrals of sine and cosine terms. For example, in the theories of Jupiter and Saturn terms with arguments containing $2\lambda - 5\lambda'$ and also its multiples $4\lambda - 10\lambda'$, etc., are associated with small divisors that constitute the essential difficulty of developing adequate theories for these planets (λ is the mean longitude = $nt+\epsilon$). This concerns the well-known long-period inequality in the motions of these planets, with a period of approximately 900 years.

LONG-TERM VARIATIONS OF THE EARTH'S ORBITAL ELEMENTS (e,π,i,Ω)

That method of the variation of arbitrary constants was formulated as early as in the first part of the eighteenth century by Euler (7) and further elaborated by Lagrange (10) and applied for 3 bodies. Laplace (11) extended the method to a 5-body problem in the solar system and introduced also discussion about its stability which is intimetely connected with the presence of secular terms in the a,e,i's. Le Verrier (12) applied the Lagrange-Laplace method to obtain short-term ephemerides for ε and e which led him to the discovery of Neptune, so providing strong support to Laplace's view of celestial mechanics.

Unfortunately, it has been seen that, if this method is used, the first-order expressions for the orbital elements, with the exception of the semi-major axis, contain terms proportional to the time. If the developments are carried to the second order similar terms factored by the square of the time appear. This progression is kept up indefinitely, each successive approximation giving rise to one higher power of the time.

The appearance of these secular and mixed secular terms is not due to any inherent quality of the equations of motion, but is a consequence of the method of integration adopted. The presence of the time in the coefficients of perturbations in planetary motion does not prevent the construction of planetary theories valid for many centuries, although the representation is not suitable for an indefinite length of time. The reason that the conventional form is of practical value for the planetary problem, while it would be hopelessly inadequate in the lunar problem, is that the secular motions of the planetary orbits are slower than those of the moon's orbit by a factor of the order of a thousand.

It is possible, nevertheless, to learn something of the character of the planetary orbits in the distant past and future by drastically simplifying the problem. This method was first developed by Lagrange. The use of Lagrange's method (7, chap. XVI) for obtaining the long term variations of the orbital elements requires that the disturbing function be limited to its secular part (it is why these perturbations are called secular perturbations in Celestial Mechanics, although we prefer to call them long-term variations for etymological reason); that is, all the periodic terms that contain the mean longitudes (or mean anomalies) of the planets in their arguments are ignored. Let us consider, as an illustration, the solution which is in the first instance limited to the inclusion, in the secular parts, of the terms of the second order in the eccentricities and inclinations.

A simplifying feature is that the indirect part of the disturbing function contains no secular terms. It is permitted, therefore, to limit the development of the disturbing function to that of the secular part of the reciprocal of the mutual distance between two planets. To the second power of the eccentricities and the mutual inclinations, the Lagrange equations for 2 planets may be written in the simplified form :

$$
\begin{aligned}
\frac{dh_1}{dt} &= \frac{1}{n_1 a_1^2}\frac{\partial R_1}{\partial k_1}, & \frac{dp_1}{dt} &= +\frac{1}{n_1 a_1^2}\frac{\partial R_1}{\partial q_1},\\
\frac{dk_1}{dt} &= \frac{1}{n_1 a_1^2}\frac{\partial R_1}{\partial h_1}, & \frac{dq_1}{dt} &= -\frac{1}{n_1 a_1^2}\frac{\partial R_1}{\partial p_1},\\
\frac{dh_2}{dt} &= \frac{1}{n_2 a_2^2}\frac{\partial R_2}{\partial k_2}, & \frac{dp_2}{dt} &= +\frac{1}{n_2 a_2^2}\frac{\partial R_2}{\partial q_2},\\
\frac{dk_2}{dt} &= \frac{1}{n_2 a_2^2}\frac{\partial R_2}{\partial k_2}, & \frac{dq_2}{dt} &= -\frac{1}{n_2 a_2^2}\frac{\partial R_2}{\partial p_2},
\end{aligned}
\qquad [10]
$$

and the integration of the equations for ϵ_1, ϵ_2 may be deferred until after these equations have been integrated. For equations [10], terms depending on a_1, a_2 only, may be omitted in the disturbing function. Hence, it is permissible to write :

$$
\begin{aligned}
R_1 &= fm_2[N_{12}(h_1^2 + h_2^2 + k_1^2 + k_2^2) - 2P_{12}(h_1h_2 + k_1k_2)]\\
&\quad + fm_2N_{12}(- p_1^2 - p_2^2 - q_1^2 - q_2^2 + 2p_1p_2 + 2q_1q_2),
\end{aligned}
\qquad [11]
$$

and

$$R_2 = \frac{m_1}{m_2} R_1 .$$

In these expressions, f has been used in the place of k^2 to avoid confusion with the variable k; N_{12} and P_{12} are related to the so-called Laplace coefficients (7, p. 471) and are function of a_1 and a_2 of degree -1.

The Lagrange equation for a :

$$\frac{da}{dt} = \frac{2}{na} \frac{\partial R}{\partial \epsilon}$$

shows that da/dt = 0 if the disturbing function is limited to its secular part.

The form of the expression [11] shows that Eqs [10] break up into two independent sets, one set for the variables h, k, and one set for the variables p, q. This separation into two sets is a consequence of the restriction in R_1, R_2 to terms of the second order in these variables. With a more complete development of R, including terms of the fourth power, this separation would no longer be possible.

Finally, the long-term variations of e, π, i, Ω may be written after some transformations :

$$\begin{aligned} e \sin \pi &= \sum M_j \sin (g_j t + \beta_j) \\ e \cos \pi &= \sum M_j \cos (g_j t + \beta_j) \end{aligned} \qquad [12]$$

$$\begin{aligned} \sin i \sin \Omega &= \sum N_i \sin (s_i t + \delta_i) \\ \sin i \cos \Omega &= \sum N_i \cos (s_i t + \delta_i) \end{aligned} \qquad [13]$$

These long-term computations, based on time-independent perturbation (as opposed to time-dependent, cf. (13)) were used by the astronomers cited in Table 1 of (14) and by Adhemar (15), Croll (16), Milankovitch (3), Vernekar (17) and Berger (2,18) to calculate insolation changes which might influence climate on the time scale of 10^3-10^7 years.

Using the same approach, Le Verrier (12, Tome II, p.133) has tried to deduce analytically to which extend his solution would change following some small differences in the planetary masses. Stockwell (19) who was aware that this relation uses the secular determinants, realised that it is impossible to be generalised to any perturbation theory. He tried nevertheless to treat the effect of each planet individually before summing them all to compute the corrections for the Earth's orbit due to the uncertainties in the masses of all the other planets. However, both techniques do not reproduce the initial conditions. Moreover, errors (as also in Harzen (21), Milankovitch

(3), Brouwer and van Woerkom (7) and Sharaf-Budnikova (22)) were discovered by Berger (20).

It is therefore significant to point out that the solution proposed by Milankovitch (3) and issued from Miskovitch (23), is based on the formulae given by Le Verrier to take into account some modifications in the planetary masses. On the other hand, the solution proposed by Milankovitch in (20) (issued from Stockwell-Pilgrim's model) is also inacceptable because the (e, π) and (i, Ω) systems are solved for 2 different values of the Earth's mass (respectively 1/335 172 and 1/368 689, in unit of the solar mass). Although Harzer (21) introduced better masses, and used the canonical variables of Poincaré and the Jacobi's method to solve the secular determinants, an error was introduced in the last section of his work. This was corrected later on by Brouwer and van Woerkom (27) who were using Newcomb' system of planetary masses and initial conditions for 1900.0 referred to the mean ecliptic and equinox 1950.0. Unfortunately again, mistakes were introduced in the longitude of the node of Venus and Earth; corrections were made by Berger (25) and Sharaf-Budnikova (22) for further computions. It is only by 1970 that the most reliable Lagrange solutions were proposed by Anolik et al. (26) and Bretagnon (30). Although differences exist in the planetary masses, the observed mean motions and the expansions that they have used, these solutions look more or less identical.

To make a synthesis of all these results, we have retained the Lagrange's type of solution by Milankovitch-Miskovitch-Le Verrier (12) and Bretagnon (30), and numerical values of the amplitudes, mean rates and phases are listed for the most important terms in Table 2 (these solutions are labelled respectively MILANK and BRE 1; the characteristics of all solutions used here are given in Table 1). The differences arise because of the accuracy of the planetary masses and of the initial conditions used by these authors as described in (25).

The method indicated here of obtaining "secular perturbations" neglects the 4th and higher powers of the e's and i's, neglects all but the secular part of the disturbing function and, in the applications thus far made, neglects the action of Pluto. In a second approximation the fourth order terms in e's and i's can be introduced which will give rise to a solution to the third degree in e's and i's. Up to 1969, Le Verrier (12) and Harzer (21) were the only ones to take into account these new terms, although they were not considering the whole system of 8 planets. It was Anolik et al. (26) and Bretagnon (30) who came for the first time with a reliable solution to the first order of the masses and the 3rd degree in e's and i's. The importance of these additional term for Venus, Earth and Mars

Table 1 Characteristics and value of the constants of integration for the obliquity, precession and eccentricity of the Earth's orbit, calculated for 7 different solutions.

	MILANK	BRE 1	BRE 2	SHARAF	BRE 3	BRE 4	BRE 5(+)
acuracy(++)	1 1 2	1 1 2	1 3 2	2 1 2	2 3 2	2 3 2 R	2 3 2 R
epoch	1950	1950	1950	1950	1950	1950	1950
ecliptic	1800	1850	1850	1950	1850	1850	1850
ε (°)	23.306263	23.318130	23.316059	23.317083	23.320548	23.319756	23.319670
$\bar{\Psi}$ ("/year)	50.471698	50.446713	50.444577	50.450194	50.439287	50.440672	50.440822
ζ (°)	4.105013	3.448476	3.472760	1.964146	3.392528	3.334857	3.328585
e_{max}	0.063865	0.063845	0.07446	0.067414	0.072864	0.073917	0.073917

The labelling of these solutions corresponds to the authors from which the developments of e,π,i,Ω originate. All further computations are following the model developed in (31). See text for details.

(++) the 3 numbers given to characterize the accuracy are related rspectively to the order to the masses, the degree with respect to e's and i's, the degree with respect to the eccentricity of the Earth's orbit in the expansion of ε and Ψ. R means that some relativity terms are included.

(+) Same as BRE 4 but where the mean rates have been changed according to expected accuracy from Bretagnon and Berger' studies.

$$e \sin \pi = \Sigma M \sin(gt + \beta)$$
$$\sin i \sin \Omega = \Sigma N \sin(st + \delta)$$
$$\Psi = \bar{\Psi} t + \zeta + \Sigma F \sin(ft + \gamma)$$
$$\tilde{\varepsilon} = \varepsilon^{*} + \Sigma A \cos(\tilde{f} t + \tilde{\delta})$$
$$e \sin \tilde{\omega} = \Sigma P \sin(\alpha t + \xi)$$
$$e = e_0 + \Sigma E \cos(\lambda t + \phi)$$

t (mathematical time of celestial mechanics) is expressed in years from 1950.0

Table 2a Amplitudes, Mean Rates and Phases in the trigonometrical expansion of the (e,π) (only the 5 largest amplitude terms are given).

	MILANK	BRE 1	BRE 2	SHARAF	BRE 3	BRE 4	BRE 5
AMPLITUDE							
1	0.016279	0.016244	0.016351	0.018340	0.018607	0.0182	0.0182
2	-0.015016	-0.014927	0.014549	0.016330	0.016275	0.0161	0.0161
3	-0.014099	0.014904	-0.014301	-0.014834	-0.013006	-0.0134	-0.0134
4	0.010565	0.010568	0.012041	0.010434	0.009888	0.0102	0.0102
5	0.005122	0.004058	0.003494	0.003916	-0.003367	0.0043	0.0043
MEAN RATE ("/year)							
1	3.66746	3.71140	3.72948	4.29590	4.20720	4.3080	4.3180
2	17.98361	18.00458	7.34586	7.34474	7.34609	7.4559	7.4659
3	7.34614	7.34658	17.83541	18.00232	17.85726	17.9025	17.9125
4	17.31308	17.33129	17.20126	17.32832	17.22054	17.2852	17.3052
5	5.44801	5.46136	5.20299	5.46325	16.84673	5.6136	5.6736
PHASE (°)							
1	28.0	27.9	27.3	29.6	28.6	28.7	28.7
2	315.7	316.6	191.6	196.9	193.7	196.7	196.7
3	20.0	192.8	307.5	318.1	308.3	307.8	307.8
4	332.6	333.4	318.7	335.4	320.1	319.1	319.1
5	86.2	87.3	83.6	92.2	279.3	87.3	87.3

The labelling of these solutions corresponds to the authors from which the developments of e,π,i,Ω originate. However, the numbers given here do not necessarily correspond to those published by these authors because all the solutions have been assigned to the same standard astronomical epoch of reference (origin of time is 1950.0).

Table 2b Amplitudes, Mean Rates and Phases in the trigonometrical expansion of (i, Ω) (only the 5 largest amplitude terms are given).

	MILANK	BRE 1	BRE 2	SHARAF	BRE 3	BRE 4	BRE 5
AMPLITUDE							
1	0.027660	0.027671	0.027673	0.0275702	0.027671	0.027671	0.027671
2	-0.024595	0.024435	0.019340	0.0244642	0.020039	0.020039	0.020039
3	0.010501	0.008524	0.012265	0.0084961	0.012075	0.012075	0.012075
4	0.006397	0.008161	0.007500	0.0081159	0.007609	0.007609	0.007609
5	0.004367	0.004520	0.005219	0.0045381	0.005082	0.005082	0.005082
MEAN RATE ("/year)							
1	0.0	0.0	0.0	0.0	0.0	0.0	0.0
2	-18.73458	-18.74620	-18.89890	-18.74358	-18.82929	-18.82929	-18.82929
3	- 5.11444	- 5.19995	- 5.64394	- 5.20153	- 5.61093	- 5.61093	- 5.61093
4	- 6.64128	- 6.57138	-17.86747	- 6.57080	-17.81876	-17.81876	-17.81876
5	-17.61019	-17.63611	- 6.79189	-17.63330	- 6.77102	- 6.77102	- 6.77102
PHASE (°)							
1	103.3	106.1	106.1	107.1	106.1	106.1	106.1
2	73.2	253.7	248.0	255.1	248.5	248.5	248.5
3	19.9	18.1	11.7	19.3	11.9	11.9	11.9
4	301.2	316.1	275.2	318.1	277.4	277.4	277.4
5	294.8	295.1	302.8	296.5	305.0	305.0	305.0

The labelling of these solutions corresponds to the authors from which the developments of e, π, i, Ω originate. However, the numbers given here do not necessarily correspond to those published by these authors because all the solutions have been assigned to the same standard astronomical epoch of reference (origin of time is 1950.0).

would be due to the following reasons : (i) the ratio of their distances to the sun (which influence the coefficients in the disturbing function) is maximum for Venus/Earth : 0.72 against 0.54 for Jupiter/Saturn; and (ii) the mean motions g_3, g_4, s_3, s_4 are very close to each other and their combinations will generate small divisors. As the constant of integration were not determined correctly by Anolik, only the numerical values of Bretagnon are listed in Tables 2a and b.

But of all the omissions, probably the most important was the omission of the second-order effect caused by certain periodic terms in the disturbing function, notably those corresponding to the great inequality between Jupiter and Saturn. G.W. Hill took these terms into account in a calculation of the mutual secular perturbations in the eccentricities and perihelia of Jupiter and Saturn; he also included the principal effects of the fourth and sixth powers of the eccentricities. Brouwer and van Woerkom (27) included the principal refinements introduced by Hill. The value of the largest annual mean rate was increased from + 23"0858 to + 27"7741 by the refinement referred to; other roots g were also modified, but to a much smaller extent. In addition to these changes, the solution of the secular variations in h and k now also contains small terms with arguments

$$(2g_5 - g_6)t + 2\beta_5 - \beta_6 \text{ and } (2g_6 - g_5)t + 2\beta_6 - \beta_5$$

More recently, as numerically demonstrated (35), Bretagnon (30) made a decisive improvement in the evaluation of the eccentricity, the longitude of the perihelion, the inclination and the longitude of the ascending node. Let us summarize the main characteristics of that solution. The elements of the Earth's orbit are referred to the mean ecliptic and the mean equinox of 1850.0. Initial elements at this epoch of reference are the most accurate and secular perturbations have been taking out of the observed mean motions, the semi-major axis of the ecliptic being then given by the third law of Kepler. Disturbing planetary masses as proposed by Kovalevsky are used. Constants of integration have been carefully determined in such a way that the solution coincides with the mean elements at the time origin 1850.0, calculation which is not found in a similar work done by Anolik et al. (26). Bretagnon took into account all the long period terms of the disturbing function up to the fourth degree in e's and i's. In a second approximation, he has also introduced the short period terms (secular part) of the disturbing function that give, at the second order of the masses, long period terms in the solution. For this contribution of the short period terms, all the terms to the 3rd degree in e's and i's which lead to a modification of the long period frequencies by more than 0.001" per year (around 50 for the only Jupiter-Saturn near resonance) have been kept for all the planets. Among the long period terms generated through these terms, only those which amplitude is greater than 10^{-4} for the inner planets and 10^{-6} for the major ones have been considered. These terms have a great influence on the frequencies; particularly in the Jupiter-Saturn couple. This solution is also given in Table 2 under the label BRE 3.

Unfortunately, for the Jupiter-Saturn near resonance namely, degree 3 is not sufficient and it is necessary to take into account the terms of degree 5 and 7 of this great inequality. Some improvements are thus still expected by introducing long period terms of fifth order and also short period terms of higher order. The realisation of such a goal needs however the construction of a general planetary theory. As it requires the integration of a system of 48 differential equations for eight planets where the disturbing function must contain several millions of terms, it is not possible now to build such an accurate solution. However, many theoretical works are available on this subject and the most advanced application of it is probably Duriez's work (29). Unfortunately, that work deals only with the four outer planets, although one of its important results as far as paleoclimates are concerned, is the determination of long period frequencies with the improvement of the largest mean rates in the system [12] (28"328 per year) with respect to Bretagnon 1974 value (26"217 per year).

Moreover, because the accuracy which is needed for the frequencies lies between hundredths and one tenth of a second per year, their modification by the relativistic perturbations and by the perturbations due to the Moon has not to be neglected. This is why Bretagnon (30) has improved the Lagrange system by bringing in the disturbing function the terms of degree 2 in eccentricity due to the general relativity and to the Moon, and by computing the constants of integration through adjustment of the solution to his short-term solution VSOP82 for 1850.0. These new Lagrange terms and the Bretagnon 1974 terms to the 3rd degree in e's and i's and to the second order to the masses, form the solution BRE 4 (Tables 1-2).

Finally, following Bretagnon and Berger's estimates of what could be the final accuracy of each frequency, we have changed the mean rates by amounts ranging from 0.01 to 0.20" per year (BRE 5 in Tables 1-2).

The procedure used for obtaining long-range changes in the elements of planetary orbits involves a drastic simplification of the astronomical problem and the results obtained are admitedly of a limited accuracy.

The planet Pluto was not included in these calculations, the difficulty being that the orbits of Neptune and Pluto may intersect if the perihelia and nodes are permitted to vary without restriction. In view of the smallness of the secular perturbations by Neptune on the planets inferior to it, it seems likely that inclusion of Pluto would not greatly alter the solution for the other planets.

The periods of the periodic terms that represent the solutions are quite long, varying from about 47 kyr to 2 000 kyr, and the largest coefficient is less than 0.03.

The most serious limitations of a practical nature arise from the uncertainties of the periods themselves. These are obtained as functions of the masses and the orbital elements of the planets. They would be modified by the inclusion of terms of higher order in masses and higher powers in e's and i's. If any one of the principal periods should need a correction of 1%, it is clear that the contribution due to this particular term would be a full period out of phase after 100 periods. The representation by these series thus becomes less and less reliable as to detail as the interval of time from the epoch of reference increases. If an uncertainty of 1% in a period of 90 000 years is a reasonable estimate, then the representation by these series has lost all its meaning as to detail in 9×10^6 years.

Moreover, due to the large influence of the Jupiter-Saturn near-resonance, the calculations must be repeated including :

(1) not only long-period terms of fifth order (terms which would affect mostly Mercury, Venus, Earth and Mars), but also,
(2) for all the planets, short-period terms of higher order in e and i's, and eventually,
(3) terms of the third order in masses, at least for the Jupiter-Saturn near-resonance.

However, qualitative and quantitative indications are also available to show that the results are nevertheless reliable (28) :

(1) The same method has been used with good success in the treatment of satellite systems in which the periods may be shorter by factors of about 10^4. Thus, 100 years in such a satellite system may correspond to a million years in the planetary system.
(2) The application of the Brouwer-van Woerkom solution to the motion of minor planets indicates a general reliability to about the third decimal place, but does not indicate anything

concerning the interval of time for which the developments may be trusted.
(3) There is an excellent agreement between the mean long-term period of ε and that computed from a numerical expression derived from the last 2000 years of observation.
(4) The frequencies corresponding to the largest amplitudes are quite stable; the present accuracy is estimated to be for precession within 1%, for obliquity, less than 0.01%, for eccentricity about 3%.

LONG-TERM VARIATIONS OF THE OBLIQUITY AND LONGITUDE OF THE MOVING PERIHELION

As the insolation requires the values of the obliquity ε (inclination of the equator on the ecliptic of date) and of the

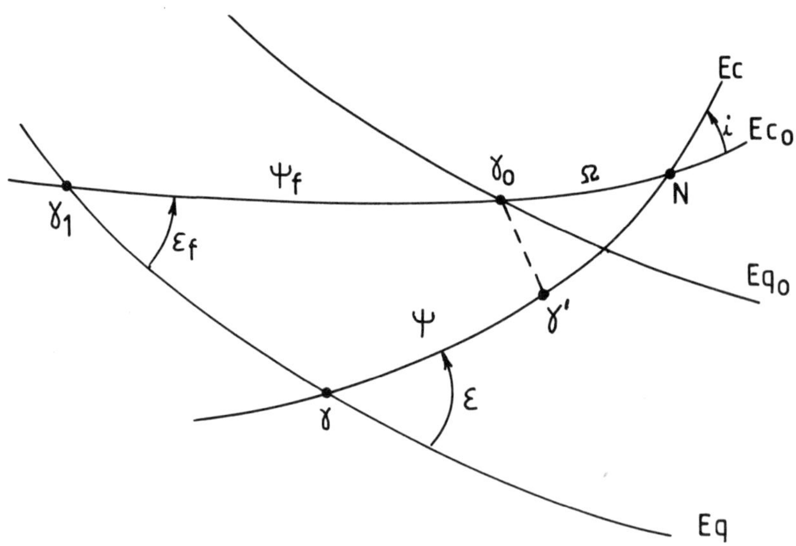

Figure 2 Precession and obliquity : Ec is the mean ecliptic of date, Ec_0 the mean ecliptic of reference; Eq the equator of date, Eq_0 the equator of reference; γ the mean vernal equinox of date; γ_0 the mean vernal equinox of reference; P the perihelion; $\gamma_0\gamma_1=\Psi_f$ the luni-solar precession in longitude; $\gamma'\gamma=\Psi$, the general precession in longitude; ε_f and ε the inclination of the equator of date respectively, on the ecliptic of reference and on the ecliptic of date.

Table 3a Amplitudes, Mean Rates and Phases in the trigonometrical expansion of the obliquity (only the 5 largest amplitude terms are given).

	MILANK	BRE 1	BRE 2	SHARAF	BRE 3	BRE 4	BRE 5
AMPLITUDE (")							
1	2994.66	-2980.56	-2389.96	-2983.03	-2462.21	-2462.11	-2462.09
2	-601.62	-604.52	-848.48	-603.72	-857.31	-857.28	-857.27
3	-482.70	-501.20	-634.15	-502.96	-629.32	-629.28	-629.28
4	-244.23	-252.13	-535.27	-250.67	-414.28	-414.26	-414.26
5	-199.92	-202.08	350.49	-201.45	-311.76	-311.75	-311.75
MEAN RATE ("/year)							
1	31.7371	31.7005	31.5456	31.7066	31.6099	31.6113	31.6115
2	24.6526	24.7055	32.5771	24.7166	32.6205	32.6219	32.6220
3	32.8615	32.8106	24.0964	32.8168	24.1722	24.1736	24.1737
4	45.3572	43.8753	31.9429	43.8793	31.9838	31.9851	31.9853
5	43.8304	45.2467	30.9115	45.2486	44.8283	44.8297	44.8298
PHASE (°)							
1	77.3	257.2	251.5	257.1	251.9	251.8	251.8
2	129.1	129.0	278.7	128.9	280.8	280.7	280.7
3	298.9	298.6	128.5	298.4	128.3	128.2	128.2
4	24.0	319.6	290.0	320.0	292.7	292.6	292.6
5	305.3	21.5	262.7	21.3	15.3	15.3	

The labelling of these solutions corresponds to the authors from which the developments of e, π, i, Ω originate, although the computation of ε and Ψ is made following (31). To have the corresponding accuracy of these expansions, refer to the first line of Table 1.

Table 3b Amplitudes, Mean Rates and Phases in the trigonometrical expansion of the general precession (only the 5 largest amplitude terms are given).

	MILANK	BRE 1	BRE 2	SHARAF	BRE 3	BRE 4	BRE 5
AMPLITUDE (")							
1	-8983.14	8939.63	7178.72	8947.08	7391.01	7390.81	7390.79
2	-2340.57	-2316.81	-2630.31	-2271.01	2555.13	2555.07	2555.06
3	1923.64	1931.04	2529.99	1928.34	2022.76	-21889.06	-2225.11
4	1436.62	1491.57	2040.40	1496.82	-1973.64	2022.66	2022.65
5	682.18	708.05	1603.19	971.93	1240.23	1240.19	1240.19
MEAN RATE ("/year)							
1	31.7371	31.7005	31.5456	31.7066	31.6099	31.6113	31.6115
2	0.6705	0.6732	0.6341	0.6740	32.6205	32.6219	32.6220
3	24.6526	24.7055	32.5771	24.7166	24.1722	0.6173	0.6073
4	32.8615	32.8106	24.0964	32.8168	0.6367	24.1736	24.1737
5	45.3572	43.8753	31.9429	3.0488	31.9838	31.9851	31.9853
PHASE (°)							
1	77.3	257.2	251.5	257.1	251.9	251.8	251.8
2	343.0	343.1	348.7	342.7	280.8	280.7	280.7
3	129.1	129.0	278.7	128.9	128.3	348.7	348.7
4	298.9	298.6	128.5	298.4	348.1	128.2	128.2
5	24.0	319.6	290.0	167.3	292.7	292.6	292.6

The labelling of these solutions correspond to the authors from which the developments of e, π, i, Ω originate, although the computation of ε and Ψ is made following (31). To have the corresponding accuracy of these expansions, refer to the first line of Table 1.

Table 4 Amplitudes, Mean Rates and Phases in the trigonometrical expansion of the climatic precession (only the 5 largest amplitude terms are given).

	MILANK	BRE 1	BRE 2	SHARAF	BRE 3	BRE 4	BRE 5
AMPLITUDE (")							
1	0.00512	0.00406	0.00349	0.00392	0.00333	0.0043	0.0043
2	-0.01410	0.01490	0.01455	0.01634	0.01628	0.0161	0.0161
3	0.01056	0.01057	0.01204	0.01043	0.00989	0.0102	0.0102
4	-0.01502	-0.01493	-0.01430	-0.01483	-0.01301	-0.0134	-0.0134
5	0.01628	0.01624	0.01635	0.01834	0.01861	0.0182	0.0182
MEAN RATE ("/year)							
1	55.920	55.908	55.647	55.913	55.638	56.054	56.114
2	57.818	57.793	57.790	57.795	57.785	57.897	57.907
3	67.185	67.778	67.646	67.778	67.660	67.726	67.746
4	68.455	68.451	68.280	68.452	68.296	68.343	68.353
5	54.139	54.158	54.174	54.746	54.646	54.749	54.759
PHASE (°)							
1	90.4	90.8	87.2	94.2	90.6	90.6	90.6
2	24.2	196.3	195.1	198.9	197.2	200.0	200.0
3	336.8	336.9	322.3	337.4	323.6	322.4	322.4
4	319.8	320.1	311.0	320.2	311.7	311.2	311.2
5	32.1	31.4	30.9	31.6	32.0	32.1	32.1

The labelling of these solutions corresponds to the authors from which the developments of e, π, i, Ω originate, although the computation $e \sin \tilde{\omega}$ is made following (31). To have the corresponding accuracy of these expansions, refer to the first line of Table 1.

longitude of the moving perihelion $\tilde{\omega}$, ε and the general precession in longitude Ψ ($\Psi:\tilde{\omega}=\pi+\Psi$) will be computed according to the procedure explained in (31). The resulting equations are obtained by solving the Poisson's equations which allow to compute the luni-solar precession in longitude, Ψ_f (Fig. 2) and the inclination ε_f of the equator on the mean ecliptic of reference (19). ε and Ψ can then be determined by resolving the classical spherical triangle $N\gamma_1\gamma$ of Fig. 2.

$$\varepsilon = \varepsilon^* + \Sigma A_i \cos (\tilde{f}_i t + \tilde{\delta}_i)$$

$$\Psi = \Psi t + \zeta = \Sigma F_i \sin (\tilde{f}_i t + \tilde{\delta}_i)$$

$$e \sin \tilde{\omega} = \Sigma P_i \sin (\alpha_i t + \xi_i) \qquad [14]$$

$$e \cos \tilde{\omega} = \Sigma P_i \cos (\alpha_i t + \xi_i)$$

$$e = e_0 + \Sigma F_i \cos (\lambda_i t + \phi_i)$$

The initial conditions being referred to 1950.0, the constants ε^*, Ψ and ζ and the amplitudes, mean rates and phases can be estimated.

Because our main interest is to test the sensitivity of the Earth's orbital elements directly related to the insolation, with regards to the accuracy of the fundamental system of celestial mechanics ($e,\pi;i,\Omega$), Tables 3 and 4 provide the characteristics of the largest terms in ε, Ψ and $e \sin \tilde{\omega}$.

NUMERICAL COMPARISONS IN THE TIME DOMAIN AND STABILITY OF THE FREQUENCIES IN TIME

From all these solutions written in an analytical form, it is quite easy to generate time-series and compare them together. This was done for the last 3.2×10^6 yr and reproduced in Figs. 3, 4, 5 for the last 1.6×10^6 yr. The Milankovitch solution has been retained for historical reason but the comparison will be made essentially between the 6 others. A visual check to these curves confirm theoretical results obtained from the analysis of the amplitudes, mean rates and phases (listed in Tables 1 to 4) : after 3×10^6 yr the "most accurate" solutions are out of phase by one third of a cycle for the eccentricity, one full cycle for precession and one fifth of a cycle for obliquity.

It would be now interesting to check whether or not the main frequencies of the these 3 orbital parameters are stable in time. It is expected that this analysis will help understanding why the main spectral peaks in proxy climatic data recorded over the Quaternary may differ for different geological epochs and from region to region over the world (32,33,34). For this purpose the whole time series has been divided into 4 sub-series (SS) of 800 000 years each. Spectral analyses (35) of these sub-time series are reproduced in Figs. 6,7,8 for the 7 different astronomical solutions. Although (i) 800 000 years represent only 2 times the length of the 400 kyr-period associated with the largest amplitude in the expansion of e (2) and (ii) the 41 kyr-period of ε is associated with a term which is by far the most important in the obliquity expansion, significant differences appear both between the solutions themselves and between the different SSs.

Sharaf eccentricity curve has a much sharper signal at 100 kyr and 400 kyr during the first and the third SSs than the others; the same is true for BRE 2 during the last SS. In a more or less uniform way for all solutions, the spectral power is about equally shared during the first and the last SSs between the 400 and 100 kyr-periods (this is especially true for the most recent solutions BRE 3,4,5), the second SS is dominated by the 100 kyr-period and the third by the 400 kyr-period.

Except for SHARAF, BRE 1 and MILANK (i.e., those which do not take into account the terms in degree 3 with respect to the e's and i's), the spectral behaviour of ε is more or less the same for all solutions : a strong peak everywhere except during the third SS where, indeed, the amplitude of the oscillations is largely reduced.

Interesting features occur also in the precessional term. There is a marked difference between MILANK, BRE 1 and BRE 2 (solutions which do not take into account the terms to the second order to the masses) and the others, namely a reversal in the relative importance of the 23 and 19 kyr spectral components which is clearly seen in the first and last SSs. As far as the stability in time is concerned, the third SS shows a dominant 23 kyr peak with an almost-zero 19 kyr component, the first and the last SSs are dominated by the 23 kyr component but with a reasonable part of the variance explained by the 19 kyr component and the second SS displays a equally-shared variance between the 23 and the 19 kyr-periods.

This behaviour in the frequency domain is confirmed by results recently obtained by Siddiqui and Wang (36) using a totally different spectral technique.

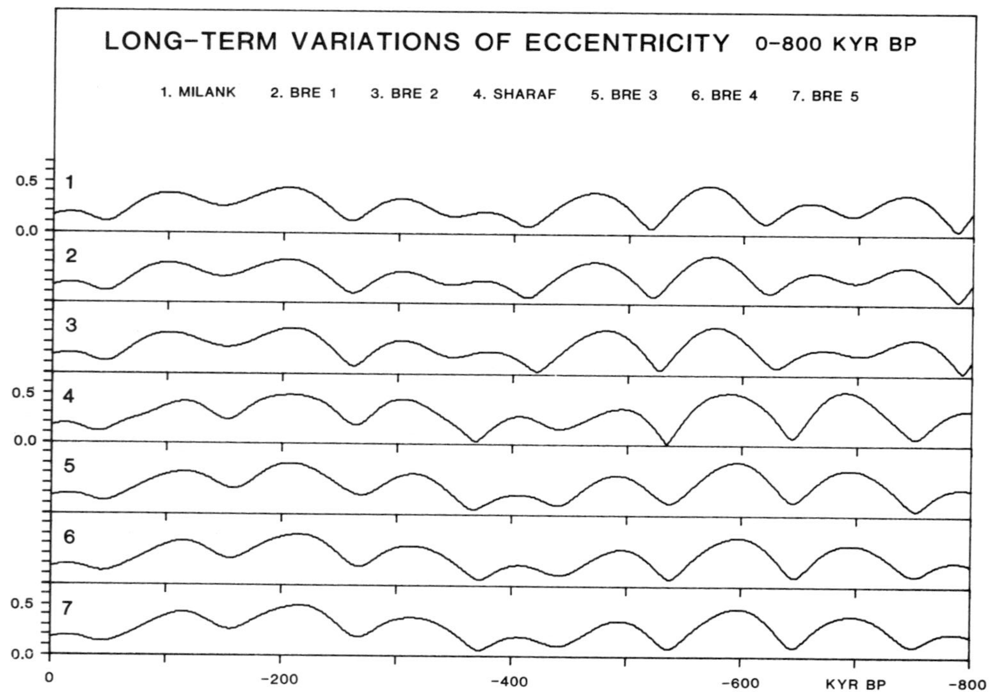

Figure 3a Long-term variations of the eccentricity over the last 0-800 kyr BP. 7 astronomical solutions are considered as given in Tables 1 and 2a.

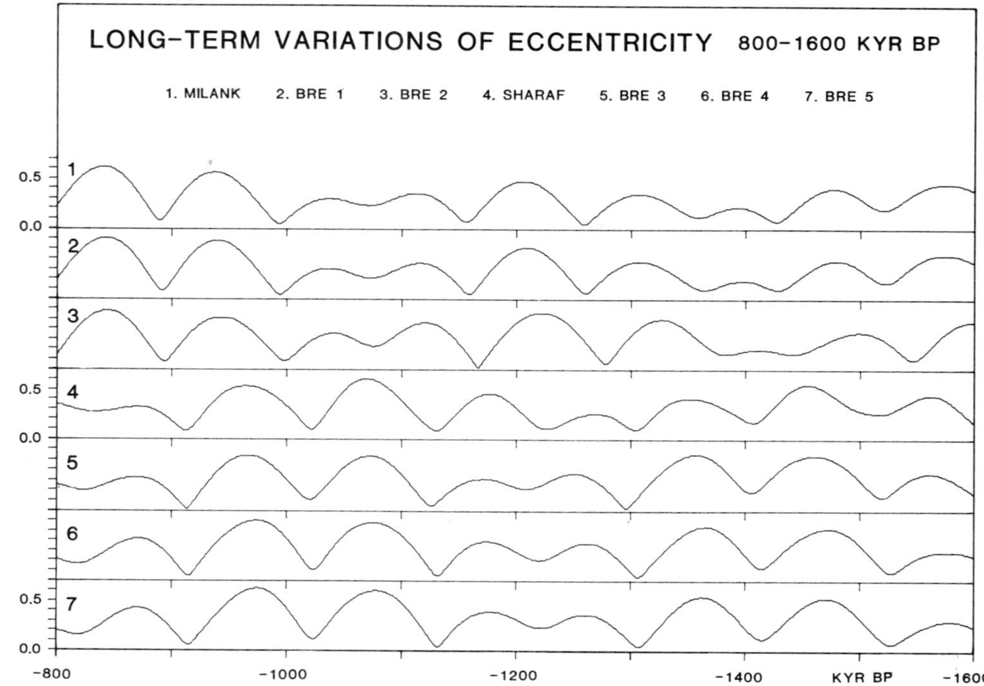

Figure 3b Long-term variations of the eccentricity over the last 800-1600 kyr BP. 7 astronomical solutions are considered as given in Tables 1 and 2a.

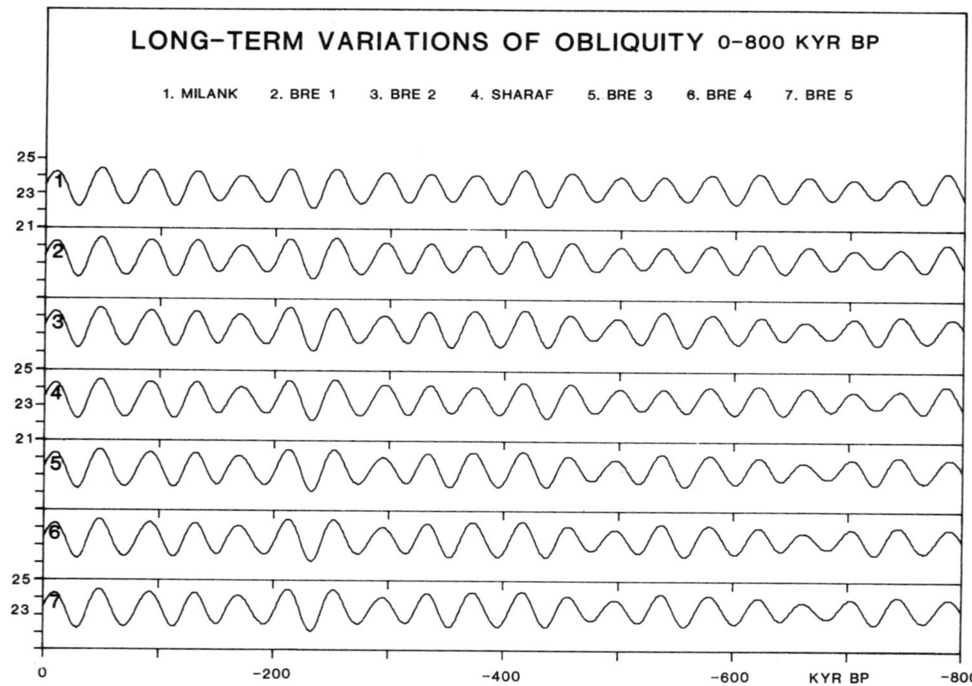

Figure 4a Long-term variations of the obliquity over the last 0-800 kyr BP. 7 astronomical solutions are considered as given in Tables 1 and 3a.

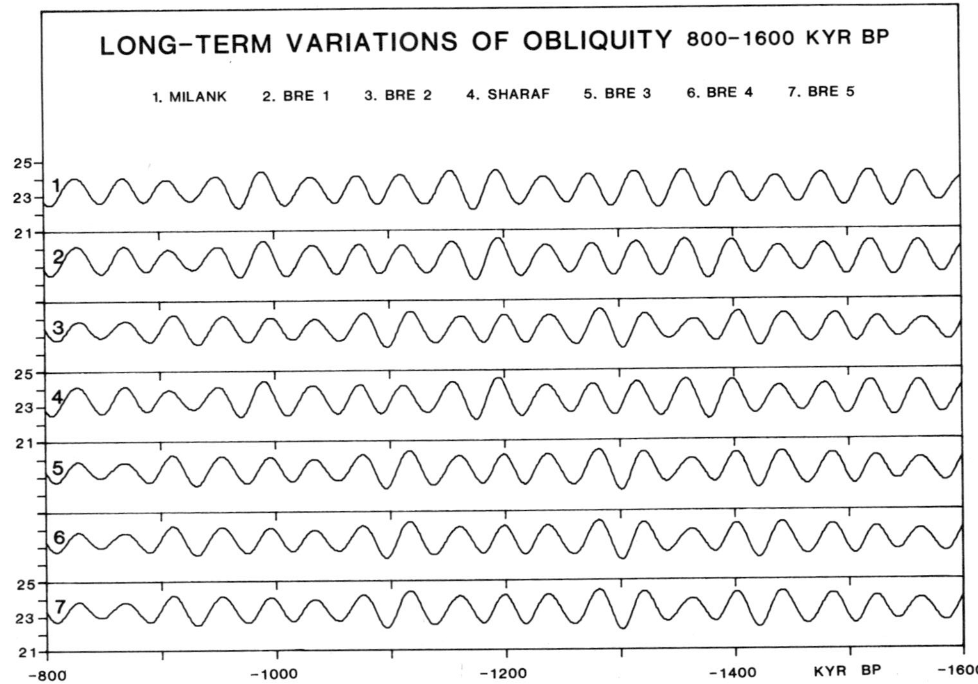

Figure 4b Long-term variations of the obliquity over the last 800-1600 kyr BP. 7 astronomical solutions are considered as given in Tables 1 and 3a.

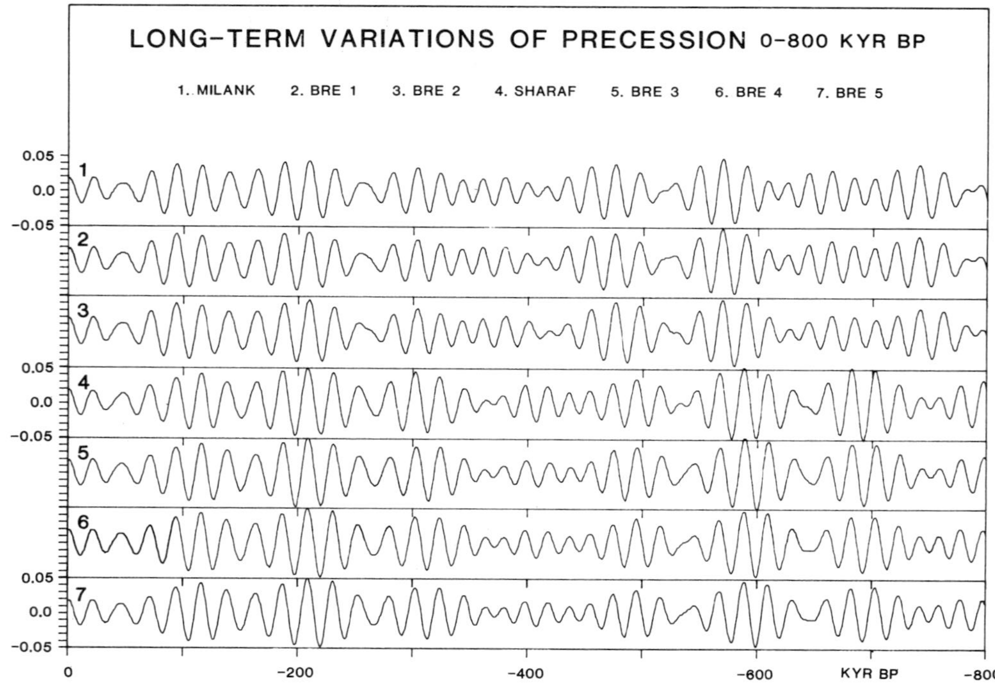

Figure 5a Long-term variations of the climatic precession over the last 0-800 kyr BP. 7 astronomical solutions are considered as given in Tables 1 and 4.

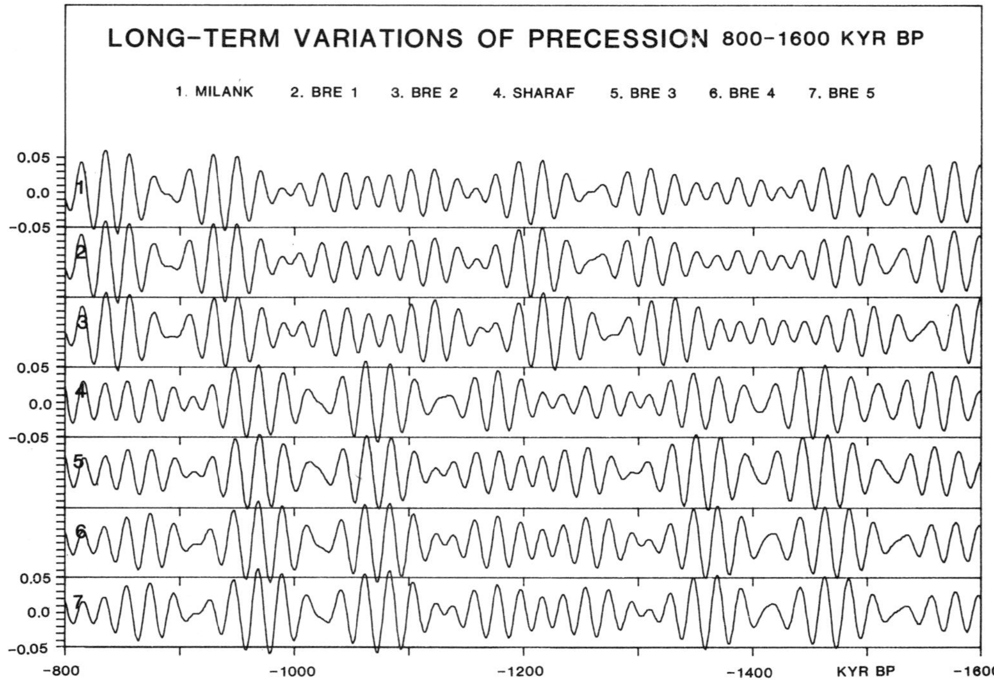

Figure 5b Long-term variations of the climatic precession over the last 800-1600 kyr BP. 7 astronomical solutions are considered as given in Tables 1 and 4.

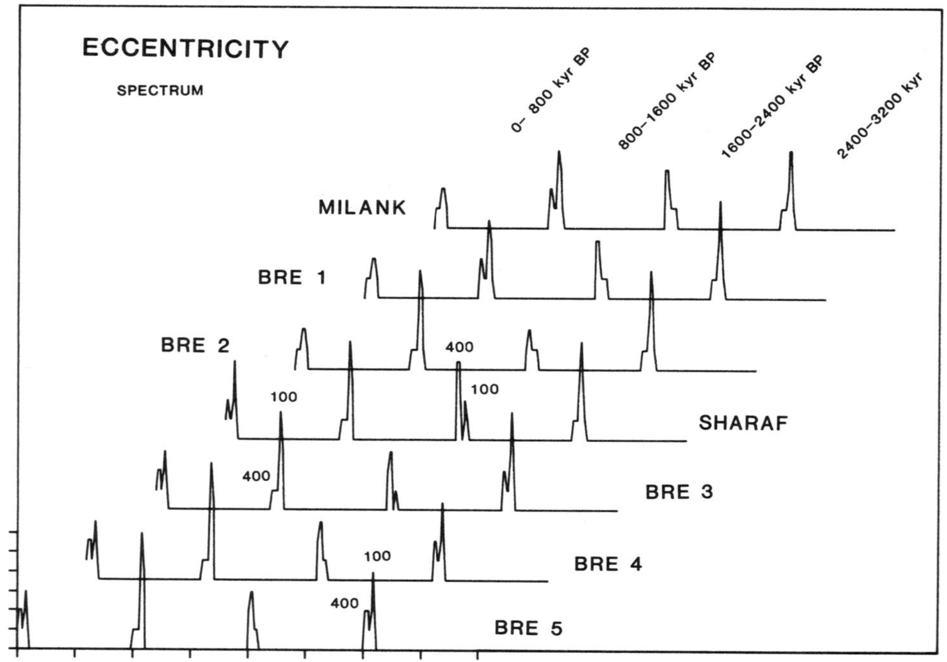

Figure 6 Spectral analysis of the eccentricity for 7 astronomical solutions (Tables 1, 2a and Figs. 3) and 4 different intervals.

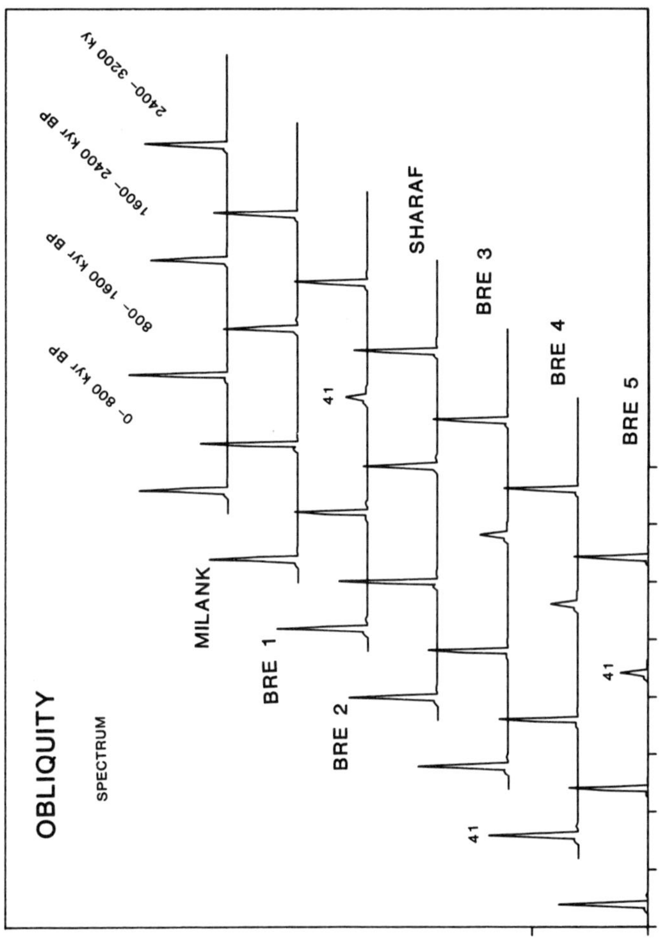

Figure 7 Spectral analysis of the obliquity for 7 astronomical solutions (Tables 1, 3a and Fig. 4) and 4 different intervals.

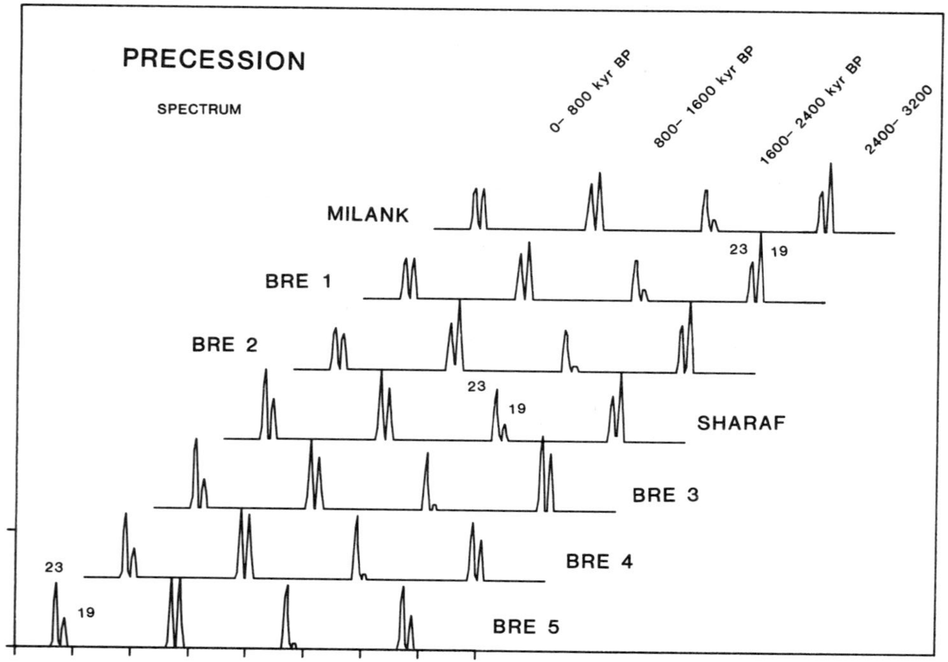

Figure 8 Spectral analysis of the climatic precession for 7 astronomical solutions (Tables 1, 4 and Fig. 5) and 4 different intervals.

CONCLUSION

The astronomical series shown here demonstrate clearly that the accuracy of these solutions depends upon the accuracy of the constants, the initial conditions, and the expansions themselves. Their critical examination has lead to the following conclusions (25) :

(1) Improvement in values for planetary masses will not have further significant influence.
(2) For eccentricity and longitude of the perihelion (e, π), terms dependent to the second order on the masses are more important than terms coming from the third degree in planetary e's and i's.
(3) For inclination and longitude of the node (i, Ω), on the contrary, these last terms are highly significant, whereas supplementary terms in masses are negligible.
(4) For obliquity and annual general precession in longitude (ε, Ψ), because of the nature of their mathematical dependence on (i, Ω), the same conclusions may be drawn. However, in this case, the truncation of the series themselves comes into account.

Consequently, and as the solution BRE 3 developed in (2) has most of the properties than the 2 more recent ones BRE 4 and BRE 5, precession, eccentricity and obliquity values given in (2) and in this paper (Fig. 9) are considered to be reliable respectively for 1.5×10^6, 3×10^6 and 4×10^6 years from present. Moreover, all their frequencies are stable enough for paleoclimate studies over 5×10^6 years at least.

If such a solution is considered, numerical experiments conducted over the previous 5 million years show that e varies between 0.0005 and 0.0607 (present value 0.0167) with an average quasi-period of 95 kyr (main spectral components at 410, 95, 120 and 100 kyr). ε varies between 22° and 24°30' (today's value 23°27'), with a very prominent and stable quasi-period of 41 kyr, although periods of 54 and 29 kyr are not negligible). The revolution of the vernal point relative to the moving perihelion (climatic precession) has a average quasi-period of 21.7 kyr (main periods are about 23 and 19 kyr, although a higher spectral resolution does exist (2)), whereas relative to the fixed perihelion of reference, this quasi-period is 25.5 kyr (astronomical precession of equinoxes). $e \sin \omega$ is presently equal to 0.01635 and oscillates roughly between -0.05 and 0.05.

Since the periods are incommensurable, it is evident that, within the limitations of the theory, the maximum value of the elements for any planet is equal to the sum of all coefficients (taken positively) in the series. For example, e_{max} computed

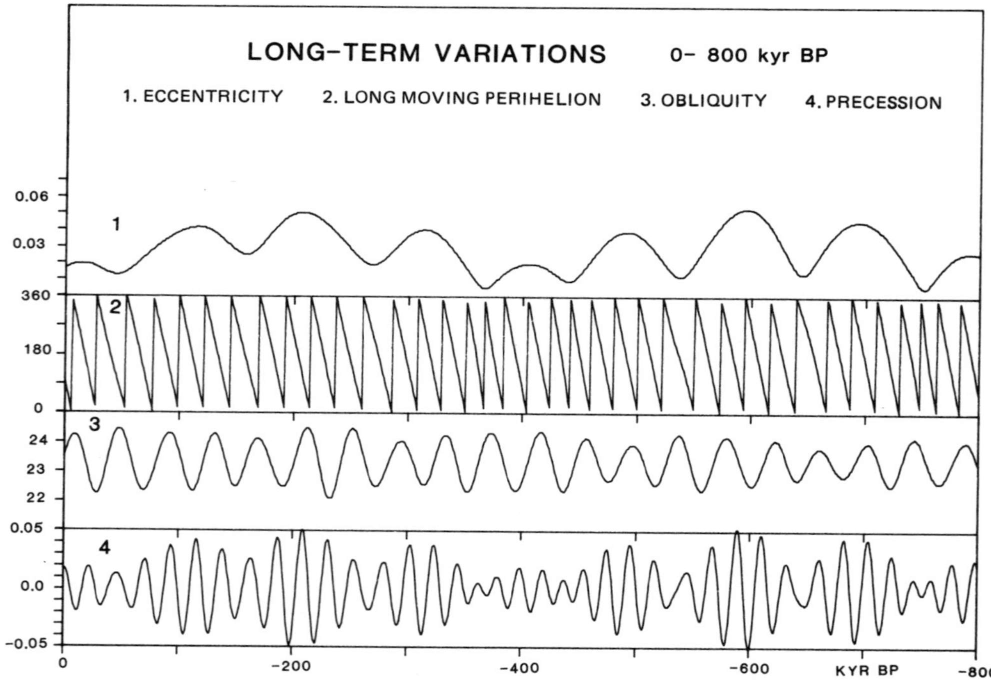

Figure 9 Long-term variations of the eccentricity, longitude of the moving perihelion, obliquity and climate precession over the last 800 kyr.

from the 7 different solutions oscillates between 0.0638 and 0.0744, and the maximal deviation from to-day value of ε is $\pm$ 2°. It is also evident that in case one coefficient is numerically greater than the sum of all the others, then a minimum value can be assigned.

For much longer time-spans of the geological past, it would be hazardous to extend this type of solution or even to extrapolate from their characteristics. A general theory of the planetary system (29), or other approach as discussed in (13), must be developed. Indeed, let us consider for example the mean rates f_i and s_i in [14]. As discussed in (20) and reminded recently (37), they depend upon the dynamical ellipticity of the Earth and in some non-linear way of the Newcomb constant of precession where one term is a function of the cube of the ratio between the semi-major axes of the terrestrial and lunar orbits. As at the geological time scale the moon is gradually moving away from the Earth and the Earth's rotation is slowing down, it could be argued that the mean precessional period will subsequently be smaller than 21 kyr in the remote past. However, this conclusion, which is very tempting and could be very helpful for the discussion of the periodicities found in the Miocene and in the Cretaceous (38,39), must be taken with caution because the form of the astronomical solution changes if these "constants" become time-dependent. Nevertheless, this is the kind of discussion which opens the field of research and is expected to stimulate further developments in the theory of the long-term variations of the Earth's orbital elements.

REFERENCES

1. Berger, A., Imbrie, J., Hays, J., Kukla, G., Saltzman, B. (Eds) : 1984, Milankovitch and Climate, Understanding the response of orbital forcing. Reidel Publ. Company, Dordrecht, Holland.
2. Berger, A. : 1978, J. Atmos. Sci. 35(2), pp. 2362-2367.
3. Milankovitch, M.M. : 1941, Canon of Insolation and the Ice-Age Problem. Beograd, Köninglich Serbische Akademie. 484pp. (English translation by Israel program for Scientific Translation and published for the U.S. Department of Commerce and the National Science Foundation).
4. Bernard, E. : 1962, Nouvelle Série XII, fasc. 1, Acad. Roy. Sc. Outre-Mer, Cl. Sc. Nat. et Med., Bruxelles.
5. Newton, I. : 1687, Principia mathematica. The Royal Society, London, Book III, Proposition VI, Theorem VI.
6. Chebotarev, G.A. : 1967, Analytical and Numerical methods of Celestial Mechanics. Elsevier Publ. Company, N.Y.
7. Brouwer, D., and Clemence, G.M. : 1961, Methods of Celestial Mechanics. Academic Press. N.Y.

8. Sterne, T.E. : 1960, An Introduction to Celestial Mechanics Interscience Publisher Inc., N.Y.
9. Tisserand, F. : 1894 : Traité de Mécanique Céleste. Gauthier-Villars. Paris.
10. Lagrange, J.L. : 1871, Théorie des Variations Séculaires des Eléments des Planètes, Nouveaux mémoires de l'Académie Royale de Berlin; publié dans Oeuvres de Lagrange, par Serret, Tomes 3,4,5 (1870), Paris.
11. Laplace, P.S. : 1798, Traité de Mécanique Céleste. 5 tomes, Paris.4e édition, Paris 1882.
12. Leverrier, U.J.J. : 1855, Recherches Astronomiques, Annales de l'Observatoire Impérial de paris, Tome II.
13. Buys, M., and Ghil, M. : 1984, in : "Milankovitch and Climate", A. Berger, J. Imbrie, J. Hays, G. Kukla, B. Saltzman (Eds), Reidel Publ. Company, Dordrecht, Holland. This volume, p. 55.
14. Berger, A. : 1980, Vistas in Astronomy 24, pp. 103-122.
15. Adhemar, J. : 1842, Révolutions de la Mer. Déluges Périodiques. Paris.
16. Croll, J. : 1875, Climate and Time in their Geological Relations. Appleton, New York.
17. Vernekar, A. : 1972, Long-period global variations of incoming solar radiation. Meteorological Monographs 12, n°34.
18. Berger, A. : 1978, Quaternary Research 9, pp. 139-167.
19. Stockwell, J.N. : 1873, Memoir on the Secular Variations of the Elements of the Eight Principal Planets, Smith. Contr. Knowledge 18(3), Washington.
20. Berger, A. : 1973, Théorie Astronomique des Paléoclimats, D.Sc. Thesis, Université Catholique de Louvain, Louvain-la-Neuve.
21. Harzer, P. : 1895, Die Säkularen Veranderungen der Bahnen der Grossen Planeten, Presschrift, Leipzig.
22. Sharaf S.G., Budnikova, N.A. : 1967, Tr. Inst. Theor. Astron. 11, pp. 231-261 (in Russian).
23. Miskovitch, V.V. : 1931, Variations séculaires des éléments astronomiques de l'orbite terrestre. Glas. Srp. Kralyerske Akad. 143, Première Classe n° 70, Belgrade.
24. Milankovitch, M. : 1920, Théorie Mathématique des Phénomènes Thermiques produits par la Radiation Solaire, Académie Yougoslave des Sciences et des Arts de Zagreb, Gauthier-Villars.
25. Berger, A. : 1977, Celestial Mechanics 15, pp. 53-74.
26. Anolik, M.V., Krassinsky, B.A., Pius, L.J. : 1969, Trud. Inst. Teor. Astron. Leningrad 14, pp. 1-48.
27. Brouwer, D., van Woerkom, A.J.J. : 1950, Astronomical papers of the American Ephemeris and Nautical Almanac 13(2), pp. 81-107.
28. Berger, A. : 1976, Astronomy and Astrophysics 51, pp. 127-135.

29. Duriez, L. : 1979, Approche d'une théorie générale planétaire en variables elliptiques heliocentriques. Docteur ès Sciences thesis, Lille.
30. Bretagnon, P. : 1984, in : "Milankovitch and Climate", A. Berger, J. Imbrie, J. Hays, G. Kukla, B. Saltzman (Eds), Reidel Publ. Company, Dordrecht, Holland. This volume, p. 41.
31. Berger, A. : 1978, Contribution n° 18, Institut d'Astronomie et de Géophysique G. Lemaître, Université Catholique de Louvain-la-Neuve.
32. Imbrie, J., Hays, J.D., Martinson, D.G., McIntyre, A., Mix, A.C., Morley, J.J., Pisias, N.G., Prell, W.L., and Shackleton, N.J. : 1984, in : "Milankovitch and Climate", A. Berger, J. Imbrie, J. Hays, G. Kukla, B. Saltzman (Eds), Reidel Publ. Company, Dordrecht, Holland. This volume, p. 269.
33. Moore, T.C., Pisias, N.G., and Dunn, D.A. : 1982, Marine Geology 46, pp. 217-233.
34. Start, G.G., and Prell, W.L. : 1982, in : "New Perspectives in Climate Modelling", A. Berger and C. Nicolis (Eds), Elsevier Publ. Company (in press).
35. Pestiaux, P., and Berger, A. : 1984, in : "Milankovitch and Climate", A. Berger, J. Imbrie, J. Hays, G. Kukla, B. Saltzman (Eds), Reidel Publ. Company, Dordrecht, Holland. This volume, p. 417.
36. Siddiqui, M.M., and Wang, C.C. : 1984, submitted to J. of Statistical Planning and Inference.
37. Bernard, E. : 1983, unpublished communication presented at the workshop on "Astronomical Signal in Pre-Quaternary Geological Data", Institut d'Astronomie et de Géophysique G. Lemaître, Université Catholique de Louvain-la-Neuve.
38. Fisher, A.G., and Schwarzacher, W. : 1984, in : "Milankovitch and Climate", A. Berger, J. Imbrie, J. Hays, G. Kukla, B. Saltzman (Eds), Reidel Publ. Company, Dordrecht, Holland. This volume, p. 163.
39. de Boer, P.L., and Wonders, A.A.H. : 1984, in : "Milankovitch and Climate", A. Berger, J. Imbrie, J. Hays, G. Kukla, B. Saltzman (Eds), Reidel Publ. Company, Dordrecht, Holland. This volume, p. 177.

[1] To be coherent with those also working in an heliocentric system (3,4) that value computed here should have been labelled Π.

[2] It would be simpler to consider, instead of S_0, S_a, the astrophysical solar parameter calculated at the distance a from the sun: it is only a function of the solar luminosity. As the mean Earth-sun distance is given by : $r_m^2 = a^2(1-e^2)^{1/2}$ we have $S_a = S_0(1-e^2)^{1/2}$.

ACCURACY OF LONG TERM PLANETARY THEORY

P. Bretagnon

Service de Mécanique Céleste du Bureau des Longitudes, F-75014 Paris, France.

SUMMARY

The global integration of the equations of celestial mechanics for the eight planets disturbing one another is a problem that has been studied several times, but so far has not reached a global solution of great accuracy. The general theory, a solution for such a problem, should produce all the short period perturbations (about the periods of the planets) and the long period ones (periods of the perihelia and the nodes in-between 50 kyr and 2 000 kyr).

Two methods are currently used to simplify the problem :

a) the long periodic terms are developed with respect to the time in the Lagrange equations (solution of Le Verrier's type). One then gets the position of the eight planets with a very good precision (some 0".01), but over short intervals of time (some thousands of years).

b) we only retain the long period perturbations of four variables giving the shape and position of the orbit, without trying to locate the planet on its orbit. Such a simplification makes it possible to know the evolution of the orbits over much longer times. The accuracy of the solution is limited mainly by the accuracy of the long period frequencies. This accuracy can be evaluated to be in-between 0".01 and 0".2/year. The accuracy of the solution therefore depreciates with time, so that the elements of the orbits are merely defined at some per cent after one million years.

A. L. Berger et al. (eds.), Milankovitch and Climate, Part 1, 41–53.

INTRODUCTION

First, we present the different kinds of solution : general theories, secular variations theories, long period theories. Next, we show how it is possible to improve our solution of 1974. Finally, we give the results of that improvement as well as the precision of the solution.

GENERAL THEORIES

The construction of a general theory for the eight major planets (Pluto excluded) consists in integrating a system of 48 differential equations. This system is of course not integrable, and it is only possible to get the solution through successive approximation in the building up of the planetary perturbations, from a solution of the 0th order, the Keplerian orbit.

For that purpose we choose to represent the solutions with the variables a, λ, k, h, q, p, where $k = e\cos\tilde{\omega}$, $h = e\sin\tilde{\omega}$, $q = \gamma\cos\Omega$, $p = \gamma\sin\Omega$, $\gamma = \sin i/2$ in which a is the semi major axis, λ the mean longitude of the planet, e the eccentricity of the orbit, $\tilde{\omega}$ the longitude of the perihelium, i the inclination, Ω the longitude of the node.

Hence we must integrate the Lagrange equations for these variables. The Lagrange equations are obtained through partial derivatives of the disturbing function R which, in the case of two planets, can be written :

$$R = \Sigma S(\alpha) h_I^{r_1} h_E^{r_2} k_I^{s_1} k_E^{s_2} p_I^{t_1} p_E^{t_2} q_I^{u_1} q_E^{u_2} \cos(i_1\lambda_I + i_2\lambda_E) \qquad [1]$$

Subscripts I and E refer to the inner planet and the outer planet respectively. The sum extends over the values of the integer exponents such as :

$$r_1 + r_2 + s_1 + s_2 + t_1 + t_2 + u_1 + u_2 < \omega \qquad [2]$$

in which ω is the maximum degree.

To get a solution within 0".001 it is necessary to keep all terms of degree inferior or equal to 15. Such a disturbing function contains, for 2 planets, several tens of thousands of terms. Afterwards, the sums of the perturbations of each planet have to be made for all the seven other planets.

The integration of the Lagrange equations thus gives the first order perturbations with respect to the masses. Very soon afterwards it gets more difficult if one intends to build perturbations of superior order with respect to the masses.

It is hence obvious that it is not possible now to build a very precise general planetary theory valid over a long time (some million years). Many numerous theoretical works have however been made on this subject. Let us mention particularly the work of Brumberg and Chapront (1). The most advanced application of such a work is probably Duriez's construction of a general planetary theory (6). Unfortunately that work only deals with the four outer planets Jupiter, Saturn, Uranus and Neptune. One of the results of this theory is the determination of long period frequencies. Particularly, the values he obtained for g_5 and g_6 (see later) are certainly the best for now.

SECULAR VARIATIONS THEORIES

The most classical method to simplify the construction of planetary theories is to state the values of elements k, h, q and p of each planet, and to calculate the perturbations under the form of polynomials of time and periodic terms depending only of the mean longitudes of the eight planets. The arguments of the periodic terms have then only 8 components (the 8 mean longitudes) instead of 24 (8 mean longitudes, 8 longitudes of the perihelia, 8 longitudes of the nodes). This is just as developing, in the solutions, the long period terms (included in-between 50 kyr and 2 million years) with respect to time. This way does simplify considerably, but of course it is against the validity-time of the theory : in the utmost, some thousands of years.

Nevertheless, if the interval of time happens to be reduced, the accuracy can be high. Thus were developed the Le Verrier-Gaillot and the Newcomb theories. In the Bureau des Longitudes, the analytical construction of secular variation theories was undertaken some ten years ago. The solutions TOP82 (2) and VSOP82 (3) reach a precision, according to the planet, of some 0."001 to 0."1 over several thousands of years around epoch J2000.

Even though, as we have already mentionned, that kind of theory is much more simplified than the general theories, 70 000 terms were nevertheless needed to represent the solutions in their present state, for all the planets.

The secular variation theories supply, apart from the periodic perturbations, the mean elements under the form of time polynomials. The mean elements are the local development, with respect to time, of long periodic terms of a general theory. They are necessary for the determination of integration constants of the long period theories (see further on).

LONG PERIOD THEORIES

In order to separate them from general theories, we call long period theories the solutions in which only long periodic terms are withheld.

For each planet i, these solutions are of the form (the notations are those of Bretagnon, (4)) :

$$\begin{aligned}
h_i &= \sum_{j=1}^{8} \lambda_{ij} M_j \sin \psi_j + \sum_{\psi,\theta} M_{i,\psi,\theta} \sin(\psi,\theta) \\
k_i &= \sum_{j=1}^{8} \lambda_{ij} M_j \cos \psi_j + \sum_{\psi,\theta} \varepsilon\, M_{i,\psi,\theta} \cos(\psi,\theta) \\
p_i &= \sum_{j=1}^{8} \mu_{ij} N_j \sin \theta_j + \sum_{\psi,\theta} N_{i,\psi,\theta} \sin(\psi,\theta) \qquad [3] \\
q_i &= \sum_{j=1}^{8} \mu_{ij} N_j \cos \theta_j + \sum_{\psi,\theta} \varepsilon\, N_{i,\psi,\theta} \cos(\psi,\theta)
\end{aligned}$$

where the notation (ψ,θ) represents the argument :

$$(\psi,\theta) = i_1\psi_1 + i_2\psi_2 + \dots + i_8\psi_8 + i_9\theta_1 + i_{10}\theta_2 + \dots + i_{16}\theta_8$$

The arguments ψ_j are the eight arguments of the Lagrange solution for the system in eccentricity; the θ_j are the eight arguments of the inclination system :

$$\psi_j = g_j t + \beta_j$$

$$\theta_j = s_j t + \delta_j$$

The quantity ε is equal to +1 or -1 :

$$\varepsilon = \sum_{m=1}^{16} i_m$$

Among recent studies on long periodic theories, we mention the work of Anolik, Krassinsky and Pius (5) who have computed, for all the planets, all the terms coming from the long period of the disturbing function, limited to degree 4. That is to say they have considered all the terms for which both $i_1 = i_2 = 0$ in the formula [1] and the degree ω of expression [2] is equal to 4.

In Bretagnon (4), have also been considered all the long period terms of the disturbing function up to degree 4. We have moreover considered short period terms (i_1, i_2 not zero) of the disturbing function [1] that give, at the second order of the masses, long period terms in the solutions. For this contribution of the short period terms, we have retained all the terms of degree 0, 1, 2 or 3 which contributed to a modification of frequencies exceeding 0".001 per year. These terms have a great influence on the frequencies, particularly in the Jupiter-Saturn couple. Unfortunately, for that couple, degree 3 is not sufficient, and it is necessary to take into account the terms of degree 5 and 7 of the great inequality between Jupiter and Saturn : $2\lambda_J - 5\lambda_S$. This accounts for the inaccuracy of our 1974 solution (g_6 = 26".217/year) compared to that of Duriez (6) (g_6 = 28".328/year).

IMPROVEMENT OF THE LONG PERIOD THEORY

Improvement of the frequencies by introducing the relativistic perturbations and the perturbations due to the Moon

As we are to see later, one can estimate the accuracy of the 16 frequencies is between 0".01 and 0".20 per year, for the problem studied in a classical way of nine point masses, the Sun and eight planets, under Newtonian mechanics. However, the modification of the frequencies g_1, g_2, g_3 and g_4 by the introducing of the relativistic perturbations and the perturbations due to the Moon is not to be neglected in front of these precisions.

We therefore re-studied the Lagrange system by bringing in the disturbing function the degree 2 terms in eccentricity due to the relativity and to the Moon. We have reported the modifications of frequencies obtained by that new system of Lagrange on the complete solution. But we did not take into account the effects of these last modifications at higher orders and degrees.

In Table 1, we have collected, for the g_1, g_2, g_3 and g_4 frequencies, the modifications due to relativity : δg_R; the modifications due to the Moon : δg_M and g, the final value of the frequency. The unit used is the second per year. The modifications for the other frequencies are negligible.

An important consequence of that improvement of the Lagrange system is the modification of the system of eigenvectors associated with eigenvalues g_1, g_2, g_3 and g_4 and hence the modification of the integration constants of which we are going to talk about in the next paragraph.

Table 1. Modification of the frequencies due to the relativity and to the Moon. The unit is the second per year.

	δg_R	δg_M	g
1	+0".413126	+0".001432	5".613637
2	+0".080274	+0".029533	7".455898
3	+0".044674	+0".019945	17".285165
4	+0".029861	+0".015376	17".902500

Improvement of the integration constants

The solution being expressed under the form [3], the 32 integration constants of the long period problem are the quantities M_j, N_j, β_j, δ_j for j=1,2,...,8.

In Bretagnon (4) these 32 integration constants had been determined through adjustment of the solution to Newcomb mean elements for epoch 1850.0. This time we used the mean elements of the VSOP82 solution (3) still for epoch 1850.0. We give these 32 integration constants in Table 2. The quantities M_j and N_j are dimensionless, angles β_j and δ_j are given in radians. One can see important differences for these integration constants, particularly for the M_j and the β_j, between the new values of Table 2 and the values of (4).

Table 2. Integration constants for 1850.0. Phases β and δ are in radians.

j	M_j	β_j	N_j	δ_j
1	0.17782480	1.521050	0.05957877	0.214872
2	0.02086688	3.429564	0.00320244	5.337468
3	0.01024586	5.561205	0.01001606	4.343749
4	0.05595392	5.364482	0.03126062	4.855160
5	0.04346096	0.500518	0.01384001	1.852648
6	0.04813174	2.229306	0.00785530	2.193319
7	0.02936651	2.027812	0.00880177	5.520060
8	0.00937703	1.265684	0.00589092	3.512822

These differences come mainly from the modifications of the disturbing function (relativity, Moon) which we mentioned above. The consequence of this lies in important variations of the matrix of the eigen vectors and hence of the integration constants. The part of the discrepancies due to the use of more precise mean elements for 1850.0 is much weaker.

Improvement of the solution through adjustment of the long period terms on the mean elements of secular variation theories.

The lack of precision of the period theories is mainly due to two reasons :

1. the lack of terms due to high degree perturbations or to the third order with respect to the masses as well as the not precise enough determination of the terms completing the Lagrange solution.
2. the level of accuracy of the 16 long period frequencies.

The first point creates in the solutions a limited uncertainty, whatever the time. Given the amplitude of the different perturbations, one can estimate that uncertainty to be located between 1 and 20 per cent for each variable according to the planet.

The second point creates a negligible uncertainty over some thousands of years. But after some hundreds of thousands of years, the solution is some percents wrong because of the inaccuracy of the frequencies. Beyond one million years, the solution is getting far from the physical reality.

It is therefore essential to improve the precision of the frequencies.

We can see here above that the mean elements of the secular variations theories are in fact the developments of the long period terms with respect to time. These mean elements are only valid for some thousands of years, for they are expressed by polynomials of time generally limited to degree 4 or 5, but the coefficients of these polynomials are determined at a very high precision.

Therefore, if the form and amplitudes of the long period solutions were perfectly known, one could determine the frequencies through adjustment of the long period solutions to the secular variation theories.

Hence, we have undertaken the adjustment of the long period solution to the VSOP82 theory. Unfortunately, as regards the inner planets Mercury, Venus, the Earth and Mars, the form of the solution is too unprecise and the uncertainty of the results can be compared to the obtained modification of the frequencies. On the contrary, for the outer planets Jupiter, Saturn, Uranus and Neptune, the degree 3 terms and over in eccentricity and inclination, and the second order terms with respect to the masses are small before the Lagrange solution.

It was hence possible, in the case of frequencies linked to the outer planets, to improve the solution of Bretagnon (4). This improvement can especially be noted for the frequencies g_5 and g_6. It is rather interesting to notice that that new determination is close to the results of Duriez (6). We give in Table 3, for the frequencies g_5, g_6, g_7, g_8 and s_6, the results of Bretagnon (4), Duriez (6) and the new determinations. The unit is the second per year.

Table 3. Improvement of the frequencies g_5, g_6, g_7, g_8 and s_6. The unit is the second per year.

	Bretagnon 1974	Duriez 1979	New values
g_5	4."2072	4."3089	4."3080
g_6	26."2168	28."328	28."1483
g_7	3."0652	3."0982	3."1534
g_8	0."6679	0."6743	0."6735
s_6	-26."2671	-26."250	-26."2090

Results and precision of the solution

The solution we give here is under the same form as that given in Bretagnon (4). It differs from the value of the 16 frequencies and the value of the 32 integration constants (Table 2) hence for the Lagrange solution of the systems in eccentricities and inclinations. On the contrary, the degree 3 terms or the second order with respect to the masses have not been recomputed and are to be taken in Bretagnon (4).

Taken into account the modification of the frequencies obtained by the terms of degree 3 in eccentricity and inclination and for the terms of the second order with respect to the masses, we have estimated the precision of each frequency. We give in Table 4 the value of the frequencies as well as their uncertainties.

Table 4. Frequencies in seconds per year.

j	g_j	s_j
1	5.6136 ± 0.06	- 5.6109 ± 0.05
2	7.4559 ± 0.01	- 6.7710 ± 0.02
3	17.2852 ± 0.02	-18.8293 ± 0.03
4	17.9025 ± 0.01	-17.8188 ± 0.02
5	4.3080 ± 0.01	0
6	28.1483 ± 0.20	-26.2090 ± 0.04
7	3.1534 ± 0.10	- 2.9998 ± 0.01
8	0.6735 ± 0.01	- 0.6914 ± 0.01

The integration constants are given in Table 2. With these new constants and matrices of eigenvectors, we have calculated the new values of the Lagrange solutions. Let us express the Lagrange solution under the form:

$$h_i = \sum_{j=1}^{8} \lambda_{ij} M_j \sin(g_j t + \beta_j)$$

$$k_i = \sum_{j=1}^{8} \lambda_{ij} M_j \cos(g_j t + \beta_j)$$

$$p_i = \sum_{j=1}^{8} \mu_{ij} N_j \sin(s_j t + \delta_j)$$

$$q_i = \sum_{j=1}^{8} \mu_{ij} N_j \cos(s_j t + \delta_j)$$

We give in Tables 5 and 6 the amplitudes of the Lagrange solution.

The complete solution is composed of the Lagrange solution of Tables 5 and 6 and of the terms of degree or superior order taken from Bretagnon (4). The frequencies g_j and s_j are those of table 4 and the phases β_j and δ_j are those of Table 2.

Let us express this solution entirely in the case of the Earth, and represent the variables h and k of the Earth under the form :

$$h_E = \sum_{j=1}^{19} H_j \sin(g_j T + \beta_j)$$

$$k_E = \sum_{j=1}^{19} H_j \cos(g_j T + \beta_j)$$

Table 5. $\lambda_{ij} M_j \times 10^8$. Amplitudes of the Lagrange solution

i \ j	1	2	3	4	5	6	7	8
Mercury	17 782 480	− 3 076 776	157 162	− 153 852	1 911 920	11 821	49 834	671
Venus	743 603	2 086 688	− 1 245 486	1 308 656	1 579 216	− 58 090	56 199	1 104
Earth	490 969	1 628 605	1 024 586	− 1 289 575	1 589 350	250 323	59 785	1 286
Mars	81 806	291 819	3 326 034	5 595 392	1 874 207	1 612 426	80 731	2 080
Jupiter	− 670	− 1 117	− 96	− 37	4 346 096	− 1 555 143	204 079	6 057
Saturn	− 615	− 1 163	− 797	− 606	3 425 491	4 813 174	186 200	6 837
Uranus	229	276	46	33	− 4 409 453	− 180 979	2 936 651	143 179
Neptune	4	11	3	2	161 225	− 13 492	− 316 862	937 703

Table 6. $\mu_{ij} N_j \times 10^8$. Amplitudes of the Lagrange solution

i \ j	1	2	3	4	5	6	7	8
Mercury	5 957 877	− 1 126 703	167 731	72 163	1 384 001	13 897	− 166 527	− 72 453
Venus	561 996	320 244	− 1 099 480	− 425 990	1 384 001	6 011	− 95 870	− 66 294
Earth	404 864	258 172	1 001 606	280 507	1 384 001	140 472	− 86 602	− 64 982
Mars	85 960	57 482	− 1 470 365	3 126 062	1 384 001	482 139	− 62 841	− 61 561
Jupiter	− 985	− 414	− 6	− 108	1 384 001	− 315 368	− 47 870	− 58 569
Saturn	− 1 260	− 584	− 196	− 1 136	1 384 001	785 530	− 39 028	− 56 456
Uranus	1 056	301	15	106	1 384 001	− 34 733	880 177	54 779
Neptune	26	16	1	12	1 384 001	− 3 851	− 103 553	589 092

Table 7. Variables h and k of the Earth. g_j is in radians per thousands of years; β_j is in radians.

j	H_j	g_j	β_j
1	0.004260	0.0272157	1.5211
2	0.016135	0.0361472	3.4296
3	0.010246	0.0838008	5.5612
4	-0.013399	0.0867938	5.3645
5	0.018173	0.0208860	0.5005
6	0.001439	0.1364670	2.2293
7	0.000598	0.0152880	2.0278
8	0.000013	0.0032650	1.2657
9	0.000182	0.0849704	2.6548
10	0.000276	0.0916930	5.8759
11	-0.003367	0.0818946	4.8531
12	0.000378	0.0897867	5.1678
13	-0.002354	0.0887000	6.0726
14	0.000857	0.0789017	5.0498
15	0.000599	0.0808079	5.7579
16	-0.000174	0.0305229	2.2690
17	0.001007	0.0328400	2.6816
18	-0.000124	0.0913001	3.6754
19	-0.000337	0.0335454	2.5416

We give in Table 7 the quantities H_j, g_j and β_j. H_j is dimensionless; we have chosen to express here β_j in radians and g_j in radians per thousands of years, T being in thousands of years as of 1850.0.

Let us express, in the same way, the variables p and q of the Earth under the form :

$$p_E = \sum_{j=1}^{15} P_j \sin(s_j T + \delta_j)$$

$$q_E = \sum_{j=1}^{15} P_j \cos(s_j T + \delta_j)$$

We give in Table 8 the quantities P_j, s_j and δ_j. P_j is dimensionless ; δ_j is in radians and s_j in radians per thousands of years, T being in thousands of years as of 1850.0.

As we already said, the imprecision of the solutions is mainly due to the uncertainty on the frequencies (see Table 4). We see on the example of the Earth that, if the errors are cumulated, the uncertainty for the variables h, k, p, q is about 15 per cent of the maximum of these quantities after one million years. Beyond one million years the solution no longer represents the physical reality.

Table 8. Variables p and q of the Earth. s_j is in radians by thousands of years; δ_j is in radians.

j	P_j	s_j	δ_j
1	0.006037	-0.0272026	0.2149
2	0.002582	-0.0328269	5.3375
3	0.010016	-0.0912870	4.3437
4	0.003802	-0.0863878	4.8552
5	0.013840	0	1.8526
6	0.001405	-0.1270650	2.1933
7	-0.000866	-0.0145436	5.5201
8	-0.000650	-0.0033522	3.5128
9	-0.000378	-0.0961862	3.8323
10	0.000499	-0.0882941	4.1470
11	0.001741	-0.0893808	5.0519
12	-0.001192	-0.0942799	4.5405
13	-0.000124	-0.0238953	0.9628
14	0.000903	-0.0361341	4.5895
15	-0.000401	-0.0335323	5.4775

It is nevertheless to be noted that the missing terms of the solution have only an important amplitude if their frequency is close to a frequency of the Lagrange solution. One can hence say that the general shape of the solution remains the same over several millions years eventhough one cannot determine at a fixed time the values of the variables h, k, p and q. Particularly, the periods met with are close to those obtained during the first million years before our era.

CONCLUSION

The results which have been presented here do not represent an original work, but merely an improvement to the solution of Bretagnon (4). It would indeed be necessary to re-start the computation of the terms coming from the long period part of degree 4 of the disturbing function, as well as the terms of the second order with respect to the masses, with the help of new integration constants. It would also be necessary to introduce the terms of degree 6 from the long period part of the disturbing function, and to study the contribution of the terms of the third order with respect to the masses.

REFERENCES

1. Brumberg, V.A., and Chapront, J. : 1973, Celes. Mech. 8, pp. 335.
2. Simon, J.L., and Francou, G. : 1982, Astron. Astrophys. 114, pp. 125.
3. Bretagnon, P. : 1982, Astron. Astrophys. 144, pp 278.
4. Bretagnon, P. : 1974, Astron. Astrophys. 30, pp. 141.
5. Anolik, M.V., Krassinsky, G.A., and Pius, L.J. : 1969, Trudy Inst. Astron. Leningrad, 14, pp. 3-47.
6. Duriez, L. : 1979, Approche d'une théorie générale planétaire en variables elliptiques héliocentriques. Thèse, Lille.

MATHEMATICAL METHODS OF CELESTIAL MECHANICS ILLUSTRATED BY SIMPLE MODELS OF PLANETARY MOTION

M. Buys[1] and M. Ghil[2]

[1]Department of Mathematics and Statistics, University of New Mexico, Albuquerque, NM 87131
[2]Courant Institute of Mathematical Sciences, New York Univerity, New York, NY 10012

ABSTRACT

Celestial mechanics studies the motions of planets, satellites and other bodies in the solar system. Various methods, analytical and numerical, of celestial mechanics are presented. Their properties and accuracy are compared and illustrated on the hand of simple examples. The structure and possible computation of stable, quasi-periodic solutions to the planetary N-body problem is outlined. The mutual implications of celestial mechanics and climate modeling are discussed.

INTRODUCTION

The detailed history of orbital variations in planetary motion plays an increasing role in understanding the paleoclimatic evolution of the Earth (1). Classical computations in celestial mechanics are based on analytic perturbations of the planets' basic elliptic motion. The advent of space ships and artificial satellites increased the importance of numerical methods in celestial mechanics. We discuss the properties of various perturbative and numerical methods, and try to estimate and compare their accuracies.

The purpose of this article is mainly expository and it addresses itself to the nonspecialist interested in celestial mechanics from the point of view of paleoclimatology. In sections 2 and 3, we present two types of perturbation methods, time-dependent and time-independent. They are applied to some

A. L. Berger et al. (eds.), Milankovitch and Climate, Part 1, 55–82.

simple, illustrative examples. Section 4 introduces time-marching numerical methods and compares them with the perturbative ones for a model problem. Hybrid, analytic-numerical methods are also mentioned. In section 5, we outline the structure of quasi-periodic solutions in celestial mechanics, and speculate on tentative approaches for their computations. Implications for paleoclimatology and its possible influence on celestial mechanics are discussed in section 6.

TIME-DEPENDENT PERTURBATION METHODS

Most problems in classical mechanics cannot be solved exactly. Exact solutions for the two-body Kepler problem, such as the Sun and the Earth interacting only by their mutual gravitational force, are found readily: the Earth moves along an elliptical orbit around the Sun, with the Sun situated in one of the foci of the ellipse.

The classical problem of three bodies interacting by their mutual gravitation force, such as the Sun-Earth-Jupiter system, is already intractable. It is therefore necessary to find approximate solutions, which can be developed by expansion in a small parameter. Basically, one considers the motion of the Sun-Earth-Jupiter system as the Kepler problem for the Sun-Earth system, with Jupiter exerting a small disturbing force; the force exerted by the Earth on Jupiter is neglected. That is, one approximates the actual orbit on the Earth in the three-body problem by perturbations, due to the third body, of the elliptical orbit. This is the reduced three-body problem, and it can be treated by perturbation methods.

Perturbation theory applied to the full three-body problem, and more ambitiously to the entire solar system, is extremely complicated. We wish therefore to discuss first some of its aspects by perturbations of the free harmonic oscillator. The motivation for this approach is the content of the following subsections.

Keplerian Motion as a Harmonic Oscillator

We show that, in an appropriate coordinate system, Keplerian motion can be viewed as a harmonic oscillator. The motion of a particle moving in a plane subjected to a central force P(r) (see Fig. 1) can be dscribed in polar form by the differential equation

$$\ddot{r} - r\,\dot{\phi}^2 = -\,P(r), \qquad [1]$$

where $\underline{r}$ is the distance of the particle with unit mass to the center, and ϕ is the angle, measured counterclockwise, the particle's radius vector makes with an axis of reference. Dot denotes differentiation with respect to time. The angular velocity equals $(P(r)/r)^{1/2}$.

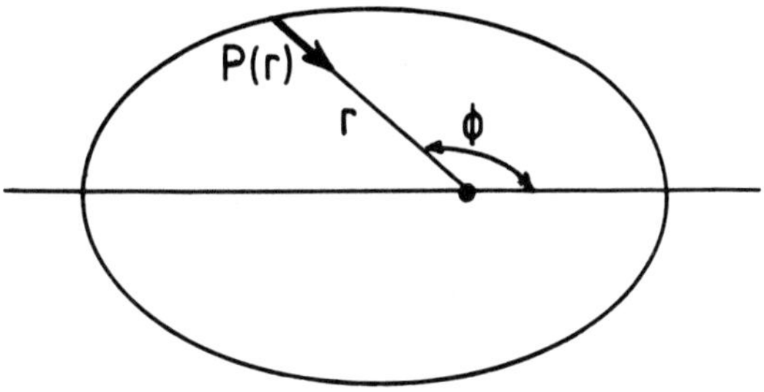

Figure 1 Coordinates for the Keplerian motion.

Examples of central force motions are :

(a) harmonic oscillation, where $P(r) = k^2 r$ and k equals the spring constant;

(b) unperturbed Kepler motion, where $P(r) = K^2/r^2$ and K equals the mass-normalized gravitational constant;

(c) perturbed Kepler motion, where $P(r) = K^2/r^2 + dV/dr$ and $V(r)$ is the perturbing potential.

The actual transformation of Eq. (1) to harmonic form is accomplished by applying several times the area law

$$r^2\dot{\phi} = c, \quad c=\text{constant},$$

using $\rho = 1/r$ as dependent variable and ϕ as the new independent variable (2,3). The differential equation then becomes

$$\frac{d^2\rho}{d\phi^2} + \rho = \frac{1}{c^2}\{K^2 - \frac{dV}{d\rho}\} .$$

Setting $K^2/c^2 = 1/p$ and making the translation $Q = \rho - 1/p$, the final equation takes the form

$$\frac{d^2Q}{d\phi^2} + Q = -\frac{1}{pK^2}\frac{dV}{dQ} , \qquad [2]$$

which is a forced harmonic oscillator. Note that in the unperturbed case $V \equiv 0$, so that

$$\frac{d^2Q}{d\phi^2} + Q = 0 \ . \qquad [3]$$

Variation of Constants

Two classes of perturbation methods are widely used in celestial mechanics (4, Sec. 11.6): time-dependent and time-independent perturbation methods. The standard approach to time-dependent perturbation theory is <u>variation of constants</u> (5, Ch. 11). It dates back to Lagrange. Variation of constants, as we shall see, is entirely appropriate for short-term computations.

The ideas of time-independent perturbation methods will be presented in the next section. Long-term computations based on these ideas, in which the short-term periods are simply neglected from the perturbing potential, are called <u>perturbation of the coordinates</u> (5, Ch. 13). The latter approach was used by various investigators for very long-term orbital computations. Their results were used in turn to calculate insolation changes which might influence climate on the time scale of 10^3-10^7 years (6,7).

In order to describe variation of constants, we need to introduce some elementary concepts. The differential equations of celestial mechanics can be described in terms of a <u>Hamiltonian</u> function $H = H(q,p,t)$ as follows :

$$\dot{q} = \frac{\partial H}{\partial p}, \qquad \dot{p} = -\frac{\partial H}{\partial q} \ ; \qquad [4a,b]$$

<u>q</u> is called the position variable, <u>p</u> the associated momentum variable (4, Ch. 8). For example, the Hamiltonian for the harmonic oscillation is

$$H = \frac{1}{2} \ p^2 + \omega^2 q^2 \ , \qquad [5]$$

where ω = constant. Variables like <u>p</u> and <u>q</u>, for which the equations of motion take the form [4], are called <u>canonical</u>.

It is frequently possible to perform a transformation from one set of canonical variables (q,p) to another such set (Q,P), so that the transformed Hamiltonian in the new coordinate system is simple, and hence the motion in these coordinates looks simple (5, Ch. 17; 4, Ch. 9). In such a case, there exists a <u>generating function</u> S(q,P,t) such that the new Hamiltonian is of the form

$$K = H + \frac{\partial S}{\partial t}, \qquad [6a]$$

and furthermore the transformation is given implicitly by

$$p = \frac{\partial S}{\partial q}, \qquad Q = \frac{\partial S}{\partial P}. \qquad [6b,c]$$

Canonical transformations of variables are the basic tool to be used in the sequel.

Let $H(q,p,t) = H_0(q,p,t) + \Delta H(q,p,t)$, where $H_0(q,p,t)$ is the Hamiltonian of the free system and $\Delta H(q,p,t)$ is the perturbing Hamiltonian. For instance, in our example [5] one can take $H_0=(1/2)p^2$, corresponding to rectilinear, uniform motion. Then $\Delta H = (1/2)\omega^2 q^2$, corresponding to the "perturbing" effect of a weak spring when ω is small. We now seek the map $(q,p) \to (Q,P)$, generated by S, so that the new Hamiltonian K_0, corresponding to H_0, vanishes identically; in effect, one seeks the constants of motion of the free system.

In the (Q,P) system, the motion is simply

$$\dot{Q} = 0, \qquad \dot{P} = 0,$$

giving $Q = \beta$ = constant, $P = \alpha$ = constant, and

$$\frac{\partial S}{\partial t} + H_0 = 0.$$

The perturbed Hamiltonian is transformed to

$$K(\beta,\alpha,t) = H + \frac{\partial S}{\partial t} = \Delta H, \qquad [7a]$$

and in these coordinates the motion it governs is described by

$$\dot{\beta} = \frac{\partial \Delta H(\beta,\alpha,t)}{\partial \alpha}, \qquad \dot{\alpha} = -\frac{\partial \Delta H(\beta,\alpha,t)}{\partial \beta}. \qquad [7b,c]$$

Note that β and α are constants of the free system, but this is no longer so for the perturbed system.

The crucial idea is that if ΔH is small compared to H_0 then (β,α) should vary slowly in time. This idea is reflected in the term "variation of constants". In the planetary case, the "constants" are the <u>orbital elements</u> describing the instantaneous ellipse on which the planet is moving, and which changes slowly due to the effect of perturbing forces.

First-order perturbation solutions are obtained by integrating equations [7] after replacing (β, α) on the right-hand side by (β_0, α_0), the unperturbed solution. The n-th order perturbation solutions are obtained similarly by replacing (β,α) on the right-hand side by $(\beta_{n-1},\alpha_{n-1})$, the (n-1)st perturbation solution.

We proceed to the perturbation treatment of the harmonic oscillator to illustrate properties of this method. The exact solution of Eq.[4] with Hamiltonian given by [5] is

$$q = \frac{p_0}{\omega} \sin \omega t ,$$

if $q(0) = 0$, $p(0) = p_0$. We shall use this simple example, so that all aspects of the procedure may be transparent.

Again,

$$H_0 = \frac{1}{2} p^2, \quad \Delta H = \frac{1}{2} \omega^2 q^2 . \qquad [8a,b]$$

Since <u>q</u> does not occur explicitly in H_0, a generating function of the form

$$S(q,\alpha,t) = \alpha q - W(\alpha,t) \qquad [9]$$

can be used; i.e., one <u>separates out</u> the <u>q</u> variable. Then

$$p = \frac{\partial S}{\partial q} = \alpha$$

and

$$\beta = \frac{\partial S}{\partial \alpha} = q - \frac{\partial W}{\partial \alpha} .$$

From this

$$\Delta H(\beta,\alpha,t) = \frac{1}{2} \omega^2(\alpha t + \beta)^2.$$

The equations of motion are

$$\dot{\beta} = \frac{\partial \Delta H}{\partial \alpha} = \omega^2 t(\alpha t + \beta), \qquad [10a]$$

$$\dot{\alpha} = - \frac{\partial \Delta H}{\partial \beta} = - \omega^2 (\alpha t + \beta) . \qquad [10b]$$

For our initial conditions, $\beta_0 = 0$ and $\alpha_0 = p_0$.

The first-order perturbation solution (β_1, α_1) is obtained by solving the equations

$$\dot{\beta}_1 = \alpha_0 \omega^2 t^2, \quad \dot{\alpha}_1 = -\alpha_0 \omega^2 t ,$$

which yields

$$\beta_1 = \frac{\alpha_0 \omega^2 t^3}{3}, \quad \alpha_1 = \alpha_0 - \frac{\alpha_0 \omega^2 t^2}{2} .$$

Hence the position and momentum are approximated to first order by

$$q_1 = \beta_1 + \alpha_1 t = \frac{\alpha_0}{\omega}(\omega t - \frac{\omega^3 t^3}{6}), \quad p_1 = \alpha_1 = \alpha_0(1 - \frac{\omega^2 t^2}{2}) .$$

Substituting (β_1, α_1) for (β, α) in the right-hand side of [10], we arrive at the second-order perturbation solution

$$q_2 = \frac{\alpha_0}{\omega}(\omega t - \frac{\omega^3 t^3}{3!} + \frac{\omega^5 t^5}{5!}), \quad p_2 = \alpha_0(1 - \frac{\omega^2 t^2}{2!} + \frac{\omega^4 t^4}{4!}) .$$

By iterating one can easily show that q_n and p_n are the (2n+1)st Taylor series approximation to $(\alpha_0 \sin \omega t)/\omega$ and $\alpha_0 \cos \omega t$ respectively.

Figure 2 shows, for $\omega = 1$, the exact solution (solid line), the first-order perturbation (dotted) and the second-order perturbation solution (dashed). Clearly, the exact solution is periodic, while the perturbation solutions are not. They will follow the exact solution for longer and longer times, as the order of the perturbation increases, but eventually they will diverge from it, and become unbounded.

In this very special case, in which successive perturbations are convergent and result in an alternating series, the maximum error in the approximation equals the first neglected term in the series. Thus the maximum error for the k-th perturbation equals

$$\frac{(\omega t)^{2k+3}}{(2k+3)!} .$$

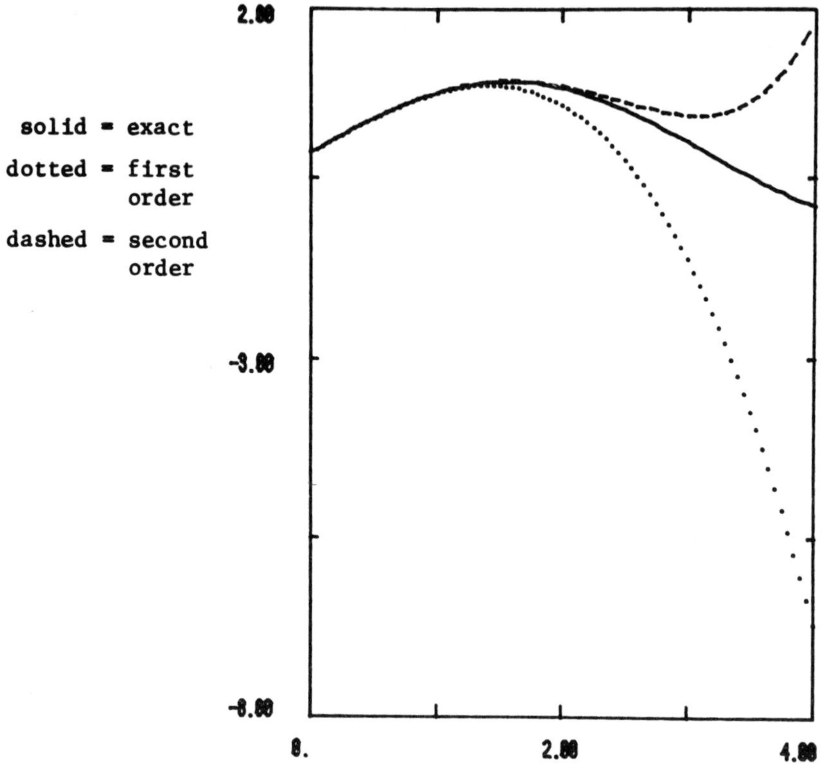

Figure 2 The free harmonic oscillator as a time-dependent perturbation of free rectilinear motion.

To be more specific, let time be measured in the sequel in units of 1000 yr, and let now $\omega = 2\pi/40$ in these units, corresponding approximately to the most important frequency of the Earth's obliquity. For the error in this perturbation solution of Eq. [10] to be at most 10^{-2}, one must then restrict the time interval to lie between 0 and t_{max}, where

$$t_{max} \simeq 6.6 \quad \text{when } k = 1 \; ,$$

$$t_{max} \simeq 11.1 \quad \text{when } k = 2, \text{ and}$$

$$t_{max} \simeq 15.8 \quad \text{when } k = 3 \; .$$

Thus an error of 1 percent in the solution will appear within one period of the exact motion even for high-order perturbations of the time-dependent type. We shall see next what happens in this method over many periods for a slightly more realistic example.

Perturbation Treatment of the Oscillator with Periodic Forcing

The Hamiltonian is given by

$$H(q,p,t) = \frac{1}{2}(p^2 + \omega^2 q^2) - \varepsilon q \sin \lambda t$$

and it is natural to take

$$H_0 = \frac{1}{2}(p^2 + \omega^2 q^2) .$$

The initial conditions $q(0) = 0$ and $p(0) = 1$ give the zeroth-order solution $\beta_0 = 0$, $\alpha_0 = 1$. Substituting α_0 and β_0 into the right-hand side of Eqs. [7b,c] yields the first-order perturbation solution

$$q_1 = \frac{\sqrt{2\alpha_1}}{\omega} \sin\omega (t + \beta_1) ,$$

where

$$\beta_1 = - \frac{\varepsilon}{2\omega} \left\{\frac{\sin (\omega-\lambda)t}{\omega - \lambda} - \frac{\sin (\omega+\lambda)t}{\omega + \lambda}\right\} ,$$

$$\alpha_1 = - \frac{\varepsilon}{2} \left\{\frac{\cos (\lambda+\omega)t}{\lambda + \omega} + \frac{\cos (\omega-\lambda)t}{\omega - \lambda}\right\} + \frac{1}{2} + \frac{\varepsilon}{2} \left\{\frac{1}{\omega+\lambda} + \frac{1}{\omega-\lambda}\right\} .$$

The true solution is given by

$$q = \frac{\sin \omega t}{\omega} + \frac{\varepsilon}{2\omega} \left\{\frac{\sin \lambda t + \sin \omega t}{\lambda + \omega} - \frac{\sin \lambda t - \sin \omega t}{\lambda - \omega}\right\} .$$

The exact solution is a superposition of two purely periodic oscillations, the free oscillation with period $2\pi/\omega$ and the forced oscillation with period $2\pi/\lambda$. Such a superposition in acoustic vibrations produces audible <u>beats</u>: the basic, free oscillation, or carrier wave, has an amplitude which is modulated by the forcing.

When λ and ω are close to each other, or nearly <u>resonant</u>, the term with $\lambda-\omega$ in the denominator will dominate the solution, unless ε is very small. The amplitude of the beats increases like $\varepsilon/(\lambda-\omega)$. In the reasonant limit of ε constant and $(\lambda - \omega) \to 0$, the solution will behave asymptotically for large <u>t</u> like

$$q \sim \frac{\varepsilon t}{2} \cos \omega t \ .$$

The amplitude of the solution then keeps increasing with time, rather than being periodic, albeit large.

Figure 3 shows the exact solution (solid line) and the first-order variation-of-constants solution (dashed) for the periodically forced harmonic oscillator. The conditions chosen are near resonance, with $\omega = 2\pi/2.1$ and $\lambda = 2\pi/2.2$, while $\varepsilon = 0.5$. The panels 3a-3c show the successive time intervals $0 \leq t \leq 4.0$, $8.0 \leq t \leq 12.0$ and $16.0 \leq t \leq 20.0$, respectively.

The high frequency visible in each panel is $(\lambda+\omega)/2 \simeq \omega$, while the increase in amplitude from one panel to the next corresponds to the near-resonant beat with frequency $(\lambda-\omega)/2 \ll \omega$. Clearly the perturbative solution is almost in phase opposition to the exact solution by t=20.0, i.e., after about ten periods of the free oscillation.

Figure 4 shows the same solutions as Figure 3, but for $\varepsilon=0.1$, $\lambda=2\pi/2.11$ and for a much longer time interval, $0 \leq t \leq 100.0$, corresponding to approximately fifty free periods. The approximate solution (heavy line, smaller amplitude) has both the wrong amplitude and the wrong phase after about ten free periods.

The difficulties encountered by time-dependent perturbation methods will become apparent after longer and longer time intervals as the order of the perturbation is increased. Such an extension of the interval of validity, however, is not indefinite, due to the nonconvergent character of the series to which these methods lead in celestial mechanics (5, p. 299; 8, Sec. 1.2).

TIME-INDEPENDENT PERTURBATION METHODS

We saw in the previous section that, for short periods of time, the full three-body problem can be approximated by the reduced three-body problem, which in turn can be treated by variation of constants. The neglect of forces exerted by the perturbed planet on the perturbing one limits the length of the time interval for which the reducing approximation is valid. Further approximations involved in the time-dependent perturbation methods, used for treating the reduced problem, limit even more this validity interval.

The planetary problem can be viewed, alternatively, as that of coupled nonlinear oscillators, each oscillator representing the Keplerian motion of one planet around the Sun. This approach goes back to the investigations of Hamilton and Liouville in the

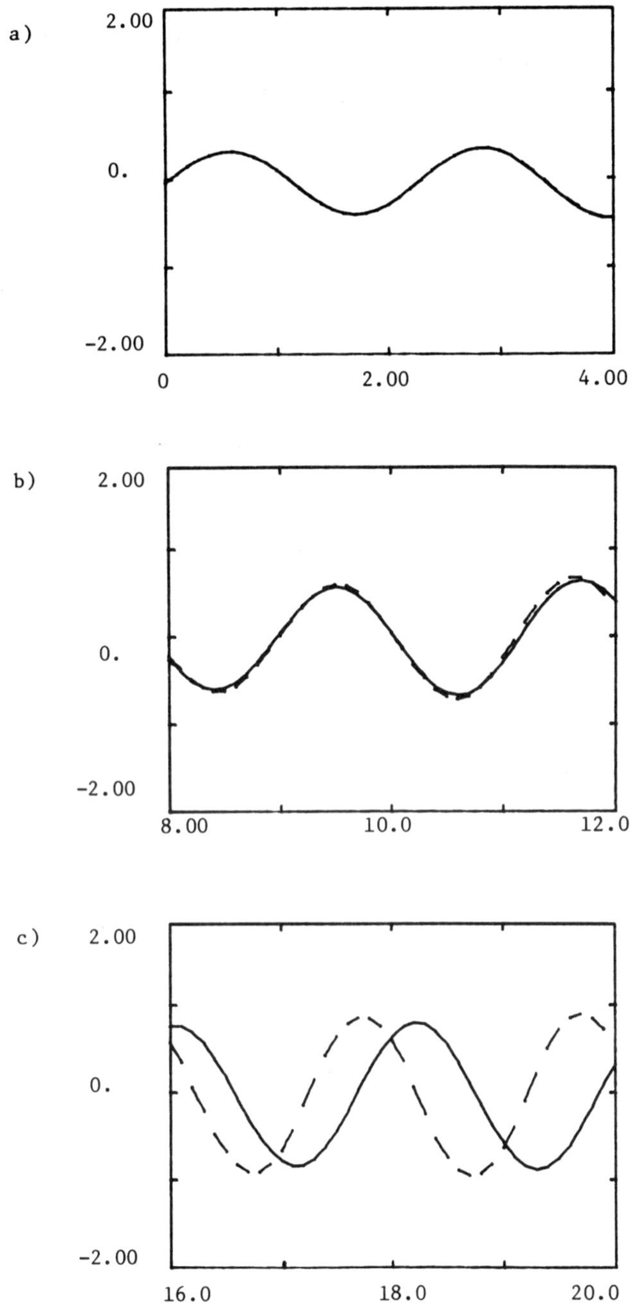

Figure 3 The periodically forced harmonic oscillator as a time-dependent perturbation of the free harmonic oscillator.

mid-nineteenth century. Toward the end of the nineteenth century, the long-term stability of coupled nonlinear systems was investigated by Poincaré (9), who devised time-independent perturbation methods. These were further applied by von Zeipel (10) to the problems of celestial mechanics.

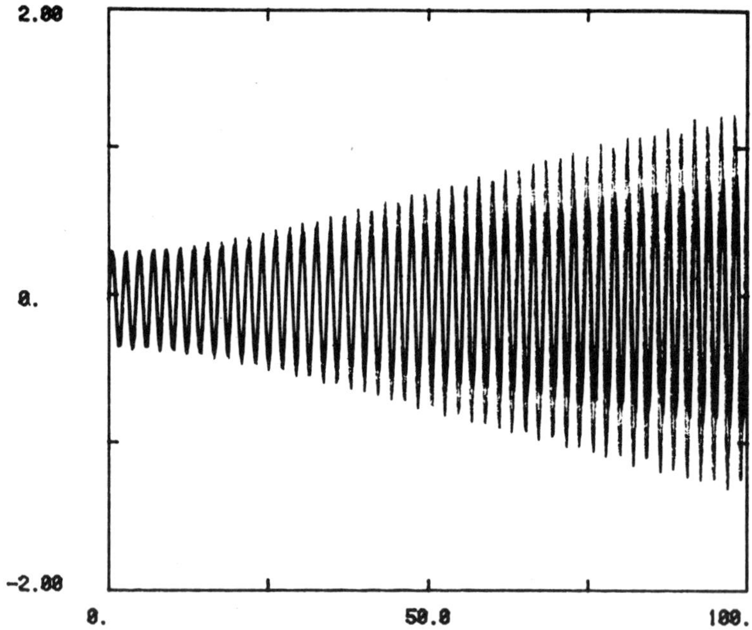

thin = exact
heavy = perturbation

Figure 4 Same as Figure 3, but for a longer time interval.

The difficulties encountered in practical, long-term calculations of the N-body problem brought Poincaré (9) and Birkhoff (11) to consider the underlying theoretical issues. This led to the emergence of the qualitative theory of differential equations, algebraic topology and other branches of modern, abstract mathematics.

Motivated by astronomical observations, the question of stability was approached by Poincaré, Birkhoff and others via the search for quasi-periodic solutions. These are solutions which consist of the superposition of trigonometric functions with rationally unrelated frequencies.

Poincaré showed the existence of periodic solutions to the full three-body problem. More recently, the KAM theorem, originally postulated by Kolmogorov (12) and proved under different restrictions by Arnold (13) and Moser (14), states, in nontechnical terms, that "most" solutions to the three-body problem are quasi-periodic.

Although quasi-periodic solutions are known to exist and be "abundant", their computation for the N-body problem is still extremely difficult. Hori (15) and Deprit (16) applied the modern Lie formalism (17) to this computation. Using symbolic manipulation and the Lie formalism on a computer, Deprit was able to verify and improve in short order the lunar calculations of Delaunay (18), who had devoted his entire life to the Sun-Earth-Moon problem.

To present some of the technical aspects of time-independent perturbation methods (32, Ch. 10; 5, Ch. 17; 4, Ch. 9), it will be useful to discuss the single nonlinear quadratic oscillator,

$$\ddot{q} = -\omega^2 q - \varepsilon q^2 .$$

This oscillator is often called <u>anharmonic</u>.

Action-Angle Variables and Averaging

In this subsection, we assume that the Hamiltonian is conservative, i.e.

$$H = H(q,p) = \alpha , \quad \alpha = \text{constant}.$$

The set of canonical variables used in time-independent perturbation theory is called <u>action-angle variables</u>. In celestial mechanics they are known as Delaunay variables. In these coordinates, the motion occurs along a straight line.

For the harmonic oscillator, the transformation from the (q,p)-space to the (w,J)-space, where w is the angle variable and J is the action variable, is given explicitly by

$$q = \sqrt{J/\omega\pi}\,\sin 2\pi w , \qquad p = \sqrt{J\omega/\pi}\,\cos 2\pi w ,$$

and the new Hamiltonian is $K = J\omega/2\pi$. Thus the motion is reduced to the linear motion

$$\dot{w} = \frac{\partial K}{\partial J} = \omega/2\pi , \qquad \dot{J} = 0 ;$$

hence $w = (\omega/2\pi)t + \beta$ and J = constant.

For a general Hamiltonian $K = K(J)$, so that

$$w = \nu(J)t + \beta ,$$

where $\nu(J) = \partial K/\partial J$ and $\dot{J} = 0$. Thus $\nu(J)$ is the frequency of the system. Since the generating function $S(q,J)$ of Eq. [6] does not depend explicitly on $\underline{t}$, $\partial S/\partial t = 0$, it follows that actually $K = H$. We shall not distinguish between the two in the sequel.

Our purpose here is to analyze the perturbed system described by $H = H_0 + \varepsilon H_1$, where ε is small. For the anharmonic oscillator, it is natural to have

$$H_0 = \frac{1}{2} p^2 + \frac{1}{2} \omega^2 q^2 , \quad H_1 = \frac{1}{3} q^3 .$$

Suppose that for the unperturbed Hamiltonian H_0 we know the action-angle variables w_0, J_0, and that $H_0 = H_0(J_0)$. In our example,

$$q = \sqrt{J_0/\omega\pi} \sin 2\pi w_0, \; p = \sqrt{J_0\omega/\pi} \cos 2\pi w_0, \; H_0 = J_0\omega/2\pi.$$

The idea is now that, for small perturbations, the action-angle variables should be close to the free action-angle variables. We therefore search for a generating function of the form

$$S(w_0,J) = w_0 J + \varepsilon S_1(w_0,J) + \varepsilon^2 S_2(w_0,J) + \dots ,$$

so that

$$w = \frac{\partial S}{\partial J} = w_0 + \varepsilon \frac{\partial S_1}{\partial J} + \varepsilon^2 \frac{\partial S_2}{\partial J} + \dots ,$$

$$J_0 = \frac{\partial S}{\partial w_0} = J + \varepsilon \frac{\partial S_1}{\partial w_0} + \varepsilon^2 \frac{\partial S_2}{\partial w_0} + \dots .$$

In the (w_0,J_0)-system, $H(w_0,J_0) = H_0(J_0) + \varepsilon H_1(w_0,J_0)$, so that in our example,

$$H = \frac{J_0\omega}{2\pi} + \varepsilon \frac{1}{3} (\sqrt{J_0/\omega\pi} \sin 2\pi w_0)^3 .$$

In the (w,J) system

$$H = \alpha(J, \varepsilon) = \alpha_0(J) + \varepsilon \alpha_1(J) + \varepsilon^2 \alpha_2(J) + \dots \qquad [11]$$

One expands now H_0 and H_1 into a power series around $J_0=J$ and matches coefficients of powers of ε in Eq. [11]. Retaining only terms up to order ε^2, one gets

$$\alpha_0(J) = H_0(J), \quad \alpha_1(J) = \nu_0(J) \frac{\partial S_1}{\partial w_0} + H_1(w_0,J) , \qquad [12a,b]$$

$$\alpha_2(J) = \nu_0(J)\frac{\partial S_2}{\partial w_0} = \Phi_2(w_0,J), \qquad [12c]$$

where

$$\Phi_2(w_0,J) = H_2(w_0,J) + \frac{\partial S_1}{\partial w_0}\frac{\partial H_1}{\partial J} + \frac{1}{2} \left(\frac{\partial Y_1}{\partial w_0}\right)^2 \frac{\partial^2 H_0}{\partial J^2} . \qquad [12d]$$

For $\underline{q}$ and $\underline{p}$ to be periodic in $\underline{w}$ and w_0, all S_k terms must be periodic functions of w_0, i.e.,

$$S_k = \sum_n B_n^{(k)}(J) \exp\{2\pi i n.w_0\}, \qquad [13]$$

with $\underline{i}$ the imaginary unit. This implies that

$$\overline{\frac{\partial S_k}{\partial w_0}} = 0 ,$$

where the bar indicates averaging with respect to w_0 over the period 1. This is why the method is also known as the method of averages. Thus

$$\alpha_0(J) = H_0(J), \quad \alpha_1(J) = \overline{H_1(w_0,J)}, \text{ and } \alpha_2(J) = \overline{\Phi_2(w_0,J)}.$$

For our example,

$$\alpha_1(J) = \frac{1}{3}\int_0^1 (\sqrt{J/\omega\pi})^3 \sin^3 2\pi w_0 \, dw_0 = 0 , \qquad [14a]$$

so that, to first order, there is no period correction of the free motion. A slightly lengthier computation yields

$$\alpha_2(J) = - \frac{5}{48}\frac{1}{\omega^2}\left(\frac{J}{\omega\pi}\right)^2 . \qquad [14b]$$

Now

$$\frac{\partial S_1}{\partial w_0} = - \frac{1}{\nu_0(J)} H_1 = - \frac{\omega}{2\pi}\frac{1}{3}(\sqrt{J/\omega\pi} \sin 2\pi w_0)^3 ,$$

and

$$\frac{\partial S_1}{\partial J} = \frac{1}{8\pi^3}\left(\frac{J}{\omega\pi}\right)^{1/2} (\cos 2\pi w_0 - \frac{1}{3}\cos^3 2\pi w_0) ,$$

which determines to first order the canonical map $(w_0, J_0) \to (w, J)$, since

$$w \simeq w_0 + \varepsilon \frac{\partial S_1}{\partial J} \quad \text{and} \quad J_0 \simeq J + \varepsilon \frac{\partial S_1}{\partial w_0} .$$

Using [11], we see that to first order

$$\nu(J) \simeq \nu_0(J) = \frac{\omega}{2\pi}$$

as stated before, and to second order

$$\nu(J) \simeq \nu_0(J) + \varepsilon^2 \frac{\partial \alpha_2}{\partial J} = \frac{\omega}{2\pi} - \varepsilon^2 \frac{5}{24} \frac{J}{\omega^4 \pi^2} .$$

Notice that

$$\nu_0 \frac{\partial S_1}{\partial w_0} = \bar{H}_1 - H_1$$

and

$$S_1(w_0, J) = \sum_n B_n^{(1)}(J) \exp \{2\pi i n . w_0\} ;$$

therefore

$$\nu_0 \frac{\partial S_1(w_0, J)}{\partial w_0} = 2\pi i \sum_{n \neq 0} B_n^{(1)}(J) (n . \nu_0) \exp \{2\pi i n . w_0\} .$$

By periodicity

$$\bar{H}_1 - H_1 = \sum_{n \neq 0} C_n(J) \exp\{2\pi i n . w_0\} ,$$

and hence the coefficients in [13] are, to first order,

$$B_n^{(1)}(J) = \frac{C_n(J)}{2\pi i (n . \nu_0)} , \quad n \neq 0 .$$

When the unperturbed system is quasi-periodic, as in the planetary problem, rather than purely periodic, the derivation above still holds. Let us assume that the system has $\underline{j}$ incommensurable periods, $j \geq 2$. Then the following interpretation is in order.

The frequency ν_0 becomes a vector of frequencies of length $\underline{j}$,

$$\nu_0 = (\nu_{01}, \nu_{02}, \ldots, \nu_{0j}) ,$$

and the other angle-related scalar variables, $\underline{n}$ and w_0, also become vectors, so that,

$$n.\nu_0 = n_1\nu_{01} + n_2\nu_{02} + \ldots + n_j\nu_{0j} .$$

Here is where the well-known problem of "small divisors" becomes apparent: if $n.\nu_0$ becomes very small for $n^2 = n_1^2+n_2^2+ \ldots + n_j^2$ going to infinity, then the trigonometric series will diverge. To understand this, consider the extreme case, when the frequencies are rationally related, so that $n.\nu_0 = 0$ for some $\underline{n}$. Then $B_n(J)$ is actually infinite. The simplest possible case of such a resonance was discussed at the end of the previous section, where $(\lambda-\omega)$ was the "small divisor".

Kronecker's lemma states that for increasing n^2, $n.\nu$ can become arbitrarily small. Hence the series [13] diverges, unless the smallness of $n.\nu_0$ can somehow be related to the value of n^2. If the unperturbed problem has a quasi-periodic solution, then the difficulty of small divisors can be avoided in the perturbed problem, for small perturbation parameter ε , provided the d'Alembert condition holds,

$$|n.\nu_0| \geq c_1(n_1^2 + n_2^2 + \ldots + n_j^2)^{-c_2} ,$$

where c_1 and c_2 are positive constants. This is essentially the content of KAM theory.

The Anharmonic Oscillator

We shall compare now the method of averages with variation of constants for the anharmonic oscillator. To obtain the exact solution, one multiplies the oscillator equation through by $\dot{q}$, which yields

$$\dot{q}\ddot{q} + \omega^2 q\dot{q} + \varepsilon\dot{q}q^2 = 0 .$$

Integrating once, one obtains

$$\frac{1}{2}\dot{q}^2 + \frac{1}{2}\omega^2 q^2 + \frac{\varepsilon}{3}q^3 = E_0 ,$$

where E_0 is the total energy of the oscillator, a constant. The solution is thus an <u>elliptic function</u> (19, Sec. 13.13) and it can be calculated by inverting the integral

$$t = \int_{q(0)}^{q(t)} \frac{dq}{\{2(E_0-\omega^2q^2/2-\varepsilon q^3/3)\}^{1/2}} ;$$

here the path of integration lies in the complex plane and should avoid the zeroes and poles of $\dot{q}$.

Transformations exist which reduce any elliptic function to the standard, tabulated Jacobi elliptic and theta functions. It turns out in practice that it is easier to compute such functions by very accurate numerical methods from their defining differential equation, as we shall see in the next section.

Figure 5 compares results for the anharmonic oscillator with $\omega = 1$ and small forcing, $\varepsilon = 0.1$. The exact solution (light solid line) was actually computed by the algorithm RKF45 of Forsythe *et al.* (20, Sec. 6.8). In Figure 5a, for $0 \le t \le 10.0$, the two first-order perturbation solutions, time-dependent (dark solid) and time-independent (dashed), are seen to lie rather close to each other, and to the exact solution. The main difference is a slight phase shift. The solutions stay very close for about twenty periods (Fig. 5b, $0 \le t \le 100.0$).

In Figure 6, the forcing has been increased, $\varepsilon = 0.5$. Due to the nonlinearity of the oscillator, the solutions differ in mean, as well as in phase and amplitude. The two perturbation solutions (dashed and solid dark lines) are closer to each other than to the "exact" (RKF45) solution (light solid). The phase difference between the perturbation solutions and the exact solution increases in time, with phase reversal after approximately ten periods. A similar increase in phase difference with time between two perturbation solutions of a realistic planetary problem can be seen in Berger (21, Figs. 2,4).

The averaging solution (dashed) stays close to the variation-of-constants solution (dark solid) in Figure 6, due to the absence of frequency correction to first order in the former, cf. [14a]. To higher order, the two methods will differ, cf. [14b].

In general, neither method can approximate the exact solution at each moment for arbitrarily long time. Time-independent perturbation methods have the advantage that they always lead to bounded solutions, and the errors in frequency are easier to estimate. Noticeable phase errors are unavoidable in any method after a few periods, while the frequencies might be approximately valid for much longer intervals.

NUMERICAL METHODS AND HYBRID METHODS

With the emergence of artificial satellites, the need for calculating orbital paths took on a new urgency. The availabi-

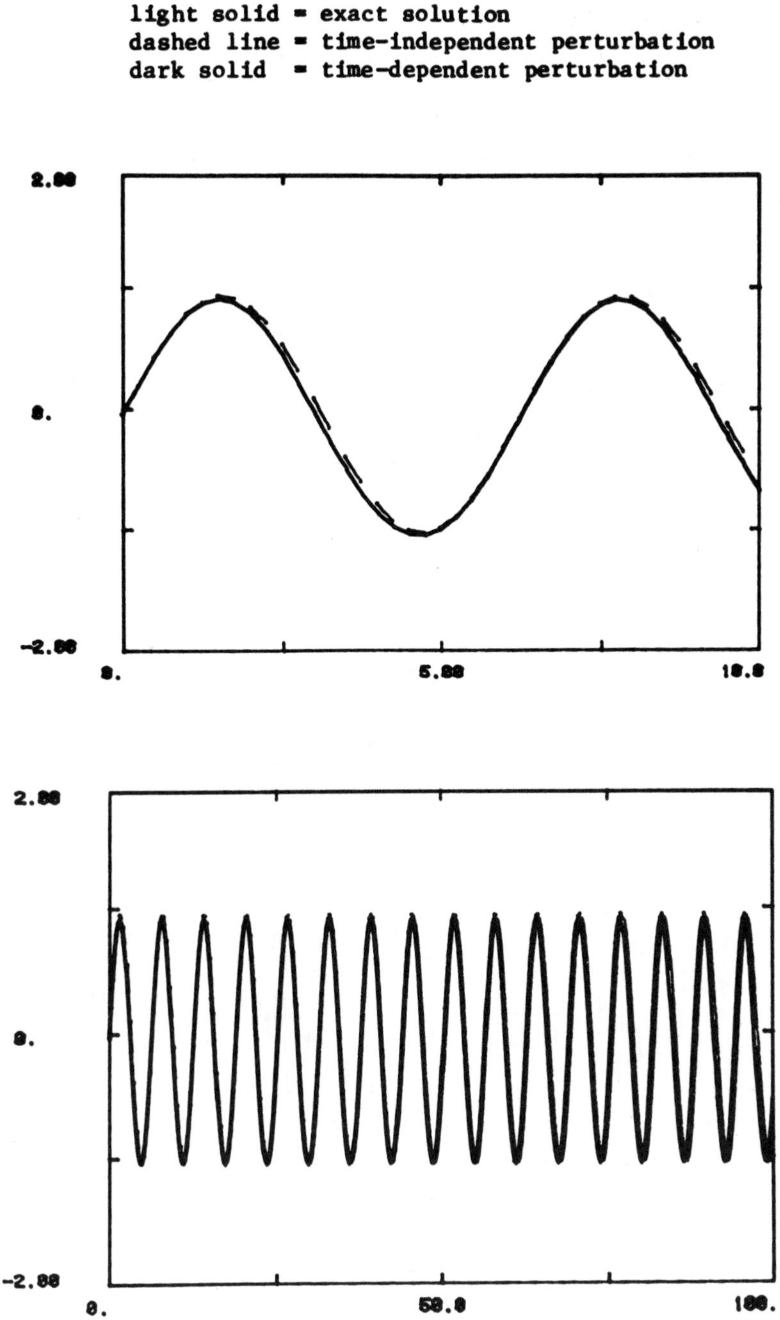

Figure 5 The anharmonic oscillator, comparison of perturbation methods for small forcing, $\varepsilon = 0.1$.

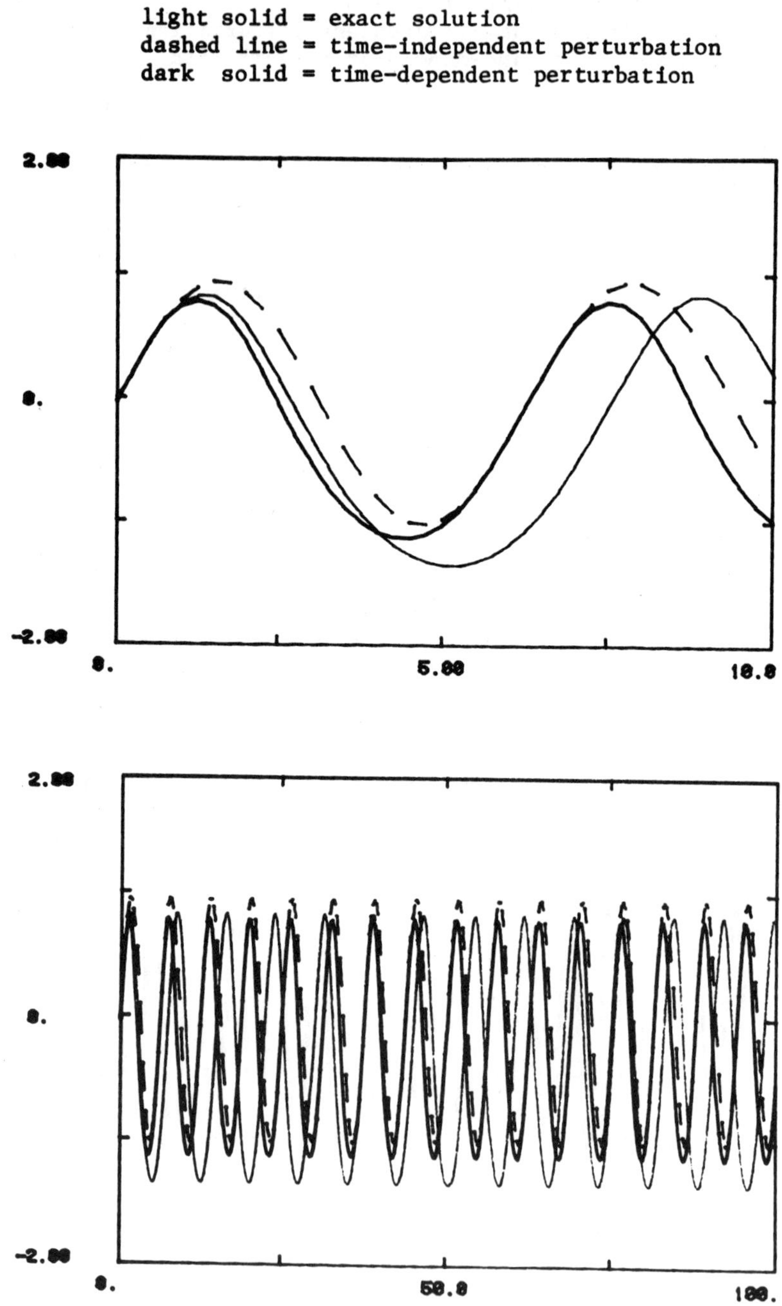

Figure 6 Same as Figure 5, but for larger forcing, $\varepsilon = 0.5$.

lity of computers facilitates this task tremendously and many techniques of numerical integration have been developed for accurately predicting paths where only a few orbital periods are involved. Even in this case, the accuracy of orbital paths can be increased considerably if, instead of the direct, brute-force numerical integration of the governing differential equations, one combines the numerical integration with a perturbation method. This is what is meant by hybrid methods.

Numerical Methods for Initial-Value Problems

We start with the description and comparison of four numerical methods for ordinary differential equations: the methods of Euler, modified Euler, Runge-Kutta-Fehlberg, and Adams-Moulton (20, Ch. 6). We apply these methods to the initial-value problem

$$\ddot{q} + q = 0 , \quad q(0) = 0 , \quad \dot{q}(0) = 1 . \qquad [15a,b,c]$$

The scalar, second-order equation [15a] can be rewritten as a system of two first-order equations

$$\dot{q} = p, \quad \dot{p} = -q$$

or, in matrix form,

$$\dot{r} = Ar, \quad A = \begin{pmatrix} 0 & 1 \\ -1 & 0 \end{pmatrix} , \qquad [16a,b]$$

where $r = (q,p)$. Euler's method is the simplest explicit time-marching method. It can be described in terms of the discrete system

$$\hat{r}(t) = (I + A\Delta t)^n r_0 , \qquad [17a]$$

where $r_0 = \begin{pmatrix} 0 \\ 1 \end{pmatrix}$, $\hat{r}(t)$ is the numerical approximation at t, $n\Delta t = t$, Δt is the step size used in the method and n the number of steps. To see this,

$$\hat{r}(t)=\hat{r}(n\Delta t)=\hat{r}((n-1)\Delta t)+\Delta t A\hat{r}((n-1)\Delta t)=(I+\Delta t A)\hat{r}((n-1)\Delta t). \qquad [17b]$$

Iterating gives [17a].

The modified Euler method is a predictor-corrector method. The predictor step is a forward Euler step, as in [17b], from $(n-1)\Delta t$ to $n\Delta t$. The corrector step is a "backward" Euler step, using the predicted value of $\hat{r}$ at $n\Delta t$ to approximate the increment of $\hat{r}$ over the last time step Δt. The two steps can be combined, since the method is still explicit, to yield

$$\hat{r}(t) = [I + A\Delta t + \frac{1}{2}(A\Delta t)^2]^n r_0 . \qquad [18]$$

The Adams-Moulton method is an implicit scheme, in which the already known value of $\hat{r}$ at $(n-1)\Delta t$, as well as the yet unknown value of $\hat{r}$ at $n\Delta t$ are used to compute the increment of $\hat{r}$ over the step Δt,

$$[I - \frac{\Delta t}{2} A]\,\hat{r}(n\Delta t) = [I + \frac{\Delta t}{2}]\,\hat{r}((n-1)\Delta t) . \qquad [19a]$$

In compact form one can then write

$$\hat{r}(t) = [(I - \frac{\Delta t}{2} A)^{-1} (I + \frac{\Delta t}{2} A)]^n r_0 . \qquad [19b]$$

When used for parabolic partial differential equations, this is the Crank-Nicholson scheme.

The Runge-Kutta-Fehlberg method is a combination of two Runge-Kutta methods, one of order four and the other of order five. The combination allows the algorithm RKF45 to estimate its own accuracy, and hence the step size needed to achieve a prescribed accuracy. The classical Runge-Kutta fourth-order method is given by

$$\hat{r}(t) = [I + \Delta t\, A + (\Delta t)^2 \frac{A^2}{2!} + (\Delta t)^3 \frac{A^3}{3!} + (\Delta t)^4 \frac{A^4}{4!}]^n r_0 ; \qquad [20]$$

for a full description of RKF45 we refer to Forsythe et al. (20, Sec. 6.8).

All four methods are stable, i.e., the solutions of the discrete problems [17-20], are at least as stable as the continuous problem [16], over a given time interval. The point of our discussion will be to compare their accuracies, as the total length T of the time interval increases.

Notice that when $\Delta t \to 0$, and the number of steps increases, $n \to \infty$, subject to $n\Delta t < T$ where T is fixed, all four methods converge to $\exp(At)r_0$, which is the true solution to the continuous problem. However if we fix Δt = constant and let $n \to \infty$, then all four methods eventually diverge from the correct solution. The situation is thus analogous to that for time-dependent perturbation methods.

Figure 7 compares the exact solution (solid) with the numerical one (dashed) for all four methods. Figure 7a shows the low, first-order accuracy of the Euler method, and should be compared with the first-order time-dependent perturbation method of Figure 2. The predictor-corrector method of Figure 7b is second-order in Δt, cf. [18], and blows up more slowly than the simple forward Euler method.

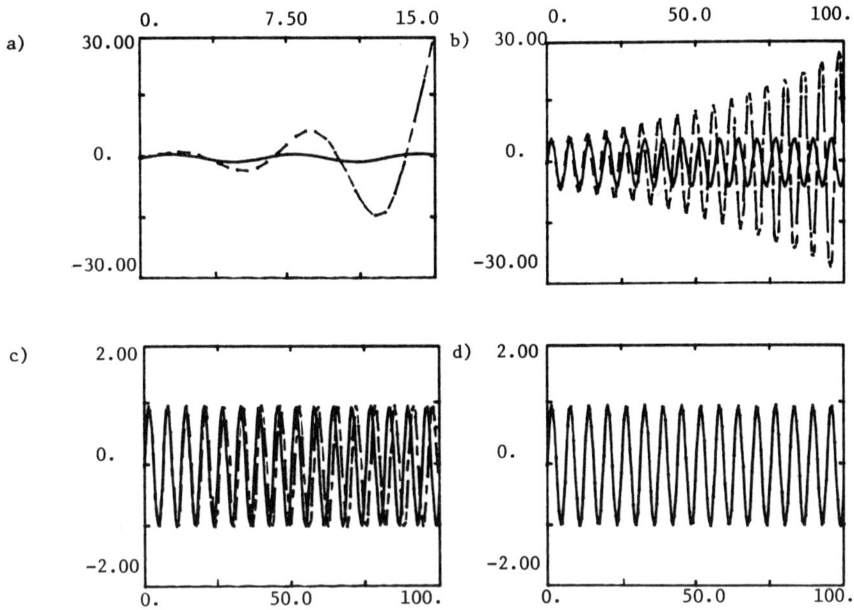

Figure 7 Numerical methods applied to the free harmonic oscillator; exact solution is solid, numerical solution is dashed. a) Euler; b) modified Euler; c) Adams-Moulton; d) RKF45.

The implicit method of Figure 7c can be shown to conserve the total energy of the numerical solution,

$$\hat{q}^2 + \hat{p}^2 = 1 .$$

Therefore $\hat{r}_n = \hat{r}(n\Delta t)$ is bounded, like the exact solution $r(t)$. Still, the phase error increases in time. The fifth-order RKF method of Figure 7d gives an extremely accurate solution over tens of periods. This and further checks provided the justification for using RKF45 to compute the exact solution in Figures 5 and 6. Still, eventually it will also diverge from the exact solution.

Hybrid Methods

The real problem in celestial mechanics is that many periodicities are present, rather than just one or two, as in our previous examples. It was mentioned after Eqs. [13,14] that these periods are rationally unrelated. Often the periods fall into "short" ones and "long" ones. Short periods are those asociated with variations in the Earth's obliquity, 41 kyr, and in its precession, 22 kyr; long periods are those associated with the orbit's eccentricity and major axis, which are of the order of 100 kyr and longer.

Variation of constants in the planetary problem leads to so-called Laplace series. These are trigonometric series in the "fast" variables, with coefficients which are power series in the "slow" variables. Thus the amplitudes and periods of the fast variables have "secular" changes, due to the slow variables.

The simplest possible form of hybrid method is then to compute the slow variables, and hence the coefficients of the Laplace series, numerically. This can be done by a time-marching scheme like [20], while using the trigonometric terms of the perturbation method up to a certain order for the fast variables. This corresponds to a numerical solution of Eqs. [10], after a number of analytic perturbation steps. The step size required is comparable to one tenth the shortest period in the system, say 1-2 kyr. Good accuracy could be maintained over a few tens of long periods, up to 1000 kyr perhaps.

Such a method would still suffer from the basic shortcomings of time-dependent perturbation methods, since the longest periods would not be explicitly apparent. In the next section, we outline the structure of solutions to the N-body problem, and discuss another type of hybrid method.

QUASI-PERIODIC AND APERIODIC SOLUTIONS

The population of the solar system is of staggering complexity. Beside the Sun and nine planets, the planets have tens of natural satellites and rings, hundreds of asteroids are in nearly elliptic orbits, while comets may also have unbounded, parabolic or hyperbolic orbits. The interactions between these bodies require their mass distribution to be taken into account, which changes in time due to short-term tides, as well as long-term physico-chemical processes. Finally, meteorites and interstellar gas modify the motion on very long time scales, along with the solar wind and nonuniformities in the galactic gravity field (33).

The stability of motion of this system has greatly preoccupied astronomers and mathematicians since the late eighteenth century. The explicit calculations to higher and higher perturbation order of the early nineteenth century proved fruitless and gave way to the abstract point of view initiated by Poincaré and Birkhoff. This road led to the achievements of KAM theory, as described at the beginning of section 3.

What is the structure of the (p,q)-phase space for the planetary problem, as described by KAM theory ? First, the system's phase space contains a large number of multi-dimensional tori, which are invariant under the canonical equations [4], and on which the quasi-periodic solutions lie (22,Sec. 1.1). Between these tori lie thin portions of phase space in which solutions are aperiodic, with an apparently random or chaotic behavior (Ibid., Sec. 3.2).

Whether the actual motion of the solar system is quasi-periodic, with a large number of incommensurable periods, or aperiodic cannot be told from existing observations of the motion (Ibid., Appendix A.1). Instrumental observations only extend over a few hundred, at most thousands of years, while the phenomena of interest are on the time scale of billions of years. In any case, this complicated structure of phase space prevents classical approaches of perturbation theory, as discussed in sections 2 and 3, from success in computing the quasi-periods as the coupling parameters between the celestial bodies increase from zero to their actual values.

In a certain sense at least, the difficulties of perturbation theory have to do with the Hamiltonian point of view itself. In a conservative system, periodic solutions and invariant tori are only neutrally stable. In a forced, dissipative system, on the other hand, limit cycles and other invariant sets are actually stable, at least in a certain neighborhood of the attracting set.

On the longest time scale, fluid friction with the interstellar gas, as well as random collisions with meteorites, provide a minute amount of dissipation, while the pressure of the solar wind provides a small, slowly changing forcing. This justifies considering the classical, Hamiltonian equations of celestial mechanics as the limit of a forced, dissipative system in which forcing and dissipation tend to zero.

Hybrid methods applied to forced, dissipative systems are rather well developed. In their simplest form, a known periodic motion is built into the solution for a certain, null parameter. The distortion of this periodic motion is then studied numerically as the given parameter varies (e.g. 23,24). Stability of the periodic motion is put to crucial use in the numerical aspects of the investigation.

Such an approach also encounters great difficulties when the simple limit cycle of the previous paragraph is replaced by a more complicated attractor set (25). Still it appears on the whole rather promising, or at least novel, and we intend to pursue it in a further publication.

CONCLUDING REMARKS

Evidence of periodicities in continuous geologic records of the Quaternary (26) has led to reasonably well-established correlations with certain short orbital periodicities, near 20 kyr and 40 kyr. Current technology, such as hydraulic piston cores and more sophisticated mass spectrometry, allow marine records to be extended back into the Tertiary, from the time scale of 10^5 yr to that of 10^6 yr.

The extended length and improved paleomagnetic and microtektite dating of deep-sea cores poses serious questions about the accuracy and constancy of the short orbital periods on these time scales. We have seen that phase information about the orbital parameters is rapidly lost over such time intervals. Still, one might hope that new approaches to orbital calculations will provide frequency information with known error bounds.

For the first time, geologic evidence of short periods emerges from the Mesozoic and even Paleozoic (27). While the issues of causal relation to orbital variations are even less settled than for the Cenozoic, it is tantalizing to consider these periods as observations of planetary behavior on the time scale of 10^7 yr to 10^8 yr. Eventually, one might hope for continuous segments of paleoclimatologic observations, however inaccurate, over the entire age of the Earth, $0(10^9$ yr).

This would throw an entirely new light on the classical stability question of the solar system. Some measure of observational verification could be expected where only speculation had prevailed, recently supplemented by powerful analytic and numerical results.

Celestial mechanics played an important role in the early stages of paleoclimatology. The time of reciprocation and further cross-fertilization seems to have come. One avenue would be the systematic investigation of simple, forced-dissipative models of the climatic system (e.g. 28,29,30,34,35), using orbital forcing based on the most accurate calculations available.

The power spectra predicted by orbitally forced climatic models can be compared with those of the records, rather than correlating the latter directly with the orbital peaks. This will allow systematic verification of independent geologic dating methods, orbital calculations, and the models themselves. The development of verification techniques, like those of numerical weather prediction (31, pp. 263-319), will greatly stimulate progress in the three interrelated areas of geochemistry, climate modeling and celestial mechanics.

ACKNOWLEDGMENTS

It is a pleasure to acknowledge useful and stimulating discussions with A. Berger, P. Bretagnon, A. Deprit, J. Moser, J. O'Keefe, J. Rennenkampff, and S. Steinberg. This work was supported in part by NSF Grants ATM-8018671 and ATM-8214754.

REFERENCES

1. Berger, A.L. : 1984, in : "Milankovitch and Climate", A. Berger, J. lmbrie, J. Hays, G. Kukla, B. Saltzman (Eds), Reidel Publ. Company, Holland. This volume, p. 3.
2. Moser, J. : 1970, Comm. Pure Appl. Math. 23, pp. 609-636.
3. Stiefel, E. : 1973, "Perturbation of the two-body motion; numerical methods", International Center for Mechanical Sciences Udine, Copernicus Session, 39pp.
4. Goldstein, H. : 1980, "Classical Mechanics", 2nd ed., Addison-Wesley, Reading, Mass., 672pp.
5. Brouwer, D. and Clemence, M. : 1961, "Methods of Celestial Mechanics", Academic Press, 598pp.
6. Berger, A.L., and Pestiaux, P. : 1984, "Milankovitch and Climate", A. Berger, J. Imbrie, J. Hays, G. Kukla, B. Saltzman (Eds), Reidel Publ. Company, Holland. This volume, p. 83.
7. Bretagnon, P. : 1984, "Milankovitch and Climate", A. Berger,J. Imbrie, J. Hays, G. Kukla, B. Saltzman (Eds), Reidel Publ. Company, Holland. This volume, p. 41.
8. Moser, J. : 1973, "Stable and Random Motions in Dynamical Systems, with Special Emphasis on Celestial Mechanics", Princeton Univerity Press, 198pp.
9. Poincaré, H. : 1892, "Les Méthodes Nouvelles de la Mécanique Céleste", Gauthier-Villars, Paris; reprinted Dover, New York, 1957, 3 vols.
10. von Zeipel, H. : 1916, Arkiv Mat. Astron. Fysik 11, No. 1 (1-58), 7 (1-62) and 9 (1-89).

11. Birkhoff, G.D. : 1927, "Dynamical Systems",American Mathematical Society, Providence, R.I.; revised, 1966, 305pp.
12. Kolmogorov, A.N. : 1954, Dokl. Akad. Nauk SSSR 98, pp. 527-530.
13. Arnold, V.I. : 1963, Usp. Mat. Nauk 18, No. 6 (114), pp. 81-92.
14. Moser, J. : 1967, "Convergent series expansion for quasi-periodic motions", Math. Ann. 169, pp. 136-176.
15. Hori, G. : 1966, Publ. Astron. Soc. Japan 18, pp. 287-296.
16. Deprit, A. : 1969, Cel. Mech. 1, pp. 12-30.
17. Lie, S. : 1888, "Theorie der Transformationsgruppen I", Teubner, Leipzig, Sec. 12.
18. Delaunay, A. : 1867, "Théorie du Mouvement de la Lune", Mém. Acad. Sci. Paris, no. 29.
19. Erdélyi, A. (Ed.): 1953, "Higher Transcendental Functions", Bateman Manuscript Project, vol. 2, McGraw-Hill Book Co., New York, 396pp.
20. Forsythe, G.E., Malcolm, M.A., Moler, C.B. : 1977, "Computer Methods for Mathematical Computations", Prentice Hall, Englewood Cliffs, NJ 07632, 259pp.
21. Berger, A.L. : 1977, Cel. Mech. 15, pp. 53-74.
22. Lichtenberg, A.J., and Lieberman, M.A. : 1983, "Regular and Stochastic Motion", Springer-Verlag, New York, 499pp.
23. Lorenz, E.N. : 1963, J. Atmos. Sci. 20, pp. 448-464.
24. Ghil, M. and Tavantzis, J. : 1983, SIAM J. Appl. Math. 43, PP. 1019-1041.
25. Ruelle, D. : 1980, Math. Intelligencer 3, pp. 126-137.
26. Imbrie, J., and Imbrie, K.P. : 1979, "Ice Ages", Enslow Publ., Short Hills, NJ 07078, 224 pp.
27. Anderson, R.Y. : 1982, J. Geophys. Res. 87C, pp. 7285-7294.
28. Ghil, M., and LeTreut, H. : 1981, J. Geophys. Res. 86C, p. 5262-5270.
29. LeTreut, H., and Ghil, M. : 1983, J. Geophys. Res. 88C, pp. 5167-5190.
30. Nicolis, C. : 1984, "Milankovitch and Climate", A. Berger, J. Imbrie, J. Hays, G. Kukla, B. Saltzman (Eds), Reidel Publ. Company, Holland. This volume, p. 637.
31. Bengtsson, L., Ghil, M., and Källen, E. (Eds) : 1981, "Dynamic Meteorology : Data Assimilation Methods", Springer-Verlag, New York, 330pp.
32. Arnold, V.I. : 1978, "Mathematical Methods of Classical Mechanics", Springer-Verlag, New York, 462 pp.
33. Vicente, R.O. : 1983, in : "Long-Time Prediction in Dynamics", C.W. Horton, L.E. Reichl, V.G. Szebehely (Eds), Wiley, New York, pp. 235-244.
34. Peltier, W.R., and Hyde, W. : 1984, in : "Milankovitch and Climate", A. Berger, J. Imbrie, J. Hays, G. Kukla, B. Saltzman (Eds), Reidel Publ. Company. This volume.
35. Saltzman, B., Sutera, A., and Hansen, A.R. : 1983, in this volume, p. 615.

ACCURACY AND STABILITY OF THE QUATERNARY TERRESTRIAL INSOLATION

A. Berger and P. Pestiaux

Université Catholique de Louvain, Institut d'Astronomie et de Géophysique Georges Lemaître, B-1348 Louvain-la-Neuve, Belgium

ABSTRACT

Seven different insolation parameters, which are used in climate modelling and for simulating the climatic variations, are reviewed as far as their computation, accuracy and spectrum are concerned. Seven different astronomical solutions, which generate the astronomical elements required in paleoclimatic studies, were computed over four different time intervals covering the last 3.2 million years. About the accuracy in time, improvements are necessary for times older than 1.5 Myr BP. About the stability of the frequencies, the fundamental quasi-periodicities (around 40, 23 and 19 kyr) do not deteriorate with time over the last 5 Myr (or at least their accuracy remains well beyond the accuracy of the geological time scale) but their relative power for each insolation parameter is a function of the time-interval considered.

SOME HISTORICAL BACKGROUND ABOUT THE ASTRONOMICAL THEORIES OF PALEOCLIMATES[1]

It is in the early part of the nineteenth century that Adhemar (3) suggested that the prime mover of the ice ages might be the variations in the direction of the Earth's axis and in the related insolations. The idea of an astronomical theory of the Quaternary glacial-interglacial alternations was born. There were after a few other scientists (5 to 6) expressing different opinions about how the motion of the Earth around the sun and about its axis could explain the Quaternary ice-ages before the second step was crossed.

A. L. Berger et al. (eds.), Milankovitch and Climate, Part 1, 83–111.

It is indeed in 1876 that a theory, opposite to Croll's view (4), was put forward by Murphy (5): long cool summer and short mild winter are the most favourable decisive factors to explain the Quaternary glacial and interglacial periods. So, the grounds were laied down for what was going to be called henceforward, the Milankovitch Theory. Indeed, in the early part of this century, M. Milankovitch, a yougoslavian astronomer, worked out, for the first time, a rational theoretical approach towards the quantitative study of climatic variations. Because of his training and his relationship with W. Köppen and A. Wegener (6), he illustrated his modelling approach through the mathematical formulation of the most well-known among all astronomical theories of paleoclimates. Nevertheless, despite the publication of his comprehensive book (7), which has become a classic, there was a continuous opposition against this theory and its followers (only about 15 recorded in the open literature for the first half of the twentieth century). The criticisms were based (i) upon the difficulty for geologists to end up with a reliable time scale for their proxy data and with an objective way to transfer them into specific climatic indices, and (ii) upon theoretical arguments advanced by meteorologists who calculated that the variations in solar heating were too small to have noticeable effect on climate.

It is around the nineteen hundred sixties that this theory revived, namely under the pressure of some geologists, such as C. Emiliani, R.W. Fairbridge, W. Broecker and G. Kukla, the astronomers D. Brouwer, A.J.J. van Woerkom, E.P.J. van den Heuvel and the climatologist E. Bernard. But the third era in the field of the astronomical theory really started in 1976 when the theoretical astronomical signals (8) were experimentally found in climatic data obtained from deep-sea cores (9). This was the results of joint efforts made in order to improve the radiometric dating, the reconstruction of climatic indices, the orbital parameters and the insolation values (10).

Since them, at least three other types of research were initiated in paleoclimatology in order to understand better the link between astronomic and climatic data; there are related to (i) monthly insolation values, their seasonal behaviour and latitudinal gradients (11,12); (ii) spectral and coherency analyses (as developed in SPECMAP under the leadership of J. Imbrie (23)); and (iii) climate modelling (from 0-dimensional models to full general circulation models) with the aim of simulating both the equilibrium and the transient response of the climate system to the astronomical forcing.

In order to contribute to this achievement, all the insolation parameters normally used in general climatology, will be reviewed in a paleoclimatic perspective. The accuracy of their long-term variations and the stability of their frequencies in time depend both upon the accuracy of the formulas used for their computation and upon the accuracy and stability of the corresponding orbital elements. The same procedure will be followed than in the companion paper (13), which means that 7 astronomical solutions will be used to test the accuracy and the stability of the insolation values over the last 3.2×10^6 years.

WHICH INSOLATION PARAMETERS ?

Among all the indices against which the geological data are tested to validate any astronomical theory of paleoclimates, the most popular ones are certainly the elements of the Earth's orbit and their linear or non-linear combinations (14,15).

However, as the climate system is thermally driven by solar insolation, there is a real interest to check wether or not there are some significant relationship between insolation parameters and climate at the global scale. The difficulty which then first arises is to determine the most realistic latitudes and to select the most sensitive periods of the year (16,17,18).

There are at least three different ways to tackle this problem. One approach would be to perform sensitivity tests of the modelled climatic system to such and such insolation parameters. A second one, probably the most direct and easiest one, is to use multivariate regressive models, which can even be extended in the frequency domain and to non-linear relationships, in order to select those latitudes and months which explain the largest part of the climatic variance (16). A simplified version of this method is the correlation analysis between climatic data and some particular insolations, 65°N Northern Hemisphere Summer being the most frequently used (7). In order to avoid problems related to a posteriori screening techniques used to select the most important subset of the complete seasonal and latitudinal distribution of solar radiation, as in (16), an a priori ordering scheme was proposed (18). This method is based on an expansion of the solar insolation in terms of a series of seasonally dependent Legendre functions, and is used to feed a model where cross spectral analysis is a basic tool to derive information on the linear relationship linking paleoclimates to paleoinsolations. The third method would be to design time-dependent models in order to study the response of the climate system to the astronomical forcing through the analysis of the climatic time series generated by such models.

The adjustment between the outputs of these models and the climatic proxy data may thus be tested in the time and/or the frequency domains. This is why the different kinds of insolation which are expected to be used for modelling the climate or for simulating the dynamics of the climatic variations, will be reviewed as far as their computations, accuracy and spectrum are concerned.

About spectrum, assuming either a linear or a non-linear response of the climate system to the external solar forcing, the frequencies found in the various insolation parameters are expected to help understanding the time and geographical distributions of the frequencies found in geological data. Indeed, since a few years, there are more and more facts which prove that the variance and spectrum of geo-climatic time series vary in space and time. For example, paleoceanographic indices from DSP site 502 show two distinct climatic regimes (24) within the Quaternary : the late Quaternary spectra display periods at around 100 kyr and 23 kyr, whereas the Early Quaternary spectra have more power at 41 kyr and 19 kyr. An evolutive maximum entropy spectral analysis of the oxygen isotope recorded in core V28-239 show also a progressive decay of the amplitude of the 100 kyr quasi-period (25), especially when the interval 0-700 kyr BP is compared to the 900-1300 kyr BP and 1300-1900 kyr BP ones. For older times, carbonate time series (DSDP site 158) shows that the Miocene record is dominated by very low frequency components (at ∿ 400 kyr) as compared to the Quaternary record (RC11-209) where additional concentrations of variance appear at frequencies corresponding to periods near 100 and 40 kyr (26).

The geographical variation of the spectra is even more complicated. The variance of the ^{18}O ice volume record (high latitudes climate estimate) is concentrated at the eccentricity, obliquity and precession frequencies, whether the cores are taken from equatorial region (27) or in temperate and polar latitudes (28). However, cycles with a period around 20 kyr dominate clearly the sea-level record determined from dated coral reefs on rising islands in the intertropical belt (29). The same predominance of the 23 kyr cycle is found in summer sea surface temperature estimated from a mid-latitudes North Atlantic core, although its isotopic record is dominated by the 100 and 41 kyr periodicities (30). The relative importance of the 41 and 23-19 kyr cycles is thus more complex (what is also well illustrated in (23) and (31)) than usually claimed by saying that precession effect seems to be recorded by proxy data only in latitudes south of 60°N while the obliquity effect is recorded at higher latitudes. This simple view of the response of the climatic system to the astronomical forcing dates back from Milankovitch's work where summer caloric half-year average insolation (departure from to-day) shows this latitudinal response to these two different orbital parameters.

However, Table 1 shows clearly that insolation, in general, is function of the orbital elements with a lot more of diversity. These insolations parameters that we review here, are : the half-year astronomical seasons (their length, their total and mean insolations), the half-year caloric seasons introduced by Milankovitch, the astronomical and meteorological seasons (their length, their total and mean insolations), the monthly mean insolations and the daily mid-month (solar date) and calendar date insolations.

Table 1 Insolations as a function of astronomical parameters (++ means stronger dependancy).

	obliquity ε	precession $e \sin \tilde{\omega}$
Mid-month insolation at equinox	−	+
at solstice	+	++
Half-year astronomical seasons		
- total insolation	+	−
- length	−	+
- mean in polar latitudes	++	+
in equatorial latitudes	−	+
Caloric seasons polar latitudes	+	−
equatorial latitudes	−	+
Meteorological seasons (astronomical definition)		
- total insolation	+	−
- length	−	+
Meteorological seasons (monthly mean)	+	++

These insolations depend on :

(i) 4 astronomical parameters which all affect the total energy received by the planet: the astrophysical solar constant[2], S_a, the length of the tropical year and of the day, the secularly variable mean distance from the Earth to the sun, r_m : $r_m^2 = a^2(1-e^2)^{1/2}$.

(ii) 2 others which re-distribute differently the energy among the latitudes and months: the climatic precession, $e \sin \tilde{\omega}$, and the obliquity, ε.

Although it is not intended to give a comprehensive review of all the formulae leading to the computation of these insolation parameters, the bases will be reminded to understand better the conclusions given in Table 1 (details may be found in (7), (21) and (22)).

The daily insolation W incident on the Earth'surface at a latitude ϕ , assuming a completely transparent atmosphere is given by :

(i) for laltitudes where there is sunrise and sunset :

$$W = \frac{S_a}{\pi \rho^2} (H_0 \sin \phi \sin \delta + \cos \phi \cos \delta \sin H_0) \qquad [1]$$

(ii) for latitudes where there is no sunset[3] :

$$W = \frac{S_a}{\pi \rho^2} \sin \phi \sin \delta \qquad [2]$$

where S_a is equal to $S_0(1-e^2)^{1/2}$ but identified to S_0(1350 W m^{-2}) in (7).
W is in W m^{-2}; to obtain W in cal cm^{-2} day^{-1}, S_a (1.95 cal cm^{-2} min^{-1}) must be multiplied by 1440.
H_0 is the absolute value of the hour angle at sunrise and sunset = $H_0(\phi,\delta)$
δ is the declination of the sun : $\sin \delta = \sin \varepsilon \sin \lambda$
ε is the obliquity
ρ is the Earth-sun distance r measured in units of a :

$$\rho = \frac{r}{a} = \frac{1 - e^2}{1 + e \cos (\omega-\lambda)}$$

λ is the true longitude of the Earth
ω is the longitude of the perigee in an geocentric coordinate system. Its numerical value is equal to the longitude of the perihelion, $\tilde{\omega}$, given in (13) plus 180°.

From [1] and [2], it is easy to compute, to the first degree with respect to the Earth's eccentricity, the insolation, W, received at the equinoxes and solstices (7,22,33) :

$$\text{Spring/Autumn equinox} : W_F^V = \frac{S_0}{\pi} (1 \mp 2 e \cos \tilde{\omega}) \cos \phi \qquad [3]$$

which is valid for all latitudes.

Summer
solstices : W^S_W
Winter

(i) for latitudes with a sunrise and a sunset

$$W^S_W = \frac{S_0}{\pi} (1 \mp 2 e \sin \tilde{\omega}) F(\phi,\varepsilon) \qquad [4]$$

the subscripts S and W refer to the summer and winter solstices, i.e. to the beginning of the Northern Hemisphere summer and winter

(ii) for latitudes where there is no sunset

$$W^S_W = \pm S_0(1 \mp 2 e \sin \tilde{\omega}) \sin \phi \sin \varepsilon \qquad [5]$$

All these formulas show that

(i) if ε increases, the latitudinal contrast decreases and the seasonal contrast increases.
(ii) at the equinoxes (Figs 1 and 3), W is only a function of precession (Fig. 5)
(iii) at the solstices (Figs 2 and 4), ε plays a similar role in both hemispheres but precession dominates although the ε effect is more important in high than in low latitudes (Fig. 5).

The long-term variations of mid-month insolations for March, June, September and December (respectively at the spring equinox, summer solstice, autumn equinox and winter solstice) are given in Figs 1 to 4 for the last 800 kyr. For a comparison, the same was done for the April, July, October and January, monthly means in Figs 8 to 11. Their spectra are reproduced in Figs 5 and 12 where the vertical scale is in normalised unit but is proportional to the variance explained by each frequency bands. The same spectral analysis has also been done for the insolation received during the astronomical (Fig. 6) and caloric (Fig. 7) seasons.

For the half-year astronomical seasons (Fig. 6), similar formulas will show that their length vary secularly as a function of the precession only and that the total amount of insolation received for any latitude is only a function of ε, although the time variations in the equatorial belt are largely attenuated. This leads to <u>mean</u> values in polar latitudes which

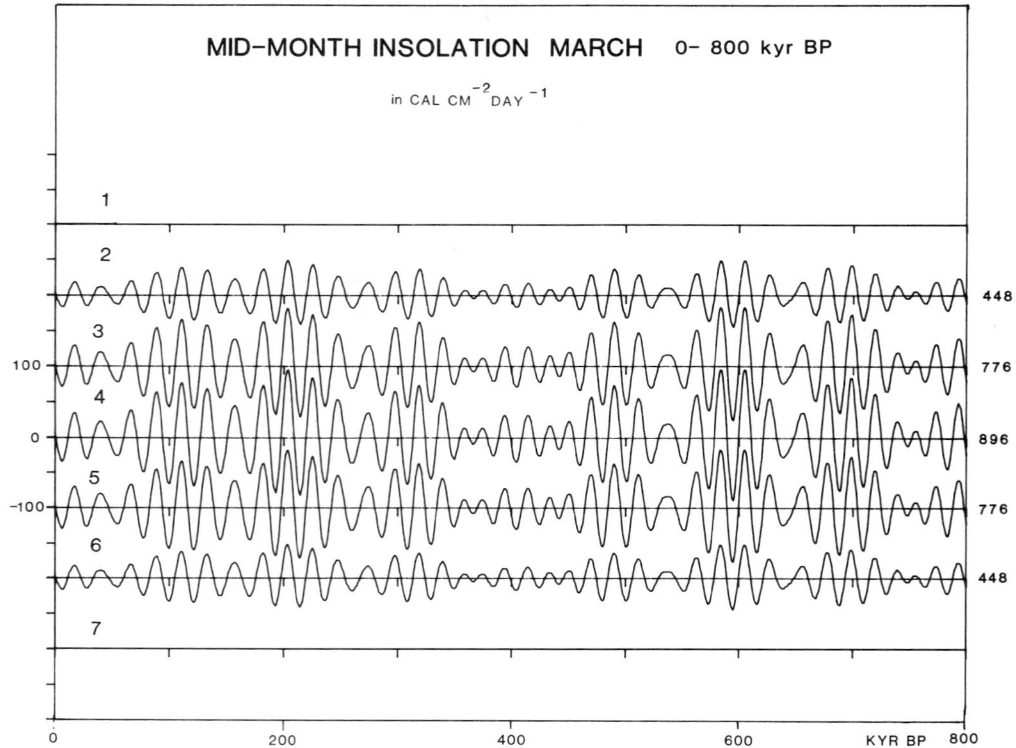

Figure 1 Long term variations of March mid-month insolation over the last 800 kyr, in cal cm^{-2} day^{-1}, for 90°N (1), 60°N (2), 30°N (3), 0° (4), 30°S (5), 60°S (6), 90°S (7). The left scale gives the deviation from the mean values listed on the right hand side of the figure for each latitude.

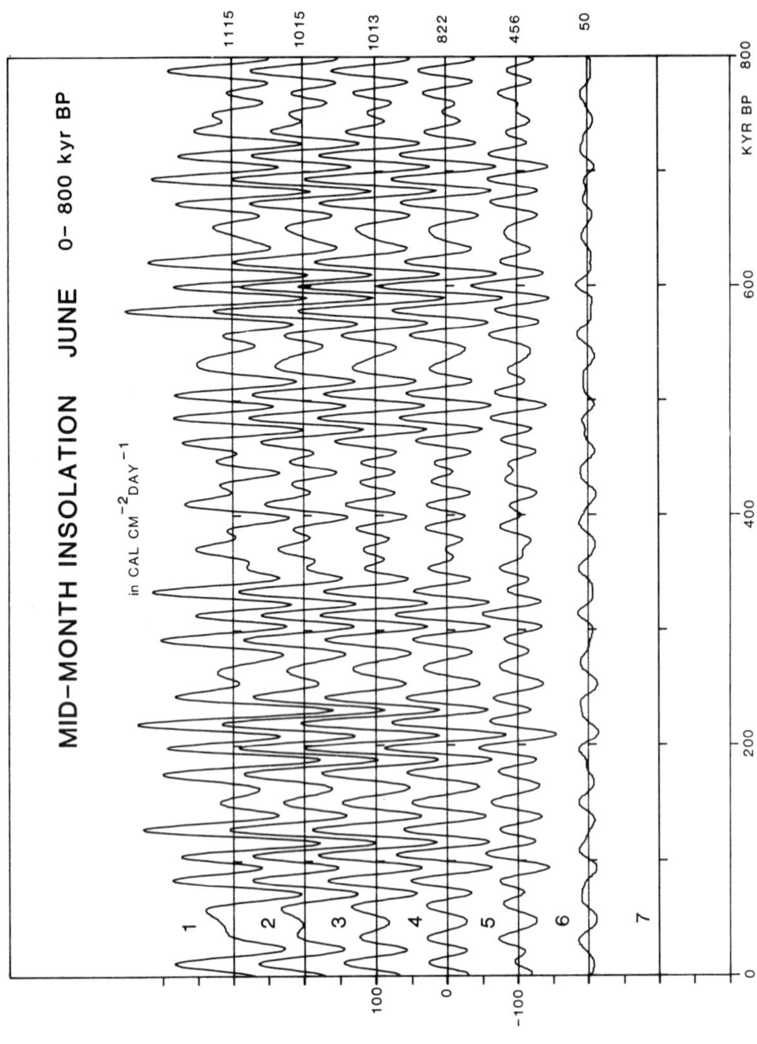

Figure 2 Same as Fig. 1 for June.

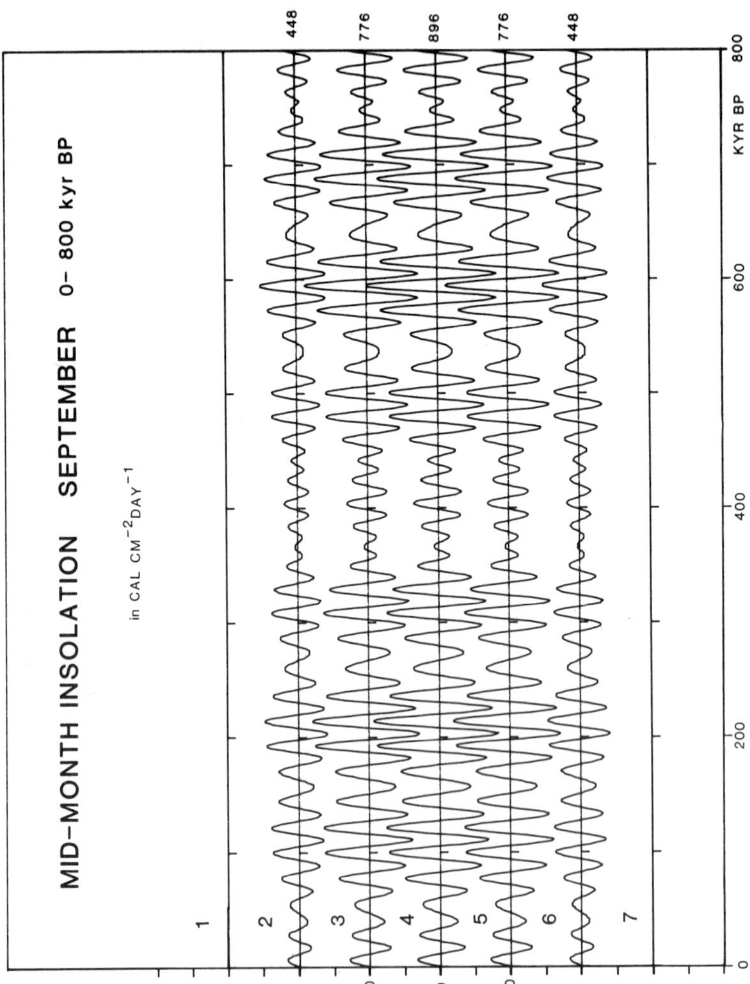

Figure 3 Same as Fig. 1 for September.

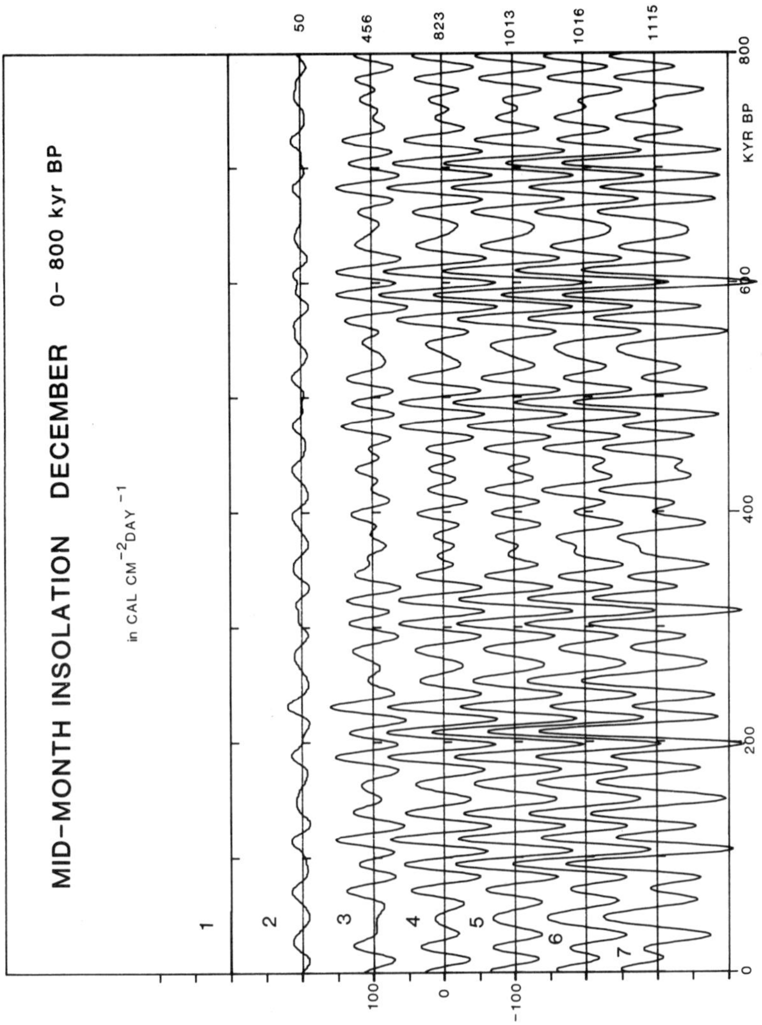

Figure 4 Same as Fig. 1 for December.

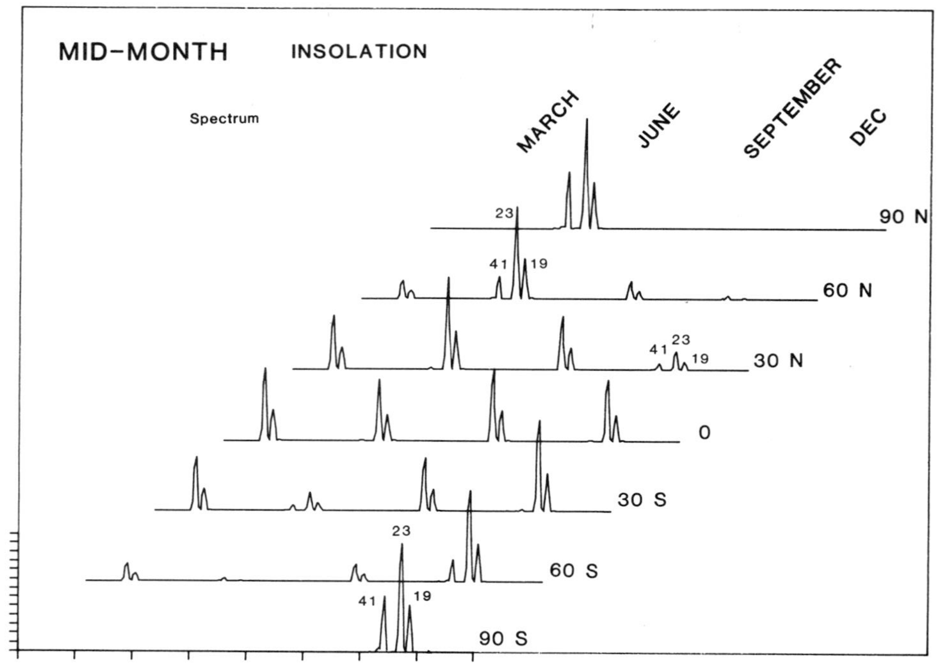

Figure 5 Spectral analysis of mid-month insolations for 7 latitudes as given in Figs 1 to 4. The vertical scale is in relative units and is proportional to the amount of variance explained by each frequency bands (periods given in kyr.)

are function of obliquity and precession, but with the ε-signal being the strongest. In equatorial latitudes, the insolation variance is explained almost entirely by the precession. The same conclusions hold more or less for the 3-month astronomical seasons, the spring being then defined by $-\frac{\pi}{4} < \lambda < \frac{3\pi}{4}$ as in (22).

In order to overcome the difficulty of dealing with a secularly variable length of the astronomical seasons, Milankovitch (7) defined the half-year caloric seasons where the $\Delta\varepsilon$'s make themselves felt in both hemispheres in the same sense, with a maximum effect in polar latitudes, whereas $\Delta(e \sin \tilde{\omega})$ has a maximum effect in equatorial latitudes but with an opposite sense in both hemispheres (Fig. 7). As in these equatorial regions, there is a double sinusoidal oscillation of the insolation during the course of a year, Milankovitch defined the caloric equator, an interesting parameter which combines both precession and obliquity effects, but with precession dominating as sin $\tilde{\omega}$ is slowly varying by a small amount only when compared to ε.

As the traditional half-year caloric averages smooth out the large seasonal variations, they are felt to be not the most relevant in all cases and the meteorological seasons or the mid-month and monthly mean insolations (Figs 8 to 11) were introduced (11). Indeed, for example, autumn insolation was stressed to be of more importance in determining whether or not snow accumulation occurs (17). These monthly insolation values which start now to be used in general circulation (19,20) and other models (34,35), show a spectrum which is half-way between the spectra of the caloric seasons insolation and of the mid-month insolation values: for the calendar monthly means, precession is always dominating but an obliquity signal appears as soon as latitude increases towards the poles and time is approaching the solstices (Fig. 12). In this respect, the amplitude of the peak for October at 85°S (Fig. 12) is remarkable and due to large variations about a relatively low mean (480 cal cm^{-2} day^{-1}); this has to be compared with similar large amplitude variations in January, but around a much larger mean of 974 cal cm^{-2} day^{-1}. These features at the precessional frequencies have not their equivalent in northern high latitudes for April (compare Figs 8 against 10).

Table 1 summarizes all this by giving the degree of dependence of the different insolation parameters upon the obliquity and precession.

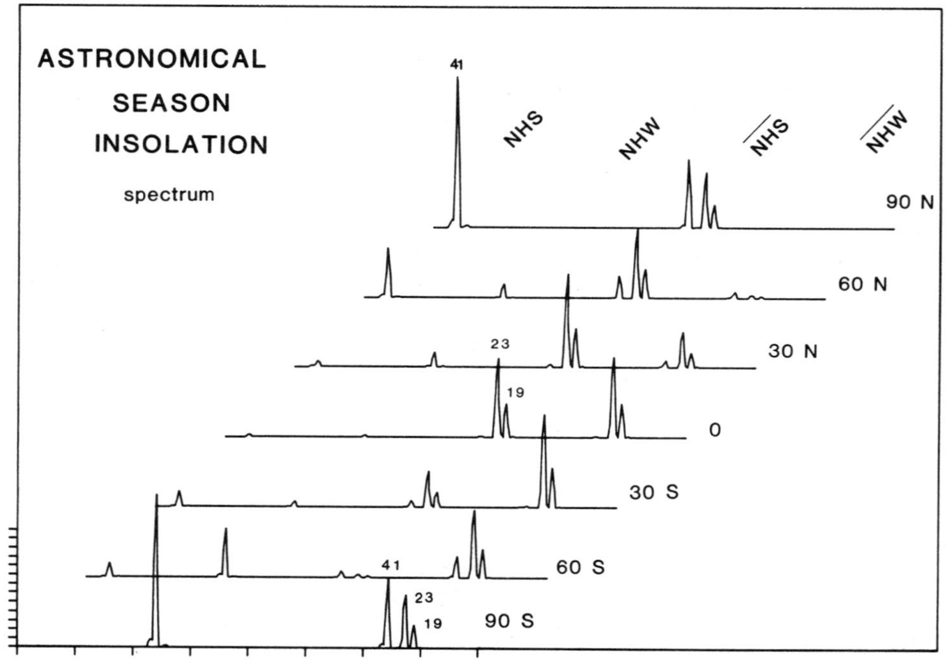

Figure 6 Same as Fig. 5 but for the astronomical seasons : NHS ($\overline{NHS}$) is for the total (mean) energy received during Northern Hemisphere summer and NHW ($\overline{NHW}$) during Northern Hemisphere winter.

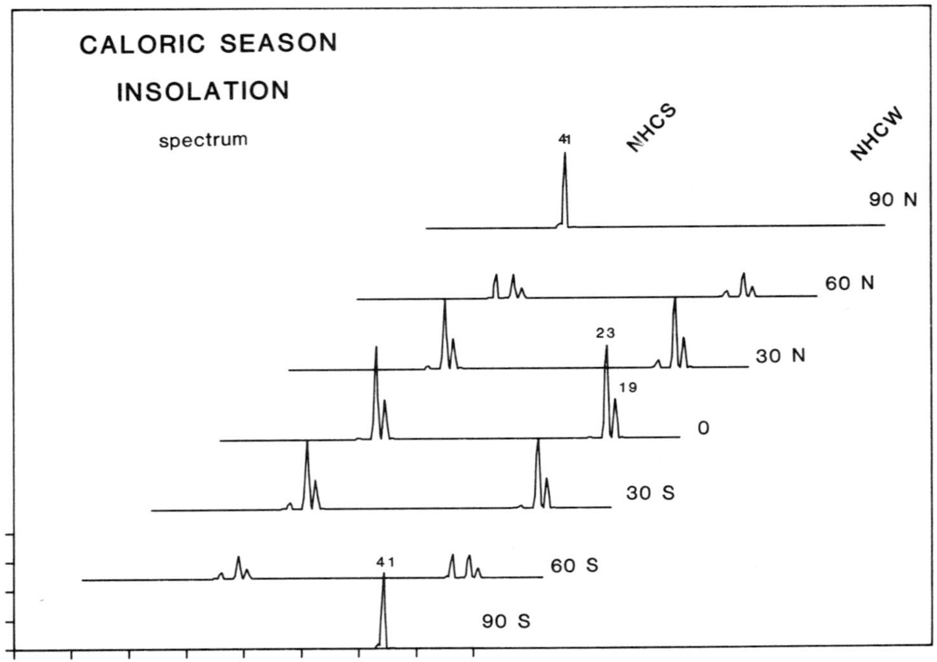

Figure 7 Same as Fig. 5 but for the Northern Hemisphere caloric summer (NHCS) and for the Northern Hemisphere caloric winter (NHCW).

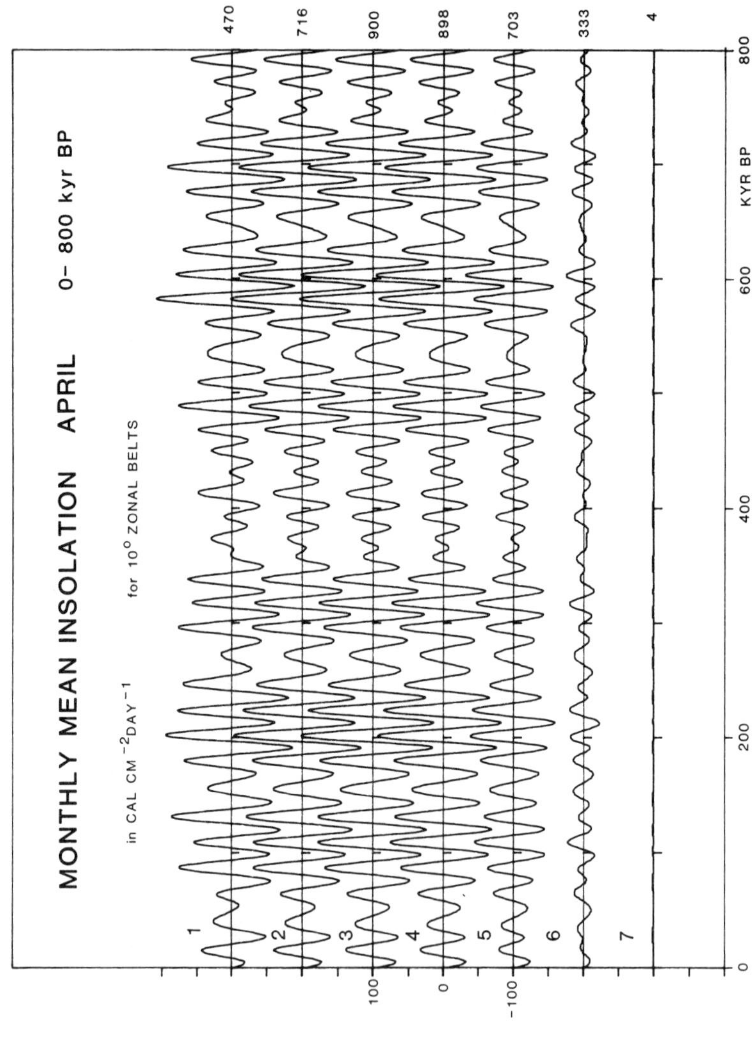

Figure 8 Same as Fig. 1 for April monthly mean insolation for 7 different 10° zonal belts centered at 85°N (1), 55°N (2), 25°N (3), 5°N (4), 25°S (5), 55°S (6), 85°S (7).

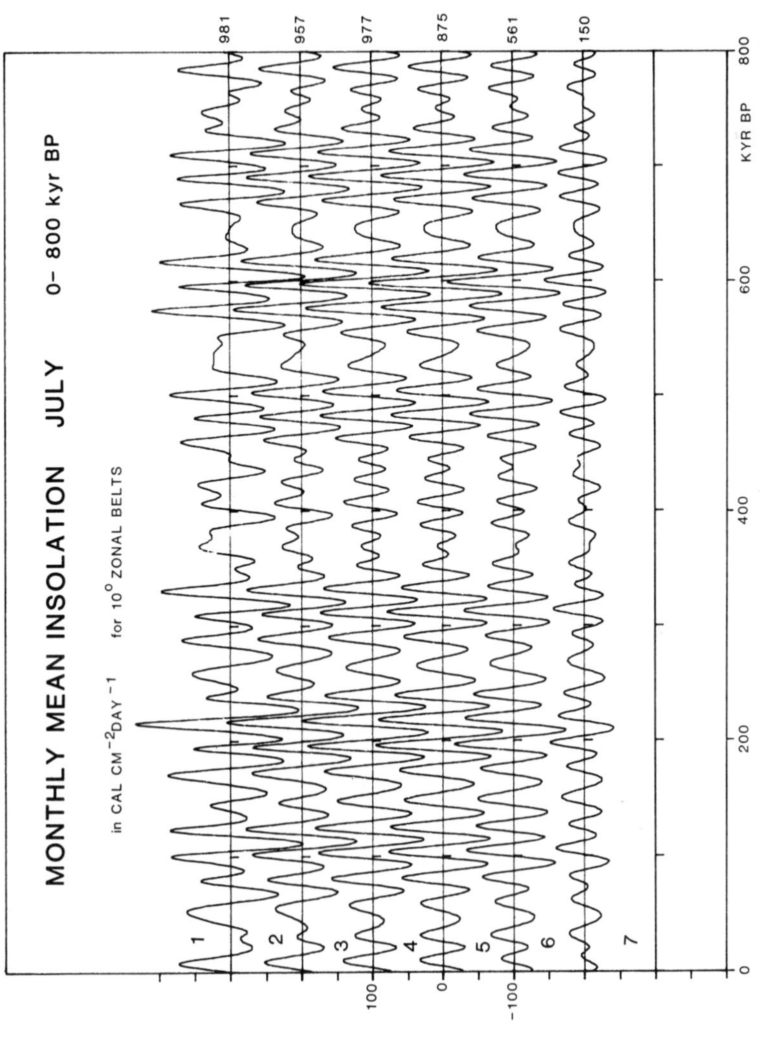

Figure 9 Same as Fig. 8 for July.

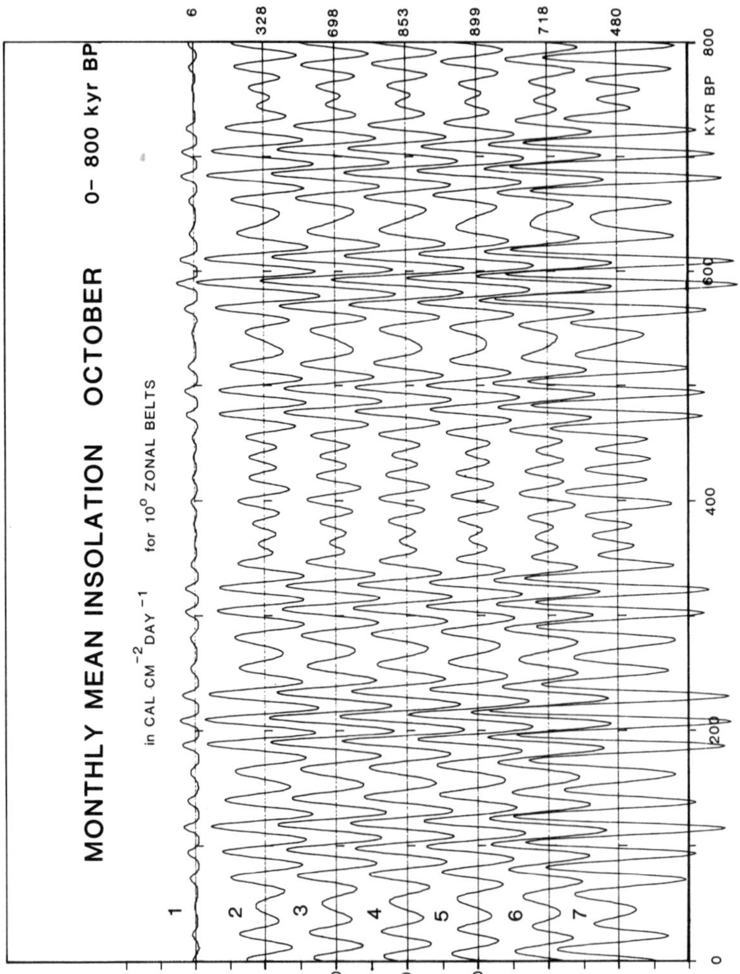

Figure 10 Same as Fig. 8 for October.

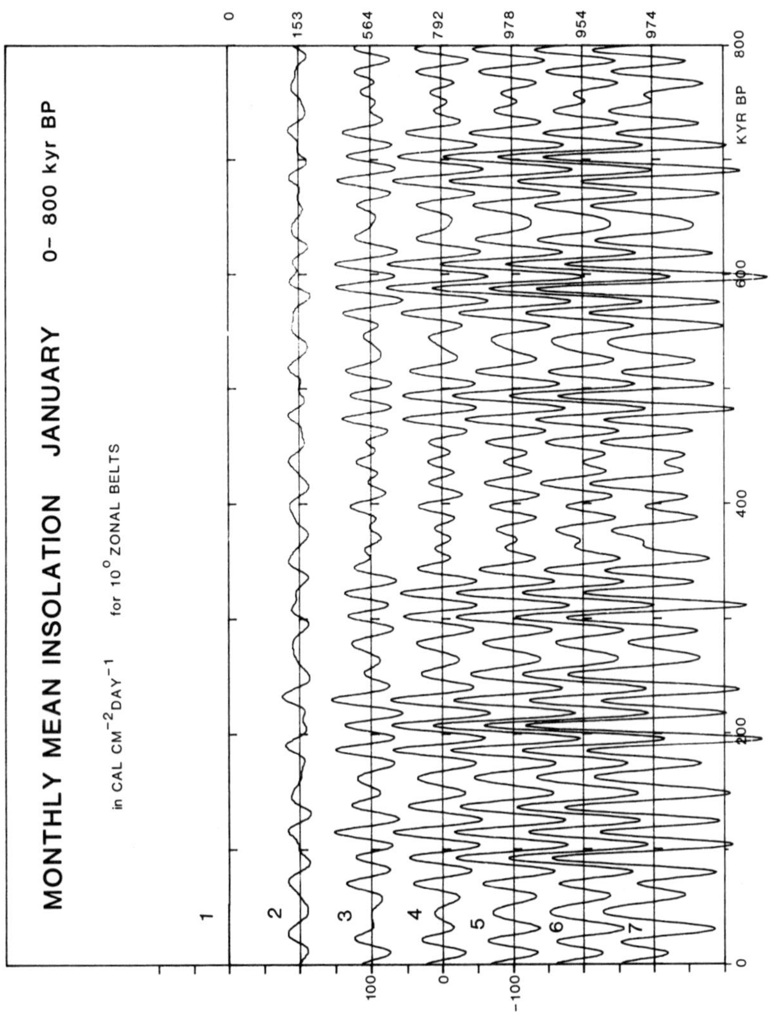

Figure 11 Same as Fig. 8 for January.

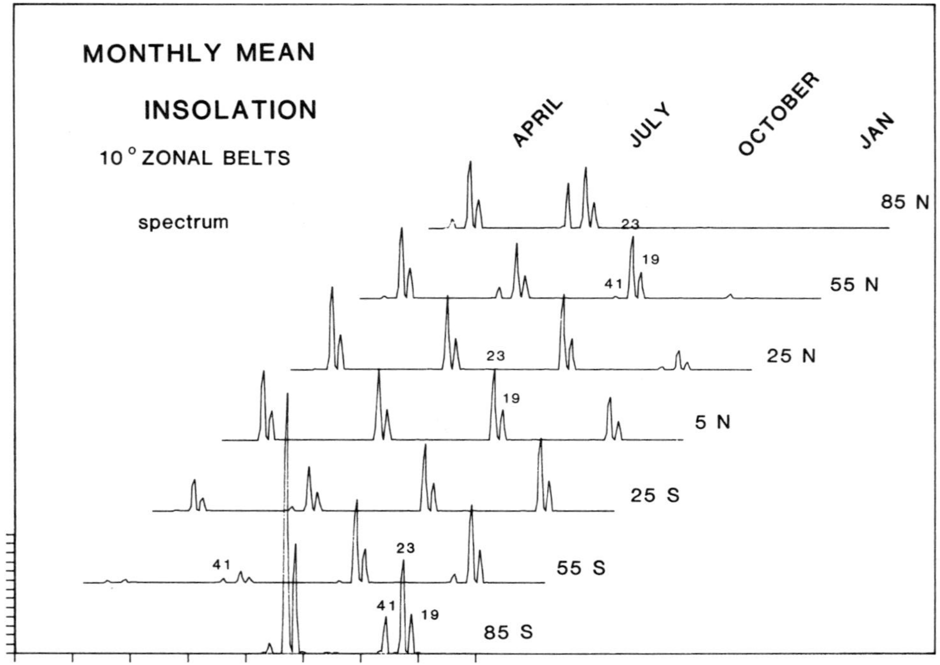

Figure 12 Same as Fig. 5 for monthly mean insolations as given in Figs 8 to 11.

ACCURACY AND STABILITY OF THE FREQUENCIES

The accuracy of these insolations has been tackled using only June mid-month insolation at 60°N. It is indeed expected that this parameter will show the most apparent progressive phase shifting with time, among all other possible insolation parameters, for the following reasons :

(i) this parameter is dependent on both precession and obliquity but with a stronger precession signal (which main period is about half the obliquity one).

(ii) The mean value, roughly 1015 cal cm^{-2} day^{-1}, is very stable over the 4 different time sub-intervals (SS) :0-800, 800-1600, 1600-2400, 2400-3200 kyr BP.

Comparing all the curves obtained from the 7 astronomical solutions described in (13), for each of the 4 time intervals, it is easy to see that the general behaviour and the amplitude of the variations are quite similar (Figs 13 to 16). This is also the conclusion which can be drawn from Fig. 17, where all the 7x4 spectra are shown. For each particular sub-interval SS, these spectra are pretty well the same, except for the earliest solutions where the relative magnitude of the 23 kyr signal against the 19 kyr one is reversed.

On the other hand, a comparison of the 4 different SSs clearly shows significant differences in the respective spectra, a common point to all solutions. As the same mathematical formulation was applied for each astronomical time series, this must result from the different behaviour of the astronomical elements during these 4 SSs. The third sub-interval (1600-2400 kyr BP) is certainly the most different with very weak 41 and 19 kyr signals. In the second one (800-1600 kyr BP), the precession variance is equally shared between the 23 and 19 kyr peaks; the first and last ones are more or less the same with a moderate 41 kyr signal, a strong 23 and a moderate to strong 19 one.

About the accuracy in time, comparing the last 4 "more accurate" time series, one can see that a progressive phase shift is appearing after 10^6 yr and starts to be significant roughly after 1.5 to 2.0 10^6 yr (even though only BRE 3,4 and 5 are considered).

CONCLUSIONS

Table 1 and all the figures show that improvements are necessary for times older than 1.5 Myr BP if insolation time-series are going to be compared with geological record in the

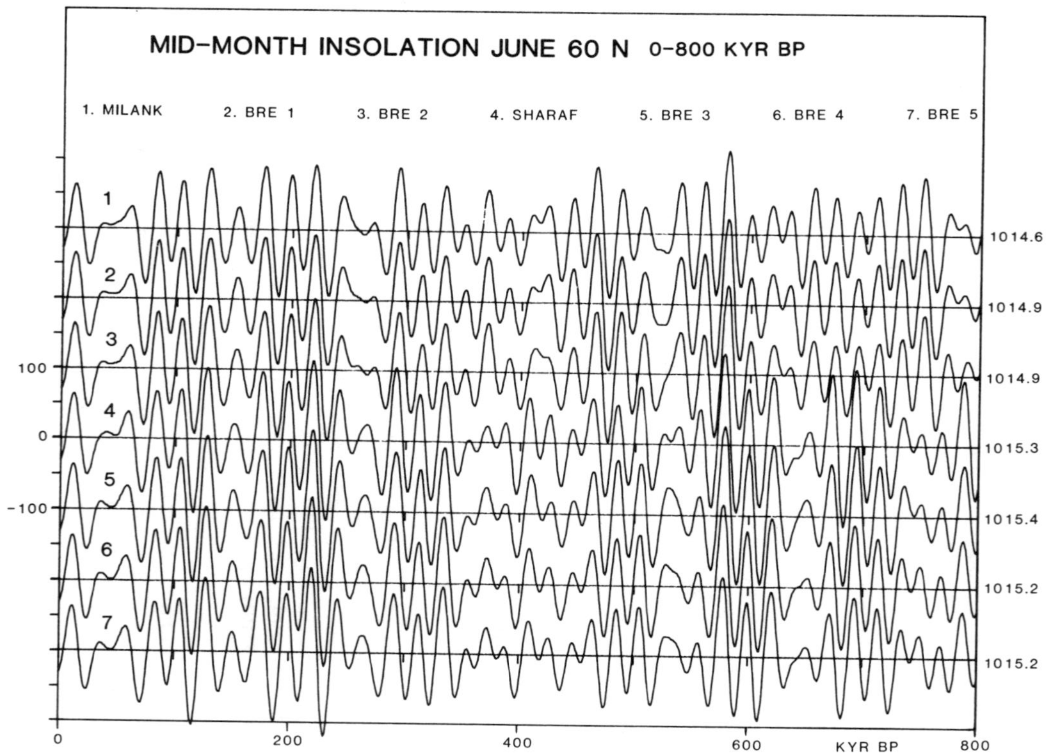

Figure 13 Long-term variations of June mid-month insolation at 60°N over the time-interval 0-800 kyr BP, for 7 different astronomical solutions : MILANK (1), BRE1 (2), BRE2 (3), SHARAF (4), BRE3 (5), BRE4 (6), BRE5 (7), described in (13). Vertical scales as in Fig. 1.

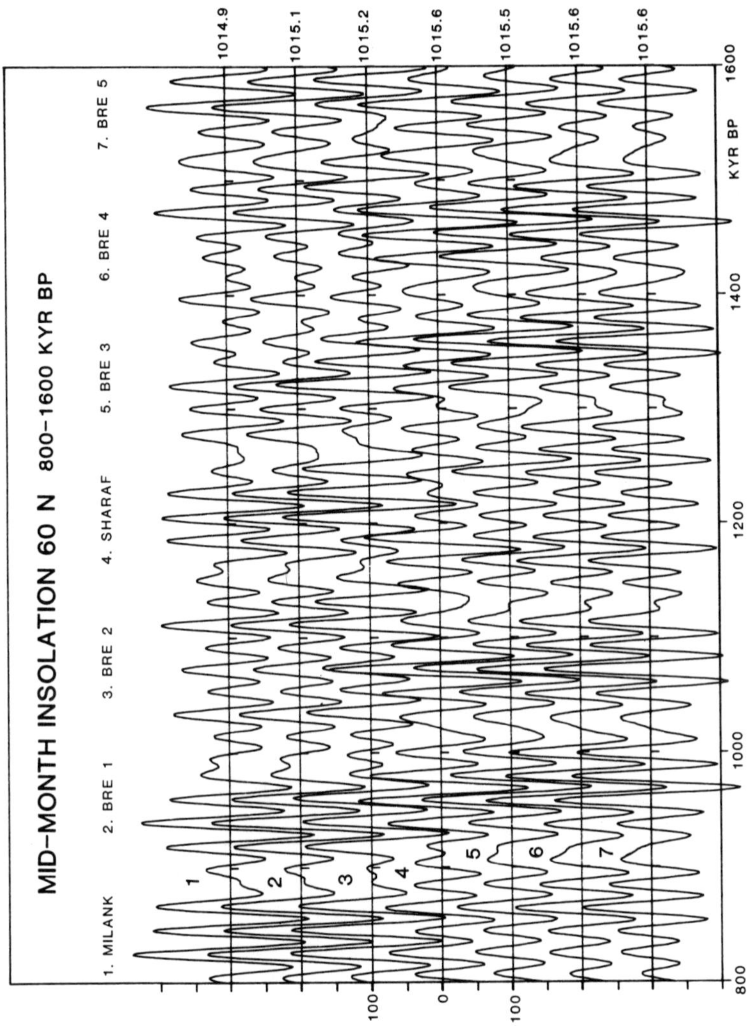

Figure 14 Same as Fig. 13 but over 800-1600 kyr BP.

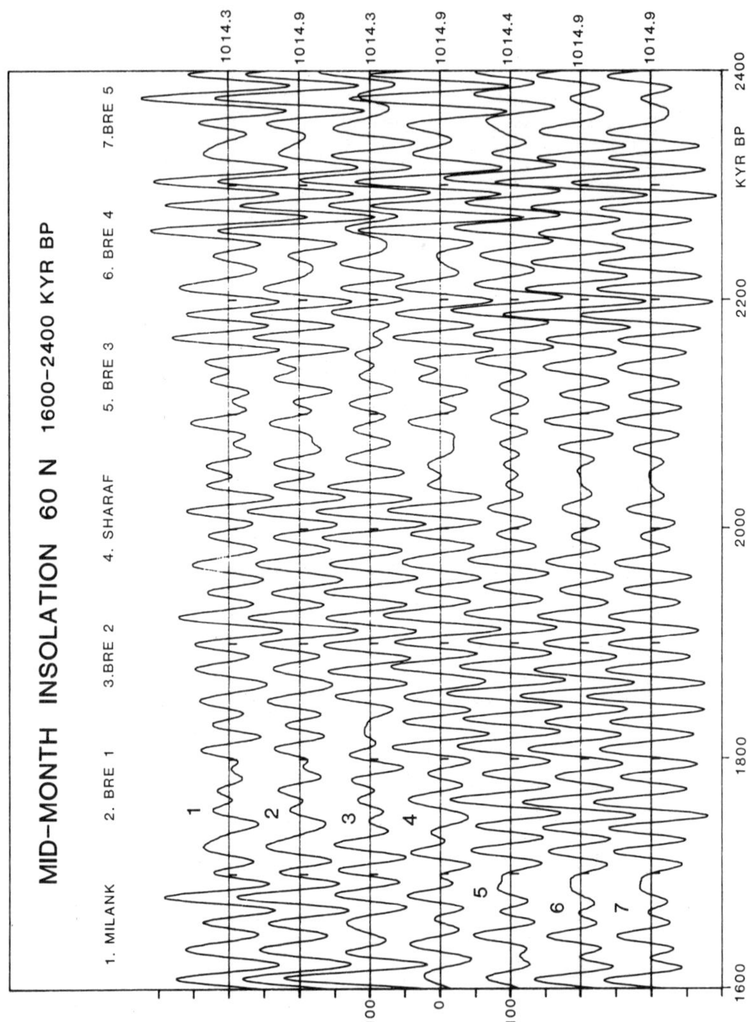

Figure 15 Same as Fig. 13 but over 1600-2400 kyr BP.

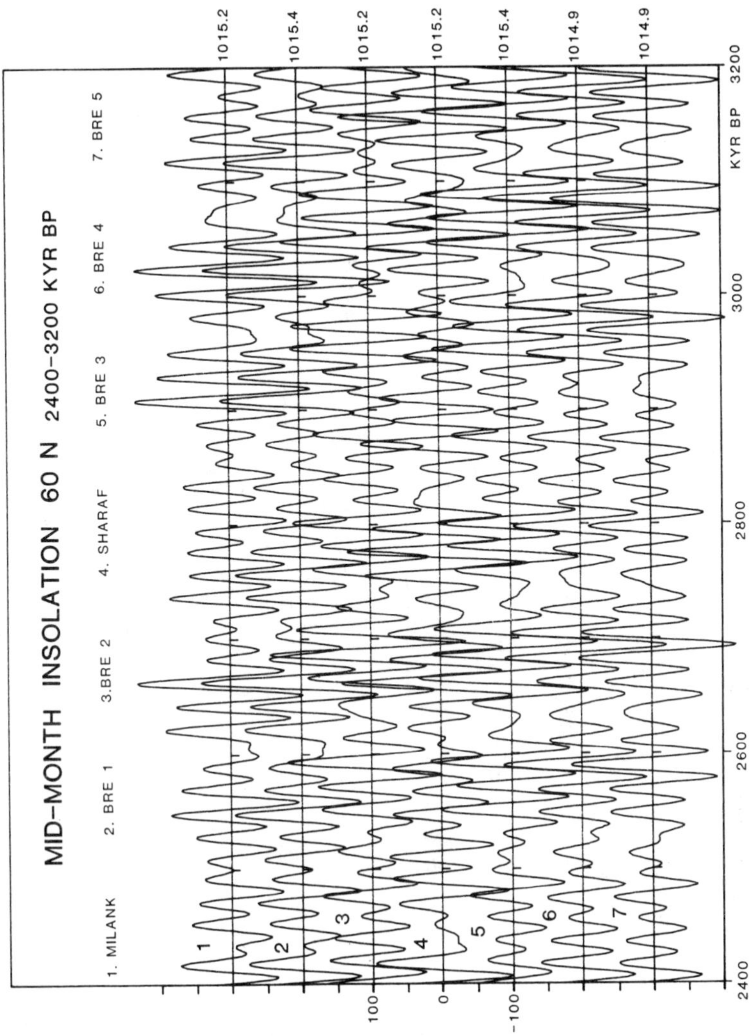

Figure 16 Same as Fig. 13 but over 2400-3200 kyr BP.

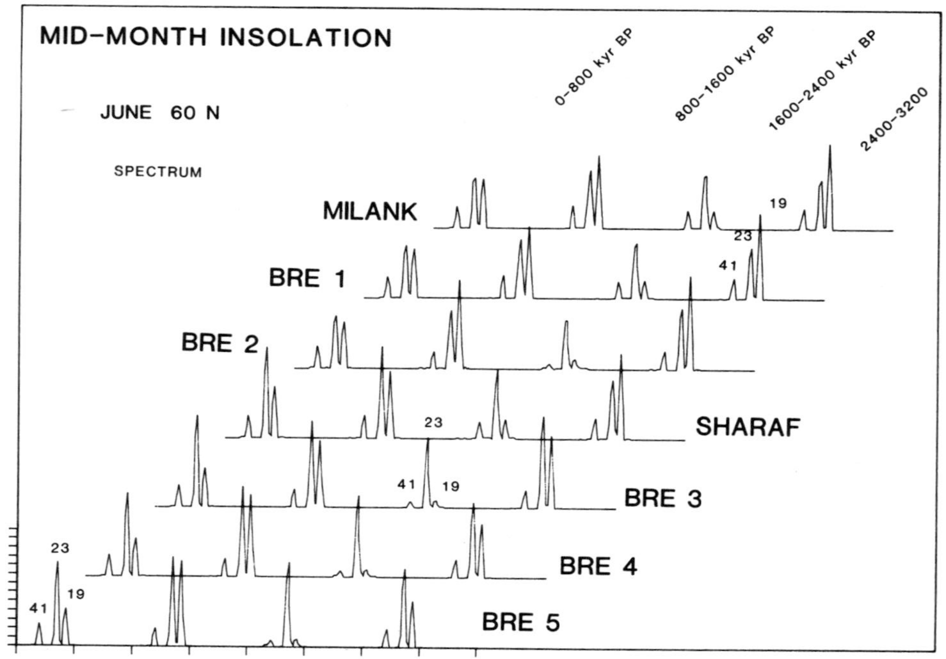

Figure 17 Spectral analysis of the insolation time series reported in Figs 13 to 16. Vertical axis as in Fig. 5.

time domain. More complete theory of long-term variations of the astronomical elements must definitely be built to allow further simulations of climatic time series back for pre-Quaternary times. Explorations undertaken recently by Duriez (36) in celestial mechanics must be extended in scope and accuracy for obtaining results which would be adequate over time spans of the order of several million years. Beyond that point, the traditional viewpoint must be totally reversed : a time will come when geology will provide astronomers with estimates of astronomical periodicities and discuss with them which paleo-astronomical effects should be added to the gravitational model used for the Quaternary.

In the meantime, any calibration of geological time scale in the frequency domain seems perfectly allowed for the last 5 Myr, at least as far as the stability and the accuracy of the astronomical frequencies is concerned and providing the geographical and temporal variability of the climatic frequencies is taken into account by considering the climate response to specific insolation parameters according to their respective spectral shape shown here.

ACKNOWLEDGMENTS

The help of H. Gallée, Chr. Goossens, F. Mercier for computing the spectra and drawing the figures is greatly acknowledged. We are grateful to Mr. F. Materne for having drawn the labels of some figures and to Mrs N. Materne-Depoorter for having typed the whole manuscript.

REFERENCES

1. Imbrie, J., Imbrie, K.P. : 1979, Ice Ages, Solving the Mystery, Enslow Publishers, Short Hills, New Jersey.
2. Berger, A.L. : 1980, in : "Sun and Climate", CNES-CNRS, Toulouse, pp. 325-356.
3. Adhemar, J. : 1842, Révolutions de la Mer. Déluges Périodiques. Paris.
4. Croll, J. : 1875, Climate and Time in their Geological Relations. Appleton, New York.
5. Murphy, J.J. : 1876, Quart. J. Geol. Soc. 32, pp. 400-406.
6. Köppen, W., Wegener, A., Bruckner, E., and Milankovitch, M. : 1925, in : "Uber die Klimate der geologischen Vorzeit". Zeitschrift für Gletscherkunde 14.
7. Milankovitch, M.M. : 1941, Canon of Insolation and the Ice-Age Problem. Beograd, Köninglich Serbische Akademie. 484pp. (English translation by Israel Program for Scientific Translation and published for the U.S.

Department of Commerce and the National Science Foundation).
8. Berger, A.L. : 1977, Nature 269, pp. 44-45.
9. Hays, J.D., Imbrie, J., Shackleton, N.J. : 1976, Science 194, pp. 1121-1132.
10. Berger, A.L. : 1978, Quaternary Research 9, pp. 139-167.
11. Berger, A.L. : 1975, in : "Long-Term Climatic Variations", WMO-IAMAP 421, Geneva, pp. 65-72.
Berger, A.L. : 1976, EOS 57(4), pp. 254.
12. Young, M.A., Bradley, R.S. : 1984 , in : "Milankovitch and Climate", A. Berger, J. Imbrie, J. Hays, G. Kukla, B. Saltzman (Eds), Reidel Publ. Company, Dordrecht, Holland. This volume, p. 707.
13. Berger, A.L. : 1984 , ibid, p. 3.
14. Kukla, G., Berger, A.L., Lotti, R., and Brown, J. : 1981, Nature 290, pp. 295-300.
also, Kukla, G., and Berger, A. : 1982, in : "La Vie et l'Oeuvre de Milutin Milankovitch 1879-1979", Académie Serbe des Sciences et des Arts, XII, Présidence, 3, pp. 29-35.
15. Imbrie, J., and Imbrie, J.Z. : 1980, Science 207, pp. 943-953.
16. Berger, A.L., Guiot, J., Kukla, G., and Pestiaux, P. : 1981, Geol. Rundschau 70(2), pp. 748-758.
17. Kukla, G. : 1975, Nature 253, pp. 600-603.
18. Herterich, K., and Sarnthein, M. : 1984 , in : "Milankovitch and Climate", A. Berger, J. Imbrie, J. Hays, G. Kukla, B. Saltzman (Eds), Reidel Publ. Company, Dordrecht, Holland. This volume, p. 447.
19. Royer, J.F., Deque, M., and Pestiaux, P. : 1983, ibid.
20. Kutzbach, J.E., and Guetter, P.J. : 1983, ibid.
21. Berger, A.L. : 1978, J. Atmos. Sci. 35(12), pp. 2362-2367.
22. Berger, A.L. : 1975, Ann. Soc. Scientifique Bruxelles 89(1), pp. 69-91.
23. Imbrie, J., Hays, J.D., Martinson, D.G., McIntyre, A., Mix, A.C., Morley, J.J., Pisias, N.G., Prell, W.L., and Shackleton, N.J. : 1984, in : "Milankovitch and Climate", A. Berger, J. Imbrie, J. Hays, G. Kukla, B. Saltzman (Eds), Reidel Publ. Company, Dordrecht, Holland. This volume, p. 269.
24. Start, G.G., Prell, W.L. : 1982, in : "New Perspectives in Climate Modelling", A. Berger and C. Nicolis (Eds), Elsevier Publishing Company, Holland.
25. Pestiaux, P., and Berger, A. : 1984, in : "Milankovitch and Climate", A. Berger, J. Imbrie, J. Hays, G. Kukla, B. Saltzman (Eds), Reidel Publ. Company, Dordrecht, Holland. This volume, p. 417.
26. Moore, T.C. Jr., Pisias, N.G., and Dunn, D.A. : 1982, Marine Geol. 46, pp. 217-233.

27. Kominz, M.A., Heath, G.R., Ku, T.L., and Pisias, N.G. : 1979, Earth Planet. Sci. Lett. 45, pp. 394-410.
28. Morley, J.J., and Hays, J.D. : 1981, Earth Planet. Sci. Lett. 53, pp. 279-295.
29. Chappell, J., and Xu Qinqi : 1983, (in press).
30. Ruddiman, W.F., and McIntyre, A. : 1981, Science 212, pp. 617-627.
31. Morley, J.J., and Shackleton, N.J. : 1984, in : "Milankovitch and Climate", A. Berger, J. Imbrie, J. Hays, G. Kukla, B. Saltzman (Eds), Reidel Publ. Company, Dordrecht, Holland. This volume, p. 467.
32. Taylor, K.E. : 1984, ibid., p. 113.
33. Bernard, E. : 1962, Théorie Astronomique des Pluviaux et Interpluviaux du Quaternaire Africain. Nouvelle Série, XII, fasc. 1. Acad. Roy. Sc. Outre-Mer, Cl. Sc. Nat. et Med., Bruxelles.
34. Adem, J., Berger, A., Gaspar, Ph., Pestiaux, P., and van Ypersele, J.P. : 1984, in : "Milankovitch and Climate", A. Berger, J. Imbrie, J. Hays, G. Kukla, B. Saltzman (Eds), Reidel Publ. Company, Dordrecht, Holland. This volume, p. 527.
35. Sellers, W.D. : 1983, ibid.
36. Duriez, L. : 1979, Approche d'une théorie générale planétaire en variables elliptiques héliocentriques. Docteur ès Sciences thesis. Lille.

[1]For a more complete detailed history and list of references, confer (1) and (2). Here we will refer more to grey litterature or to papers generally left out from usual lists of references.

[2]S_a is defined at the distance a from the sun (a is the semi-major axis of the Earth's orbit) and is related to the solar constant, S_0, by : $S_a=S_0(1-e^2)^{1/2}$.

[3]For polar latitudes the developments used by Milankovitch (7) are not convergent, a difficulty which was resolved in (22) by using elliptic integrals and in (32) by using an orbital longitude taken to be zero at the Northern Hemisphere winter solstice.

FOURIER REPRESENTATIONS OF ORBITALLY INDUCED PERTURBATIONS IN SEASONAL INSOLATION

K.E. Taylor

Department of Physics, University of Florida, Gainesville, Florida 32611, USA

ABSTRACT

Fourier series representations for the seasonal variations in insolation are derived. At all latitudes more than 99% of the seasonal variance is captured by the annual average and first two harmonics in the series. The perturbations in the coefficients due to slow variations in the earth's orbital characteristics are also presented, so that if the astronomical parameters are known for a given period, insolation can be derived for any particular latitude and time of year. The Fourier representation can improve our intuitive sense of how each of the orbital parameters affects insolation. It also can simplify the procedure for calculating average insolation amounts (say, for a month period) and frequency spectra of insolation anomalies caused by the orbital perturbations.

INTRODUCTION

The obvious first step in studying the connection between the orbital variations and climate (and the easiest part of the problem theoretically) is to calculate the orbitally induced changes in distribution of insolation. This can be accomplished in rather straightforward fashion by calling on high speed computers to calculate the seasonal variation in insolation at all latitudes for all past orbital configurations (1,2). The unwieldy list of numbers generated by this procedure can be used as input to detailed climate models that are supposed to

A. L. Berger et al. (eds.), Milankovitch and Climate, Part 1, 113–125.

simulate the response of the climate system to changes in forcing.

There is another approach, however, if one is seeking a qualitative understanding of how insolation depends on orbital characteristics: the rather complicated pattern of seasonally and latitudinally varying insolation can be reduced to a few parameters (Fourier coefficients) that retain in a simplified way, most of the information contained in the original equation governing daily average insolation. This present work aims to do this and then to plot curves showing how each of these depends on the orbital configuration. With this Fourier representation, the seasonal dependence of insolation at each latitude can be seen to respond to each of the orbital parameters in a rather straightforward manner. In addition, this analysis simplifies the calculation of different measures of insolation such as running averages for a season or a month. Finally, developing such an intuitive sense of the qualitative changes in insolation patterns is valuable in that conceptual models can be developed more easily.

After substantially completing this manuscript, the author obtained a copy of Milankovitch (3) and discovered that a similar approach was taken in this pioneering work. Fourier coefficients for seasonal insolation (for latitudes outside the polar caps) were computed by Milankovitch because this was the most practical way to do his calculation without the assistance of high speed computers. He did not, however, treat the polar regions in this manner since his series expansions that are used to evaluate the Fourier coefficients analytically do not converge there, as demonstrated in (1) by means of the exact integration of the insolation problem using elliptic integrals.

Milankovitch used the Fourier approach as a means of calculating insolation as a function of orbital <u>longitude</u>. Here, in contrast, we derive the Fourier representation to give insolation as a function of <u>time</u> of year. This makes the formulas more useful for paleoclimatic applications since the equations governing the climate system normally carry time as the independent variable. Even so, it should be clear that much, but not all, of the derivation that appears in the next section can be found in Milankovitch (3), and if the concise nature of the outline presented here is insufficient, the earlier work should be consulted for further discussion. In any case, Fourier coefficients published here should be used in actual applications since some numerical errors appear in the tables of Milankovitch, especially at high latitudes.

THEORY

In preparation for deriving the Fourier series, we use the following form for the intensity of daily average solar radiation incident at latitude ϕ :

$$S = \frac{S_0}{4} \left(\frac{r_0}{r}\right)^2 \psi(\lambda,\phi,\varepsilon) = \frac{S_0}{4(1-e^2)^{1/2}} \psi(\lambda,\phi,\varepsilon) \frac{d\lambda}{dt} \qquad [1]$$

where ψ is a normalized distribution function describing how insolation varies at each latitude throughout the year :

$$\psi = \frac{4}{\pi} (\sin H \cos \phi \cos \delta + H \sin \phi \sin \delta) \qquad [2]$$

For our purposes, it is desirable to express insolation as an explicit function of time rather than orbital longitude. Toward this end, we normalize time t such that it changes by 2π over a year. The relationship between t and orbital longitude λ is then given by :

$$\frac{d\lambda}{dt} = \left(\frac{r_0}{r}\right)^2 (1-e^2)^{1/2} = \frac{[1+e \cos (\lambda-\omega)]^2}{(1-e^2)^{3/2}} \qquad [3]$$

In the above formulas $r(\lambda)$ is the distance from the Earth to the sun, δ is the solar declination, H is the absolute value of the hour angle at sunrise and sunset, S_0 is the solar constant (taken here to be 1350 W/m^2), r_0 is the semi-major axis of the Earth's elliptical orbit (a constant), e is the eccentricity of the orbit, ε is the obliquity of the ecliptic, λ is the orbital longitude (taken here to be zero at the Northern Hemisphere winter solstice), and ω is the longitude of the perihelion (measured relative to the moving Northern Hemisphere winter solstice).

Integration of ψ over the entire Earth yields 1, so that the total radiation received by the earth varies inversely with r^2 according to [1], but is otherwise independent of the orbital parameters.

The procedure for determining the exact solar insolation on a particular day, as recalled in (2) and this volume, is to solve [3] for the orbital longitude λ on that day, and then calculate the insolation with [1]. The Fourier approach to representing the annual variation in insolation will simplify the above procedure in a way to sharpen our understanding of the relationship between orbital variations and the insolation distribution.

The Fourier series that converges to $\psi \frac{d\lambda}{dt}$ can now be written down :

$$\psi \frac{d\lambda}{dt} = \frac{a_0}{2} + \sum_{n=1}^{\infty} [a_n \cos nt + b_n \sin nt] \qquad [4]$$

where

$$\begin{pmatrix} a_n \\ b_n \end{pmatrix} = \frac{1}{\pi} \int_0^{2\pi} \begin{pmatrix} \cos n t \\ \sin n t \end{pmatrix} \psi(\lambda,\phi,\varepsilon) \frac{d\lambda}{dt} dt \qquad [5]$$

The integrals can be evaluated most easily by integrating over λ , not t. This is accomplished by writing t as a function of λ where it appears as an argument in the trigonometric functions. For the special case of n=0 (i.e. for a_0) this is unnecessary, and we immediately find that a_0 depends only on latitude (ϕ) and on the earth's obliquity (ε); variations in eccentricity and the precession of the equinox do not affect it. The annual average insolation $\hat{S}$ at latitude ϕ is consequently given by

$$\hat{S} = \frac{S_0}{8} \frac{a_0(\phi,\varepsilon)}{(1-e^2)^{1/2}} \qquad [6]$$

This means that the <u>fractional</u> change in insolation due to secular variations in e is very nearly equal to $e^2/2$ and is the same at all latitudes.

Evaluation of the other coefficients requires t be written as a function of λ according to [3]. Following North and Coakley (4) we write the relationship as a truncated power series in e from which we obtain

$$\begin{pmatrix} \cos nt \\ \sin nt \end{pmatrix} = \begin{pmatrix} \cos n\lambda \\ \sin n\lambda \end{pmatrix} + 2ne[\sin(\lambda-\omega) + \sin\omega] \begin{pmatrix} \sin n\lambda \\ -\cos n\lambda \end{pmatrix} \qquad [7]$$

For simplicity, we neglect higher order terms in e which is justifiable because e^2 has always been small ($\lesssim 0.005$, according to Berger (5)).

To emphasize the effects that orbital perturbations have on the insolation distribution, we resolve each Fourier coefficient into three components,

$$a_n = \bar{a}_n(\phi, \varepsilon_0) + \frac{\Delta\varepsilon(t')}{\varepsilon_0} a_n^*(\phi, \varepsilon_0) + e(t')\, \alpha_n(\omega(t'), \phi, \varepsilon_0)$$

$$b_n = \bar{b}_n + \frac{\Delta\varepsilon}{\varepsilon_0} b_n^* + e\,\beta_n \qquad [8]$$

where $\Delta\varepsilon$ is the deviation from present day obliquity (ε_0) and t' appears to indicate which parameters vary slowly over thousands of years. For a circular orbit with present obliquity, $a=\bar{a}_n$ and $b_n=\bar{b}_n$. The terms involving (a_n^*, b_n^*) and (α_n, β_n) describe how precession and secular variations in obliquity and eccentricity affect insolation. A good approximation has been made in replacing ε by ε_0 in the above coefficients since $\Delta\varepsilon / \varepsilon_0$ has varied by no more than $\pm$ 0.06 during the past several million years (6). We note that the last terms above depend on the longitude of the perihelion, but shortly we shall show that this dependence can be simply factored out to yield :

$$a_n = \bar{a}_n + a_n^* \frac{\Delta\varepsilon}{\varepsilon_0} + a_n' \, e \cos\omega$$
$$b_n = \bar{b}_n + b_n^* \frac{\Delta\varepsilon}{\varepsilon_0} + b_n' \, e \sin\omega \qquad [9]$$

where now all the coefficients are functions of latitude alone, the present obliquity being given : $\varepsilon_0 = 23.45°$.

The coefficients for a circular orbit will be treated first. Several of these coefficients are identically zero :

$$\bar{a}_n = 0 \text{ for all odd } n \neq 1$$
$$\bar{b}_n = 0 \text{ for all } n. \qquad [10]$$

Exact values for the even cosine coefficients must be numerically determined and are given in Table 1 and Figure 1, but $\bar{a}_1$ can be found analytically :

$$\bar{a}_1 = -2 \sin\varepsilon \sin\phi \qquad [11]$$

The perturbations due to changes in obliquity are accounted for by a_n^* and b_n^* and can either be determined analytically to first order or numerically. The values are given in Table 2 and will be discussed in the next Section.

With some effort (α_n, β_n) can be found analytically and expressed in terms of the coefficients ($\bar{a}_n, \bar{b}_n$). Keeping only the highest order terms in e and dropping all terms involving b_n since these are identically zero, we find :

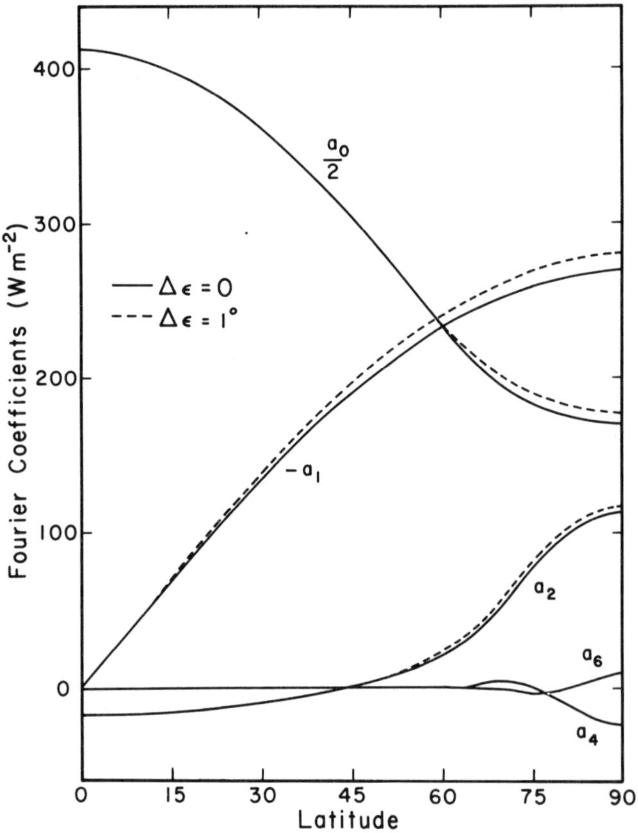

Figure 1 Latitudinal dependence of Fourier coefficients for a circular orbit (e=0). Solid curves are for present obliquity ($\Delta\varepsilon$=0), and dashed curves are for an increase in obliquity of 1°.

$$\alpha_n = a'_n \cos\omega = n(\bar{a}_{n-1} - \bar{a}_{n+1}) \cos\omega$$
$$\beta_n = b'_n \sin\omega = n(\bar{a}_{n-1} - 2\bar{a}_n + \bar{a}_{n+1}) \sin\omega \qquad [12]$$

Furthermore, $\alpha_n = a'_n = 0$ for even $n \neq 2$ since $\bar{a}_n = 0$ for odd $n \neq 1$.

As we anticipated, the coefficients show a simple dependence on precession which allows us to combine the effects of eccentricity and precession into a single parameter e sin ω (or e cos ω). Once the Fourier coefficients for a circular orbit

Table 1 Fourier coefficients ($\bar{a}_n$) at several Northern Hemisphere latitudes for a circular orbit (e=0), present obliquity (ε_0=23.45°) and solar constant of 1350 W m^{-2}

LATITUDE	$\bar{a}_0/2$	$\bar{a}_1$	$\bar{a}_2$	$\bar{a}_3$	$\bar{a}_4$	$\bar{a}_5$	$\bar{a}_6$
0	412.16	0.00	-17.74	0.00	-0.19	0.00	-0.00
5	410.73	-23.41	-17.54	0.00	-0.19	0.00	-0.00
10	406.45	-46.65	-16.91	0.00	-0.18	0.00	-0.00
15	399.38	-69.53	-15.85	0.00	-0.16	0.00	-0.00
20	389.57	-91.88	-14.36	0.00	-0.13	0.00	-0.00
25	377.13	-113.53	-12.42	0.00	-0.09	0.00	-0.00
30	362.20	-134.32	-9.99	0.00	-0.04	0.00	0.00
35	344.95	-154.09	-7.03	0.00	0.02	0.00	0.00
40	325.60	-172.68	-3.48	0.00	0.11	0.00	0.01
45	304.42	-189.96	0.77	0.00	0.22	0.00	0.01
50	281.78	-205.79	5.92	0.00	0.37	0.00	0.02
55	258.18	-220.06	12.27	0.00	0.60	0.00	0.04
60	234.40	-232.65	20.48	0.00	1.01	0.00	0.08
65	211.96	-243.47	32.13	0.00	1.97	0.00	0.24
70	195.25	-252.44	52.66	0.00	4.97	0.00	0.37
75	184.15	-259.49	76.51	0.00	1.24	0.00	-2.94
80	176.73	-264.56	96.49	0.00	-8.89	0.00	-0.85
85	172.43	-267.62	109.51	0.00	-18.79	0.00	6.04
90	171.02	-268.64	114.01	0.00	-22.80	0.00	9.77

Table 2 Coefficients (a_n^*) for calculating perturbations due to a change in obliquity in units of W m^{-2}.

LATITUDE	$a_o^*/2$	a_1^*	a_2^*	a_4^*	a_6^*
0	-39.2	0.0	-40.1	-1.0	-0.0
5	-38.7	-24.7	-39.6	-1.0	-0.0
10	-37.3	-49.3	-38.2	-0.8	-0.0
15	-35.0	-73.4	-35.6	-0.7	-0.0
20	-31.6	-97.0	-32.1	-0.6	-0.0
25	-27.1	-119.9	-27.6	-0.4	-0.0
30	-21.7	-141.8	-21.8	-0.2	0.0
35	-15.0	-162.7	-14.8	0.2	0.0
40	-6.9	-182.3	-6.3	0.6	0.0
45	2.9	-200.5	3.9	1.2	0.1
50	14.7	-217.3	16.5	2.0	0.2
55	29.7	-232.3	32.7	3.3	0.3
60	49.8	-245.7	55.1	5.9	0.7
65	82.1	-257.0	94.2	14.8	3.6
70	129.7	-266.6	144.7	8.7	-13.5
75	154.0	-274.0	143.9	-23.5	-7.6
80	169.2	-279.3	133.4	-32.2	11.0
85	177.7	-282.6	124.0	-27.7	13.2
90	180.6	-283.6	120.4	-24.1	10.3

are known, the perturbation coefficients a_n' and b_n' are easily calculated using [12] and are given in Table 3.

Table 3 Coefficients (a_n',b_n') for calculating perturbations due to nonzero eccentricity in units of W m^{-2}. The coefficients, a_0', a_4', and a_6', are identically zero and consequently have been omitted.

LATITUDE	a_1'	b_1'	a_2'	b_2'	a_3'	b_3'	b_4'	a_5'	b_5'	b_6'
0	842.1	806.6	0.0	71.0	-52.7	-53.8	1.5	-0.9	-1.0	-0.0
5	839.0	850.8	-46.8	23.3	-52.0	-53.2	1.5	-0.9	-1.0	-0.0
10	829.8	889.3	-93.3	-25.7	-50.2	-51.2	1.4	-0.9	-0.9	-0.0
15	814.6	922.0	-139.1	-75.6	-47.1	-48.0	1.2	-0.8	-0.8	-0.0
20	793.5	948.5	-183.8	-126.3	-42.7	-43.5	1.0	-0.6	-0.6	-0.0
25	766.7	968.9	-227.1	-177.4	-37.0	-37.5	0.7	-0.4	-0.5	-0.0
30	734.4	983.0	-268.6	-228.7	-29.8	-30.1	0.3	-0.2	-0.2	0.0
35	696.9	991.0	-308.2	-280.0	-21.2	-21.0	-0.2	0.1	0.1	0.0
40	654.7	993.1	-345.4	-331.4	-10.8	-10.1	-0.9	0.5	0.6	0.1
45	608.1	989.5	-379.9	-383.0	1.7	3.0	-1.7	1.0	1.1	0.1
50	557.6	981.1	-411.6	-435.2	16.6	18.9	-3.0	1.8	1.9	0.2
55	504.1	968.8	-440.1	-489.2	35.0	38.6	-4.8	2.8	3.2	0.5
60	448.3	954.6	-465.3	-547.2	58.4	64.5	8.1	4.7	5.4	1.0
65	391.8	943.0	-486.9	-615.4	90.5	102.3	15.8	8.7	11.1	2.9
70	337.8	948.0	-504.9	-715.5	143.1	172.9	-39.7	23.0	26.7	4.4
75	291.8	963.8	-519.0	-825.0	225.8	233.3	-9.9	20.9	-8.5	-35.3
80	257.0	979.1	-529.1	-915.1	316.1	262.8	71.1	-40.2	-48.7	-10.2
85	235.4	989.6	-535.2	-973.3	384.9	272.2	150.3	-124.2	-63.7	72.5
90	228.0	993.3	-537.3	-993.3	410.4	273.6	182.4	-162.8	-65.2	117.2

It is interesting to note that if orbital longitude is taken to be zero at one of the equinoxes (as it was by Milankovitch (3)), then the Fourier representation (with time as the independent variable) becomes much more complicated for nonzero e and the results are consequently less illuminating. This might be why Milankovitch stopped short of deriving [12].

DISCUSSION

One advantage to the Fourier representation of insolation derived above is that the effect of orbital perturbations on the annual cycle can be visualized. Toward this end we plot with unbroken curves in Figure 1 the first five non-zero Fourier coefficients for a circular orbit. We are not surprised to find that the annual average insolation $\bar{a}_0$ decreases poleward and the amplitude of the fundamental frequency (seasonal component $-\bar{a}_1$) increases poleward. The semi-annual component $\bar{a}_2$ is important in the tropics where it accounts for the biannual transit of the sun across the equator. It is also important near the poles where it offsets $\bar{a}_1$ in the winter keeping the insolation nonnegative but near zero and where it contributes (with $\bar{a}_1$) to the substantial insolation during summer (when there is no night). The higher harmonics are insignificant except within a few degrees of the poles.

A numerical analysis shows that $\bar{a}_1$ and $\bar{a}_2$ together account for more than 99% of the variance in insolation during the year at all latitudes. To further illustrate this point, Figure 2 clearly shows that $\bar{a}_0$, $\bar{a}_1$ and $\bar{a}_2$ are sufficient to characterize the insolation at low, middle and high latitudes. The comparison between the exact calculation of insolation and the Fourier representation shows that $\bar{a}_2$ is very important at the poles because without it the maximum summer insolation would be grossly underestimated and the winter insolation would be unacceptably negative.

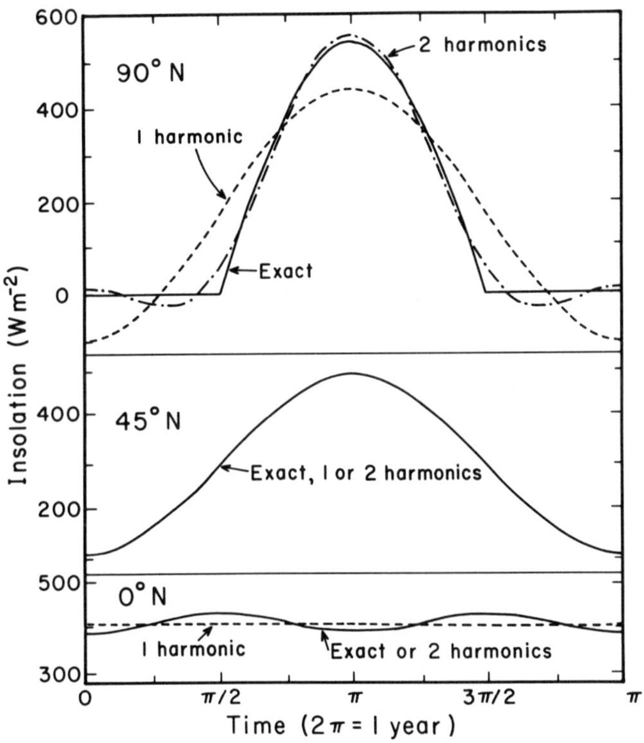

Figure 2 The seasonal variations in insolation at three latitudes (for a circular orbit) calculated exactly using [1] (solid curves), and calculated with a Fourier series truncated after the first harmonic (dashed curve) or second harmonic (dash-dot curve).

We next examine how the coefficients are modified by perturbations in the obliquity. Table 2 and Figure 1 indicate that an increase in obliquity of 1° (which is close to the maximum perturbation calculated for the last several million years), causes only minor changes except near the poles. In response to the increase in "tilt", the annual average insolation increases at the pole by about 4% with smaller changes at lower latitudes. The seasonal component $|a_1|$ also increases, again with maximum perturbations at high latitudes. The semiannual component a_2 increases to keep the insolation from becoming negative in the winter and to increase the summer maximum insolation.

The response of insolation to changes in eccentricity and the precession effect is more complicated because although the annual average insolation at each latitude is constant, both amplitude and phase of the various harmonics are affected. The perturbations due to eccentricity can be written :

$$e \sum_n A_n(t) \cos (\omega - \lambda_n)$$

where

$$A_n = (a_n'^2 \cos^2 nt + b_n'^2 \sin^2 nt)^{1/2}$$

and

$$\tan \lambda_n = \frac{b_n'}{a_n'} \tan nt .$$

The first harmonic (n=1) is easiest to analyze. According to the above expression, when perihelion coincides with winter or summer solstice (ω=0 or π), the first harmonic perturbation is given by :

$$\pm e\, a_1' \cos t$$

where the plus sign applies when ω=0 and minus sign applies when $\omega = \pi$. For these orbital orientations then, the absolute value of the perturbations is maximum near the solstices and minimum near the equinoxes (see dashed curve labeled $- a_1$ in Fig. 3). If perihelion occurs near either equinox, on the other hand, the perturbation is equal to :

$$\pm e\, b_1' \sin t$$

where the minus sign applies when $\omega=3\pi/2$ and the plus sign applies when $\omega = \pi/2$ (see solid curve labeled b_1 in Fig. 3).

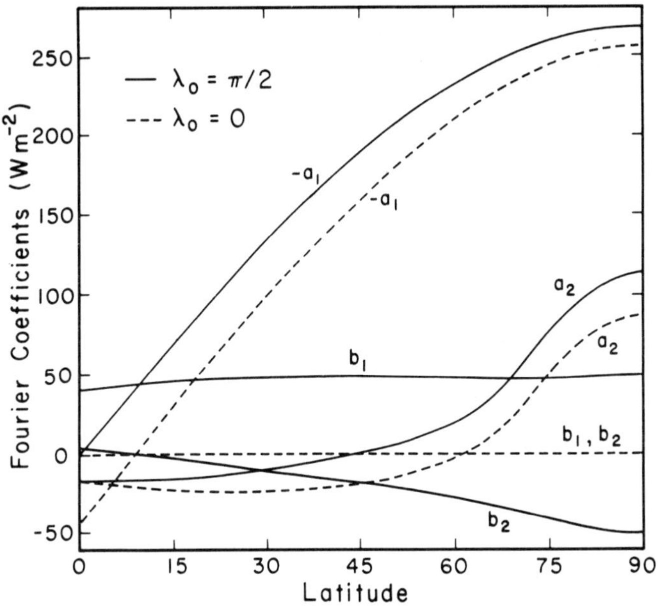

Figure 3 Latitudinal dependence of Fourier coefficients for eccentricity of .05 with perihelion coinciding with winter solstice (solid curve) or lagging winter solstice by three months (dashed curve).

In general the first harmonic describes the first order effects of eccentricity. When the Earth is relatively close to the sun, the insolation perturbation is positive and vice versa. A closer look at Table 3 reveals that near the equator the amplitude of the perturbation is not affected much by precession because, according to Figure 3 or Table 3, $a_1' \simeq b_1'$. Near the poles, on the other hand, $b_1' >> a_1'$ so that the perturbations are strongest when perihelion occurs near the equinoxes. Thus the precession will most strongly affect insolation at high latitudes near the time of equinoxes.

The second harmonic insolation perturbation due to precession and changes in eccentricity can also be qualitatively analyzed. According to Table 3 and Figure 3, a_2' and b_2' are zero at the equator and decrease monotonically poleward (becoming more and more negative). This means that in the tropics the insolation perturbations are dominated by changes in the first harmonic alone. In the middle latitudes $a_2' \simeq b_2'$ so that the perturbations can be approximated by

$a_2' \cos(\omega - 2t)$.

The above expression indicates that in middle latitudes the largest perturbations (in an absolute value sense) occur when $t=\omega/2$ and at 3-month intervals after that time. For example if perihelion coincides with vernal equinox ($\omega = \pi/2$), positive insolation anomalies due to this second harmonic will be found during the spring and fall seasons ($t=3\pi/4$, $7\pi/4$) and negative anomalies during winter and summer ($t=\pi/4$, $5\pi/4$). (Note that $a_2' < 0$). The opposite is true when perihelion coincides with the autumnal equinox.

Near the poles $|b_2'|$ is about twice $|a_2'|$ and we find that the largest insolation anomalies occur when perihelion coincides with one of the equinoxes ($\omega = \pm\pi/2$). If, perihelion coincides with one of the solstices the typical insolation anomalies are roughly half as large and the phase of maximum anomaly shifts by $\pi/4$ (i.e., 1.5 months).

CONCLUDING REMARKS

We have approximated the rather complicated formula governing insolation as a truncated Fourier series to help develop a qualitative understanding of how perturbations in the Earth's orbit affect the seasonally varying insolation at each latitude. This representation with the coefficients given in Tables 1-3 will allow quick and accurate calculations of forcing functions in climate models used to test various hypotheses for orbitally induced climate change. Average insolation for a season or month can be computed by simply adding the Fourier coefficients after determining the appropriate weighting factors. In addition it should be possible after some further analysis to generate frequency spectra of different measures of insolation anomalies caused by the orbital perturbations as it is done in (8). These spectra can then be compared with paleoclimatic data (7) to help determine what latitudes and times of year are most important in linking the insolation perturbations to changes in climate.

The results show that the annual average and first two harmonics provide a sufficiently accurate approximation to the insolation. The computational and conceptual advantages in using the Fourier series make it particularly well suited for applications by paleoclimatologist and climate modelers who are trying to extract the essential mechanisms that link climate to orbital variations. It is a tribute to Milankovitch that an analytical approach he initiated 50 years ago can still facilitate progress in understanding the ice ages.

ACKNOWLEDGMENT

This material is based upon work supported by the National Science Foundation under Grant No. ATM-8105024.

REFERENCES

1. Berger, A.L. : 1975, Ann. Soc. Scient. Bruxelles 89 (I), pp. 69-91.
2. Berger, A.L. : 1978, J. Atmos. Sci. 35 (12), pp. 2362-2367.
3. Milankovitch, M. : 1941, Kanon der Erdbestrahlung und seine Andwendung auf das Eiszeitenproblem. Roy. Serb. Acad. Spec. Publ. 133, pp. 1-633. (English version published by the Israel Program for Scientific Translations, Jerusalem, 1969, available from U.S. Department of Commerce).
4. North, G.R., and Coakley, J.A. : 1979, J. Atmos. Sci. 36, pp. 1189-1204.
5. Berger, A.L. : 1977, Nature 269, pp. 44-45.
6. Berger, A.L. : 1977, Astron. Astrophys. 51, pp. 127-135.
7. Imbrie, J. : 1982, Icarus 50, pp. 408-422.
8. Berger, A.L. and Pestiaux, P. : 1984, this volume, p. 83.

PART II

GEOLOGICAL EVIDENCE FOR LONG-TERM CLIMATIC VARIATIONS AT ASTRONOMICAL FREQUENCIES

SECTION 1 - PRE-PLEISTOCENE EVIDENCE OF ORBITAL FORCING

PERIODICITY OF LAKE-LEVEL CYCLES IN THE LATE TRIASSIC LOCKATONG FORMATION OF THE NEWARK BASIN (NEWARK SUPERGROUP, NEW JERSEY AND PENNSYLVANIA

P.E. Olsen[1]

Peabody Museum, Box 6666, 170 Whitney Avenue, New Haven, Connecticut 06511.

The short (ca. 5m) sedimentary cycles which Van Houten first described from the Lockatong Formation of the Newark Basin were produced by the climate controlled rise and fall of large lakes. During their high stands many of these lakes covered over 7000 km^2 and were over 100 m deep, but during their low stand they were reduced to playas or dried out completely. Annual laminations (varves) present in many short cycles show that the lakes which produced them oscillated in depth with a periodicity of about 21 800 years. Lockatong short cycles make up longer, compound cycles, 25 m and 100 m thick, which reflect periodic changes in the magnitude of high-stands of the 21 800 year lake-level cycles. These lower frequency cycles show a 101 400 and a 418 000 periodicity, respectively. These periodicities are within the tight independent constraints placed on the duration of these cycles by radiometric dates and sediment thickness. During the Triassic the Newark Basin was located at about 15 N, paleolatitude and the periodicities and the ratios of the short and compound cycles are in very close agreement with the Milankovitch predictions for that paleolatitude.

During the early Mesozoic, Pangea rested on the equator (Fig. 1) and a long series of rift valleys formed around the zone which was to become the Atlantic Ocean. These rift valleys filled with thousands of meters of sediments and igneous rocks and the North American contingent of what remains of these deposits is called the Newark Supergroup (1). The exposed portions of the Newark Supergroup consist largely of lacustrine deposits and these rocks preserve a record of changing climate spanning some 35 million years over a distance of over 2000 kilometers. The largest and thickest sequences are preserved in the Newark

A. L. Berger et al. (eds.), Milankovitch and Climate, Part 1, 129–146.

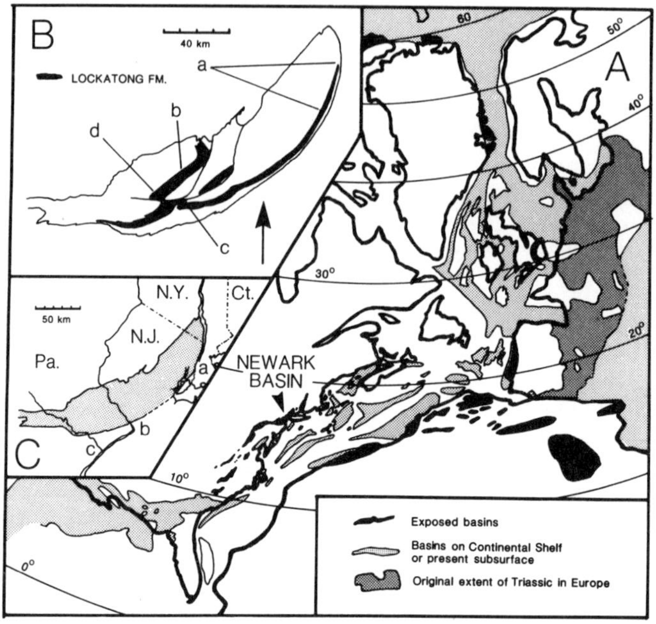

Figure 1 Lockatong Formation in the Newark Basin : A, Predrift (Late-Triassic, Early Jurassic) position of rift basins (Newark Supergroup consists of basins exposed in eastern North America - continental positions from (6) - geology adapted from (1,6,7)) ; B, distribution of Lockatong Formation in Newark Basin - intrusions omitted (a, position of sections in Weehawken area (sections A-F in Figure 5); b, Delaware River section; c, Rushland I quarry section; d, Eureka Quarry section); C, major cities around Newark Basin (a, New York City; b, Trenton; c, Philadelphia).

Basin division of the Newark Supergroup in New York, New Jersey and Pennsylvania. Van Houten (2,3) was one of the first to recognize that much of the Newark Basin record is cyclic and that this cyclicity reflected periodically changing climate. He suggested that this climate change was in turn controlled by the precession of the equinoxes. This paper is essentially a reexamination, extension, and confirmation of Van Houten's original work.

There are 9 formations in the Newark Basin section (4,5) (Fig. 2) and of these the Late Triassic Lockatong and overlying Passaic formations comprise the longest continuous lacustrine record. The Lockatong (Figs 1 and 2) consists almost entirely of a spectrum of thin (ca. 5 m) sedimentary cycles, the end

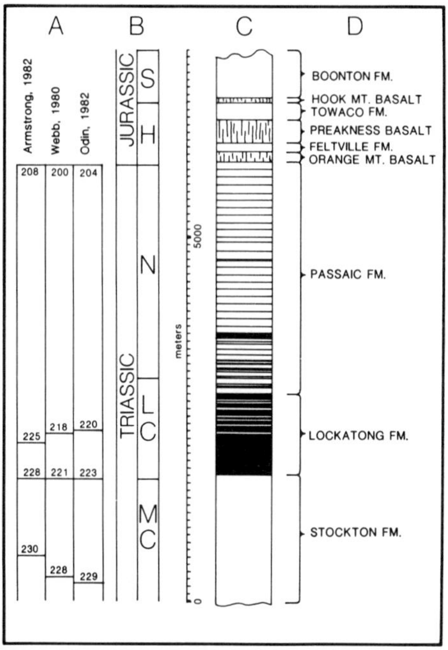

Figure 2 Formations of the Newark Basin and their ages : A, radiometric scales for the Late Triassic (Late Carnian is here assumed to be 1/3 of Carnian time and the Mid-Late Carnian and Triassic-Jurassic boundaries are correlated with the basin section by biostratigraphic data); B, system and stage boundaries based on biostratigraphy, radiometric dates, and paleomagnetics; C, diagram of Newark Basin section (black horizontal lines and black bars represent gray and black units of the Triassic portion of the section and white areas and bars are principally red beds) ; D, formations of the Newark Basin (from 4,5).

members of which Van Houten (2,3) termed detrital and chemical (Fig. 3). The vertical sequence of fossils and sedimentary structures found in the cycles show that they owe their origin to the rise and fall of lakes. Each detrital cycle averages 5.7 m and can be divided into three lithologically distinct divisions (Fig. 3) (7) : division 1 consists of platy to massive gray mudstone sometimes showing current bedding deposited during lake transgression; division 2 is a fine calcareous black mudstone often platy to microlaminated and organic rich, deposited during lake high-stand; and division 3 is made up of platy to massive gray mudstone deposited during lake regression, low-stand, and lake bottom exposure. Chemical cycles are, on the average thinner than detrital cycles (4.5 m) and consist of a lower platy gray mudstone and an upper much more massive gray or red mudstone often rich in sprays of analcime and dolomite crystals and pseudomorphs after gypsum, glauberite and halite - hence Van Houten's epithet chemical cycles.

Van Houten (2,3) reasoned that the vertical sequence of bed types with short cycles reflected the expansion and contraction of lakes. Detrital cycles were produced by lakes which were deep enough to have reached their outlet and were hence through-flowing. Chemical cycles, in contrast, were produced by lakes which never reached their outlet and therefore they concentrated salts during their entire existence. Van Houten argued that all these lakes were relatively shallow and that their depths were governed by changes in precipitation and thus the individual short cycles record regional cyclic changes in precipitation.

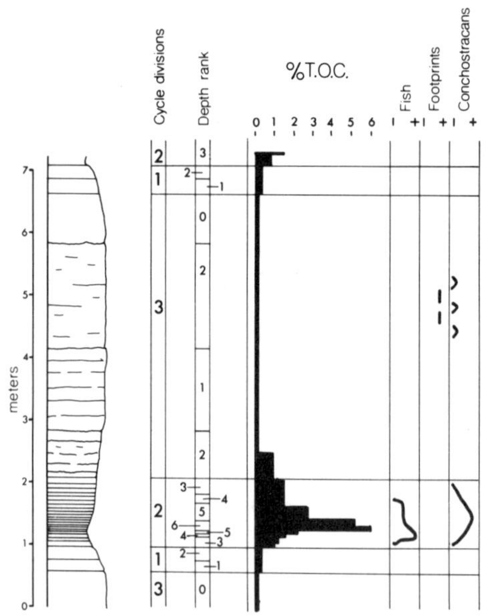

Figure 3 Major features of Lockatong detrital cycles. This cycle is marked SH in Figure 9.

The alternative explanation to changing climate is that the short sedimentary cycles were produced by the filling in of small shallow lakes by sediments, the differences between the cycles being due to local hydrographic differences, and the development of the lake basins being due to local tectonics. Chemical cycles might then form geographically adjacent to

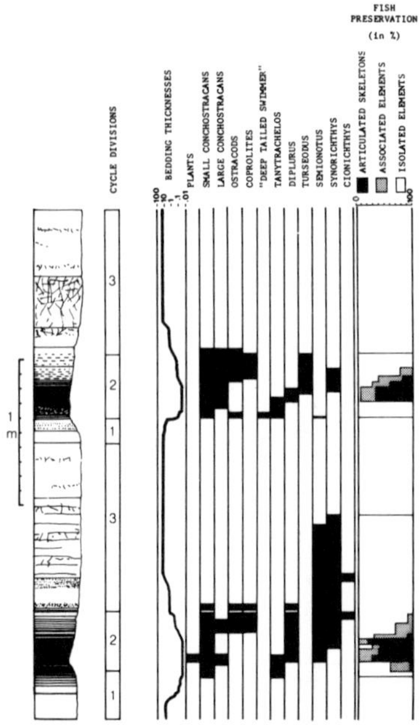

Figure 4 Detrital cycles W-5 (above) and W-6 (below) at excavation at Weehawken, New Jersey showing distribution of major fossils and their preservation : "deep tailed swimmer" and Tanytrachelos are small reptiles, and Diplurus, Turseodus, Semionotus, Synorichthys, and Cionichthys are fishes. This is locality A in Figure 5.

detrital cycles. Information on the lateral extent of cycles is needed to select between these two explanations.

Over the last six years I have been attempting to trace individual Lockatong cycles laterally. This is made difficult principally because of : 1) the scarcity of large, continuous exposures; 2) the presence of lateral facies changes; and 3) the general similarity of all the sedimentary cycles. Detailed investigations of single sections, however, have shown that each cycle can be uniquely defined by the details of the vertical changes in the kinds, preservation, and diversity of fossils (Figs 4 and 5). It has become evident that it is a property of detrital cycles that these vertical changes seen in single cycles remain consistent laterally (Fig. 5). This property allows for individual cycles to be identified in vertical sections of many cycles and allows individual cycles to be traced over large distances (Figs 5 and 6). I first worked out a cycle-by-cycle

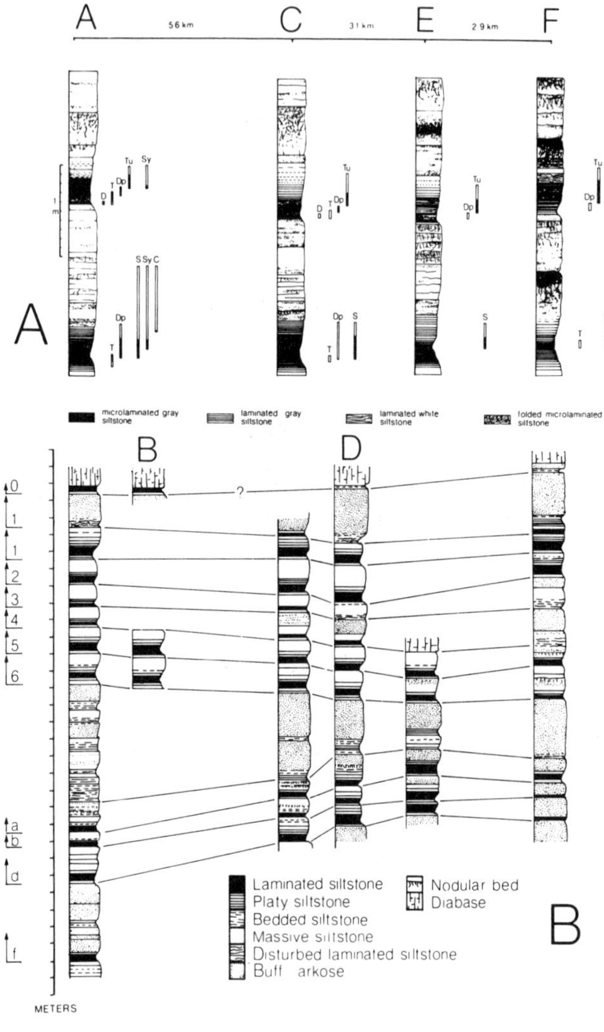

Figure 5 Lateral extent of Lockatong detrital cycles from Weehawken to Fort Lee, New Jersey: A, detailed correlation by the vertical distribution of fossil fishes of cycles W-5 (above) and W-6 (below) [abbreviations of vertebrate fossils - D, "deep tailed swimmer", T, Tanytrachelos, Dp, Diplurus, Tu, Turseodus, Sy, Synorichthys, S, Semionotus, and C, Cionichthys] B, correlation of all exposed cycles laterally based on the vertical distribution of fossil fishes. Localities of sections A - F shown in Figure 1 and given in detail in (8).

stratigraphy for 18 cycles in the Hoboken to Fort Lee area (7) where outcrops are closely spaced (about 1 per 2 km for 20 km (Figs 5 and 6)). Recently, a large series of new outcrops have been identified in the central and southern Newark Basin which permit the cycles found in the Hoboken - Fort Lee area to be traced over most of the basin. In addition, these newly found exposures allow the same cycles originally worked on by Van Houten to be traced over large areas of the central Newark Basin (Fig.6). It is now apparent that many individual detrital cycles can be traced over most of the Newark Basin and that these cycles retain their particular faunal identities over these areas. It is also apparent that the short sedimentary cycles of the Lockatong reflect changes in the depths of lakes which covered much, if not all, of the Newark Basin and that changes in precipitation and evaporation rates are the most plausible cause of the lake-level change.

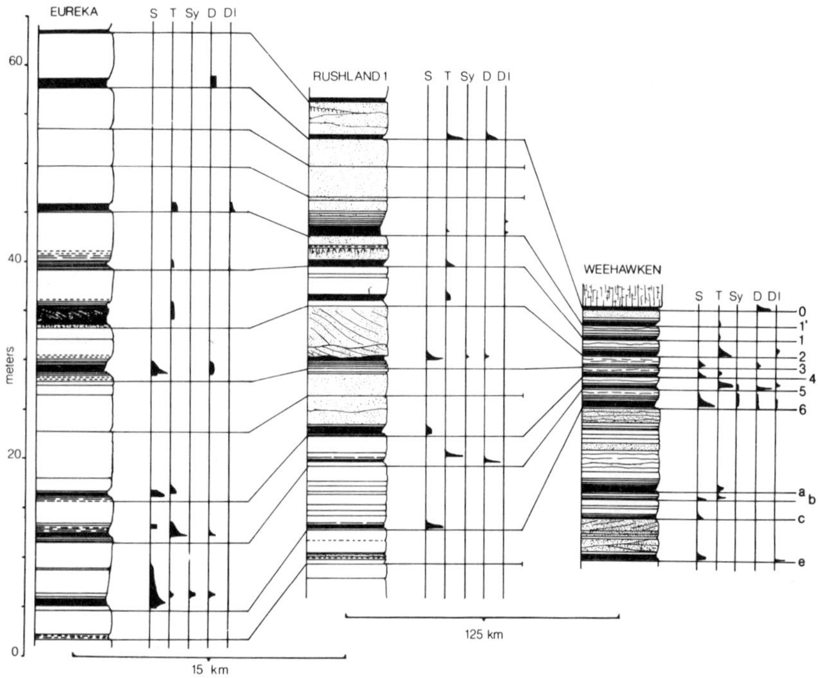

Figure 6 Correlation across Newark Basin of detrital cycles of Weehawken member of lower Lockatong (see Figure 7) showing distribution of most abundant fish. Abbreviations of fish taxa as follows : S, Semionotus, T, Turseodus, Sy, Synorichthys, D, Diplurus, and Dl, large coelacanth. Positions of sections shown in Figure 1.

A consequence of the ability to trace individual cycles laterally is that lithological and paleontological features which are associated with various degrees of lateral continuity can be identified. Those cycles fitting Van Houten's detrital category prove to be traceable individually over much longer distances than those fitting the chemical category which are restricted to the central 60 km of the basin. Furthermore, those detrital cycles which contain a microlaminated division 2 are traceable over the largest distances with the least change. The microlaminated portions of these cycles contain the best preserved vertebrate remains. The very fine laminae and the fine preservation of fossil fish and other delicate organisms in the microlaminated portions of division 2 show that deposition of these units could only have occurred below wave base (7,9).

The lateral continuity of the microlaminated portions of division 2 allows for an estimation of the minimum extent and depth of the Lockatong lakes during their maximum transgression. I have developed a new method of estimating the depths of ancien lakes which uses the familar relationship between the maximum fetch of a water body, wind speed and the depth of wave mixing (9). Using this method, the fact that the microlaminated (i.e. varved) fish-bearing portion of individual Lockatong cycles cover over 7000 km^2 means that the lake which deposited that unit must have covered more than 7000 km^2 and must have been more than 100 m deep. the fact that the portions of Lockatong cycles which were deposited during lake low stand can also be traced over the extent of the formation illustrates that the lakes actually did become very shallow and frequently dried out entirely. Thus, those detrital cycles with a microlaminated division 2 resulted from tremendous fluctuations in water depth, similar to or greater in magnitude than the changes known to have occurred in many of the lakes of the Great Basin in the western United States (10,11) and the Great Lakes of Africa (12,13,14).

Detrital and chemical cycles do not occur randomly in vertical section. Clusters of 1 to 4 detrital and 1 to 4 chemical cycles make up 25 m cycles (added up to a total of 4 to 6 short cycles) (Fig. 7) and clusters of these 25 m cycles alternately dominated by chemical or detrital cycles clusters make up 100 m cycles (Fig. 7) (2,3). The pattern of 100 m cycles allows the Lockatong formation to be broken up tentatively into 11 members (Fig. 7). This pattern of 100 m cycles continues into the overlying Passaic Formation. In the latter, however, the chemical cycles disappear and their position is taken by red beds (Figs 2 and 7).

The classification of sedimentary cycles types developed by Van Houten and followed in my own previous papers is

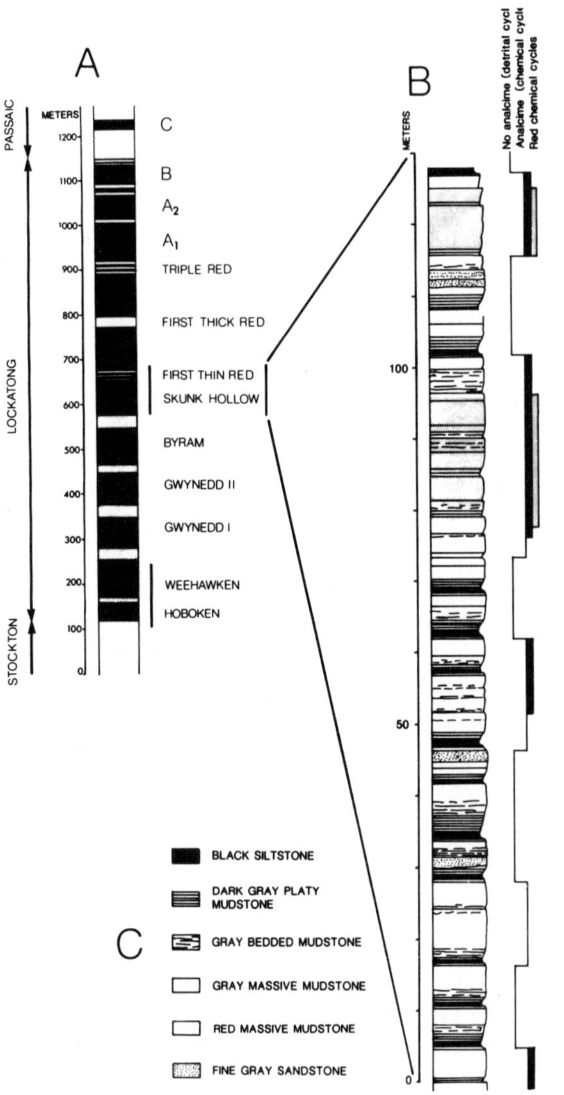

Figure 7 A, tentative division of the Lockatong Formation into 100 m members as exposed along the Delaware River in the Hunterdon Plateau Fault Block: Black horizontal bars represent portions of the Lockatong dominated by detrital cycles, white bars indicate portions of Lockatong made up mostly of red chemical cycles or red beds, gray bars indicate portions made up mostly of gray chemical cycles. Black vertical bars indicate portions of Lockatong shown in Figures 9 and 10. B, measured section of McLaughlin's (17) First Thin Red and the Skunk Hollow Member of this report. C, key for B.

essentially a typological one. The method of classification forces cycles to be identified either as chemical or as detrital. The operational definition of chemical cycles requires that evaporitic minerals, especially zeolites and dolomite, be present in the cycle. Thus, even if in all other respects a cycle without evaporitic minerals looks exactly other chemical cycles and is the lateral equivalent of a "true" chemical cycle it is classified as detrital because it lacks the essential aspect of a chemical cycle. This purely semantic problem produces confusion in interpretation when by definition, chemical cycles turn into detrital cycles laterally. In addition, in this sort of typological classification system all the information inherent in intermediate cycles is lost. This is the nature of typological classifications.

As suggested by Van Houten (2,3) and Olsen (7) various features of the sedimentary fabric of the rock types which make up Lockatong short cycles have characteristics which can be interpreted in terms of water depth, at least in a relative sense. Thus, division 2 of detrital cycles is interpreted as having been deposited in deeper water than divisions 1 or 3 because of the absence of indications of exposure to the air, presence of undisturbed laminations, lack of roots, etc. The vertical sequences of sediment fabric types through a cycle shows directional change in several characters which reflect the expansion and contraction of the lakes in which they were deposited. I have developed a tentative classification of sedimentary fabrics within Lockatong cycles with seven categories (Fig. 8) ranked from 0 to 6 in order of the relative depth of water in which they were deposited. This sequence is seen in vertical succession through typical detrital cycles as 1 2 3 4 5 4 3 2 1 0 (from the bottom up). Walther's law suggests that these same

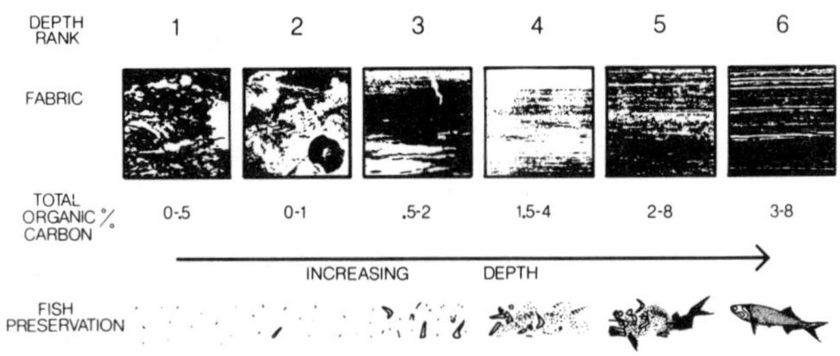

Figure 8 Ranks of sedimentary fabrics of mudstones and siltstones of Lockatong Formation arranged in order of the interpreted relative depth of water in which they were deposited and their relationship to organic carbon content and fossil fish preservation. Rank 0 (not shown) is a microbrecciated and disrupted massive mudstone sometimes with evaporitic minerals.

fabrics might be reflected in lateral changes from the center of the basin outwards, as well, and for the most part they are (7).

When the rank of the fabrics of beds which compose Lockatong short cycles are graphed against the measured section (Figs 9 and 10), the rank can be read as a indicator of water depth and hence a proxy indicator of (at least) local climate. The curve produced by this method is analogous to curves produced

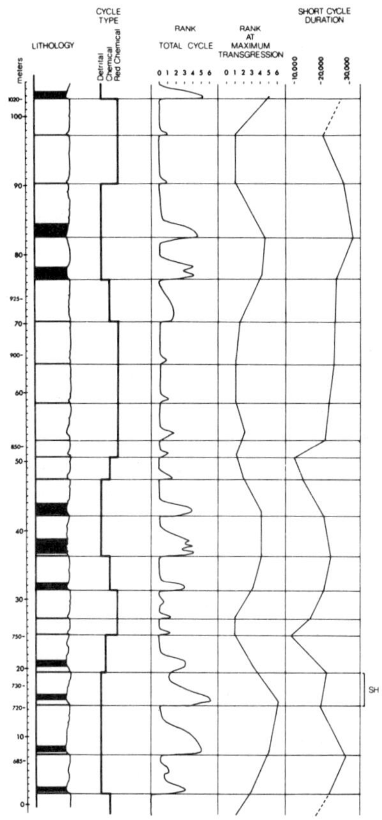

Figure 9 Section of First Thin Red and Skunk Hollow members of Lockatong along Delaware River (see Figure 7) showing the classification of cycle type according to Van Houten (2,3), the application of depth ranks based on Figure 8, and the duration of short sedimentary cycles. Duration is equal to 0.24 mm X cycle thickness and this value is placed at base of cycle. SH is cycle drawn in Figure 3.

by graphing oxygen isotope ratios or the derived bottom water temperatures against core depth in cores of the ocean bottom (15,16). By use of this depth rank, it is no longer necessary to identify sedimentary cycles or to classify the cycle types into end members, although this is still a useful tool. The larger cycles of 25 m and 100 m also show up in the curve as modulations of the maximum magnitude of the higher frequency cycles. All the information present in the typological classification of cycles and the higher order cycles are preserved in this curve. Because the ranks are based on sedimentary fabrics which are related to water depth, the rank curve canbe interpreted as a lake-level curve with rank 6 equivalent to depths in excess of 100 m and ranks 0-1 corresponding to very shallow, saline water, or complete dessication.

Two long sections through different portions of the Lockatong (the Skunk Hollow Member and the Weehawken and Hoboken members (Figs 9 and 10)) are dealt with here, but the same pattern can be seen at other outcrops within the center of the basin and in the Passaic Formation as well. Peaks in depth rank occur at about 5 m intervals, and when these peaks alone are graphed against the section, a 25 m cycle of maximum rank becomes clear. Peaks in this 25 m cycle occur at 100 m intervals, although the two measured sections presented here are too short to show this fully. The peaks occurring at 5 m intervals are the short cycles identified by Van Houten. At the Delaware River section, most of those peaks occuring at 5 m intervals which do not exceed rank 3 belong to cycles identified by Van Houten as chemical cycles. Most of those peaks which have ranks of 4 to 6 belong to Van Houten's detrital cycles. The 25 m cycles seen in depth rank correspond to Van Houten's 25 m alternations of chemical and detrital cycles and the 100 m cycles are also equivalent. The main advantage of this method is that the structure of these curves contains much more information than a typological classification, especially in sections where no evaporitic minerals are present in cycles which otherwise look like chemical cycles but which do not fit the definition. These curves are also amenable to the type of wave theory analysis used with so much success in the deep sea curves (16,18); such procedures are not possible with a typological classification of cycles.

The microlaminated portions of division 2 of short cycles (corresponding to the peaks of 5 and 6 in rank) are composed of couplets of a lamina of very low carbonate - high organic carbon mudstone and a lamina of higher carbonate - low organic carbon mudstone. These couplets are traceable over very large areas and are indistinguishable from the annual laminations produced today in anoxic aquatic environments such as the bottoms of deep lakes (7,19). If these couplets are of annual origin, and there is no reason to believe they are not, they are non-glacial varves (each couplet = 1 varve) and the average thickness of a varve is the sedimentation rate per year after compaction. This sedimentation rate can then be used to calibrate both the curves of ranks and the individual cycles (Figs 9 and 10) (Table 1). Van Houten used exactly this property of microlaminated portions of Lockatong short cycles and concluded that the short cycles had a period of about 21 000 years, the 25 m cycles a period of 100 000 years, and the 100 m cycles a period of 500 000 years.

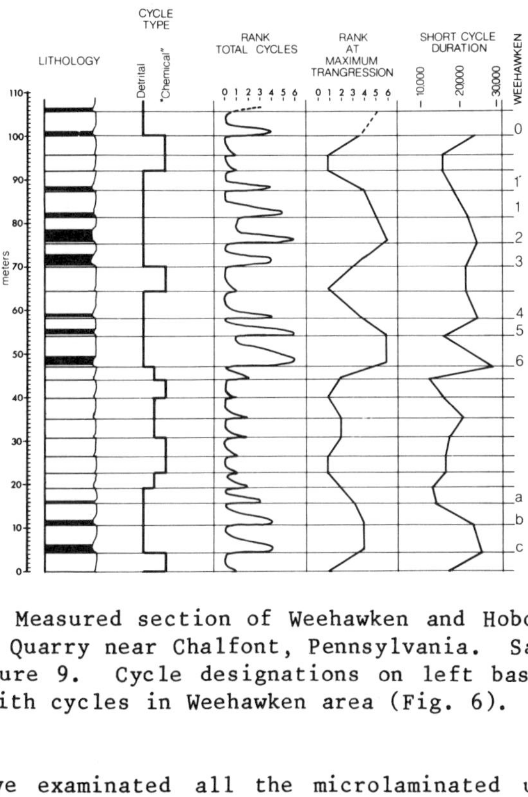

Figure 10 Measured section of Weehawken and Hoboken members in Eureka Quarry near Chalfont, Pennsylvania. Same conventions as Figure 9. Cycle designations on left based on correlation with cycles in Weehawken area (Fig. 6).

I have examinated all the microlaminated units in short cycles in the sections presented in Figures 9 and 10, as well as other cycles within the central Newark Basin. The mean sedimentation rate derived from 10 measurements of non-overlapping portions of 4 different cycles exposed in 2 different members in the Lockatong is 0.24 mm/yr. When this sedimentation rate is applied to the sections measured in Figures 9 and 10 the periodicities for the short and longer frequency cycles are derived (Table 1). The mean periods of the cycles in the Lockatong as shown by the curves of rank and the mean sedimentation rate are thus about 20 900, and 101 400. There are about 220 short cycles in the Lockatong and in the 1100 m of this formation, there are 11 100 m cycles. There are thus about 20 short cycles per 100 m cycle and assuming 20 900 years per cycle the 100 m cycle takes about 418 000 years.

Table 1 Periods of cycles in Lockatong based on varve calibration.

<u>Main periods of all cycles</u>

20 800 : 101 400 : 418 000 years

<u>Main periods of short cycles</u>

Eureka :

All short cycles, N=26, 20 500 ± 643 years
Detrital cycles, N=15, 22 800 ± 1659 years
Chemical cycles, N=11, 17 300 ± 841 years

Delaware River :

All short cycles, N=19, 21 300 ± 1449 years
Detrital cycles, N=7, 25 200 ± 1667 years
Chemical cycles, N=12, 19 900 ± 1810 years

<u>Periods of "25 m" cycles</u>

Eureka :
N=5, 101 500 years
Delaware River :
N=4, 101 400 years

<u>Period of "100 m" cycles</u>

418 000 years (see text for explanation)

Van Houten's classification of cycles into chemical and detrital types is applied to the sections in Figures 9 and 10, chemical cycles have a mean periodicity of 23 800 years and detrital cycles have a mean periodicity of 18 800 years. Unfortunately, this difference only reflects the fact that chemical cycles tend to be thinner than detrital and it is very difficult for me to believe that sedimentation rates were so constant between cycles that such a small difference in thickness can be significant in terms of time. It seems much more likely that the small differences in cycle thickness reflect differences in rates of sedimentation during the arid intervals represented by the upper parts of chemical cycles.

The above calibration of cycles in the Lockatong does, of course, depend on the assumption of a constant sedimentation rate - an assumption which might be right on a large scale, but which is certainly wrong on a very fine scale. Fortunately, there is another means than varve counts available for approximating the periodicity of Lockatong lake-level cycles. Newark Basin stratigraphy has, over the last 10 years been investigated on increasingly finer levels. The age of the Lockatong is early Late Triassic (Late Carnian) on the basis of both correlation by pollen and spores (20,21) and reptiles and amphibians (5,8) and the top of the overlying Passaic Formation corresponds, more or less to the Triassic - Jurassic boundary on the basis of abundant radiometric dates from the overlying lava flows (8,22), paleomagnetic reversal sequences (23), pollen and spores (20), and reptile remains (8). Using these correlations, the duration of the Lockatong plus Passaic formations can be estimated by using published radiometric scales (Fig. 2). Three somewhat different radiometric scales have been published for the Triassic but, using either, the Lockatong plus Passaic column took about 20 million years to deposit. The pattern of 100 m cycles seen in the Lockatong (Fig. 7) continues up through the Passaic Formation. There, they show up as intervals of gray and black detrital cycles separated by red beds. These gray and black intervals have been traced over much of the Newark Basin by McLaughlin (17) and they show up clearly on a map of 1:250 000 scale as well as on LANDSAT photos. The top of the Passaic Formation is not preserved in the area in which the sections described in this paper occur because of post-Early Jurassic erosion. However, the entire thickness is preserved in adjacent fault blocks and after correction for systematic decreases in thickness of 100 m cycles outside the center of the basin (5) the total sediment column in the center of the basin is estimated to be about 4190 m. Since there are about 42, 100 m cycles in this interval (most have been mapped) the periodicity of the 100 m cycles was, on the average, 476 000 years. Dividing by the number of 25 m cycles per 100 m cycle (i.e.4), and 5 m cycles per 25 m cycle (i.e. 5), the 25 m cycles take up 119 000 years and the 5 m cycles 24 000 years. Using either varve counts of radiometric - paleontological methods to obtain calibration for Lockatong cycles, the main periods which show up are fairly close to 21 000, 100 000 and 400 000 years.

The main periodicities seen in the lake-level cycles of the Lockatong are also seen in the deep-sea proxy records for the

Pleistocene and both records agree with major periods predicted by the Milankovitch astronomical theory of climate. During the Triassic the Newark Basin was located at about 17 N paleolatitude (Fig. 1). On the basis of celestial mechanics, at this latitude solar insolation changes should reflect the cycles of precession (21 000 yrs) and eccentricity (100 000 and 400 000 yrs) but not obliquity (42 000 yrs) (24) and there is no sign of a 42 000 year cycle in the Lockatong record. The ratio of thickness (and inferred duration) of the short Lockatong cycles to the thicker compound cycles is 1 : 5 and 1 : 20. Even if sedimentation rates were strongly variable within short cycles, these ratios match only the precession and eccentricity portions of the spectrum of Milankovitch astronomical periodicities.

Hypothetical alterations of the periodicity of short cycles are constrained by the radiometric-paleontological data from the sediments. The implications of assignments of the short cycles (and hence the compound cycles as well) to periodicities of even 2 x 21 000 years would involve gross changes in the duration of the Late Triassic, age of the Lockatong, thicknesses of the Lockatong and Passaic Formations, or stratigraphic position of the Triassic-Jurassic boundary. The magnitude of the changes necessary to accomodate a doubling of the duration of a Lockatong short cycle would be out of proportion of what appears to be even a very pessimistic view of the confidence in the correlations and radiometric ages. What can be safely said at this time is that very large lakes in the Newark Basin fluctuated in depth over periods on the order of magnitude of 21 000 years and that the ratios of the higher frequency fluctuations to modulations of the magnitude of those fluctuations correspond to 1 : 5 and 1 : 20 which are the same as the ratios of the terms of precession and eccentricity. These intepretations of Lockatong lake-level cycles appear to be strong evidence of Milankovitch type forcing of climate in the Late Triassic. They also provide evidence that the main periods of precession and eccentricity were not very different 220 million years ago from today.

REFERENCES

1. Olsen, P.E. : 1978, Newsletters on Stratigraphy. 7, pp. 90-95.
2. Van Houten, F.B. : 1962, Amer. Jour. Sci. 260, pp. 561-576.
3. Van Houten, F.B. : 1980, in : "Field Studies in New Jersey Geology and Guide to Field Trips", 52nd Annual Meeting of the New York State Geological Association, W. Manspeize (Ed.), Newark College of Arts and Sciences, Rutgers University, pp. 264-276.
4. Olsen, P.E. : 1980, New Jersey Academy of Science, Bulletin 25, pp. 25-51.

5. Olsen, P.E. : 1980, in : "Field Studies in New Jersey Geology and Guide to Field Trips", 52nd Annual Meeting of the New York State Geological Association, W. Manspeizer (Ed.), Newark College of Arts and Sciences, Rutgers University, pp. 2-39.
6. Smith, A.G. : 1981, Geol. Rundschau 70, pp. 91-127.
7. Olsen, P.E. : 1980, in : "Field Studies in New Jersey Geology and Guide to Field Trips", 52nd Annual Meeting of the New York State Geological Association, W. Manspeizer (Ed.), Newark College of Arts and Sciences, Rutgers University, pp. 352-398.
8. Olsen, P.E., McCune, A.R., and Thomson, K.S. : 1982, Amer. Jour. Sci. 282, pp. 1-44.
9. Manspeizer, W. and Olsen, P.E. : 1981, in : "Field Guide to the Geology of the Palaeozoic, Mesozoic, and Tertiary Rocks of New Jersey and the Central Hudson Valley", G.W. Hobbs (Ed.), Petroleum Exploration Society of New York, New York, pp. 25-103.
10. Benson, L.V. : 1981, Quat. Res. 16, pp. 390-403.
11. Gilbert, G.K. : 1890, Lake Bonneville, U.S. Geol. Surv., Monogr. 1, 438pp.
12. Hamilton, A.C. : 1982, Environmental History of East Africa : A Study of the Quaternary. New York, Academic Press, 328pp.
13. Kutzbach, J.E. : 1980, Quat. Res. 14, pp. 210-223.
14. Livingston D.A. : 1965, Limnol. Oceanogr. 10, pp. 607-610.
15. Emiliani, C. : 1966, Jour. Geol. 74, pp. 109-126.
16. Imbrie J. : 1982, Icarus 50, pp. 408-422.
17. McLaughlin, D.B. : 1946, Mich. Acad. Sci. Papers 32, pp. 295-303.
18. Hays, J.D., Imbrie, J., and Shackleton, N.J. : 1976, Science 194, pp. 1121-1132.
19. Twenhofel, W.H. : 1932, Treatise on Sedimentation, 2nd ed. Baltimore, Williams and Wilkens, 926pp.
20. Cornet, W.B. : 1977, The palynostratigraphy and age of the Newark Supergroup. Ph.D. Thesis, University of Pennsylvania, State College, 506pp.
21. Cornet, W.B. : 1977, In : "Geobotany", Romans, R.C. (Ed.), New York, Plenum Press, pp. 165-172.
22. Armstrong, R.L. : 1982, in : "Numerical Dating in Stratigraphy", G.S. Odin (Ed.), John Wiley and Sons, London, pp. 509-513.
23. McIntosh, W.C. : 1976, Paleomagnetic reversals in the Newark Group Brunswick Formation of eastern Pennsylvania and central New Jersey. Senior Thesis, Princeton University, Princeton, 72pp.
24. Berger, A.L., Quat. Res. 9, pp. 139-167.

[1] Present affiliation : Department of Paleontology, University of California, Berkeley, California 94 720.

ORBITAL FORCING OF EVAPORITE SEDIMENTATION

R.Y. Anderson

Department of Geology, University of New Mexico, Albuquerque, NM 87131, USA

ABSTRACT

The link between climatic forcing and evaporites is close and direct; orbital climatic forcing has initiated and terminated some evaporite deposits in the past. In the varved Permian Castile evaporites, the initiation and termination of deposition, annual thickness trends, and symmetry of the response is consistent with control by the 100 000-year eccentricity term of orbital variation. The precession cycle is recorded in the Castile as nearly symmetrical changes in the rate of calcium sulfate deposition with a period near 20 000 years; the low latitude of the recording site may be responsible for the absence of the obliquity cycle in the record. The climatic signal in the Castile evaporites can be demonstrated to be external to the basin and was established before the development of evaporite conditions. During the evaporite phase, the climatic pulse was transferred directly to geochemical changes which were recorded as variations in individual components, deposited on a seasonal schedule. The varve thickness changes are interpreted as a direct response to orbitally influenced climatic change, retaining most of the symmetry associated with orbital variation of insolation.

Other sequences, such as the Pennsylvanian Paradox Basin evaporites, the Jurassic Todilto evaporites, and the Pleistocene Searles Lake evaporites, have less precise time control than the Castile, but have time relationships consistent with orbital forcing.

A. L. Berger et al. (eds.), Milankovitch and Climate, Part 1, 147–162.

INTRODUCTION

Net water loss by evaporation, as shown by the distribution of modern and ancient evaporites (1), occurs over latitudes of the globe ranging from the equator to about 50 degrees, with optimum conditions between 20 degrees and 40 degrees latitude. Within this climatic belt, and under favorable conditions, evaporites have the potential of directly recording insolation effects by means of geochemical responses to evaporation and concentration and the precipitation of chemical sediments. The specific geochemical response is determined by type and concentration of salts, common ion effects, water temperature, kinetics of precipitation, salinity stratification, and mixing. In the case of marine evaporites, changes in sea level often control influx and reflux of waters into and out of the basin so that the recorded geochemical response may be several processes removed from the direct forcing by insolation related to planetary perturbations.

Evaporite sedimentary basins tend to be delicately balanced hydrologic systems and are, by their nature, sensitive recorders of climatic change. Evaporite sedimentation is also quite rapid, with rates ranging from tenths of millimeters to centimeters per year. Just as evaporites are climatically sensitive, so are they short-lived. In fact many evaporite records are either too senstivive, have too high a proportion of clastics, or are too short to record the long-period responses associated with orbital forcing. Others do not contain sufficient chronologic information to permit evaluation. However, some evaporite basins do have the proper conditions, and these suggest that orbitally regulated climatic forcing is involved in the initiation, termination, and even the regulation of evaporite deposition.

Four depositional basins, each representing a different hydrologic setting, are briefly examined here to show that orbital control is a reasonable possibility. One is a closed lake system; the others have different degrees of involvement with eustatic change. Varving is used in two of the examples to help calibrate deposition. The evaporites in the Permian Castile Formation, are varved throughout and have been studied in sufficient detail to show that insolation changes related to precession and eccentricity may have been transferred directly to the varved sediment through evaporation and geochemical changes.

Precession or eccentricity cycles have been reported in the marine Pleistocene (2) and in varved sequences, including the Eocene Green River Formation (3) and the Triassic Lockatong Formation (4). This discussion, however, is restricted to evaporites.

SEARLES LAKE EVAPORITES

Pleistocene Searles Lake occupied a closed tectonic depression east of the Sierra Nevada in south central California. The drainage area of 1600 km^2 contains an assortment of sediments, plutonic rocks, and volcanics. Searles Lake sediments, include halite, trona, borax, and other evaporite minerals which were deposited during low lake stands and represent episodes of dessication and higher salinity levels alternating with higher lake stands and lower salinity.

Searles Lake evaporites have been studied in detail (5) and G.I. Smith (personal communication) is now preparing a report on a 930m core in which a paleomagnetic chronology permits an evaluation of the timing of the episodes of evaporite deposition in the 3.2 Myr record. Smith recognizes 9 hydrologic regimes with an average duration of 395 kyr. He notes that during the last 1.75 Myr the regime boundaries coincide with changes in sea surface temperatures in the south Atlantic and suggests that the regimes are related to the 400 kyr orbital eccentricity cycle. The wettest and dryest regimes associated with the 400 kyr oscillations are not sensitive to shorter period cycles but intermediate regimes have recorded fluctuations with periods of about 20 kyr and 40 kyr.

Attempts by Smith (5) to correlate some of these fluctuations with other records of late Pleistocene change, including the marine record, other lakes, and sea level changes are only partly successful, but are more convincing in the younger part of the core. Other closed lakes in the Great Basin have fluctuating lake levels related to air mass movements so that one would expect local insolation impact to be modified by general circulation. The controls of salinity and deposition are at least partly removed from the most direct type of forcing. The Searles Lake system, however, was hydrologically sensitive, and the timing of evaporite deposition is consistent with a climatic response to perturbational controls.

TODILTO EVAPORITES

The Upper Jurassic Todilto evaporite sequence, in northwestern New Mexico, is thin (30m) but was deposited over a wide (34 600 mi^2; 90 000 km^2) area. The pre-evaporite environment was eolean sand and the short-lived evaporite phase graded upward into nonmarine mudstone and siltstone. The evaporites themselves were considerd nonmarine to marginal marine (6). Subsequent isotopic work by D.W. Kirkland (personal communication) indicates that the basin was connected to the ocean.

However, the evaporite sequence never progressed to the point of halite precipitation, and the occurrence of insects and brackish water fishes suggests a substantial nonmarine influence.

Climatic-eustatic factors rather than tectonic controls were probably involved in developing and sustaining the broad, shallow, mostly inland water body. The Todilto evaporites are varved so that it is possible to obtain a fairly accurate estimate of the elapsed time for the sequence. Varve counts indicate that the basal 2m thick limestone unit was deposited in 14 kyr. A transition zone ocupied 3 kyr, and the main anhydrite-gypsum body another 3 kyr. Assuming that chemical sedimentation was controlled by climate, the limestone mode represents part of a larger cycle and the calcium sulfate mode represents part of the same cycle. Taken together, the duration of the entire limestone-evaporite sequence conforms to a response near the period of the precession cycle. Of course, one episode cannot make a case for control, but given the sensitivity of the physical system, as suggested by the morphometry, the duration of deposition is at least consistent with a response to the precession cycle.

PARADOX EVAPORITES

The Paradox evaporites in southwest Colorado and southeast Utah can be correlated laterally with carbonates and other sediments which bear evidence for eustatic control on their deposition (7). The evaporites were deposited in a deep trough against the Uncompaghre Uplift in mid-Pennsylvanian time, are about 1600 m thick, and cover an area of 11 000 km^2. There are 29 distinct evaporite cycles within the basin, beginning with anhydrite and progressing through a cycle of silty dolomite, black shale, dolomite, anhydrite, and halite. The cycles are asymmetrical and represent, from the base upward, rising sea level until the development of black shale conditions, falling sea level to halite deposition, followed by a disconformity correlated with a break in shelf carbonate deposition.

Halite laminae in the Paradox salt units have an average thickness of 4 cm. Hite and Bukner (7) estimated the rate of deposition for the anhydrite, dolomite, and black shale for the second evaporite cycle in the sequence, which is one of the thicker cycles, and obtained an elapsed time of 104 kyr to 111 kyr for the complete cycle. This is only a rough approximation, however, because the rates, especially for the black shale unit, are based on several assumptions. Most of the other 29 cycles in the Paradox are a quarter to half as thick as the second cycle and presumably these might reflect oscillations of equivalently shorter duration. The timing of the evaporite cycles in the Paradox probably cannot be estimated more precisely. They do, however, represent a case for eustatic control of evaporite sedimentation that may have been indirectly responsive to perturbational control. It has been suggested that glaciation was established in Australia and South America by the Pennsylvanian (Namurian-Westphalian; (8)) so that it is possible that Paradox evaporite cycles were indirectly regulated by a glacio-eustatic mechanism responsive to orbital perturbations.

CASTILE EVAPORITES

Nature of the Record

A deep sediment-starved basin developed in western Texas and southeastern New Mexico at the end of the Permian (Fig. 1). The Delaware Basin was ringed by a reef which held back clastic sediment from the deeper central part of the basin. After reef growth, and with a lowering of sea level, the reef acted as a still or gate which regulated the inflow of marine waters into and out of the basin. A delicate balance between net water loss by evaporation, fresh and marine inflow, and marine reflux was maintained for nearly a quarter-million years as evaporites precipitated from the surface waters and accumulated on the floor of the basin. Eventually, 600 metres of varved evaporites, the Castile Formation, filled the initially deep basin.

The Castile Formation is divided into anhydrite and halite members, with the rate of accumulation much faster in the halite units (Table 1). Halite accounts for nearly one-third of the thickness of the Castile but less than one-fiftieth of the time of deposition. Most of the material consists of thin laminae of nearly pure anhydrite ($CaSO_4$) alternating with even thinner laminae of dark brown, organic-rich calcite (Fig. 2). The average thickness of a calcite-anhydrite couplet is about 2mm. The anhydrite has a "pile of bricks" texture and shows no original grading. Calcite, where it has not been recrystallized, occurs as minute rhombs in a layer that has a sharp lower contact with anhydrite laminae. The number of rhombs diminishes upward into the overlying anhydrite and it is apparently the calcium carbonate that is precipitated seasonally. Each couplet of anhydrite and calcite represents an annual cycle of deposition or varve (see 9 for details of petrography).

During times when halite is being precipitated, the deposition of calcium carbonate is greatly reduced. Laminae of halite, several centimeters thick, are "inserted" between the anhydrite laminae. There are also times when the deposition of calcium sulfate virtually stops. During these episodes, calcite laminae

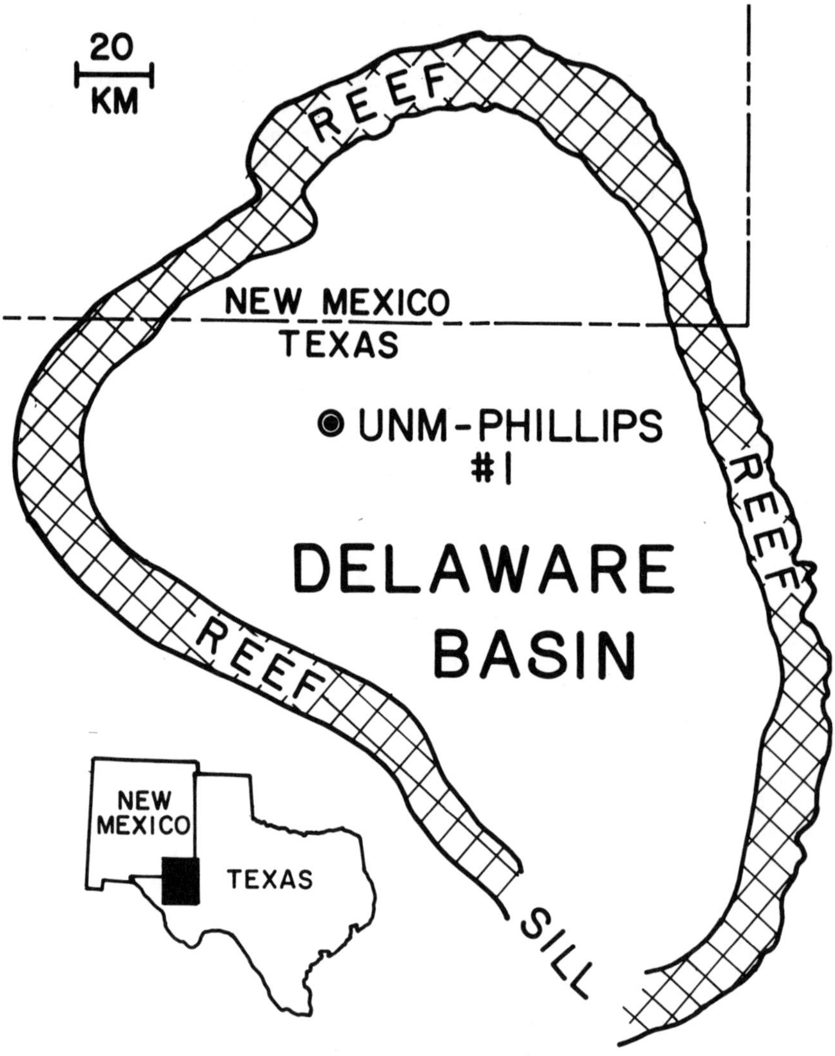

Figure 1 Index map showing Delaware Basin and location of Castile core (for details see (9)).

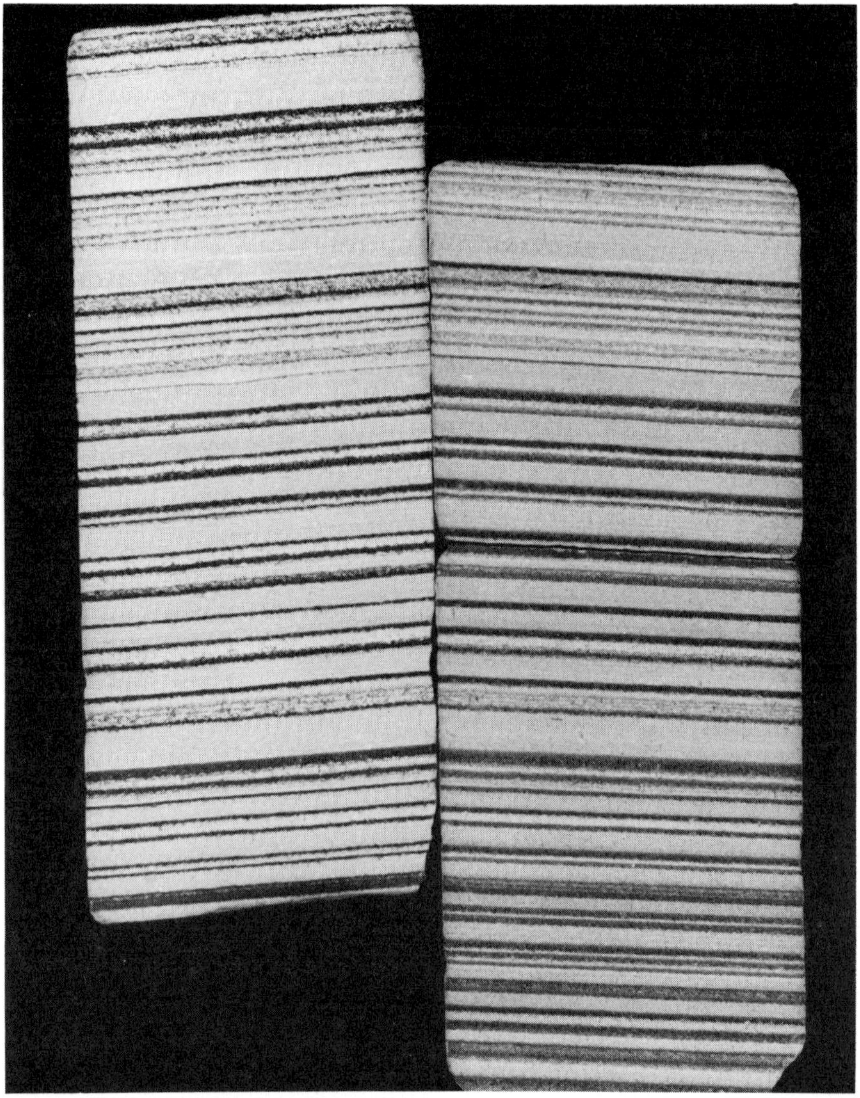

Figure 2 Correlative slabs of Castile calcite-anhydrite laminations. Distance between cores is 14.5 km. Couplets are about 2mm-4mm tick. Subseasonal synchroneity of deposition in the whole basin indicates climatic forcing.

persist and are set off by organic-rich calcite or minor anhydrite. The result is a laminated limestone. The continuity of the lamination process is maintained during these different modes of deposition and it is this continuity that has made it possible to construct an unbroken record of climatic oscillation over an interval of more than 200 000 years (Table 1).

Table 1 Thickness and time relationships of the members of the Castile Formation.

Member or unit	Description	Thickness (meters)	Elapsed Time (years)
Anhydrite IV	Laminated anhydrite, with beds of halite and limestone.	210	89 600
Halite III	Laminated halite, with beds of anhydrite and limestone.	80	17 900
Anhydrite III	Laminated anhydrite	100	46 600
Halite II	Laminated halite, with thin beds of anhydrite	50	1 800
Anhydrite II	Laminated anhydrite	30	14 400
Halite I	Laminated halite	70	1 000
Anhydrite I	Laminated anhydrite	60	38 400
Basal Limestone	Laminated limestone	0.1	600
	Total	600	210 300

The episodes of reduced sulfate (limestone) deposition occurred when the waters in the basin were freshened and diluted. Similarly, halite deposition occurred when waters became more concentrated. These fluctuations in salinity impacted the basin on a schedule between 2-3 kyr (2700-year period, (10)). As the deep basin filled in with sediment and the depth and volume of water were reduced, the impact of these freshening events increased and resulted in more episodes of halite and limestone deposition in the upper part of the Castile (Table 1).

Controls on Deposition

The precipitation of materials from surface waters was regulated by seasonal changes in temperature, evaporation, and organic productivity. Climatic forcing that was external to the basin is clearly demonstrated in the remarkable correlations of individual laminae over great distances (Fig. 2) and, in fact, across the entire basin. It is this response of the whole basin in what must have been time intervals of weeks or even days that indicates that the forcing mechanism was climatic (weather) change that affected the entire basin simultaneously.

The simplest and most direct response to climatic change, and the one most likely to have been involved in the direct forcing of chemical precipitation from surface waters by insolation changes, is found in the calcium sulfate system. The transfer sequence is from insolation → temperature → concentration → precipitation. Calcium sulfate deposition is little effected by changes in ionic strength or temperature. Calcium carbonate, on the other hand, has more complex and conflicting controls involving temperature, salinity, and photosynthetic activity. The more complex response of calcium carbonate is reflected in the observed changes in the time series (10, Fig. 1). The conflicting behavior of carbonate and sulfate, and their sensitivity to salinity differences have proved to be a type of "tracer" for identifying their responses to climatic forcing (discussed later).

The Delaware Basin, because of its particular morphometry and relationship to influx and reflux, was "tuned" selectively to climatic forcing at different frequencies. That is, the climatic signal affected the geochemical response through several processes that changed dominance with different frequencies. For example, climatic oscillations in the range of 2-3 kyr regulated the deposition of major units of halite, anhydrite, and limestone. Although the basin was not "tuned" to the longer climatic oscillations associated with orbital perturbations, the same evaporation and geochemical controls that regulated varve thickness over seasonal and shorter periods were operating to record the longer oscillations.

Sulfate Response to Climatic Forcing

The calcium sulfate time-series displays nearly symmetrical oscillations at the precession frequency that is also reflected in the spectrum for sulfate (10). In addition, there is an almost symmetrical longer-period oscillation of about 100 kyr that could be interpreted as a response to the eccentricity cycle (Fig. 3). The record is too short to completely separate the longer period from progressive changes in the basin, but the reversal in sulfate thickness midway through the sequence is a part of an oscillation with a symmetry that might be produced by a direct response to changes in seasonal insolation accompanying changes in eccentricity.

There are 9 to 11 oscillations with an average period of about 20 kyr that most likely reflect the precession cycle. These oscillations are most clearly defined with a smoothing interval of 10 kyr (see (10), Fig. 2). The clarity of this particular period of oscillation is not altered by reducing the smoothing to 8 kyr, as in Figure 3, and is even maintained with a 5 kyr smoothing (Fig. 4). Closer inspection of the Castile plots shows a considerable departure from a 23 kyr period, especially in the earlier part of the sequence, and an average period of 19.4 kyr. It is not known how much of this departure from 23 kyr is the result of difficulties of varve interpretation, how much might be climatic modification of insolation accompanying precession, or how much is from the character of the cycle. Varve interpretation was conservative, with a tendency to consider doubles as a single couplet, so that errors are in the direction of too few varves in the sequence and this probably accounts for some of the difference. Varve clarity and oscillation symmetry, as well as basin sensitivity, is best developed in the latter part of the sequence where oscillations display a longer period (Fig. 4).

Insolation vs Reflux and Freshening

Marine inflow supplied the materials of deposition. The flow of marine waters into the basin was accompanied by nearly continuous reflux of brines from the basin. Such a system must have been delicately balanced and sensitive to small changes in sea level. Reflux and freshening may also have been responsive to changes in wind patterns (10) and freshening waters may also have been supplied by runoff. The longer oscillations observed might be explained in terms of eustasy, freshening and reflux. However, the symmetry of the response as well as an interesting relationship between carbonate and sulfate, suggest that insolation, played a direct role in regulating deposition.

The association between calcium carbonate and calcium sulfate changes dramatically with the period of response. For periods less than 200-400 years, the association is strongly positive (see (10), Fig. 8) and reflects the dominance of temperature (insolation) in regulating both evaporation (sulfate deposition) and dissolved carbon dioxide (carbonate deposition). This association shifts to strongly negative as the period of oscillation lengthens to 2-3 kyr (see 10, Figs 5,6). This switch from a positive to a negative association is brought about by

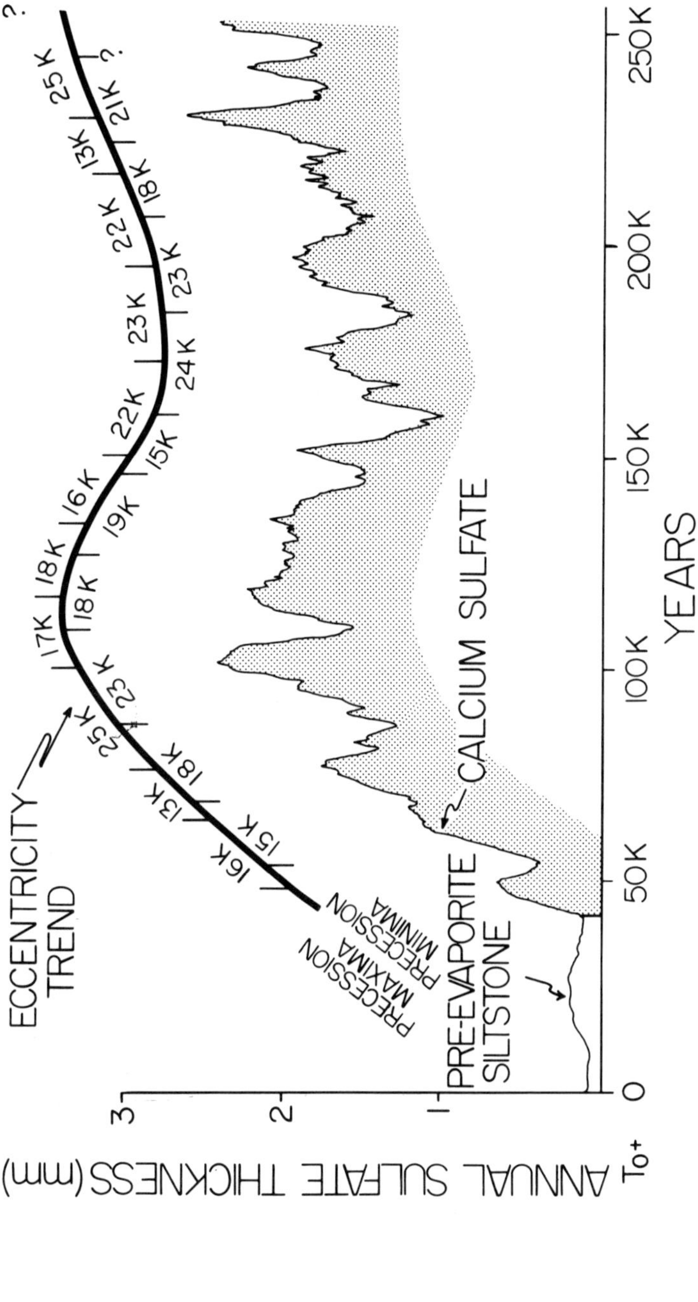

Figure 3 Smoothed plot of absolute thickness of calcium sulfate in the Castile Formation. Note the dominant oscillation in the period range of the precession and eccentricity cycles. Smoothing interval is 8 kyr. The intervals between the successive maxima and minima of the sulfate thickness given in thousands years along the heavy line ("ecc. trend") and marked as "precession maxima" and "precession minima".

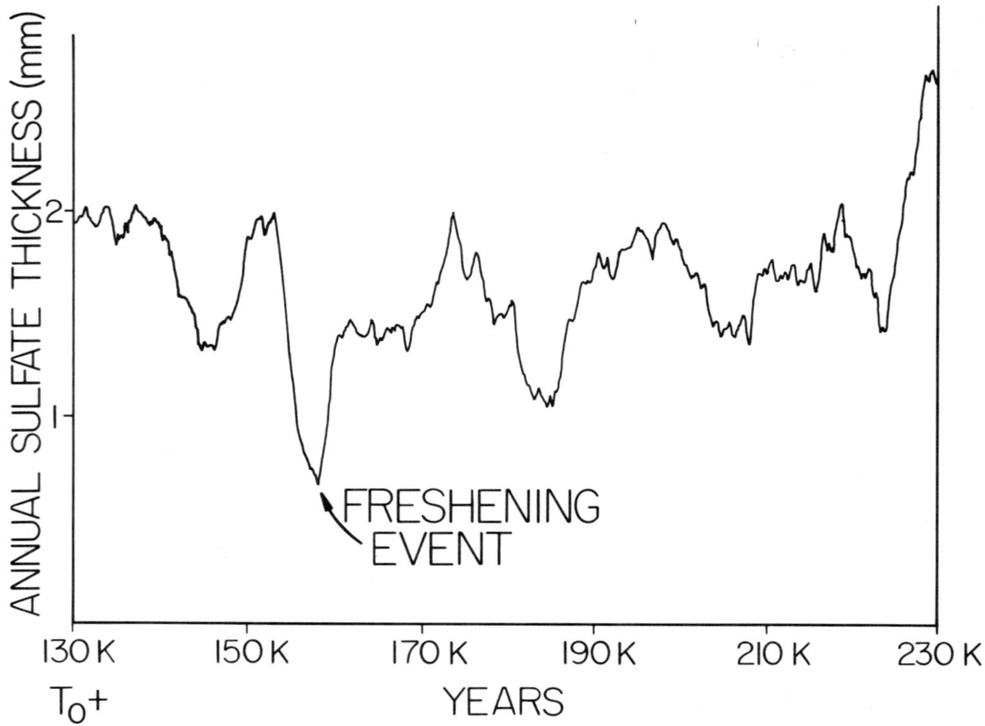

Figure 4 Smoothed plot of a segment of the sequence in Figure 3. Smoothing interval is 5 kyr. Note that a freshening event appears to interrupt the progress of a longer precessional oscillation.

freshening events that also shift the isotopic composition to lighter oxygen and carbon.

Moving correlation coefficients approach -0.8 near the 2-3 kyr frequencies, as the freshening water in the basin greatly reduces or even shuts off sulfate deposition and promotes carbonate deposition. As the period of oscillation lengthens beyond 3 kyr and approaches the range of perturbational effects, the negative association weakens (Fig. 5). Moving correlation that resolve the longer oscillations also reveal interesting alternations in the intensity of the negative association, with a pattern that is similar to that of the precession period (compare Figs 3 and 5). The negative association weakens and even disappears in a pattern similar to the development of maxima and minima in the precession cycle.

The weakening of the negative relationship between carbonate and sulfate in the longer periods indicates that reflux and freshening events have maximum effect within a relatively narrow period range (2-3 kyr). This control by freshening is replaced by control by temperature (insolation) at both the shorter and longer periods. Freshening events and reflux were not sufficiently strong to mask the precession effect which arrived directly through insolation and was transferred through evaporation. An Example can be seen in Figure 4 where a systematic change in thickness at the precession period is interrupted by one of the more severe freshening events in the Castile.

The symmetry of the longer period oscillations (Figs 3,4) also suggest a direct response to insolation rather than a eustatic movements. Typically, glacio-eustatic responses are assymmetrical, with rapid rise followed by a more gradual lowering. The circulating and refluxing Delaware basin might be expected to respond by sudden termination of sulfate deposition, followed by gradual recovery. There is a subtle assymmetry in this direction at the precession period, but this is hardly sufficient to warrant comparison with Pleistocene fluctuations.

The freshening events have the greatest impact on the basin on a 2-3 kyr schedule (see (10), Fig. 3). If glacio-eustasy was involved, the dominant ice-volume response time in the late Permian was an order of magnitude shorter than in the Pleistocene. The fact that the basin remained delicately balanced to influx and reflux for over 200 kyr suggests a stable sea level. If sea level fluctuations had been of the same period and magnitude as in the Pleistocene, then sea level certainly would have been raised high above the reef, and probably would have eliminated evaporite conditions altogether. Finally, precession rather than obliquity appears to dominate the low-latitude climatic response in the marine Pleistocene (11,12). The Delaware Basin was within

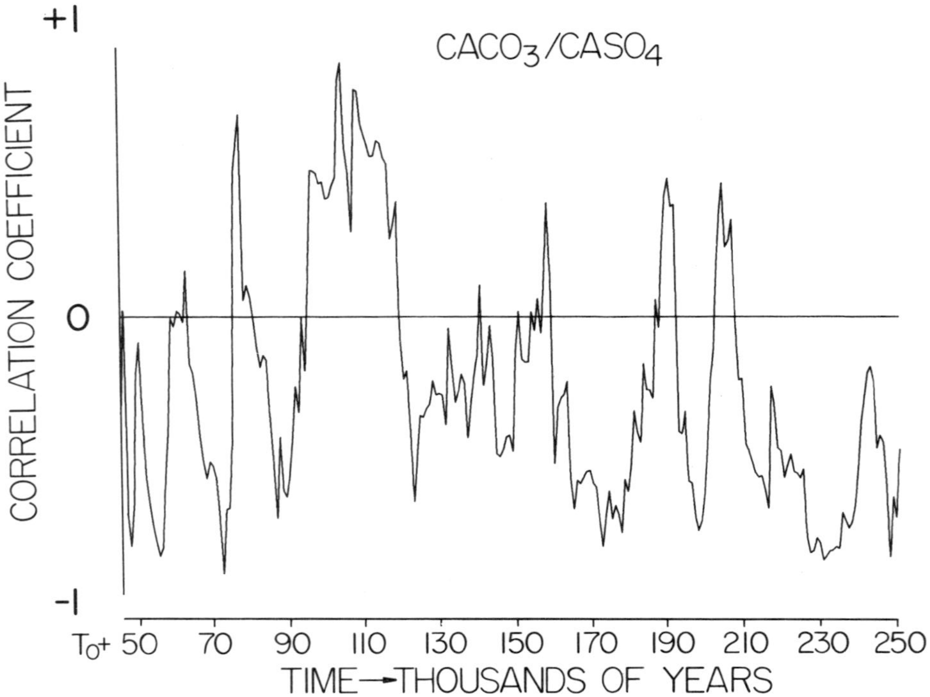

Figure 5 Moving correlation coefficient for absolute calcium carbonate and absolute calcium sulfate in Castile time-series. Moving correlation interval is 8.8 kyr. Note that the generally negative association resolved by this correlation interval weakens in a pattern similar to the precession oscillations (see 10 for methods).

10 degrees of the Permian equator. If insolation rather than glacio-eustasy were the dominant process controlling deposition, one would expect to find only the precession and eccentricity cycles in the Castile, and indeed, this is what the record shows.

CONCLUSIONS

Where the evaporitic environment has persisted for intervals sufficiently long to record perturbational effects, the sediments in the evaporite basins appear to have responded at these frequencies. This is true for Searles Lake, the ephemeral Todilto basin, and for the eustatically regulated Paradox basin.

The precession cycle, and perhaps the eccentricity cycle, appear to have controlled calcium sulfate deposition in the Castile sequence. Departures from a more idealized precession series may be due to the changing character of the cycle itself, to climate modification of insolation, or to difficulties of varve interpretation.

The interpretation that the precession cycle has been directly transferred through insolation to the Castile sequence is strengthened by evidence for the "tuning" of the basin. The tuning evidence indicates that freshening and reflux effects dominated a restricted frequency range and that a more direct response to temperature and insolation recorded the orbital effects.

Finally, the oscillations recorded in the Castile are remarkably close to what one would predict if insolation were the dominant process in regulating evaporite deposition. The absence of the obliquity term and the dominance of precession in the Castile resembles insolation curves for the low paleolatitudes.

REFERENCES

1. Meier, R. : 1981, "The geographic and paleogeographic distribution of Phanerozoic evaporite deposits and the latitudinal position of the Zechstein Basin", Int. Symposium Central European Permian, Proceedings, Geol. Inst., Warsaw, pp. 317-323.
2. Hays, J.D., Imbrie, J., and Shackleton, N.J. : 1976, Science 214, pp. 1121-1132.
3. Bradley, W.H. : 1929, "The varves and climate of the Green River Epoch", U.S. Geol. Survey Prof. Paper 158, pp. 87-110.

4. Van Houten, F.B. : 1964, in : "Cyclic lacustrine sediments in (Upper Triassic) Lockating Formation, central New Jersey and adjacent Pennsylvania", D.F. Merriam (Ed.), Symposium on cyclic sedimentation, State Geol. Survey of kansas Bull 169, pp. 476-531.
5. Smith, G.I. : 1979, "Subsurface stratigraphy and geochemistry of late Quaternary evaporites, Searles Lake, California, U.S. Geol. Survey Prof. Paper 1043, 130p.
6. Anderson, R.Y., and Kirkland, D.W. : 1960, Am. Assoc. Petroleum Geologists Bull. 44, pp. 37-52.
7. Hite, R.J., and Buckner, D.H. : 1981, "Stratigraphic correlations, facies concepts, and cyclicity in the Pennsylvanian rocks of the Paradox Basin: Rocky Mountain Assoc. of Geologists, Field Conf. Guidebook, pp. 147-159.
8. Frakes, L.A. : 1979, "Climates throughout geologic time", Elsevier Scientific Publication Co., new York.
9. Anderson, R.Y., Dean, W.E.Jr., Kirkland, D.W., and Snider, H.I. : 1972, Geol. Soc. Amer. Bull. 83, pp. 59-86.
10. Anderson, R.Y. : 1982, J. Geophys. Res. 87, pp. 7285-7294.
11. Ruddiman, W.F., and McIntyre, A. : 1981, Science 212, pp. 617-627.
12. McIntyre, A., Karlin, K., and Molfino, B. : 1982, "Orbital forcing and the response of the ice-age tropical Atlantic Ocean", Geol. Soc. Amer. (abs), Annual Meeting, 561p.

CRETACEOUS BEDDING RHYTHMS UNDER ORBITAL CONTROL?

A.G. Fischer[1], W. Schwarzacher[2]

[1]Department of Geological and Geophysical Sciences, Princeton University, Princeton, NJ, USA
[2]Department of Geology, The Queen's University, Belfast, N. Ireland

ABSTRACT

Limestones deposited in the Italian Apennines in the general interval of 90-110 m.y. BP show a hierarchy of four periodicities in stratification, attributable to climatic rhythms. The low-frequency rhythms remains poorly defined because of inadequate sampling. While the periods of the other rhythms cannot be accurately measured via the radiometric time-scale, they show numerical ratios very close to those existing between the present precessional, tilt, and short eccentricity cycles. This and the similarity in the fine structure between insolation curves calculated and the Cretaceous bedding sequences observed support the proposition that orbital variations remained essentially constant since early Cretaceous times, and induced climatic fluctuations with similar periods regardless of the degree of global glaciation.

INTRODUCTION

Milutin Milankovitch established the quantitative basis for the old theory that Pleistocene climates varied rhythmically, in response to the variations in the Earth's orbit. This theory can now be considered as established, though the nature of the linkage remains controversal. Did climates fluctuate in this manner and for the same causes throughout Earth History, even in its nonglacial modes?

A. L. Berger et al. (eds.), Milankovitch and Climate, Part 1, 163–175.

Repetitive bedding patterns abound in the pre-Pleistocene record. As early as 1895 Gilbert (1) recognized that many of them must involve temporal rhythms in the depositional environment, a matter formulated by Sander (2) in the rule space rhythm=time rhythm. Sedimentary rhythms are varied (3), and include the "punctuated aggradational units" or PACs of Goodwin and Anderson (4) in shelf sediments; varved lake sequences (5,6); varved evaporites (7); rhythmically emerged carbonate platforms (8); rhythmically interbedded shales and marls (9,10); and the rhythmically interrupted limestones such as those of this paper.

One kind of rhythm consists of regularly spaced bedding planes or an alternation of two rock types. Commonly such alternations are grouped into bundles, in sets of 4-6 (11,12), implying superposition of two or more rhythms. We have found up to four. Such bundled rhythms occur throughout the Phanerozoic. Their occurrence in Cretaceous pelagic limestones is the subject of this paper.

BARREMIAN AND CENOMANIAN - RHYTHMS IN APENNINES

General Character

The Umbrian Apennines of Italy contain a continuous record of deep sea deposits - marls and limestones - extending over 100 m.y., from late Jurassic time to the Miocene. Rhythms appear throughout, but are particularly well developed in the Maiolica Limestone (Tithonian-Aptian), in the succeeding Scisti a Fucoidi Marls (Aptian-Albian), and in the Scaglia Bianca Limestone (Cenomanian, about 91-95 m.y. BP). We here present an extension of work done on the upper Maiolica and on the upper Scaglia Bianca (13), while de Boer (9,10) has dealt with intervening beds.

Both of these limestones were coccolith oozes. Burial and folding have converted them into dense, conchoidally fracturing rocks. Limestone beds of dm-thickness are separated by shaly bedding planes, of mm-dimensions. 1 m thick bundles of such beds are separated by one or two more pronounced interruptions, in which the shale may reach cm-dimensions, or may give way to a radiolarian chert of mm or cm thickness. Thus the entire sequence is articulated by a high frequency bedding rhythm (a) and a lower-frequency bundle rhythm.(c).

While many bedding-parallel discontinuities were observed in the field, major, continuous bedding planes, thin shales or radiolarites may be separated as primary features of sedimentation. Beds defined by such planes average 28.26 cm thick and

4.88 to the bundle in the Maiolica, and 21.69 cm thick and 4.61 to the bundle in the Scaglia (Table 1).

Spectral Analysis

Schwarzacher and Fischer (13) measured a section of the upper Maiolica (36.45m) and a section of the upper Scaglia Bianca (18m) in the vicinity of Gubbio. Basing the time dimension of their time-series study on the assumption of linear sedimentation rates, they sampled the sequence for bed-thickness at 10 cm intervals, and constructed from this a curve of sequential bedding thickness. Power spectra of these curves (Fig. 1) lack the bedding period, since bed thicknes is what was measured. The spectra show great scatter, probably because of deviations from linear sedimentation rate, but three well-defined frequency peaks appear.

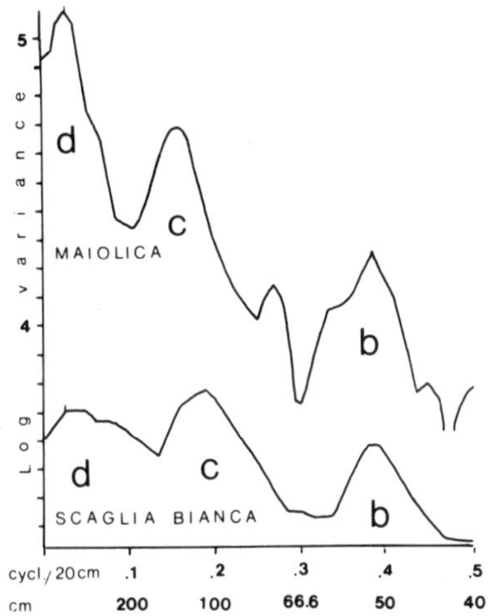

Figure 1 Power spectra of sequential curves of bed-thickness.

Peak b, at 51 and 52 cm respectively, is not clearly apparent in the field. Peak c, at 108 cm in the Scaglia is slightly longer than the 100 cm mean thickness of bundles logged in the field. To achieve a match (Table 1) we assume that one of the bundle boundaries logged in the field is spurious, and that the correct number of bundles is 17 rather than 18. The corresponding peak in the Maiolica Limestone, at 124 cm, calls for a reduction in bundle number from 32 to 28, to achieve a match. The spurious boundaries are readily apparent in Schwarzacher and Fischer (13), Figure 3 (boundaries 10, 20, 22, and 28).

A low frequency peak, d, lies in the domain above 400 cm, but is not clearly defined due to shortness of sections analyzed.

Table 1 Statistical data on bedding rhythms.

SCAGLIA	Major beds (a)	51 cm peak (b)	Bundles (c) uncor.	Bundles (c) correct.
Number	83	35.29	18	17
Thickness av.(cm)	21.69	51		105.88
Av. no. in bundle	4.88	2.08		1
MAIOLICA				
Number	129	70.09	32	28
Thickness av.(cm)	28.25	52		130.18
Av. no.in bundle	4.61	2.50		1

Sedimentology

The sedimentology of this sequence has been discussed by Arthur and Fischer (14), Arthur (15), and Schwarzacher and Fischer (13). The major bedding features resulted from a depositional alternation of purer carbonate ooze with more marly sediment, and from an occasional excursion into deposition of radiolarian ooze. Subsequent diagenesis has heightened the contrast by moving carbonate from the more marly to the more calcareous beds, and by converting the radiolarian ooze to chert. Three possible mechanisms exist for producing the limestone-marl alternation: fluctuations in the supply of terrigenous detritus; fluctuations in biogenic carbonate production; and fluctuations in the rate of carbonate dissolution on the sea floor. All go back ultimately to climatic causes.

The existence of changes in planktonic faunas and productivity is demonstrated by the sporadic occurrence of radiolarian cherts. Variations in rate of carbonate dissolution on the seafloor are demonstrated by a comparison of many thin sections. In some, the full spectrum of the foraminiferal fauna, with large and small specimens, with thick or thin wals, is well preserved. In other sections the tests are ragged, and in many the small forms are only visible as ghosts or are lacking altogether. Thus both changes in carbonate productivity and changes in dissolution rates played a role in the development of bedding rhythms but the details remain to be worked out. Carbonate productivity may well have been related to local climates, whereas the dissolution factor reflects characteristics of the bottom water which may have been acquired in far distant regions. If the bedding planes represent short excursions of the depositional system to or beyond the margins of the carbonate field, the bundle boundaries represent longer and more intense ones.

Timing

The interest of earlier geologists (1,16) in sedimentary rhythms and their possible link to orbital periods stemmed in large part from the great need to geologists for chronometers. Gilbert used what he believed to be a 21 000 year precessional cycle to set up a chronology for the Cretaceous period, before the discovery of radioactivity and its application to Earth history. This conference has made it plain that such constancy of orbital periods is not to be taken for granted. There are two questions: (1), are the sedimentological rhythms reflections of orbital variations? and (2), do these orbital variations maintain their characters and periods over such long stretches of geological time? Yet, in practice, it seems unlikely that (1) will be answered without recourse to (2).

Sedimentary rhythms in the pre-Pleistocene record may be timed either via varves or via reference to radiometric dates. The varve approach (5,6,7,17) is the more direct one. However, very few sedimentary sequences retain a record of seasonal fluctuations: most, such as the Maiolica and Scaglia limestones, are deposited too slowly and are mixed by burrowers.

The alternative is to date sedimentary rhythms by reference to the "radiometric time scale" (18,19). While this scale is one of the triumphs of 20th century geology, it remains a blunt tool for this purpose, in all but the youngest parts of the Phanerozoic, for the following reasons:

(1) minerals well suited for dating are not common in the record of bedded rocks. Dating of intervals in a sequence of Cretaceous sediments, for example, is not generally possible by direct means, but involves patching together radiometric dates from different parts of the world, by reference to "time-stratigraphic units" - generally Epochs (on the order of ten million years long) or Stages (on the order of 5 million years long) recognized on the basis of paleontological zones.

(2) Accuracy of radiometric dating generally decreases with increasing age. The radiometric determinations critical to the

dating of Cretaceous stage boundaries generally carry error bars of a million years or more, and these errors are not amenable to correction by averaging.

(3) The biostratigraphic correlations involved in tying distant dates into a given sequence also carry errors in the million-year range.

(4) In most stratigraphic sequences, strongly cyclic parts, or parts characterized by a given type of cycle, rarely persist through as much as a stage, so that extrapolation is required.

Greater accuracy is to be obtained in the younger Past, such as the Neogene, and improvements are on the horizon. New methods such as that of argon-argon dating will provide more and better dates; magnetic stratigraphy and the tie of classical stratigraphic data to the relative constancy of seafloor spreading (20) will provide better control, especially for the last 150 m.y. The problem at present, however, is illustrated by the cycles here discussed.

Three time-scales for the Cretaceous are currently in use, and their applications to our data are shown in Table 2. Kauffman (21) assigns the Cenomanian 2.5 m.y., Obradovich and Cobban (22) 4, Van Hinte (23) 8. Application of the Van Hinte scale to our sequence yields sedimentation rates that seem too low for such relatively pure carbonate ooze, and too low in the context of the whole sedimentary sequence. The Obradovich-Cobban values seem consistent with the sediment, and are based on analyses (biotite and sanidine, in volcanic ashes interbedded with marine sediments) that are generally held to be comparatively reliable. Arguments against the Kauffman scale, a variant of the Obradovich-Cobban scale, have been advanced by Fischer (24). Furthermore, the recently published radiometric time scale by Odin (19) also assigns 4 m.y. to the Cenomanian. We therefore incline toward the Obradovich-Cobban values. Still, for the reasons discussed above, none of these numbers can be taken at face value.

Errors of correlation and extrapolation are to be added. The statistics of our Scaglia Bianca section refer to 17 bundles, occupying 18 m of stratigraphic thickness. This is precisely half of the thickness assigned to the Cenomanian in this area by Premoli Silva et al. (25), and we have therefore assigned to it half of Cenomanian time. Since the more shaly lower half of the stage may well have been deposited at a slower rate, the periods calculated may be somewhat excessive.

Table 2 Periods of the Scaglia Bianca rhythms, in years, using three different values for Cenomanian time.

Cenomanian Stage	2.5 m.y. (Kauffman)	4.0 m.y. (Obradovich -Cobban)	8.0 m.y. (Van Hinte)	Corresp. orbital periods
Sedimentation rate (m/million years)	14.40	9.00	4.50	
Bundle (c)	73 529	117 647	235 294	100 000
51 cm peak (b)	35 417	56 668	113 336	41 000
Bedding (a)	15 067	24 108	48 216	19 000 -23 000

Match to orbital periods?

As discussed above, we favor the Obradovich-Cobban scale. If these rhythms are related to orbital variations, then one might expect the bedding to be related to the precession, the b-rhythm to the tilt cycle, the bundling to the short cycle of eccentricity, and the d-rhythm to the long cycle of eccentricity. The values calculated by the Obradovich-Cobban scale are roughly comparable : values for bedding and bundling are 14 to 18% greater than the corresponding orbital periods of to-day. The discrepancy for the b-rhythm, however, is much greater.

But we have already seen that the value of 2 m.y. extrapolated for the Cenomanian section studied by us carries a considerable uncertainty, and that these numbers cannot be taken at face value. What is not affected by such calculations is the relative timing of the rhythms to each other. As a test for the match to to-day's orbital variations, we therefore in Table 3 normalize the bundle to the value of the present-day short eccentricity cycle - 100 000 years. This brings the other periods closer to those of the corresponding orbital variations, and also permits us to incorporate the Maiolica data, by assuling that the duration of the bundles was the same in both formations. The final averages - 21 244 for the bedding cycle and 42 537 for the b-cycle - come very close to the present values for the precession and the tilt cycle : so close as to make a strong case for "Milankovitch control" of Cretaceous sedimentation.

Table 3 Timing of bedding rhythms normalized to bundle = 100 000 years.

	Scaglia 17 bundles	Maiolica 28 bundles	Combined 45 bundles	Corresponding orbit periods
Sedimentation rate, m/m.y.	10.59	13.02		
Bundle (c)	100 000	100 000	100 000	100 000
51-52 cm peak (b)	48 168	39 176	42 573	41 000
Bedding (a)	20 492	21 700	21 244	19 000 -23 000

Matching bundle structure and insolation patterns

Sedimentology suggests that local climate, i.e. insolation, was an important factor in the development of these bedding rhythms. We therefore proceed to test the match between bedding features and orbital cycles by comparing the structure of the limestone bundles observed with the structure of calculated insolation curves.

If the bundles correspond to the short cycle of orbital eccentricity, the shaly or cherty bundle boundaries most probably represent the strong lows which segment the low-latitude insolation record at ca. 100 000 year intervals as a result of the interplay between precession and eccentricity (26). Reasoning that limestone beds within the bundle may correspond to periods of steady insolation, and that carbonate deposition may have been interrupted during episodes of lowered summer insolation, we compare the two records in Figure 2.

For the climatic curve, we computed the history of equatorial insolation at the vernal equinox, calculated according to Berger (26), for a period of 20 m.y. Intense insolation minima of short duration define the ca. 100 000 year cycle, within which minor insolation lows occur. The cycles were normalized to 100 000, and Figure 2A shows the frequency distribution of minor insolation lows within that cycle, as computed from 200 cycles, and plotted in 50 classes. If insolation lows occurred randomly through the cycle, they would plot near the probability 1 line. Instead of this, the precessional cycle, with its changes and multimodality in length, concentrates the insolation lows in some parts of the eccentricity cycle, and leave other parts virtually untouched.

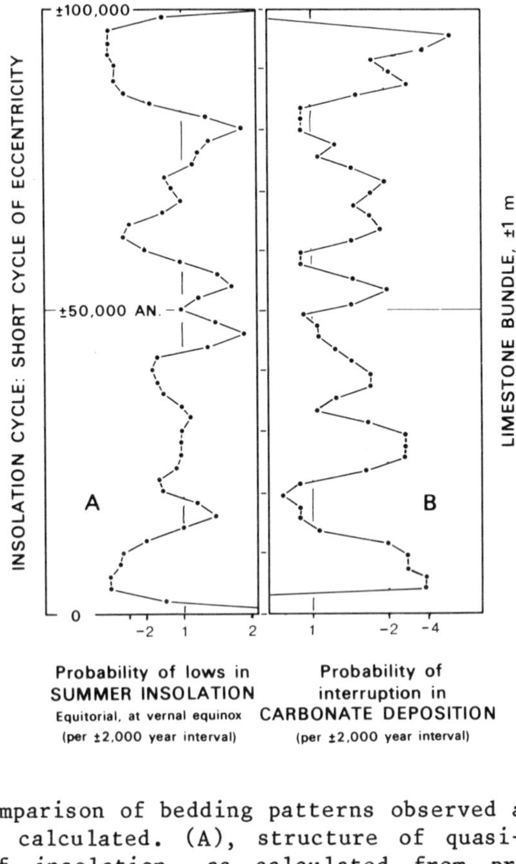

Figure 2 Comparison of bedding patterns observed and insolation patterns calculated. (A), structure of quasi-100 000 year cycle of insolation, as calculated from present orbital variations. (B), bedding patterns observed within the bedding bundles (Maiolica and Scaglia) tentatively attributed to the same cycle. Times when insolation lows are infrequent (A peaks to left) match times at which uninterrupted carbonate sedimentation produced the major limestone beds (B peaks to right); times of frequent insolation minima match times when bedding planes, shale and chert beds were developed. Both curves go off scale in at beginning and end of cycle.

To construct a comparable curve for the Cretaceous rock record, B, we normalized all of the recognized bundles to 100 kyr, and plotted the probability of bedding-plane occurrences within them, for 50 classes. In this we used all bedding-parallel surfaces, not only the main ones used in Table 1. These curves, plotted back-to-back, appear remarkably similar.

The rock record lags slightly behind that of the insolation curve, but makes up the difference at the top (end) of the cycle, where the last "limestone bed" seems anomalously thin as compared to the length of the corresponding climatic signal. These differences we attribute to a flaw in our initial assumption that sedimentation rates were linear throughout : a "first approach" simplification. There is every reason to believe that shale deposition was slower than limestone deposition, and that the bundle boundaries should therefore receive a greater share of the 100 000 year period than they have in our plot. A correction would compress the rest of the curve, for a better match to the insolation patterns. In addition, it seems likely that a few centimeters of carbonate were physically or chemically removed from the tops of the bundles, during the extreme insolation minima, rendering the uppermost of the limestone beds too thin in reference to the corresponding climatic signal.

If bedding and insolation were indeed linked, as these curves suggest, then the precessional patterns of the Cretaceous were much like those of to-day: they were multimodal, and their number per eccentricity cycle remained the same.

COMPARISON WITH OTHER CRETACEOUS SEQUENCES

Rhythmicity in other Cretaceous sequences has been summarized by Fischer (24,27). Some sequences are dominated by multiple (bundled) rhythms such as those described above, in which bedding bundles may reflect the short cycle of eccentricity, and beds the precession. A possible tilt cycle may or may not be recorded.

Other sequences are dominated by a simple limestone-shale alternation. In the Cenomanian at Peille, near Nice, occurrence of some 92 evenly spaced limestone beds in shale provides an apparent period (by Obradovich-Cobban scale) of 43 478 years, suggesting a match to the cryptic 51-52 cm cycle in the Cretaceous of Umbria, possibly linked to the cycle in axial tilt.

Milankovitch showed that the climatic effects of the precession-eccentricity cycles is greatest in the low latitudes, and de Boer and Wonders (10) have been impressed with the development of the corresponding complex bedding rhythms in the lower paleolatitudes, susceptible to shifts in the heat equator. The tilt cycle, on the other hand, affects climate chiefly in the polar regions. One might therefore expect the simple "40 000 year" cycles to be found in the higher paleolatitudes. Yet the matter appears to be not so simple: while the sequence at Nice is simple, complex cycles occur in the Fosse Vaucontienne to the north. Also, the cycles described by Gilbert ((1); see also (24)) from the Cretaceous of Colorado seem to include both simple cycles (Greenhorn Formation) and complex ones (Niobrara Formation). Any given depositional setting is influenced by many climatic factors, some generated locally and others far away; the surface waters, for example, may reflect local climate, while the temperature and chemistry of bottom waters may have been imprinted in some far-distant part of the world, where they sank. Thus the relationship of cycle type to latitude may not be simple.

CONCLUSIONS

(1) Cretaceous (Barremian and Cenomanian) pelagic limestones in the Umbrian Apennines show a hierarchy of four stratification rhythms: a bedding rhythm (a) in the dm range, a periodicity (b) in the half-m range, a bundling of beds (c) in the 1 m range, and a rhythm (d) in the 4-8 m range.

(2) While a variety of factors can be called on to produce these rhythms, all are ultimately controlled by climate. We conclude that the rocks record a hierarchy of four climatic rhythms. Are these related to the four orbital cycles?

(3) Periods of these rhythms cannot be accurately measured by radiometry. However, the Obradovich-Cobban value of 4 m.y. for the Cenomanian, also adopted by Odin, yields periods that roughly match the bundle with the short cycle of eccentricity and the bedding rhythm with the precession. If the bundle is normalized to 100 000 years (Table 3) the mean period of the half-meter cycle is 42 573 years, and that of the bedding 21 700 years.

(4) A comparison of the fine structure of the calculated insolation cycle of ca. 100 000 years with the bedding structure of the bundles (Fig. 2) shows good correlation: times when insolation lows are probable, as calculated from present-day orbital parameters, correspond to times when the probability of carbonate interruptions (bedding planes) is observed to have been high.

(5) These observations support the view that Cretaceous climates were linked to orbital variations, much as were Pleistocene climates. This implies that the non-glacial Earth responds to orbital forcing in much the same manner as the glacial Earth. It also implies that the orbital periods have not changed drastically in the last 100 m.y.

ACKNOWLEDGMENT

Our work has been supported by National Science Foundation Grants EAR-8107648A01 and INT-815265.

REFERENCES

1. Gilbert, G.K. : 1895, J. of Geology 3, pp. 121-127.
2. Sander, B. : 1937, Tschermaks Mineralogische und Petrographische Mitteilungen 48, pp. 27-139 (Engl. transl. American Assoc. Petrol. Geol., 1951).
3. Einsele, G. : 1982, in : "Cyclic and Event Stratification", G. Einsele and A. Seilacher (Eds), Springer Verlag, pp. 8-53.
4. Goodwin, P.W., and Anderson, E.J. : 1982, in : "Punctuated Aggradational Cycles and Carbonate Facies", G.M. Friedman et al. (Eds), Helderberg Group, New York State, 11th International Congress on Sedimentology, Field Excursion Notebook 17A, Hamilton, Ontario.
5. Bradley, W.H. : 1929, "The varves and climate of the Green River epoch", U.S. Geological Survey Professional Paper 645, 108, pp. 45 pls.
6. Olsen, P.E. : 1984 , in : "Milankovitch and Climate", A. Berger, J. Imbrie, J. Hays, G. Kukla, B. Saltzman (Eds), Reidel Publ. Company, Holland. This volume, p. 129.
7. Anderson, R.Y. : 1982, J. Geophys. Res. 87, pp. 7285-7294.
8. Fischer, A.G. : 1964, in : "The Lofer Cyclothems of the Alpine Triassic", D.F. Merriam (Ed), Symposium on Cyclic Sedimentation, Kansas Geological Survey Bull. 169, pp. 107-150.
9. de Boer, P.L. : 1982 : in : "Cyclic and Event Stratification", G. Einsele and A. Seilacher (Eds), Springer Verlag, pp. 456-475.
10. de Boer, P.L. and Wonders, A.A.H. : 1984 , in : "Milankovitch and Climate", A. Berger, J. Imbrie, J. Hays, G. Kukla, B. Saltzman (Eds), Reidel Publ. Company, Holland. This volume, p. 177.
11. Schwarzacher, W. : 1954, Tschermaks Mineralogische und Petrographische Mitteilungen ser. 3, 4, pp. 44-54.
12. Schwarzacher, W. : 1975, "Sedimentation Models and Quantitative Stratigraphy. Elsevier Publ. Co., 377 pp.

13. Schwarzacher, W., and Fischer, A.G. : 1982, in : "Cyclic and Event Stratification", G. Einsele and A. Seilacher (Eds), Springer Verlag, pp. 78-95.
14. Arthur, M.A., and Fischer, A.G. : 1977, Geological Society of America Bull. 88, pp. 367-371.
15. Arthur, M.A. : 1979, "Sedimentologic and geochemical studies of Cretaceous and Paleogene pelagic sedimentary rocks : the Gubbio sequence". Dissertation, Princeton University, part 1, 174pp.
16. Blytt, A. : 1889, "The probable cause of the displacement of beach lines, an atttempt to compute geological epochs". Videnskabs-Selkabs Forhandl., Christiania, 1883, n.1, 93pp.
17. Anderson, R.Y. : 1984, in : "Milankovitch and Climate", A. Berger, J. Imbrie, J. Hays, G. Kukla, B. Saltzman (Eds), Reidel Publ. Company, Holland. This volume.
18. Harland, W.B., Smith, A.G., and Wilcock, B. (Eds) : 1964, in : "The Phanerozoic Time-Scale", Geological Society of London, Special Publ. no5.
19. Odin, G.S. : 1892, Episodes 3, pp. 3-9.
20. Napoleone, G., Premoli, S.I., Heller, P.C., Corezzi, S., and Fischer, A.G. : 1983, Geological Society of America Bull., in press.
21. Kauffman, E.G. : 1977, The Mountain Geologist 14, pp. 75-274.
22. Obradovich, J.D., and Cobban, W.A. : 1975, "A time scale for the late Cretaceous of the western interior of North America", Geological Association of Canada Special Paper 13, pp. 31-54.
23. Van Hinte, J. : 1976, Bull. A.A.P.G. 60, pp. 498-516.
24. Fischer, A.G. : 1980, in : "The Scientific Ideas of G.K. Gilbert", E. Yochelson (Ed.), Geological Society of America Special paper 183, pp. 93-104.
25. Premoli, S.I., Paggi, L., and Monecchi, S. : 1977, Memorie, Societa Geologica Italiana 13, pp. 31-32.
26. Berger, A.L. : 1978, Contribution 18, Université Catholique de Louvain, Institut d'Astronomie et de Géophysique G. Lemaître, 17pp.
27. Fischer, A.G. : 1981, in : "Biotic Crises in Ecologic and Evolutionary Time", M. Nitecki (Ed.), Academic Press, pp. 103-131.

ASTRONOMICALLY INDUCED RHYTHMIC BEDDING IN CRETACEOUS PELAGIC SEDIMENTS NEAR MORIA (ITALY)

P. L. de Boer[1], A. A. H. Wonders[2]

[1]Comparative Sedimentology Division, Institute of Earth Sciences, Box 80.021, 3508 TA Utrecht, the Nederlands. (rep. nr 41)
[2]B. P. Research Centre, Chertsey Road, TW16 7LN Sunbury-on-Thames, United Kingdom

ABSTRACT

A Late Albian/Cenomanian pelagic sedimentary succession in the Umbrian Apennines (Italy) contains limestone-marl couplets which cover a mean depositional cycle period of 20 000 years. The thickness distribution pattern of the successive carbonate rich beds shows a clear correspondence to the present pattern of astronomically induced climatic changes at low latitudes, as e.g. related to successively extreme latitudinal positions of the caloric equator.

Relating variations of the carbonate content in the sediments to the fluctuations of biogenic carbonate production in the surface waters of the Middle Cretaceous Tethys Ocean and to variations of atmospheric circulation and of circulation intensity of ocean waters, caused by astronomically induced climatic changes, it is suggested that the rhythmicity of the sequence was controlled by astronomical variables, primarily by precession related fluctuations of distribution and intensity of solar radiation.

The suggested link between astronomical parameters and bedding rhythmicity permits estimates of the duration of stratigraphic intervals, and of the rates of geologic, biologic and other processes. The obvious possibility that astronomic frequencies change in the course of geologic time, urges to consider such estimates as tentative figures which allow for mutual

A. L. Berger et al. (eds.), Milankovitch and Climate, Part 1, 177–190.

comparisons of the length of adjacent stratigraphic intervals. They should not be taken as absolute time determinations defined in terms of present-day time constants.

INTRODUCTION

Rhythmic alternations in carbonate content and other characters of pelagic sediments are found in many stratigraphic intervals. Suggested mechanisms for the formation of such sequences include variations in the supply of the sediment components, dissolution, and diagenetic processes. For a review about the ideas and literature on this subject see Einsele (1). Mean periodicities of near 20 000, 40 000 and/or 100 000 years have been calculated for deposition of individual carbonate-marl couplets in the Cretaceous and Lower Tertiary of the Apennines (2, 3) for pelagic sediments drilled in the open ocean (4 - 6), for Triassic shallow marine carbonates in the Northern Alps (7, 8) and for Eocene (9) and Triassic lacustrine sediments (10, 11) in U.S.A.. Frequently reference is made by the authors to astronomical influences as a possible cause of the rhythmicity which was found.

The above periodicities are also found in the parameters which define the orbital elements precession, obliquity and eccentricity (cf. 12).

In order to test the hypothetical relationship between sedimentary rhythmicity and astronomical variables, a Cretaceous pelagic sequence in the Umbrian Apennines (Italy), consisting of limestone-marl alternations, was measured and sampled for micropaleontological, calcimetric and statitical analyses.

LOCATION, LITHOLOGY AND ZONATION

The studied section (Fig. 1; 43°33'N; 12°42'E) is a complete exposure along the road to the summit of the Monte Petrano, near the cemetery of Moria, a small village near Cagli, province of Pesaro and Urbino. The Middle Cretaceous sequence in Umbria has been subject of study by previous authors (3, 13 - 15).

The 75 meters discussed here (Fig. 1), comprise the transition from the _Scisti a Fucoidi_ to the overlying _Scaglia Bianca_. The upper part of the Scisti a Fucoidi consists of regularly alternating thin marls (light-grey to black) and marly limestones (light-grey to almost white). Both contain ichnofossils of the _Chondrites_-type ("fucoidi"), which are especially frequent in the marls. Often the marls are darker coloured in the middle

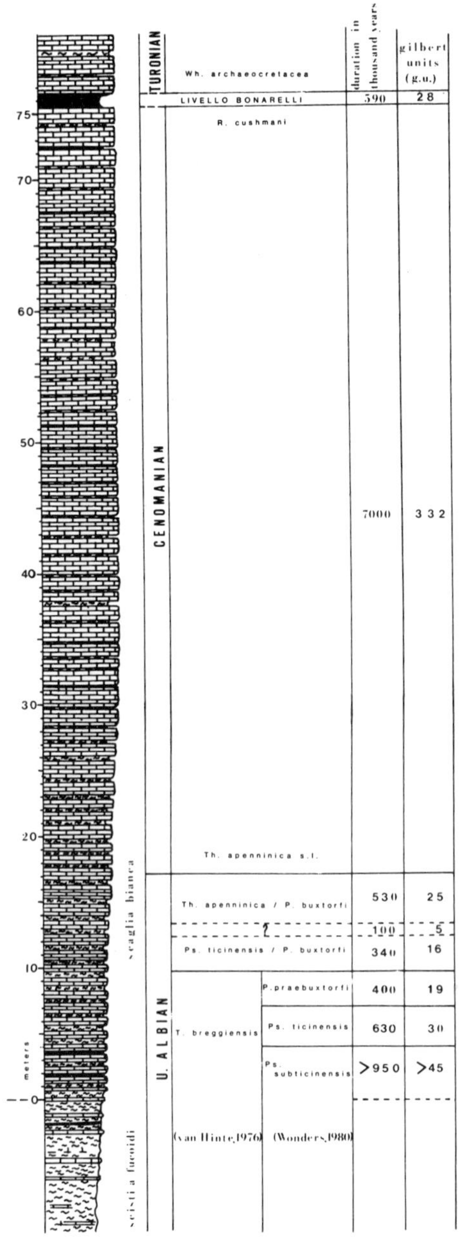

Figure 1. Columnar section of the interval studied near Moria, showing schematic lithology, planktonic foraminiferal zonation and duration of stratigraphic intervals in 1000 years based on the tentative assignment of a 21 000 year period for each of the carbonate-marl rhythms.

of the beds than at the rims, and they are sometimes completely black. This can be the result of the presence of pyrite rather than of abundant organic matter (16).

The contacts between marl and limestone beds are gradational. The transition from the Scisti a Fucoidi to the overlying "Scaglia Bianca" is gradual, and involves an increase of average carbonate content and a lightening of colour.

The regularly bedded limestones of the Scaglia Bianca have thickness of one to a few decimeters, and are separated by very thin to centimeter thick marly interbeds, mostly with gradational contacts. They were deposited in the open ocean at a depth of one to two kilometres, well above the carbonate compensation depth (C.C.D.; the level in the ocean below which calcite dissolves) (14), which was at some 3 to 4 km in that time (17, 18). Indeed, foraminifera are well preserved, suggesting that dissolution has not sgnificantly reduced the original amount of calcite. Electron microscopy shows that the larger part of the carbonate consists of calcareous nannofossils. The percentage of carbonate in the sequence generally varies between 60 and 80%, the limestone beds containing 5 - 15% more $CaCO_3$ than adjacent marly intervals. The contrast between "carbonate-rich" and "carbonate-poor" or marly intervals in the Scisti a Fucoidi and in the lower part of the Scaglia Bianca, as seen in the outcrop, has been much enhanced by weathering. Differences in $CaCO_3$ content as small as 5 to 10% allow weathering out of massive ledges separated by "shaly" slopes.

In fresh exposures, created by the removal of some decimetres of sediment, the difference is less clear or not visible at all. Beds with mass-flow phenomena were found only occasionally.

Stratigraphically the studied sequence extends from the Late Albian (Pseudothalmanninella subticinensis Zone) to the Cenomanian-Turonian boundary marked by the Livello Bonarelli (Whiteinella archaeocretacea Zone).

The good preservation of planktonic foraminifera in most of the sequence allows for a detailed zonation. All the zones described by Wonders (19) from Southern Spain were recognized, from the Ps. subticinensis Zone (Wonders, (14); = middle part of the Ticinella breggiensis Zone of van Hinte (20) to the top of the Thalmanninella appenninica - Planomalina buxtorfi Zone. As most zonal boundaries are defined by evolutionary appearances and because gradations from one species to the other could be traced from bed to bed, the record of this interval near Moria appears to be complete. The Cenomanian part of the section was not studied in detail, but from previous studies it is known that the Scaglia Bianca probably is a continuous and complete sequence of Cenomanian pelagic sediments (13, 14). For the Albian part of the section the number of bedding rhythms per zone is almost exactly known (Fig. 1), for the Cenomanian the accurate positions of zonal boundaries in relation to the sequence of bedding rhythms were not established in the present study.

In the entire studied section, which covers a timespan of the order of 8 to 11 Ma (on the basis of radiometric dating ; see Fig. 4), 472 marl-limestones couplets were counted (Fig. 1). This yields a mean cycle duration in the range of 17 000 to 26 300 years.

CARBONATE CONTENT AND THICKNESS OF THE BEDS

Calcimetric analysis of the lower 135 couplets reveal that the thickness of the carbonate-marl couplets (calculated as the thickness of each carbonate bed plus half of the thickness of the two adjacent marly beds) is positively correlated with the carbonate content (Fig. 2). The absolute amount of HCl-insoluble matter, inclusive biogenic silica, in each carbonate-marl couplet found in this calculation may fluctuate considerably, but it is of subordinate influence on the thickness of the couplets. On the average the insoluble residue accounts for about 3.1 cm (st. dev. 1.1 cm) of the total thickness of the carbonate-marl couplets. Processes such as dissolution and reprecipitation of carbonate are unlikely to cause the rhythmicity in the sequence because of the good preservation of foraminifera, the small differences of $CaCO_3$ content between the "limestones" and "marls", and because of the stable oxygen isotope ratios of carbonate. These generally show lower values in the marly intervals whereas in the case of a diagenetic redistribution of carbonate they would have shown lower values in the limestone beds (21). It is, therefore, suggested that this sedimentary sequence is the result of a relatively continuous and regular sedimentation of inorganic non-carbonate sediment, with a regulary fluctuating sypply of carbonate.

As stated above, the stable oxygen isotope ratios of carbonate are generally higher in "limestone" beds than in adjacent marly intervals. This points to differences of temperature during time of formation of some few degrees, with the limestone beds having been formed during periods with "cooler" surface waters (21).

The production of biogenic carbonate depends on the amount of nutrients available. In the open ocean, the supply of

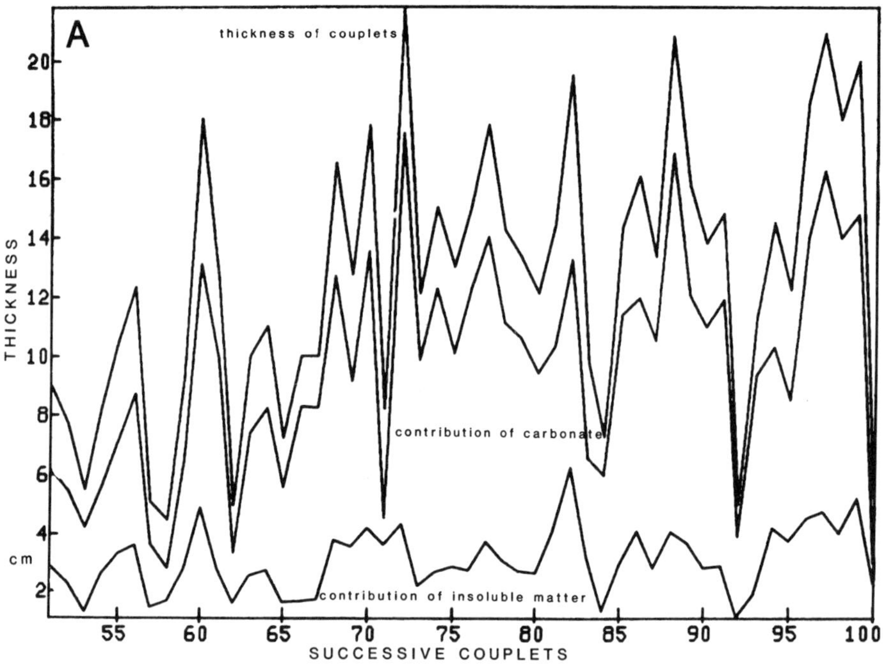

Figure 2. Upper curve : Thicknesses of the lower 100 carbonate-marl couplets in the Moria section, calculated as the thickness of the carbonate-rich beds plus half the under- and overlying carbonate-poor intervals. Middle curve : Contribution of carbonate to these thickness values. Lower curve : Contribution of insoluble matter to these thickness values.

nutrients to the surface waters, with resulting production andsinking of carbonate is a function of circulation intensity. It is obvious to relate the relatively low temperature of formation of the carbonate in the limestone ("carbonate-rich") beds to a better mixing of ocean waters with a relatively high nutrient supply.

ASTRONOMICAL INFLUENCES AND REGULARITY OF FLUCTUATIONS OF BEDDING THICKNESS

Changing orbital parameters of the Earth have been suggested as a possible cause of climatic change long ago (22). Hays et al. (23) established a correlation between changes in insolation at the top of the Earth's atmosphere resulting from changes in the astronomical variables, and the global ice volume during the last few 100 000 years as determined by oxygen isotopic analysis of deep sea cores. However, only 50 to 70% of the variance of the ice volume record can be ascribed to variations of astronomical parameters (24), and the correlations found, mainly concern variances at 19 000 and 23 000 years (precession cycle) and 41 000 years (obliquity cycle). The rather weak correlation is explained by the fact that ice sheet/bedrock dynamics have a large response time, leading to a cycle period of about 100 000 years, and thus reduce variations of orbital parameters to a trigger mechanism for the start of growth and melting of the northern-hemisphere ice sheets (25 - 27). Due to the inertia of ice sheet/bedrock dynamics, the large amplitude of climatic changes at the middle and high latitudes during the subrecent geological history seems to be mainly the result of the very process of growth and melting of the icecaps, obscuring the influence of varying orbital parameters.

As stated earlier, given the 8 to 11 Ma timespan of the 472 carbonate-marl units in the studied sequence, a mean duration of 16 000 to 26 000 years can be calculated for each carbonate-marl couplet. This period is suggestive of astronomical influences.

Thicknesses of the lowermost 150 carbonate-rich beds from the Moria section, where they were best exposed and least disturbed by weathering, by diagenetic and/or tectonic processes, have been spectrally analysed according to the method of Jenkins and Watts (28). As stated by these authors, such analysis does not necessarily imply an assumption of equal time elapsed between successive levels. Consequently, spectral analysis of the thickness pattern of the carbonate-rich beds does not stand for a priori assignment of equal timespans to the successive carbonate-marl couplets. The analysis (Fig. 3, shaded) reveals a dominant and significant peak at a frequency of 0.23, indicating a repetition of a thickness distribution pattern with a periodicity of about 4.3 carbonate-rich beds (CRB). The value of 4.3 found in the spectral analysis, equals the present ratio between the mean period of the eccentricity cycle (100 000 years) and the most important period of the precession cycle (23 000 years). This agreement, however, only relates to the relative time ratios and does not necessarily mean that the average time period represented by the carbonate-marl rhythms was same as it is today. The frequencies of both astronomical features, measured in present day time constants, may have changed during the last 100 Ma.

Analysing the thicknesses of only the carbonate beds implies a strong aliasing. Spectral analysis allows only the recognition of periods amounting more than twice the period of the sample interval, which is, in this case, of the order of 20 kyr. The most obvious periodicity in the carbonate signal seen in the field (the thickness and the related $CaCO_3$-content of the carbonate-rich beds) was taken as the basis for the analysis, and therefore, the spectral analysis only reveals the modulation of the thicknesses of the successive carbonate-rich beds, separated by marly intervals. That is, only periods of more than about 40 kyr can be detected by this method.

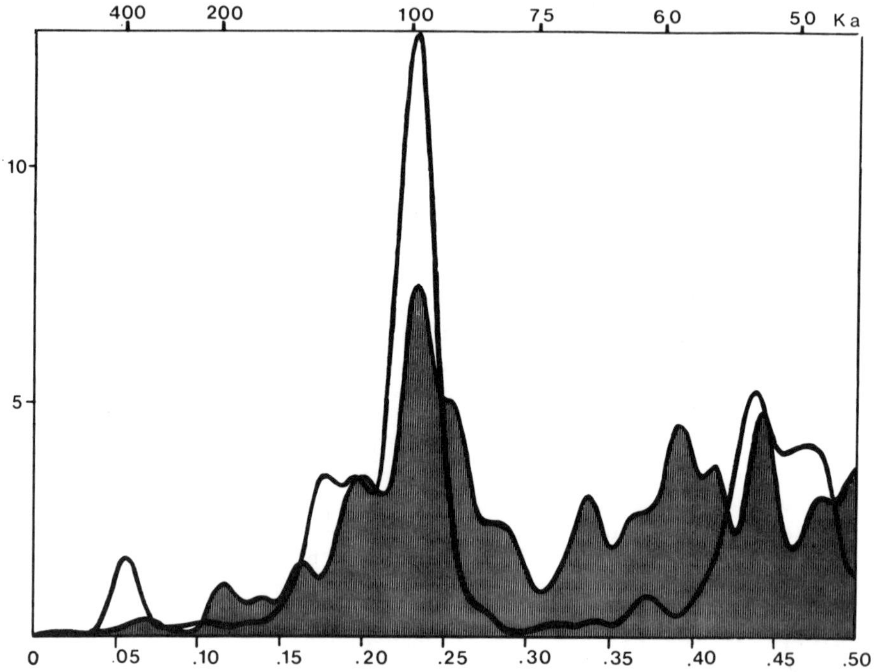

Figure 3. Spectral density curves; unshaded curve with highest peak value is the frequency spectrum of the successively extreme latitudinal positions of the caloric equator. The above time scale indicates periods based on astronomical data for present day. The shaded curve is the spectral distribution of thickness data of a series of carbonate-rich pelagic beds (nrs 1-150, Fig. 1) from the Middle Cretaceous (100 Ma BP) in Umbria.

In order to further check the possible relation to astronomical influences, a model curve, indicative of the impact of astronomical variables upon climate at low latitudes, was generated, from the astronomical parameters as given by Berger (12). It closely resembles the changing position of the caloric equator in degrees latitudes N and S of the geographic equator vs. time (cf. Figure 3 of Berger, 12b). Berger states that the caloric equator is a perfect integrator of the precession and obliquity effects at low latitudes. Since the present phases were not taken into consideration, the curve does not stand for any special time interval, but rather represents the general behaviour of the caloric equator over millions of years, based on present-day "constants". From the model curve, the heights of the successive peaks, resembling the successively most northerly (or southerly) latitudinal positions of the caloric equator in time, separated from each other by timespans in the range of about 15 000 to 27 000 years, were subjected to the same spectral analytical technique as applied to the field data. The resulting spectral density curve (Fig. 3 unshaded), and the one based on the field data show a good resemblance.

These results support the idea that the analysed rhythmic limestone-marl alternations from the Middle Cretaceous sequence in Umbria do reflect the influence of astronomical parameters upon pelagic sedimentation. They suggest that the Middle Cretaceous (100 Ma ago) sedimentary rhythms in Umbria are related to astronomic influences upon climate, with the precession cycle being the major tuner. Moreover the data suggest that the ratio between the major periodicities of the eccentricity and the precession was similar to that of the present day.

ASTRONOMICAL INFLUENCES UPON CLIMATE AND SEDIMENTATION

The ultimate cause of all movements in the ocean is the supply of solar energy (29). Orbital parameters produce differences in the intensity and distribution of solar radiation on the surface of the Earth, which e.g. results in regular shifts of the caloric equator in between about 10°N and 10°S with a mean periodicity of, at present, about 21 000 years (12). Changes of the distribution and the intensity of insolation lead to changes of atmospheric circulation patterns. It was stated that due to the influence of orbital parameters, climatic contrasts at about 30°N should have been much larger 9 000 years ago than at present (30). Astronomical data predict that solar radiation would have been about 7% higher during summer and 7 to 8% lower during winter as compared to the present day (30). The amplified seasonal cycle of solar radiation would have caused an intensified monsoon circulation during the Northern Hemisphere summer.

If the behaviour of the orbital elements during the Cretaceous has been comparable to that of the present day, as was suggested above, then comparable changes of the position of the caloric equator, of summer-winter contrasts and of monsoon circulation intensity should have occured (see also 31). Such changes must have influenced the circulation and the stratification of ocean waters.

Following the interpretation of the limestone-marl cycles in the Middle Cretaceous of the Apennines, given above, these factors should have influenced the temperature of surface waters, the circulation intensity and, through the circulation controlled supply of nutrients to surface waters, the production of biogenic carbonate. It thus is obvious to relate the limestone-marl cycles to astronomic influences.

Climate influences the character of many sedimentary environments. The influence of astronomically induced changing climatic conditions upon the sedimentation in Triassic lakes, represented by alternating evaporitic and normal lacustrine deposits as the result of a changing proportion between precipitation and evaporation was suggested earlier by Bradley (9). The typical colour bandings in paleosol profiles present in sedimentary successions at many places also invite to look for possible relations to astronomically defined climatic changes.

TIMESCALE

In Figure 1 the number of bedding rhythms present in the studied stratigraphic interval in the Middle Cretaceous pelagic series in the Apennines is given. On the basis of the apparent resemblance of the pattern of thickness distribution of the carbonate-rich beds to the present behaviour of the caloric equator and of long-term changes in summer winter contrast, with the cycles of precession and eccentricity as the most important defining factors (Fig. 3), it is attractive to give estimates of the timespan covered by each of the stratigraphic intervals

Consequently, in terms of the present-day average period of 21 000 years of the cycle of precession, the data would suggest that the interval between the base of the Th. appenninica Zone in the Upper Albian to the top of the Cenomanian would span 7 Ma, the Ps. ticinensis Zone 0.63 Ma, the P. praebuxtorfi Zone 0.40 Ma, the Ps. ticinensis/P. buxtorfi Zone 0.39 (±0.05) Ma, the Th. appenninica/P. buxtorfi Zone 0.58 (± 0.05) Ma, and that the Cenomanian/Turonian "oceanic anoxic event" lasted 0.6 Ma.

However, for several reasons care should be taken. First, the number of bedding rhythms measured in each of the stratigraphic intervals was derived from only one section. Measurements were made with fair accuracy, but errors, either subjective or because of the presence of noise in the sedimentary record can not be excluded. Secondly there is the question if the astronomic parameters as measured for the present are valid also for periods as far as 100 Ma ago. Changes of the order of some few percent as observed e.g. in the rotational velocity of the Earth (32) should not be excluded.

The data presented here suggest that the ratios between the different astronomical periods during the Middle Cretaceous are comparable to those of the present day. This, however, does not imply that the periods themselves were equal to the present ones. From Figure 4 and from literature data it is obvious that, as yet, modern radiometric dating techniques can not give an explicit answer to this question. Using different existing time-scales leads to considerable differences in the estimates of astronomical periodicities in the past. Therefore it seems useful to introduce a chronology independent of present day time constants. The duration of stratigraphic zones based on the counting of precession induced rhythmic sedimentary cycles can be expressed in relative time units. We propose the term "gilbert unit", after Gilbert (1895) who was the first to recognize the importance of astronomical influences upon pelagic sedimentary facies, and who was successful in giving a fairly precise estimate for the duration of the Late Cretaceous (33). A "gilbert unit" is defined as a climatostratigraphic unit which represents the (variable) time period between successive extreme climate conditions at low latitudes of the order of (at present) 21 000 years, induced by the precession cycle. For example, in time, two extreme latitudinal positions (North or South) of the caloric equator would be separated by one gilbert unit. In the same way, successive extremes of the summer - winter contrast at latitudes of around 30° would fit to this property (cf. 12, 30).

These features are defined mainly by the astronomic factor $e \sin \omega$ (where e is the eccentricity and ω the longitude of the perihelion; 12). The obliquity of the earth's axis is of minor importance at low latitudes, but with increasing latitude it gains importance (12). This implies that features such as described in this paper are to be expected only at latitudes lower than about 50 degrees (cf. Fig. 2 in Berger, 12b).

In order to get a reflection of astronomical influences upon a sediment, a sensitive sedimentary facies is needed to allow the relatively small, astronomically induced, climatic changes to leave a recognizable trace. The fact that periodicities reminding of astronomical influences are often found at latitudes of about 30 degrees (2-11) suggests that such sensitivity is especially there. Indeed, at present the boundary between tropical and subtropical climates, and the subtropical convergence in the ocean is found close to this latitude. It is obvious to relate the cyclicity described in this paper to changes of character and/or of intensity of oceanic circulation, induced by astronomical influences. Similarly, astronomically induced rhythmicities in continental deposits seem to be defined

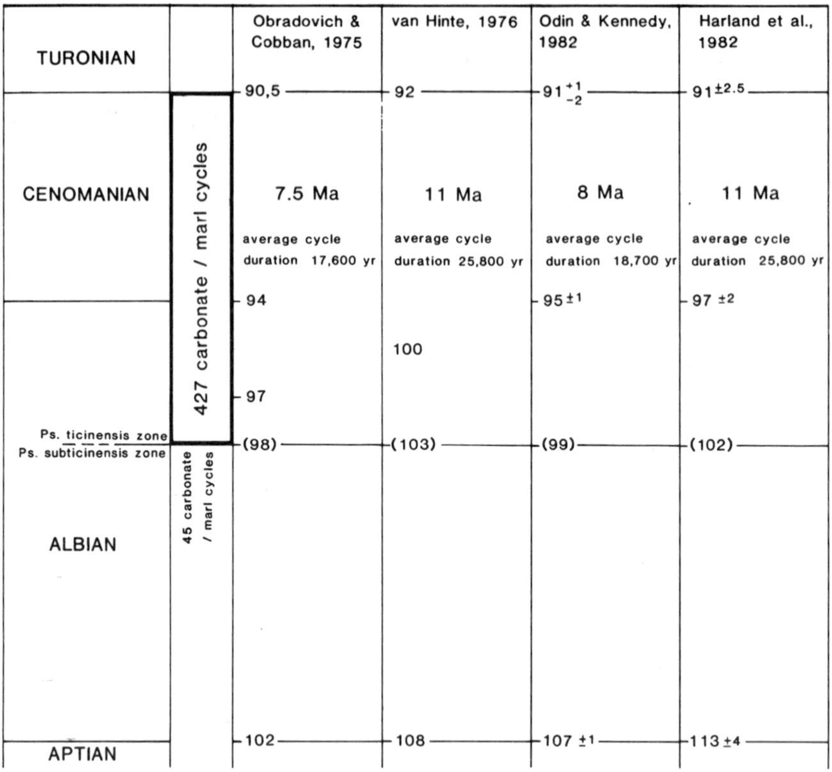

TURONIAN
CENOMANIAN
Ps. ticinensis zone
Ps. subticinensis zone
ALBIAN
APTIAN
427 carbonate / marl cycles
45 carbonate / marl cycles
Obradovich & Cobban, 1975
van Hinte, 1976
Odin & Kennedy, 1982
Harland et al., 1982
90,5
92
91 +1 -2
91±2.5
7.5 Ma
11 Ma
8 Ma
11 Ma
average cycle duration 17,600 yr
average cycle duration 25,800 yr
average cycle duration 18,700 yr
average cycle duration 25,800 yr
94
95±1
97 ±2
100
97
(98)
(103)
(99)
(102)
102
108
107 ±1
113±4

Figure 4 Estimates of the timespan covered by 472 limestone-marl cycles in the Upper Albian and Cenomanian near Moria in the Apennines, and of the mean time-span covered by individual limestone-marl cycles, based on estimates of absolute age by several authors. Age estimates between brackets were derived by interpolation of these latter data. The rough average of these estimates and those of other authors is about 22 000 years. The lower 45 cycles were not involved in the calculation, whereas the basis of the Ps. subticinensis zone of which these form part, was not established.

by climate related changes of the ratio between precipitation and evaporation.

ACKNOWLEDGEMENTS

We are greatly indebted to P. Marks and G. van Graas for cooperation during the fieldwork which was financially supported by the Netherlands Organisation for the advancement of pure research (Z.W.O.). We acknowledge the reviews of successive drafts of this paper by P. Marks, A.L. Berger, A.G. Fischer, J.E. van Hinte, M.A. Arthur, G.E. Birchfield and S.O. Schlanger.

REFERENCES

1. Einsele, G.: 1982, in: "Cyclic and event stratification", Einsele G. & Seilacher, A. (Eds.), Springer, pp. 8-53.
2. Arthur, M.A.: 1977, Mem. Soc. Geol. It. 15, pp. 9-20.
3. Arthur, M.A. and Fischer, A.G.: 1977, Bull. Geol. Soc. Am. 88, pp. 367-371.
4. Dean, W.E., Gardner, J.V. and Jansa, L.F.: 1977, in: "Initial Reports of the Deep Sea Drilling Project Vol. 41 ", Lancelot, Y. ,Seibold, E. et al. (Eds.), Wash., U.S. Governm. Printing Office, pp. 965-989.
5. Arthur, M.A.: 1979, in: "Init. Rep. D.S.D.P. 47/2 ",Ryan, W.B.F. & Sibuet, J.C. (Eds.), pp. 719-738.
6. McCave, I.N.: 1979, in: "Initial Reports of the Deep Sea Drilling Project Vol. 43 ", Tucholke, B., Vogt, P. et al. (Eds.), pp.411-416.
7. Schwarzacher, W.: 1954, Tchermaks Mineral. Petrograph. Mitt. 4, pp. 44-54.
8. Fischer, A.G.: 1964, Kansas Geol. Survey Bull. 169, pp. 107-149.
9. Bradley, W.H.: 1929, U.S. Geol. Surv. Pap.158-E, pp. 87-110.
10. van Houten, F.B.: 1964, Kansas Geol. Survey Bull. 169, pp. 497-531.
11. Olsen, P.E. , Remington, C.L. , Cornet, B. and Thompson, K.S. : 1978, Science 201, pp. 729-733.
12. Berger, A.L.: 1978a, J. Atm. Sci. 35, pp. 2362-2367.
Berger, A.L.: 1978b, Quat. Res. 9, pp.139-167.
13. Premoli Silva, I. and Paggi, L.: 1977, Mem. Soc. Geol. It. 15, pp. 21-32.
14. Wonders, A.A.H.: 1980, Utrecht Micropal. Bull. 24, pp. 157 p.
15. Arthur, M.A. and Premoli Silva, I.: 1982, in: "Nature and origin of Cretaceous carbon-rich facies", Schlanger, S.O. and Cita, M.B. (Eds.), Acad. Press, pp. 7-54.
16. van Graas, G.: 1982, in: "Organic geochemistry of Cretaceous black shale deposits from Italy and France", Thesis, Delft Univ. Press, 95 pp.
17. van Andel, T.H.: 1975, Earth Plan. Sci. Lett. 26, pp. 187-194.

18. Winterer, E.L. and Bosellini, A.: 1981, Bull. A.A.P.G. 65, pp. 394-421.
19. Wonders, A.A.H.: 1975, Proc. Kon. Ned. Akad. Wet. Series B. (78) 2, pp. 83-93.
20. van Hinte, J.: 1976, Bull. A.A.P.G. 60, pp. 498-516.
21. de Boer, P.L.: 1982, in: "Nature and origin of Cretaceous carbon-rich facies", Schlanger, S.O. and Cita, M.B. (Eds.), Acad. Press, pp. 129-143.
22. Croll, J.: 1864, Philos. Mag. 28, pp. 121-137.
23. Hays, J.D., Imbrie, J. and Shackleton, N.J.: 1975, Science 194, pp. 1121-1132.
24. Berger, A. , Guiot, J. , Kukla, G. and Pestiaux, P.: 1981, Geol. Rundsch. 70, pp. 748-758.
25. Oerlemans, J.: 1980, Nature 287, pp. 430-432.
26. Birchfield, G.E. , Weertman, J. and Lunde, A.T.: 1981, Quatern. Res. 15, pp. 126-142.
27. Moore, T.C. , Pisias, N.G. and Dunn, D.A.: 1982, Marine Geol. 46, pp. 217-233.
28. Jenkins, G.M. and Watts, D.G.: 1968, "Spectral analysis and its applications", Holden-day, San Francisco, 525 pp.
29. Defant, A.: 1961, "Physical Oceanography", vol. 1, Pergamon, 729 pp.
30. Kutzbach, J.E. and Otto-Bliesner, B.L.: 1982, J. Atm. Sci. 39, pp. 1177-1188.
31. Lloyd, C.R. : 1982, J. Geol. 90, pp. 393-413.
32. Pannella, G. : 1972, Astrophys. and Space Sci. 16, pp. 212-237.
33. Fischer, A.G. : 1980, G.S.A. Spec. Pap. 183, pp. 93-104.
34. Odin, G.S., and Kennedy, W.J. : 1982, C.R. Acad. Sc. Paris t. 294, serie II, pp. 383-386.
35. Obradovich, J., and Cobban, W.A. : 1975, Geol. Assoc. Can. Spec. Paper 13, pp. 31-54.
36. Harland, W.B., Cox, A.V., Llewellyn, P.G., Pickton, C.A.G., Smith, A.G., and Walters, R. : 1982, A geologic time scale. Cambr. Univ. Pr.110p.

RHYTHMIC BEDDING IN MESOZOIC-CENOZOIC PELAGIC CARBONATE SEQUENCES: THE PRIMARY AND DIAGENETIC ORIGIN OF MILANKOVITCH-LIKE CYCLES

M.A. Arthur[1], W.E. Dean[2], D. Bottjer[3], P.A. Scholle[2]

[1]Department of Geology, University of South Carolina, Columbia, SC 29208, USA. (now at: Graduate School of Oceanography, University of Rhode Island, Narragansett, R.I. 02882)
[2]U.S. Geological Survey, Box 25046, Denver Federal Center, Denver, CO 80225, USA
[3]Department of Geological Sciences, University of Southern California, Los Angeles, CA 90089, USA

ABSTRACT

Rhythmicity is a pronounced characteristic of nearly all Cretaceous and Cenozoic pelagic carbonate sequences whether deposited in shallow or deep-water environments. Intercalation of carbonate-rich and carbonate-poor beds, on the order of tens of centimeters thick, are particularly common in environments where there is also an abundant supply of clay. In anoxic or marginally oxic depositional environments, intervals of oxygen-depletion are periodic as well, and enrichment of organic carbon occurs in the relatively clay-rich intervals. In highly compacted pure chalks, the rhythmicity is reflected by decimeter-thick limestone beds separated by thin stylolitic seams. The estimated average periodicities of all most obvious types of cycles in Cretaceous-Cenozoic pelagic strata usually are either about 20 kyr or 40 kyr; groups of beds ("bundles") often form less obvious cycles with periods of 100 kyr. This is in contrast to the dominant 100 kyr periodicity in some Quaternary pelagic carbonate sediments. However, because of presently inadequate absolute time-scales for the Mesozoic, the exact periodicities are difficult to establish.

Glacial-interglacial changes in rates of deep-water production in high latitudes and consequent changes in carbonate dissolution probably cannot be called upon to explain the cyclicity

A. L. Berger et al. (eds.), Milankovitch and Climate, Part 1, 191–222.

in Cretaceous strata deposited during a period of globally warm climate. We propose, however, that periodic changes in insolation, evaporation, wind stress, and/or rainfall in a wide variety of environments caused changes in input of terrigenous detritus, water mass stratification, surface productivity, deepwater oxygen content, and rates of carbonate dissolution. A number of lines of evidence, including stable isotope and geochemical profiles across individual cycles support these inferences. The importance of different climate-related forcing mechanisms may have varied between depositional environments (e.g., different deep ocean basins or shallow epicontinental seas) and between paleolatitudes, but the overall periodicities are the same, and the manifestations in lithologies are similar regardless of the mechanism that caused the cycles. Cycles in pelagic carbonate sequences with Milankovitch-like periodicities are typical of all periods of time from at least the Late Jurassic to the present. Unfortunately, diagenesis commonly renders the cycles unsuitable for study of primary environmental signals, and progress in understanding the causes of such cyclicity will be slow.

INTRODUCTION

Most pelagic carbonate sequences of Jurassic through Quaternary age are characterized by rhythmic alternations of relatively more and less calcareous beds on the order of a few to tens of centimeters thick. Quaternary carbonate cycles in the deep sea have been attributed mainly to cyclic fluctuations in carbonate dissolution and/or periodic dilution by terrigenous material. Variations in productivity of phyto- and zooplankton also may be important, but as yet have not been convincingly deciphered in the sedimentary record. Substantial evidence now exists to ultimately link the cycles to changes in climate that are induced by periodic variations in the earth's orbit and axis of rotation (1-3) as long ago proposed by Croll (4). The major solar-terrestrial orbital cycles that have been correlated to climate and carbonate stratigraphy have average periodicities of 23 kyr, 41 kyr and 100 kyr (5-7). There is much more difficulty however, in demonstrating that similar pre-Quaternary carbonate cycles are of primary (i.e. depositional) origin, that the cycles are periodic with frequencies corresponding to the orbital parameters defined by Milankovitch (5), and that the origin of the cycles (causal mechanism) can be linked to orbital variations, particularly in buried, compacted and lithified pelagic sequences. These difficulties arise mainly because of inadequate absolute time scales and the postdepositional effects of bioturbation and diagenesis.

The purpose of this paper is to briefly review evidence that the ubiquitous carbonate cycles in Mesozoic-Cenozoic pelagic sequences are indeed primary and quasi-periodic, with periods of between 20 and 50 kyr that correspond to Milankovitch frequences of orbital cycles. We discuss evidence that the primary carbonate cycles frequently are enhanced, modified, or even obliterated during diagenesis. Most pre-Pleistocene cycles have estimated periods of between 20 and 50 kyr, and most likely are due to climatically induced changes in detrital influx (terrigenous dilution), in the rate of carbonate dissolution, or possibly in depositional energy. Variations in productivity of calcareous plankton also are plausible but more difficult to demonstrate.

DESCRIPTION OF RHYTHMIC BEDDING AND EVIDENCE FOR PRIMARY ORIGIN

Cyclic alternations of more- and less-argillaceous carbonate beds are common to most pelagic sequences deposited in both Jurassic-Cretaceous epicontinental seas and in deeper water environments now exposed in mountain belts or penetrated in Deep Sea Drilling Project drillholes. The lithologies and thicknesses of cyclic interbeds may vary from one environment to another and apparently depend on a relative interplay of rate of carbonate sedimentation versus rate of dilution by terrigenous material, primarily clay and clay-sized minerals. For the purpose of this paper, we will describe two types of primary cycles or rhythmic bedding. The first is the typical alternation found in pelagic sequences of at least Jurassic through Cenozoic age consisting of lime (stone) or marl (stone) interbedded with marl (stone) or clay (shale) (see Fig. 1 for examples). The more carbonate-rich intervals generally are thicker, and the individual bedding couplets typically range in thickness from a few centimeters to several tens of centimeters. The second type of cycle is found mainly, but not exclusively, in pelagic and hemipelagic sequences of lower to middle Cretaceous age and consists of a redox cycle, commonly superimposed directly over the more typical carbonate cycle. The marginally oxic to anoxic depositional environments in which the redox cycles are inferred to have formed apparently were characterized by fluctuating intensity of redox conditions at or above the sediment/water interface. Such fluctuations led to a variety of rhythms, the basic one being that of laminated black claystone (shale) or marlstone, relatively rich in organic matter (i.e. > 1% Corg.), alternating with homogeneous to burrow-mottled gray to green claystone, marlstone or limestone. These lithologies imply an oxygen deficient depositional environment. If the depositional environment was slightly more oxic, the cycles may be manifested as interbedded red and green limestone, marlstone, or claystone. The carbonate content of all these lithologies apparently

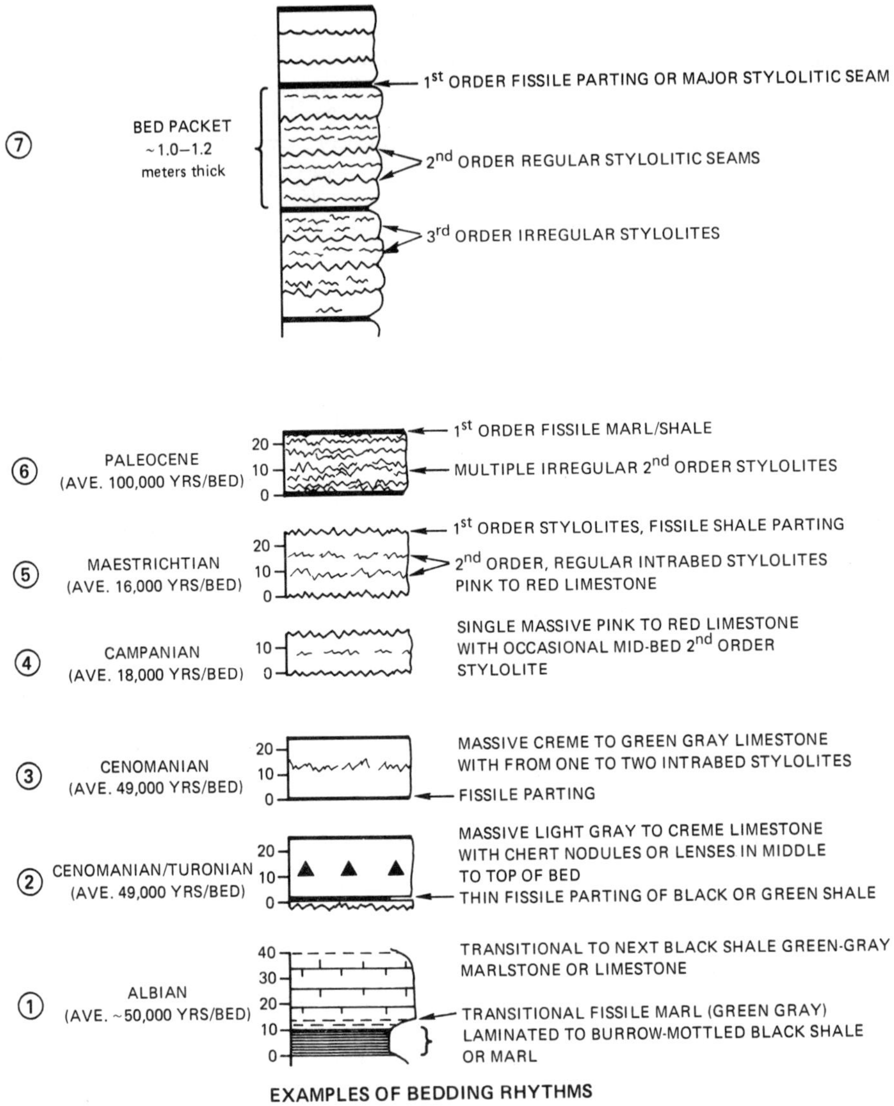

Figure 1 Examples of bedding rhythms (carbonate and redox cycles) found in the pelagic sequence of Neocomian through Paleogene age in Umbria, Italy (11). Period of cycles calculated using age scale of (62). (see 11,21,56 for discussion).

depends largely on the rate of supply of carbonate and the depth of deposition relative to the carbonate compensation depth (CCD).

Carbonate-Clay Cycles

Although evidence for the primary origin of rhythmic bedding in some pelagic limestone sequences is ambiguous (8-10), many sequences exhibit sedimentary structures and geochemical signatures which suggest that there were primary lithologic differences during deposition, although the differences may have been as subtle as a slight variation in amount of organic matter. In polished slabs, the rhythmically bedded Cretaceous pelagic limestones exposed in the Appennines of Italy show decimeter-thick pink carbonate beds that are separated by thin (less than 1 or 2 cm) seams of red fissile shale or stylolitic contacts (11). Burrows near the tops and bottoms of the limestone beds are filled with darker, more argillaceous material than the host limestone (Fig. 2), and some burrows contain even lighter colored, less argillaceous material. This suggests that intervals of lower and higher carbonate content existed during deposition and that these contrasting lithologies were partially mixed by burrowing organisms.

Paleocene pelagic carbonate strata exposed along the north coast of Spain (Zumaya and San Sebastian) also exhibit rhythmic bedding in which reddish marl interbeds are nearly as thick as the subjacent pink to grey limestone beds in each couplet (average thickness of couplets approximately 35 cm). There again, burrowing organisms have mixed sediment from one bed into the upper part of the underlying bed of contrasting lithology. The passage from marlstone to limestone, therefore, is transitional and reflects a primary contrast in carbonate content. Chalk-marl cycles of Miocene to Late Eocene age from DSDP Site 366 in the eastern North Atlantic (12,13) have not been as extensively lithified as examples cited above, but exhibit similar patterns of primary lithologic contrasts and bioturbation which often are quite subtle. The cycles at Site 366 continue into the Lower Eocene part of the section where they are complicated by a diagenetic overprint of silicification.

The bedding rhythms in many parts of the Scaglia Formation in the Italian Appennines (Fig. 1) do not have gradational limestone-marlstone alternations; instead, the decimeters thick limestone beds are separated by well-developed stylolitic seams or very thin, fissile calcareous shale seams. Obviously, diagenesis has played some part in the development of the bedding and has led to a fairly sharp distinction between beds and bedding planes (Fig. 2). In the example illustrated in Figure 2, $CaCO_3$ contents of limestones, average about 90 percent and do not vary much in profiles across individual limestone beds. However, profiles of iron content in the same beds (Fig. 3) demonstrate that there is a pronounced gradient from a bedding plane to the center of each bed. This illustrates the fact that minor components often are much more sensitive than major components (e.g., $CaCO_3$) in detecting gradations in lithology or chemistry across beds. The reason for this is essentially that when the initial insoluble residue content is low, substantial amounts of carbonate must be dissolved in order to reduce the relative percentage of $CaCO_3$ (14), but the relative percentage of a minor component (e.g. clay or iron) may change considerably. The equation

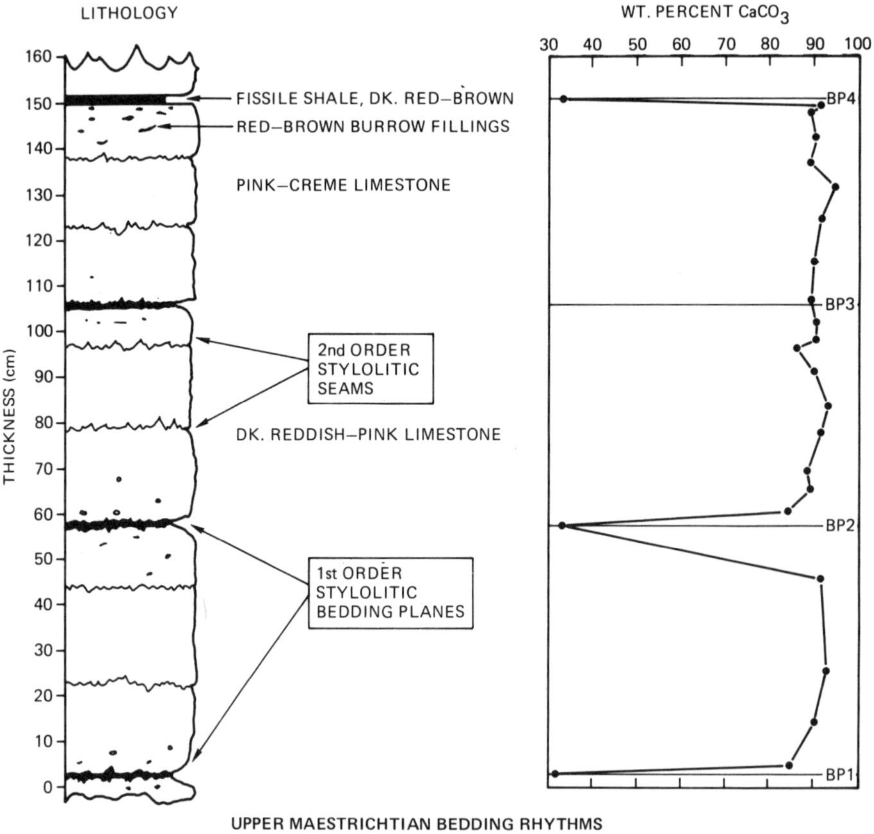

Figure 2 $CaCO_3$ profiles across compacted and cemented pelagic limestone beds. (Maestrichtian; Gubbio, Italy; 11). First order stylolitic bedding planes separate major limestone beds with about a 20 kyr period. Note concentration of red-brown burrow fillings near bedding planes.

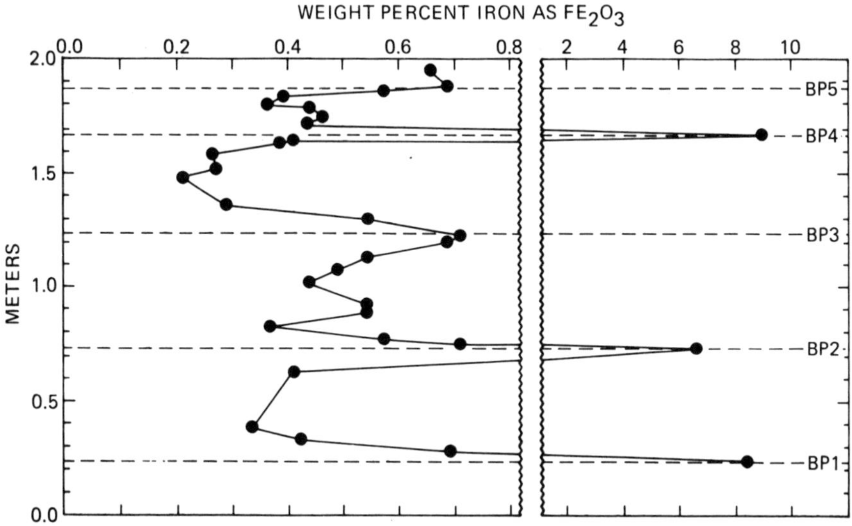

Figure 3 Total iron (expressed as Fe_2O_3;11) profiles across beds shown in Figure 2 (BP-4 is equivalent to 150 cm). Note gradational increases towards top and bottom of each bed.

that expresses the relative change in percent $CaCO_3$ by dissolution is :

$$L = [100\ (1 - \frac{R_0}{R})]/C_0$$

L = percent of carbonate lost
R_0 = initial fraction of insoluble residue
R = measured fraction of residue
C_0 = initial fraction of $CaCO_3$

A graph of the amount of dissolution necessary to change $CaCO_3$ percentages by a given amount assuming R_0=15% is given in Figure 4.

We argue that the minor-element chemical gradients across beds are evidence of primary, albeit often subtle, gradational changes in carbonate and insoluble residue content, and are not the result of diagenetic processes that produced the stylolitic or shale seams and well-defined limestone beds, because the gradations exist across parts of beds that have not been affected

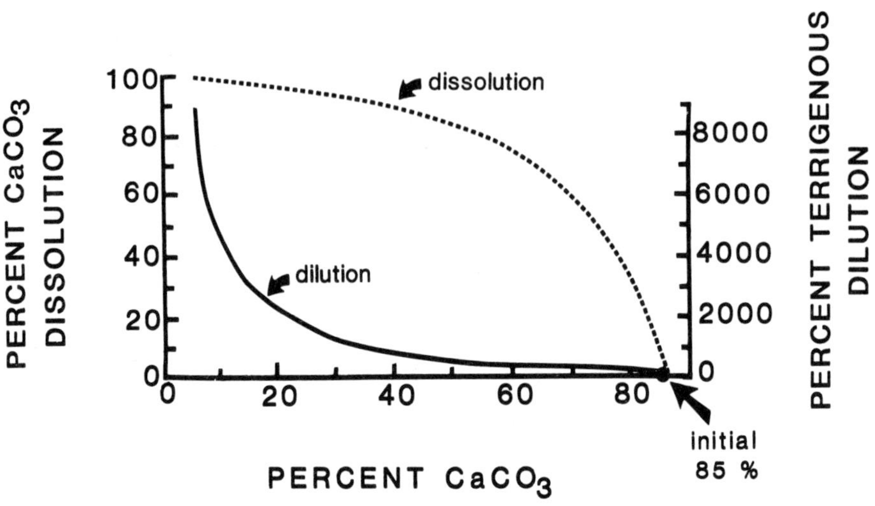

Figure 4 Graph of changes in $CaCO_3$ content as a function of increasing dissolution of $CaCO_3$ or dilution of $CaCO_3$ by terrigenous clays or other material (13; see text for explanation).

by stylolites or other diagenetic dissolution phenomena.

A primary depositional origin of rhythmically bedded carbonate beds is also suggested if individual beds can be traced laterally for some distance with little change in thickness or character. Such an exercise necessitates either good exposure in a continuous outcrop belt and/or intermittent exposure with several adequate marker horizons such as distinctive volcanic ash beds. Perhaps the best example is that provided by Hattin (15) from the Greenhorn Formation of mid-Cretaceous age in the western interior of North America. He was able to trace distinctive individual beds in the limestone-marlstone alternations of that unit over 750 km with the aid of several bentonite marker horizons. Bausch et al. (16) were able to trace similar limestone-marlstone alternations in the Oxfordian (Upper Jurassic of southern Germany) for over 100 km; Bausch et al. (16) and Ricken and Hembelen (17), as well as Seibold (18), also outlined lithologic criteria, similar to those discussed above, for the primary depositional origin of the same Oxfordian carbonate cycles. Individual beds in the Cretaceous and Paleocene examples from Italy and Spain discussed previously could be traced along the extent of an outcrop, but because of the lack of suitable marker horizons, beds could not be traced unequivocably for more than 1 km. Because of incomplete recovery and the lack of multiple marker horizons, it has not yet been possible to correlate individual beds between DSDP cores from the same depositional basin.

Redox Cycles

The other main type of sedimentary cycle found in ancient pelagic sequences, and only to a minor extent in modern ones, is a redox cycle which may be directly superimposed on a carbonate-clay cycle. Such a cycle typically, but not always, involves an alternation of dark and light intervals on a decimeter scale. The most obvious redox cycles consist of dark (commonly dark grey to black), organic-carbon rich layers which alternate with lighter colored layers relatively low in organic carbon (example in Fig. 1-1). The dark-colored interval commonly is laminated but may be homogeneous to burrow-mottled; the light-colored intervals are nearly always bioturbated and appear homogeneous to mottled. Such redox cycles have been described from Lower to middle Cretaceous sequences recovered at Atlantic DSDP Sites (12,19,20) and in exposed Cretaceous Tethyan deeper-water pelagic sequences (21-23) as well as in Cretaceous pelagic strata deposited in epicontinental seas (24-26). Gardner et al. (27) and Dean and Gardner (28) have documented somewhat similar cycles of organic carbon and carbonate in Upper Miocene to Holocene sediments recovered in DSDP Site 532 on Walvis Ridge in the South Atlantic Ocean.

That such redox cycles are primary is indicated by the sequence of primary sedimentary structures and the burrows which commonly penetrate and mix contrasting lithologies at stratal boundaries. However, the contacts between the alternating lithologies may be either sharp or gradational, and such sequences are not uniformly simple (12,19,20). More subtle redox cycles also occur, such as alternations of red and green clay, claystone, marlstone, or limestone found in some Atlantic DSDP sites in strata of Cretaceous age (12). Although it is more difficult to attribute these cycles to primary causes, we believe that many of these cycles reflect, to a lesser degree, the same changes in environmental variables as the more pronounced cycles of organic carbon and carbonate.

ORIGIN OF PRE-PLEISTOCENE PELAGIC CARBONATE AND REDOX CYCLES

A complete analysis of the possible causes of cyclicity in ancient pelagic carbonate sequences is beyond the scope of this paper. It is often difficult to ascertain the environmental changes responsible for apparent cyclicity due to diagenetic overprints and because the primary variables commonly differ from one environment to another. The reader is referred to Arthur and Fischer (20), Dean et al. (12,13), Volat et al. (30)

and Dean and Gardner (28) for general treatment of this topic. For the purposes of this paper, we briefly discuss several possible causes for cyclicity and present examples below.

There are five main ways in which cyclic or rhythmically bedded, pelagic carbonate sequences can be produced: 1) by cyclic changes in production of carbonate in surface waters; 2) by cyclic changes in intensity of carbonate dissolution due to undersaturation in the water column or below the sediment/water interface; 3) by cyclic variation in amount of dilution of carbonate by non-carbonate material (biogenic or terrigenous) supplied by rivers, downslope movement and/or wind ; 4) by cyclic variations in water depth and/or depositional energy in shoal-water pelagic environments favoring alternating deposition and non-deposition of carbonate and differential early diagenesis (32); and 5) by early diagenetic "unmixing" of carbonate into discrete layers which would necessarily bear no relation to a primary cyclicity in carbonate content (8,10,33).

Diagenetic unmixing may explain the origin of some rhythmically bedded nodular pelagic limestone units, but the excellent correspondence between carbonate cycles and climate changes in most Quaternary pelagic carbonate sequences (2,30,34) belies the possibility that early diagenetic unmixing is universally significant. Because of the evidence from the more recent record and because many ancient pelagic carbonate sequences show clear evidence for primary cyclicity, even though the ancient deposits are now overprinted by diagenesis (see below), we believe that simple diagenetic unmixing satisfactorily explains only few ancient examples.

Productivity

Cyclic variations in productivity, though they may occur (35), are very difficult to demonstrate even in the Quaternary record (14,30,36). Variations in productivity were proposed originally by Arrhenius (37) to explain Quaternary carbonate cycles in the equatorial Pacific. A few studies (35, 38-40) have suggested that productivity may cause cyclically interbedded sequences, but most have assumed that productivity is not a major cause of cyclicity in deep-sea pelagic sequences. It is possible that productivity cycles may be detected in cores in shallow carbonate sequences deposited above the calcite lysocline (35,39) but in deeper water sequences the effects of variations in productivity are masked by dissolution effects. The major problem is that we lack dependable quantitative indicators of productivity changes. De Boer (23,41) has argued that productivity changes were the cause of the rhythmically bedded limestone-marlstone sequences of mid-Cretaceous age exposed in the Northern Apennines of Italy, but he can offer no definitive evidence for his assertion. Figure 5C illustrates the effects of cyclic changes in carbonate productivity on carbonate content and bed thickness, assuming that each hemicycle is one-half the total time represented by a cycle and an initial insoluble residue content of 10%. Productivity changes of a factor of two would be necessary to create significant detectable differences in bed thickness and carbonate content. We suggest that productivity variations, although they may occur, are not the main cause of rhythmic bedding in ancient pelagic carbonate sequences; their effects are more subtle and easily masked by other processes.

Dilution and Dissolution

Periodic terrigenous dilution and carbonate dissolution are probably the main factors which produced pre-Quaternary rhythmically bedded pelagic sequences. Several workers have favored dilution of Pleistocene carbonate sediments in the low-latitude Atlantic by terrigenous material (42-48). Dilution by terrigenous clastics also has been cited as the main cause of carbonate cycles recovered at DSDP Site 532 on Walvis Ridge in the South Atlantic ocean (27,28) and Site 502 in the Caribbean.

Figure 4 illustrates the change in weight percent $CaCO_3$ induced by varying amounts of dilution vs. dissolution, assuming an initial insoluble residue content of 15%. These curves show, for example, that to decrease the $CaCO_3$ content from 85% to 50%, either 82% of the original $CaCO_3$ must be dissolved, or there must be an addition of 467% more clay by dilution (i.e., 70 weight units must be added to equal the 85 weight units of $CaCO_3$). In terms of actual volumes of materials, however, the dissolution process involves a much larger change. For example, to decrease the $CaCO_3$ content from 85% to 50%, about six times more $CaCO_3$ must be dissolved than clay added in the dilution example to achieve the same change (12). Changes in volume, in terms of bed thickness, of hypothetical carbonate cycles produced by the two processes (assuming equal duration of the carbonate and clay hemicycles and an initial insoluble residue content of 10%) are shown in Figures 5A and 5B. Notice that a 200% increase in dilution (dilution factor of 2 x) produces a change of only 1 cm in bed thickness (from 10 cm to 11 cm). However, only 20% $CaCO_3$ dissolution produces a 1.8-cm change in bed thickness (from 10 cm to 8.2 cm). In other words, dissolution produces a much greater absolute volume change, whereas dilution produces a greater relative volume change in a sediment that contains an initially large percentage of $CaCO_3$. We feel that it is this relative (percentage) change in the effects of a process that is most important when considering the processes involved in dissolution and dilution.

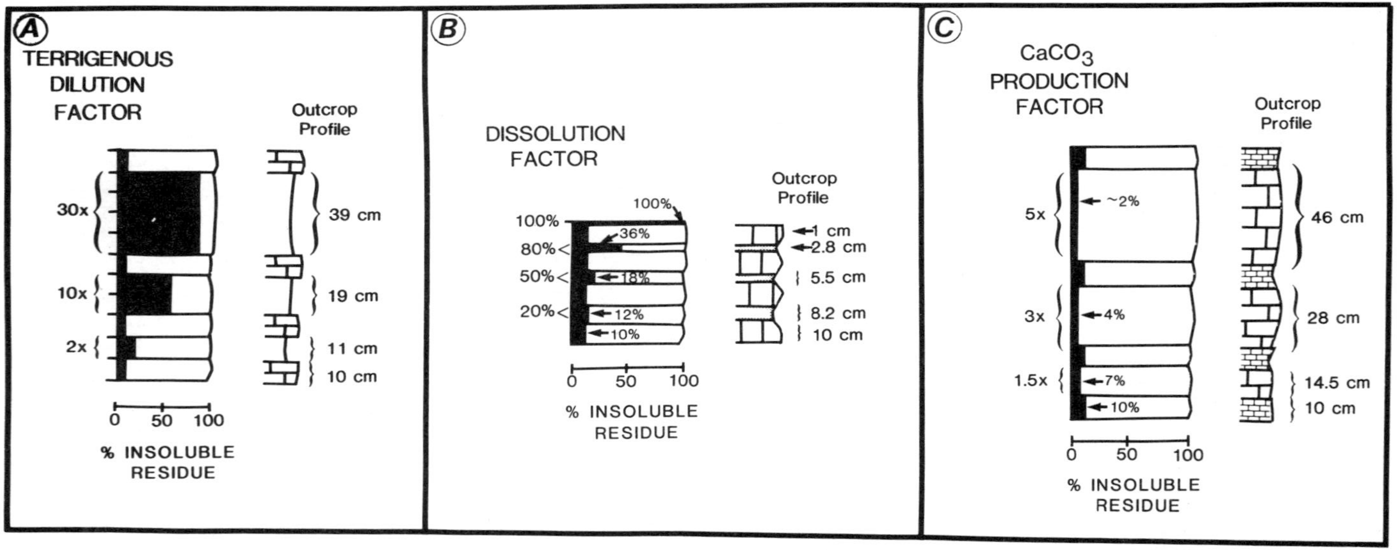

Figure 5 Evaluation of factors which lead to carbonate cycles in pelagic sequences: all examples assume an initial background flux of 0.5 cm/ky (90% $CaCO_3$ and 10% insoluble residue) but fluxes vary during part of each cycle as shown (equal hemicycles of 20 kyr). (A) Terrigenous dilution factor (2X=200% increase, 10X=1000% increase); note increase in insoluble residue (Fig. 4) as well as in thickness of dilution hemicycle with increasing dilution factors; (B) Dissolution factor; note relatively gradual increase in insoluble residue content (as in Fig. 4) with increasing dissolution as well as progressive decrease in thickness of dissolution hemicycle volume change); (C) $CaCO_3$ production factor (1.5X=150% increase, etc.); thickness of hemicycle is marked by an increase in $CaCO_3$, whereas insoluble residue content decreases. Dissolution and productivity cycles are difficult to distinguish from one another without independent criteria for dissolution during one hemicycle.

Fluctuation in intensity of carbonate dissolution in response to changes in deep water chemical characteristics forced by cyclic climate change is the most commonly cited and demonstrated cause of carbonate cycles in Quaternary pelagic sequences (30,36,49,50). Dean et al. (12,13) demonstrated that Eocene through Miocene carbonate cycles recovered in DSDP Site 366 on the Sierra Leone Rise in the eastern North Atlantic were due mainly to cyclic fluctuations in carbonate dissolution. This conclusion was reached on the basis of studies of changes in preservation of calcareous nannofossils across the cycles and the relative amounts of dilution vs. dissolution required to produce the changes in carbonate content and interval thicknesses. This study is probably the best documented example of cyclicity and its causes in an older (e.g. pre-Late Neogene) pelagic sequence. The cores studied were ideal in that they represent a continuous sequence of pelagic sedimentation on an aseismic rise 2500 m above the surrounding abyssal plain, and the sediments were not significantly altered by burial diagenesis. Rhythmically bedded pelagic carbonates of Late Cretaceous-Paleogene age at Gubbio, Italy (11) also are thought to have formed by carbonate dissolution. The limestone beds are 10-50 cm thick and contain between 80 and 90% $CaCO_3$ (Fig. 2), and are separated by much thinner (2 cm) clay seams. Preservation of carbonate constituents in the clay seams is relatively poor, although this may be as much due to diagenesis as to primary fluctuations in intensity of dissolution. The Eocene-Miocene strata from Site 366 and the Upper Cretaceous-Paleogene strata from Gubbio are both inferred to have been deposited in water depths near the lysocline (13,20,51). Therefore these Sites were in a position to experience periodic changes in dissolution rate as the lysocline depth fluctuated, perhaps in response to cyclic variations in climate and production of bottom-water. Geochemical and stable isotope data across individual Eocene cycles at Site 366 (Fig. 6) suggest, but do not prove, that diagenesis was relatively unimportant in producing the cycles. The Sr/Ca ratio is high and changes little with changes in $CaCO_3$ content across the cycles, and the amplitude of associated $\delta^{18}O$ values is only about 2‰, which suggests that there has been little redistribution of carbonate cement. The $CaCO_3$-rich intervals usually are the sites of preferential cementation, yet $\delta^{18}O$ values are reasonably low in these intervals, within the expected range for a primary signal (52,53). Like Quaternary carbonate cycles, the Eocene cycles show a positive relationship between $\delta^{18}O$ values and carbonate content, which suggests that there was a climatic control with warmer surface water temperatures corresponding to times of apparently less deep-water dissolution. Another aspect of these cycles may be the possibility that productivity plays a role as well. Total SiO_2 and the SiO_2/Al_2O_3 ratio increase drastically in relatively radiolarian-rich intervals, having lower $\delta^{18}O$ values of $CaCO_3$. Such radiolarian-rich intervals within the

Eocene cycles may represent periods of increased surface productivity and dilution of $CaCO_3$ by biogenic silica. Lower $\delta^{18}O$ and more negative $\delta^{13}C$ values of the carbonate suggest colder surface-water temperatures and higher rates of upwelling (supply of isotopically light carbon) during times of increased radiolarian abundance. Stable isotope analyses of whole rock carbonate across the similar cycles in the Gubbio sequence (Fig. 8) show that there are only very subtle changes in both $\delta^{18}O$ and $\delta^{13}C$ which easily could have been caused by diagenesis. For the Gubbio cycles, the relative difference in thickness between limestone beds and interbedded shale seams argues for the importance of dissolution rather than dilution (see Fig. 5).

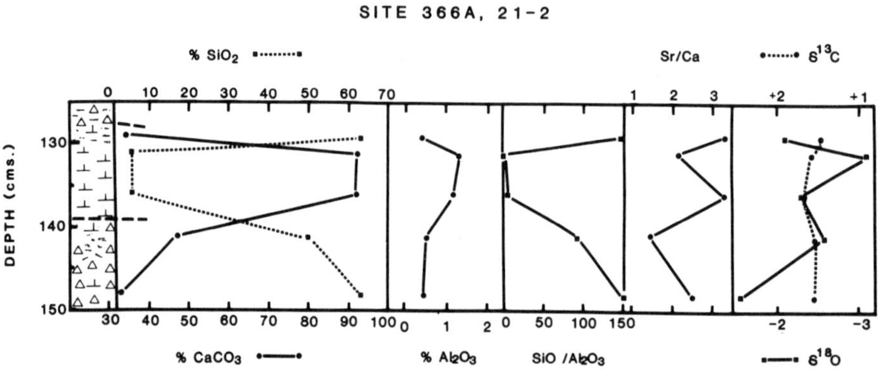

Figure 6 Selected geochemical profiles across Eocene carbonate cycle at DSDP Site 366 (eastern equatorial Atlantic); see (12) and text for details.

An example of the effects of terrigenous dilution is the cyclic pelagic carbonate sequence of the Greenhorn Formation of Cenomanian-Turonian age found in the mid-continent region of the United States (25,54,55,56). This type of rhythm is actually a combination redox and carbonate dilution cycle; the factors that produced terrigenous dilution also created changes in organic carbon supply and/or oxygenation of the water column. The Greenhorn Fm.(Bridge Creek Ls. member) was deposited in a relatively shallow (e.g.< 600 m) epicontinental sea (55). Therefore, it is unlikely that dissolution could have been the cause of the pronounced cyclicity in carbonate content. Individual cycles are on the order of 20 to 60 cm thick and consist of alternation of two main lithologies of subequal thickness: 1) a dark, commonly laminated, typically calcareous shale to marlstone relatively rich in organic carbon (0.7-6.0 wt%), and 2) a lighter colored, intensively bioturbated marly limestone to limestone with low or-

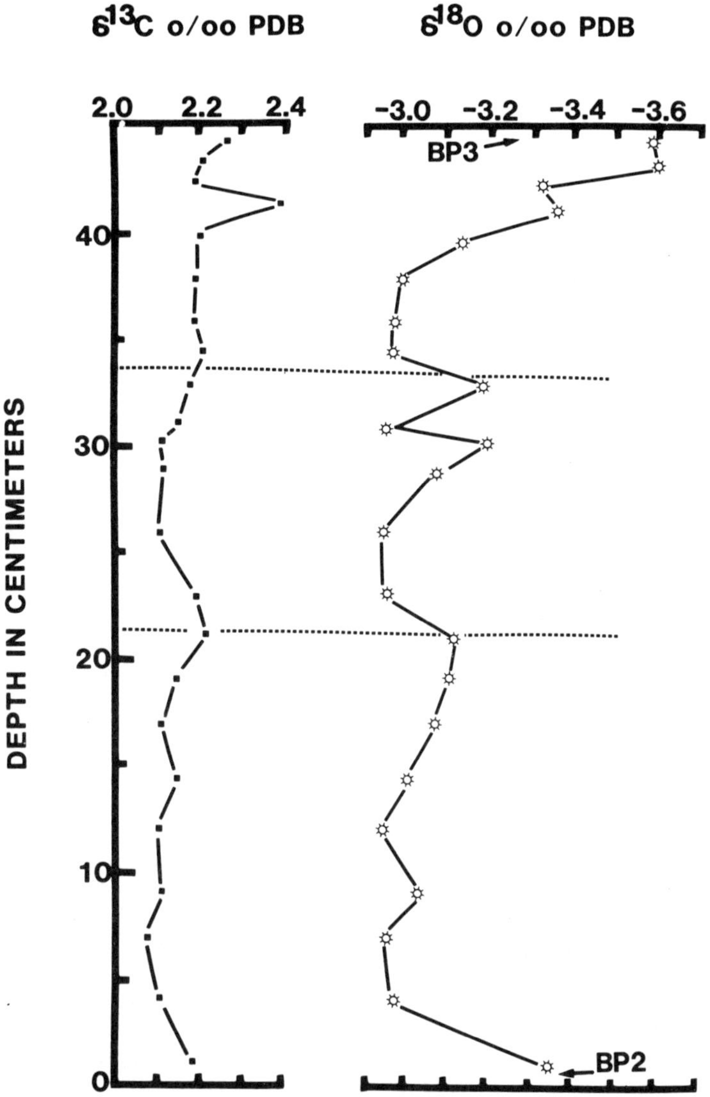

Figure 7 Stable isotope records across one highly diagenetically altered Maestrichtian carbonate cycle (BP-2 to BP-3; see Fig. 2) at Gubbio, Italy. Note relatively homogeneous $\delta^{18}O$ and $\delta^{13}C$ values.

ganic carbon content (0.1-0.7 wt%)(see Fig. 8A,B). The high organic carbon content and common lamination of the dark layers imply that bottom waters were dysaerobic or anoxic at the seafloor which led to exclusion of a benthic infauna and enhanced preservation of organic carbon; such conditions alternated with apparently well-oxygenated conditions during which time pelagic carbonate detritus accumulated and was bioturbated. Pratt (26) studied the sequences of sedimentary structures and mineralogy of the Greenhorn cycle in detail. She concluded that the clay mineral assemblage in the intervals enriched in clay and organic-carbon reflects derivation mainly from fluvial input, whereas the clay-mineral assemblage in the carbonate rich intervals is dominated by smectite, an alteration product of volcanic ash. Consequently, the alternation of relatively carbonate-rich and -poor beds is most likely due mainly to periodic terrigenous dilution, probably related to climatic cycles of increased and decreased rainfall. Our stable isotope studies of the same cycles support Pratt's (26,57) conclusions. Several examples of cycles in the Greenhorn Ls. are illustrated diagrammatically in Figure 8. The $\delta^{18}O$ values are more negative than most diagenetically altered chalks (52) and probably reflect lower than normal salinity in the restricted Cretaceous western interior seaway at the time. Values of $\delta^{18}O$ are most negative (lightest) in the organic-carbon rich (carbonate-poor) intervals. This suggests that surface water salinity during deposition of the carbonate-poor beds may have been lower by 3 to 10 ppt relative to surface-water salinity during deposition of the limestone beds. Such a salinity change provides a mechanism to enhance the stability of the water column and promote oxygen depletion in deeper (i.e. below wind and wave mixing) waters, thereby leading to enhanced preservation of organic carbon. Productivity may or may not have changed across the cycle, but one might expect lower productivity with a more stratified water column because of slower rates of nutrient upwelling from bottom waters. Some support for this view also comes from $\delta^{13}C$ values which are lighter in the limestone beds deposited during more oxygenated episodes, probably indicating better mixing of nutrients (and isotopically lighter carbon) to the surface. The data are internally consistent, but we cannot rule out some diagenetic overprint on the isotopic data.

Similar redox cycles, with or without carbonate cycles, occur in many Lower to middle-Cretaceous pelagic deeper water sequences recovered at DSDP Sites (12,19,20,28,58) but there is probably not one single cause that is capable of explaining all of the known examples (59). Redeposition of organic matter, either terrestrial or marine, is probably responsible for some of the observed cyclicity (dilution cycles) in Cretaceous pelagic/hemipelagic sequences (29,60). The alternation of organic-carbon-rich and-poor strate in other cycles undoubtedly are due

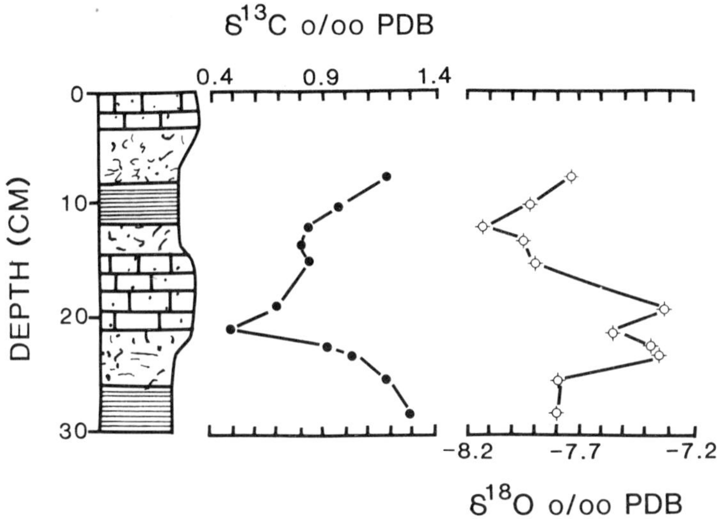

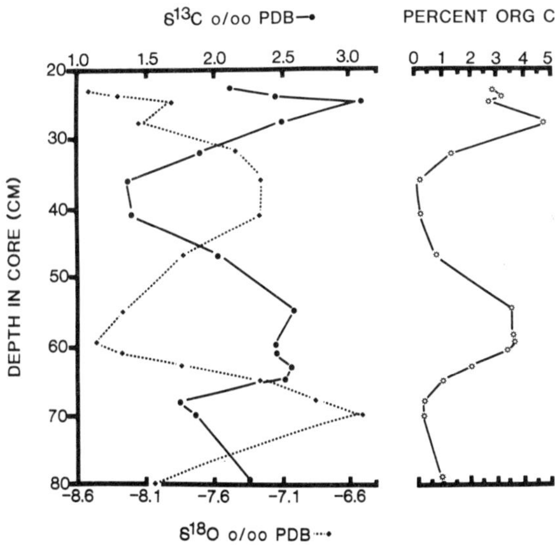

Figure 8 Examples of stable isotope and organic carbon profiles across redox/carbonate cycles of Cenomanian-Turonian age in the Bridge Creek Ls. of Colorado, U.S.A., from a core near Pueblo (25,26,57) (see text for explanation). Laminated pattern represents organic C-rich, laminated intervals; speckles represent bioturbation; block pattern represents limestone beds.

to periodic changes in oxygenation of the water column related to changes in bottom-water residence time and/or in surface productivity (12,19,20). All of these periodic environmental changes probably are caused directly or indirectly, by changes in climate.

Changes in Water Depth and Depositional Energy

Cyclicity in Upper Cretaceous shallow-water chalk sequences deposited in dominantly oxygenated settings may have been induced by periodic changes in depositional energy (32,60). These hypothesized changes in current velocity produced winnowed calcarenite layers or hardgrounds (seafloor lithified omission surfaces) during high energy episodes and pelagic nannofossil chalk layers during inferred lower energy depositional periods. The alternation of high and low energy conditions may have been related to cyclic changes in water depth, although evidence to support this is sparse. The estimated periodicities of the rhythmic bedding in these Upper Cretaceous chalk sequences are similar to those of other carbonate cycles (32). Diagenesis has produced the characteristic nodular aspect and flaser-like solution seams.

THE TIME SIGNATURE OF PRE-PLEISTOCENE CARBONATE CYCLES

A number of estimates have been made of the periodicities of pre-Quaternary carbonate cycles in a variety of localities (Table 1). The estimates are usually obtained by dividing average rates of sedimentation by average bed thickness (or number of beds per known time interval). There are obvious uncertainties in this method. The accuracy of such estimates depends on completeness of sequences and a high resolution chronostratigraphy which becomes less ideal with increasing age. Uncertainties in the length of certain stages of the Cretaceous are as high as a factor of two. For example, estimates for the duration of the Cenomanian are 8 My, 4 My, and 6.5 My (62,63,64). These problems notwithstanding, most estimates for bedding periodicities range between about 20 kyr and 100 kyr which are similar to the periodic variations in the earth's orbit and axis of rotation (precession-19-23 kyr, obliquity-41 kyr, eccentricity-100 kyr) that are manifested in global or regional changes in climate and ocean circulation. Fischer and Schwartzacher (65,66) and de Boer and Wonders (67) attempted spectral analysis of bed thickness data from several localities representing several Cretaceous stages. The results are intriguing and suggest that there are 3 groups of frequencies of bedding thickness. The power of spectra of these Cretaceous cycles has the same shape as spectra of Pleistocene cycle periodicities. However, we feel that it is a bit premature to assign precise time values to the bedding thickness frequencies. Ultimately, this may be a way to "tune" the Cretaceous and other time scales, but only after satisfactory documentation of cycle periods is available.

One further problem in establishing the time value of ancient carbonate cycles is bioturbation in relation to sedimentation rate. Burrowing organisms may continuously mix sediment in most uncompacted pelagic carbonate sequences to a depth of up to 15 cm below the sediment/water interface (68,69). This depth may correspond to more than 10-15 kyr of stratigraphic mixing, depending on overall sedimentation rates.

Table 1 Estimated Cycle (carbonate or redox) Durations in pre-Quaternary Pelagic/Hemipelagic Carbonate Sequences.

Age	Unit/ location	Duration of cycle	Method	Source
Early Lower Jurassic	Adnet limestone (Austria) (nodular limestone/ red shale)	25-80 ky	Average thickness	(83)
Oxfordian	(South Germany) (limestone-marlstone)	15 ky	-------do-------	(18)
Kimmeridgian	(South Germany) (limestone-marlstone)	15-20 ky	-------do-------	(84)
Tithonian-Barremian	DSDP Site 367 (Cape Verde Basin) (limestone-marlstone)	37 ky	-------do-------	(12)
Hauterivian-Albian	DSDP Site 398 (North Atlantic) (Redox, carbonate cycles)	44 ky	-------do-------	(20)
Tithonian-Aptian	Maiolica Limestone (Italy) (limestone-shale)	43, 100 ky (bundles) 413 ky	Power Spectra of bed thickness	(65)
Aptian-Albian	DSDP Sites 386, 387 (W.N. Atlantic) (Redox cycles; mudstone)	20 ky	Average thickness	(19)
Albian-Cenomanian	Scisti a Fucoidi (Italy) (carbonate cycles)	23 ky 100 ky	Power Spectra of bed thickness	(23)
Cenomanian	Scaglia Limestone (Italy) (carbonate cycles)	43 ky 100 ky (bundles) 413 ky	-------do-------	(65)
Albian-Paleocene	Scaglia Limestone (Italy) (carbonate cycles)	16 ky-100 ky range mean 20 ky using (63) mean 32 ky using (62)	Average thickness	(11)(21)
Cenomanian-Turonian	Greenhorn Limestone (Colorado) (carbonate cycles/ Redox cycles)	18-22 ky	-------do-------	(25)
Late Cretaceous	Boreal Cretaceous (NW Germany)	30-40 ky	-------do-------	(85)
Late Cretaceous	The Chalk (United Kingdom) (chalk-marl, nodular limestone)	~40-50 ky	-------do-------	(32)
Early Eocene-Early Miocene	DSDP Site 366 (N. Atlantic) (carbonate-marl)	26-50 ky range Oligocene-Miocene 44 ky Middle-Late Eocene 19 ky	-------do-------	(12)(13)
Late Miocene-Recent	DSDP Site 532 (S. Atlantic)	25-50 ky	-------do-------	(27)(28)

At very slow rates of deposition, the contrasts of short term cycles (e.g. periods of about 21 kyr) may be completely mixed so that only the longer cycles are adequately recorded by the contrasts in carbonate content. Another possibility is that periodic cycles are recorded only intermittently which would compromise any later estimates of periodicities. Bioturbation has been recognized as a possible factor in distorting stable isotope signals in Quaternary carbonate cycles (70) and attempts have been made to deconvolve the record on the basis of bioturbation models, but this technique is not practical for ancient lithified sequences. Figure 9 illustrates an example of probable sedimentation rate control on the resolution of cycle frequencies in a lithified pelagic limestone sequence of Cretaceous-Paleocene age from Gubbio, Italy. Arthur (11) calculated average bedding periodicities in the Gubbio sequence for Cretaceous stages and Cretaceous and Paleogene magnetozones. Figure 9A illustrates that average bed thickness does not vary much (about 20 cm) for any time interval, but the calculated periodicity does vary significantly. Figures 9B and 9C show that the average calculated periodicity (average bed duration) of the bedding rhythms decreases as rates of sedimentation (compacted) decrease. We argue that this effect is due to the efficiency of sediment mixing by bioturbation at slow sedimentation rates, as well as the later obscuring effects of compaction and chemical diagenesis discussed in the next section.

DIAGENETIC OVERPRINTS

A further major problem in studying ancient carbonate cycles and in establishing a primary origin for them is the overprint of early and late diagenesis. By that we mean the sum of post-depositional modification of the original sediment during burial, not including seafloor dissolution and bioturbation which have been discussed above. Compaction, dissolution and cementation of pelagic carbonate sediments occur during burial (52,53,71,72). These processes lead to changes in texture, chemical composition (including stable isotope), and volume of the original sediment. These acquired aspects commonly overprint or even enhance small-scale primary lithologic variations. Although most pelagic chalks are relatively simple chemical systems in comparison to shallow-water carbonates, and although deep-sea diagenetic rates are relatively slow, the most deeply buried and intensively altered pelagic limestones may not retain much of their original chemical, textural or biologic character. Therefore, even if cyclicity is manifested in a given sequence it may be difficult to identify the process(es) that led to the cyclicity, other than possible diagenetic enhancement.

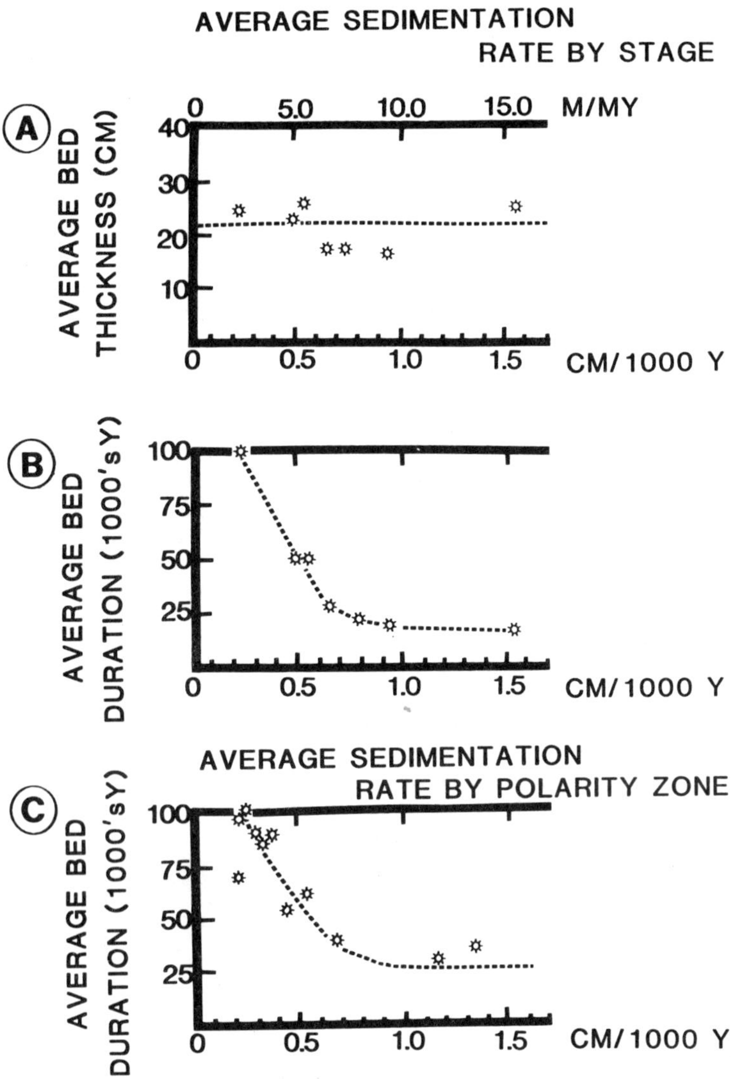

Figure 9 Plots of (A) average bed thickness (cms.) vs. average sedimentation rate by stage or epoch for the Cretaceous-Paleogene pelagic sequence at Gubbio, Italy (11); (B) Average bed duration (in kyr) vs. average sedimentation rate for the Cretaceous-Paleogene sequence at Gubbio; (C) calculated average period (duration) of carbonate cycles vs. average sedimentation rate by magnetic polarity scale for the Cretaceous-Paleogene.

Because chalks are a relatively simple chemical system, their diagenesis is well enough understood that we can ascribe a primary origin for bedding rhythms or carbonate cycles in most cases (53,71,72). Except for the least compacted or otherwise relatively unaltered chalks, however, chemical and stable isotope data may provide little information about the primary depositional environment. We emphasize that such data must be very carefully interpreted. Because of space limitations only a few examples of diagenetic overprints are discussed briefly below.

Figure 10 illustrates the basic principles and processes in diagenesis of pelagic carbonates (11). The first column shows a typical uncompacted Quaternary deep-sea carbonate sequence. Carbonate cycles of several frequencies occur in the core. Two complete 100 kyr cycles of about 160 cm thick are shown; superimposed on these are shorter period cycles. The relatively low-carbonate intervals contain more highly dissolved calcareous assemblages and are considered to have a lower "diagenetic potential" (71) than intervening calcareous intervals. During the first 300 m or so of burial, 40 to 50% of the primary porosity is destroyed by mechanical compaction. Relatively little chemical change has occurred, although incipient carbonate dissolution-reprecipitation may have begun (71,73,74). At this point in diagenesis of most chalk sequences, chemical and paleontologic analysis will still yield generally valuable insights to primary depositional conditions.

Further porosity reduction during burial must occur by "chemical compaction" because of increases in temperature and pressure, and the formation of a more-or-less rigid grain framework in the progressively lithified chalk. In most deep-sea and many shallower water chalks the addition of cement must take place by selective dissolution and internal solution transfer of calcium carbonate because external sources of carbonate are not readily available. Therefore some intervals of the sequence may become donor horizons whereas others are selectively cemented. On the basis of several studies (11,52,61,71,75) it appears that those beds that originally had higher carbonate contents (higher "diagenetic potential") are loci for preferential cementation; the intervals richer in insoluble residue (lower initial $CaCO_3$) are the source of most $CaCO_3$ for cementation. This transfer of $CaCO_3$ from relatively carbonate-poor to carbonate-rich intervals generally occurs over distances of a few tens of centimeters. The end result is shown in column 3 of Figure 10. The intervals that originally were carbonate-poor intervals in this model are reduced to thin (<5 cms) shale layers or solution seams (stylolites), and the resulting cycles appear similar to the familiar rhythmic bedding in pelagic carbonate sequences shown in Figure 1. Diagenesis has emphasized the original lithologic contrasts

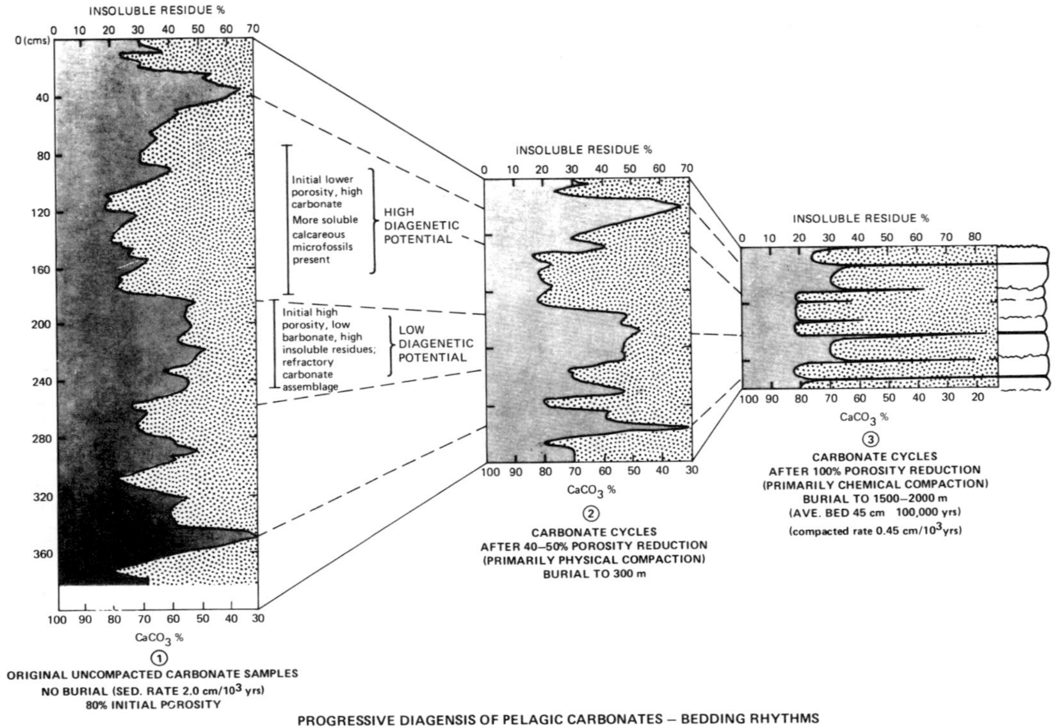

Figure 10 Diagenetic model for pelagic carbonates during progressive burial (11; see text for explanation).

across the primary carbonate cycles, rendering them more strikingly visible, yet obliterating most primary chemical signals.

Figures 6 and 7 contrast stable oxygen isotope profiles across carbonate cycles from a relatively unaltered pelagic sequence and a highly lithified one. The $\delta^{18}O$ values across the cycle in Figure 7 change relatively little and suggest a redistribution and homogenization of the original $\delta^{18}O$ signals. This is not surprising because diagenetic models suggest that $\delta^{18}O$ values of carbonate cements should become more negative with greater burial and increasing temperatures (76-78) (Fig. 11), and the solution transfer of carbonate to sites of cementation should lead to homogenization of $\delta^{18}O$ values in the limestones, assuming that cementation generally is homogeneous. At earlier stages of chemical compaction, however, whole rock carbonate $\delta^{18}O$ values from limestones vs. marls might actually be the reverse of their original relationships. Figure 12 shows such an example from the Hauterivian-Barremian (640 m burial depth) of Site 387 in the Western North Atlantic. The dark marl beds have heavier $\delta^{18}O$ values (-1.5 to -3 °/oo) than the overlying limestone bed (-4 to -5.5 °/oo). The isotopically light values in the limestone are too negative to be representative of original Cretaceous open ocean surface water values (perhaps -3 °/oo or less (79), and undoubtedly represent a diagenetic shift (compare to burial values in Fig. 11). The Sr/Ca ratio (Fig. 12) in the carbonate confirms the diagenetic interpretation; the Sr/Ca is higher in the marls, which have more reasonable "primary" $\delta^{18}O$ values, and lower in the limestones which have been cemented by low-Sr calcite. We conclude that in this case there is little primary information in the stable isotope or most of the other geochemical record.

Carbon isotopic values of pelagic carbonates are more conservative because of the high ratio of initial rock to water carbon (81). However, early and late diagenetic reactions involving organic matter can cause substantial $\delta^{13}C$ changes in carbonate cements (80,82), particularly within intervals having originally low in carbonate (e.g. < 35% $CaCO_3$). We would therefore be hesitant to interpret the $\delta^{13}C$ trends across the cycle shown in Figure 12 as a primary one, because the marl interval contains up to 5 wt. percent organic carbon, the degradation of which could have been a source of isotopically light carbon during cementation of the adjacent limestone.

CONCLUSIONS

The ubiquitous presence of carbonate and/or oxidation-reduction cycles in ancient pelagic carbonate sequences of virtually all paleoenvironments and the common pronounced rhythmi-

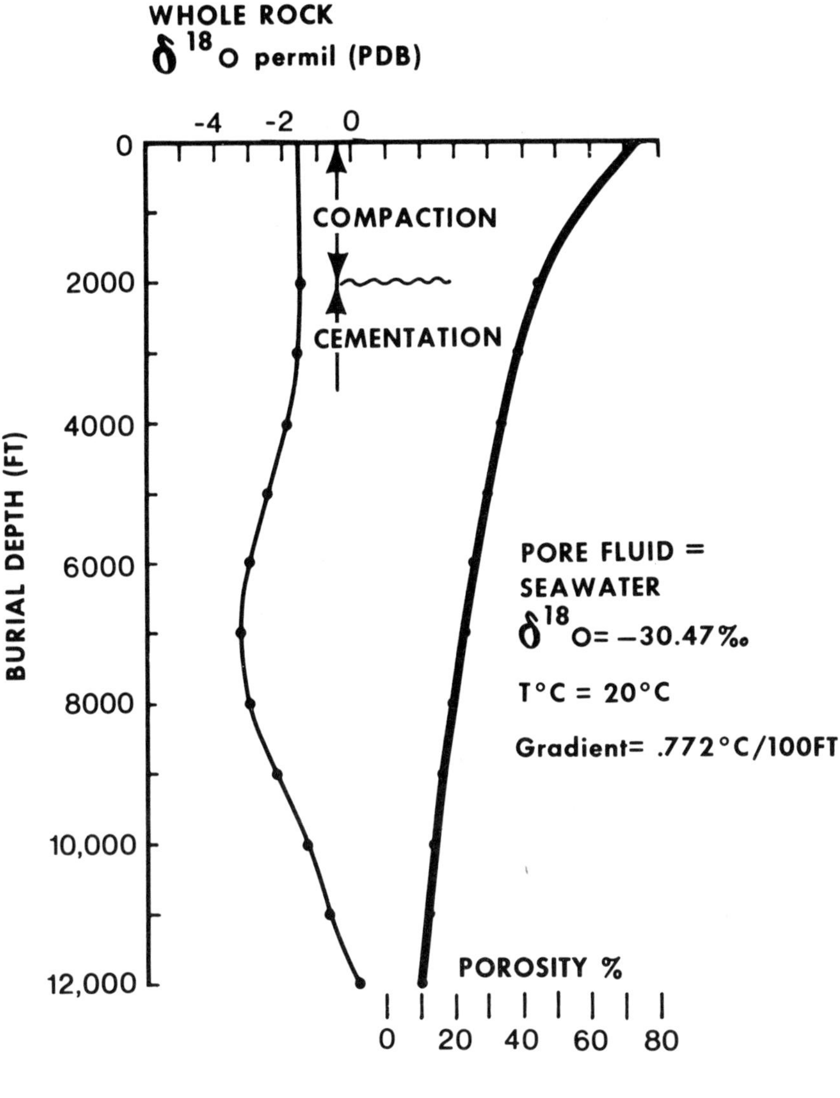

Figure 11 Model of the expected diagenetic shift of $\delta^{18}O$ values in whole rock pelagic carbonate (79). The model assumptions are shown on the diagram. Essentially the assumptions are a starting value of $\delta^{18}O = -1.5$ ‰ for unaltered carbonate, marine pore waters, a U.S. Gulf Coast geothermal gradient, and relatively closed-system alteration. The computer model is iterative with equilibration of discrete amounts of $CaCO_3$ dissolved at each level (25 m burial intervals) with pore waters and averaging of discrete amounts with existing whole rock values from the previous iteration.

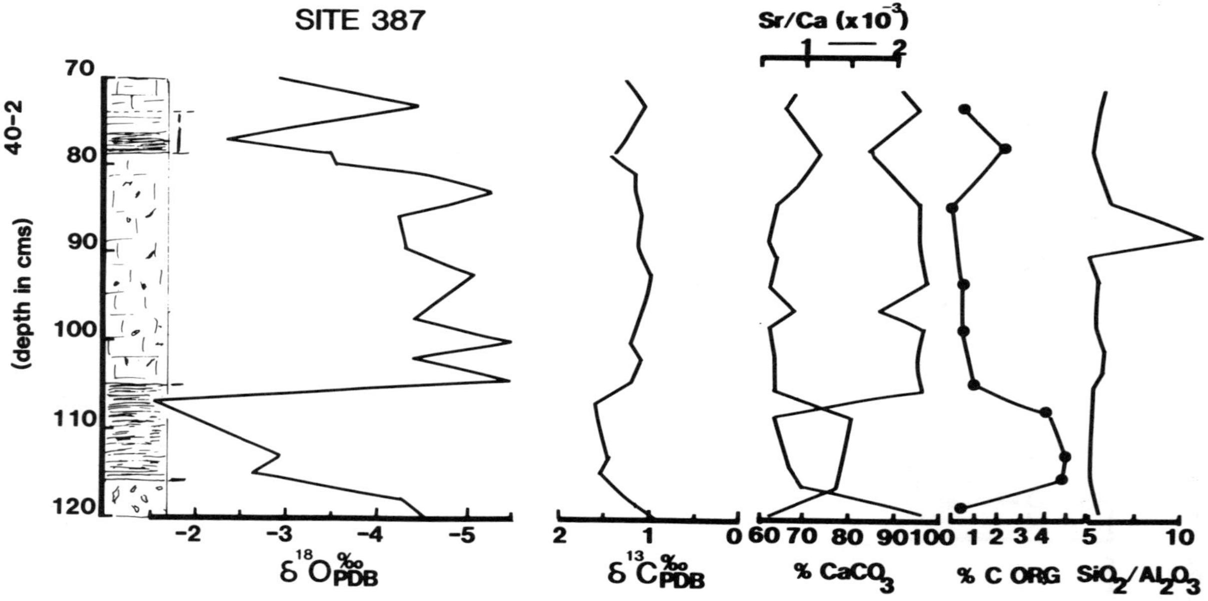

Figure 12 Selected geochemical profiles across a redox/carbonate cycle at DSDP Site 387 in the Western North Atlantic (see text for explanation).

city of these cycles suggest to us that the cyclicity is a result of periodic or quasiperiodic variations in the depositional paleoenvironment of most pelagic sequences. Although the periodicity of the cycles is difficult to accurately prove, estimates of around 20, 40, and 100 kyr repeatedly appear (e.g. Table 1), and it is likely that the Milankovitch orbital parameters, a dominant climatic forcing function during the Quaternary, have influenced pelagic sedimentation in some way at least back through the Mesozoic.

The way in which changes in the earth's orbit or axis of rotation may have had such a pronounced influence on Mesozoic climate, ocean circulation and sedimentation in the absence of major ice caps is not well understood at present. The mechanism may have differed from one environment to another, but we suggest that the influence of insolation variations on local and regional patterns of evaporation and precipitation is the most likely cause. Results of our ongoing research indicate that periodic salinity variations in surface and deep waters, and possibly changes in surface wind stress, probably influenced nutrient availability, rates of primary productivity, rates of deep-water generation, rates of carbonate dissolution, deep-water oxygen content, and other parameters of deep-water chemistry.

More detailed studies of ancient Milankovitch-like cycles are needed, including possible climate modeling of insolation effects, and we encourage careful, multidisciplinary efforts to distinguish primary from diagenetic signals.

ACKNOWLEDGEMENTS

We thank the convenors of this symposium for encouraging us to present this paper. Discussions with A.G. Fischer, L.M. Pratt, and E.G. Kauffman are gratefully acknowledged. We also thank J.V. Gardner and L.M. Pratt for their helpful reviews of an earlier manuscript.

REFERENCES

1. Hays, J.D., Imbrie, J., and Shackleton, N.J. : 1976, Science 194, pp. 1121-1132.
2. Imbrie, J., and Imbrie, K.P. : 1979, "Ice Ages - Solving the Mystery", Enslow Publishers, 224p.
3. Imbrie, J., Hays, J.D., Martinson, D.G., McIntyre, A., Mix, A.C., Morley, J.J., Pisias, N.G., Prell, W.L., and Shackleton, N.J. : 1984, in : "Milankovitch and Climate", A. Berger, J. Imbrie, J. Hays, G. Kukla, B.

Saltzman (Eds), Reidel Publ. Company, Holland. This volume, p. 269.
4. Croll, J. : 1875, "Climate and Time", Daldy, Isbister and Co., London, 577pp.
5. Milankovitch, M. : 1941, Belgrade, Royal Serb. Acad., Spec. Publ. 133, pp. 1-633.
6. Berger, A.L. : 1980, Vistas in Astronomy 24, pp. 103-122.
7. Berger, A.L. : 1976, Astron. Astrophysics 51, pp. 127-135.
8. Hallam, A. : 1964, J. Geology 72, pp. 157-168.
9. Brückner, W.D. : 1953, J. Sediment. Petrol. 23, pp. 235-237.
10. Jenkyns, H.C. : 1974, in : K. J. Hsu and H.C. Jenkyns (Eds), Internat. Assoc. Sedimental. Spec. Pub. 1, pp. 249-271.
11. Arthur, M.A. : 1979, Sedimentologic and geochemical studies of Cretaceous and Paleogene pelagic sedimentary rocks : The Gubbio sequence : unpubl. Ph.D. Dissertation, Princeton Univ., Part I, 174pp.
12. Dean, W.E., Gardner, J.V., Jansa, L.F., Cepek, P., and Seibold, E. : 1977, in : "Initial Reports of the Deep Sea Drilling Project", Y. Lancelot, E. Seibold et al. (Eds), 41, Washington (U.S. Govt. Print. Off.), pp. 965-989.
13. Dean, W.E., Gardner, J.V., and Cepek, P. : 1981, Marine Geol. 39, pp. 81-101.
14. Berger, W.H. : 1971, Marine Geol. 11, pp. 325-358.
15. Hattin, D.E. : 1971, Am. Assoc. Petrol. Geol. Bull. 55, pp. 412-431.
16. Bausch, W.M., Fatschel, J., Hofman, D. : 1981, in : G. Einsele and A. Seilacher (Eds), Springer-Verlag, Berlin, pp. 54-62.
17. Ricken, W., and Hambelen, C. : 1982, in : G. Einsele and A. Seilacher (Eds), Springer-Verlag, Berlin, pp. 63-71.
18. Seibold, E. : 1952, N. Jb. Geol., Abb. 95, pp. 337-370.
19. McCave, I.N. : 1979, in : "Initial Reports of the Deep Sea Drilling Project", B.E. Tucholke, P.R. Vogt et al. (Eds), 43, Washington (U.S. Govt. Print. Off.), pp. 411-416.
20. Arthur, M.A. : 1979, in : "Initial Reports of the Deep Sea Drilling Project", J.C. Sibuet, W.B.F. Ryan et al. (Eds), 47, pt.2, Washington (U.S. Govt. Print. Off.), pp. 719-751.
21. Arthur, M.A., and Fischer, A.G. : 1977, Geol. Soc. Am. Bull. 88, pp. 367-389.
22. Weissert, H., McKenzie, J., and Hochuli, P. : 1979, Geology 7, pp. 147-151.
23. de Boer, P.L. : 1982, in : G. Einsele, and A. Seilacher (Eds), Springer-Verlag, Berlin, pp. 456-475.
24. Arthur, M.A., Dean, W.F., and Pollastro, R. : 1980, Am. Assoc. Petrol. Geol. Bull. 64, pp. 671-672.
25. Fischer, A.G. : 1980, in : E.L. Yochelson (Ed.), Geol. Soc. Am. Spec. Publ. 183, pp. 93-104.

26. Pratt, L.M. : 1982, in : "Cyclic and Event Stratification", G. Einsele, and A. Seilacher (Eds), Berlin, Springer-Verlag, pp. 96.
27. Gardner, J.V., Dean, W.E., and Wilson, C. : 1983, in : "Initial Reports of the Deep Sea Drilling Project", W.W. Hay, J.C. Sibuet et al. (Eds), 75, Washington (U.S. Gvt. Print. Off.), in press.
28. Dean, W.E., and Gardner, J.V. : 1983, Communication made at the "Milankovitch and Climate" symposium, Lamont Doherty Geological Observatory, Palisades, N.Y., December 1982.
29. Stow, D.A.V., and Dean, W.E. : 1983, in : "Initial Reports of the Deep Sea Drilling Project", W.W. Hays, J.C. Sibuet et al. (Eds), 75, Washington (U.S. Gvt. Print. Off.), in press.
30. Volat, J.L., Pastouret, L., and Vergnaud-Grazzini, C. : 1980, Marine Geology 34, pp. 1-28.
31. Einsele, G. : 1982, in : G. Einsele, and A. Seilacher (Eds), Springer-Verlag, Berlin, pp. 8-53.
32. Garrison, R.E., and Kennedy, W.J. : 1977, Sediment Geology 19, pp. 107-137.
33. Eder, W. : 1982, in : G. Einsele, and A. Seilacher (Eds), Springer-Verlag, Berlin, pp. 98-112.
34. Shackleton, N.J. : 1977, in : "The Fate of Fossil Fuel CO_2 in the Oceans", N.R. Anderson and A. Malahoff (Eds), Plenum Press, N.Y., pp. 401-427.
35. Adelseck, C.G.Jr., and Anderson, T.F. : 1978, Geology 6, pp. 388-391.
36. Berger, W.H. : 1977, in : "The Fate of Fossil Fuel CO_2 in the Oceans", N.R. Andersen, and A. Malahoff (Eds), Plenum Press, N.Y., pp. 505-542.
37. Arrhenius, G. : 1952, "Rep. Swedish Deep-Sea Expedition, 1947-1948", 5, pp. 1-228.
38. Ruddiman, W.F., and McIntyre, A. : 1976, in : R.M. Cline, and J.D. Hays (Eds), Geol. Soc. Amer., Memoir 145, pp. 111-146.
39. Prell, W.L., and Hays, J.D. : 1976, in : R.M. Cline, and J.D. Hays (Eds), Geol. Soc. Amer., Memoir 145, pp. 201-220.
40. Luz, B. : 1977, Palaeogeogr., -climatol., -ecol. 22, pp. 61-78.
41. de Boer, P.L. : 1984, in : "Milankovitch and Climate", A. Berger, J. Imbrie, J. Hays, G. Kukla, B. Saltzman (Eds), Reidel Publ. Company, Holland. This volume.
42. Folger, D.W., Burckle, L.H., and Heezen, B.C. : 1967, Science 155, pp. 1243-1244.
43. Delany, A.C., parkin, D.W., Griffin, J.J., Goldberg, E.D., and Reinmann, B.E.F. : 1967, Geochim. Cosmochim. Acta 31, pp. 885-909.
44. Folger, D.W. : 1970, Deep-sea Res. 17, pp. 337-352.

45. Ruddiman, W.F. : 1971, Geol. Soc. Amer. Bull. 82, pp. 283-302.
46. Carlson, T.N., and Prospero, J.M. : 1972, J. Appl. Meteorl. 11, pp. 283-297.
47. Hays, J.D., and Perruzza, A. : 1971, Quaternary Research 2, pp. 355-363.
48. Gardner, J.V., and Hays, J.D. : 1976, in : R.M. Cline, and J.D. Hays (Eds), Geol. Soc. Amer. Memoir 145, pp. 221-246.
49. Gardner, J.V. : 1975, in : "Dissolution of Deep-sea Carbonates, Cushman Found.", W.V. Sliter, A.W.H. Bé, and W.H. Berger (Eds), Foraminiferal Res. Spec. Publ. 13, pp. 129-141.
50. Luz, B., and Shackleton, N.J. : 1975, Cushman Found. Forminiferal res. Spec. Publ. 13, pp. 142-150.
51. Premoli Silva,I., and Paggi, L. : 1983, Rivista Ital. Paleont. Strat., in press.
52. Scholle, P.A. : 1977, Amer. Assoc. Petrol. Geol. Bull. 61, pp. 982-1009.
53. Matter, A., Douglas, R.G., and Perch-Nielsen, K. : 1975, in : "Initial Reports of Deep Sea Drilling Project", R.L. Larson, R. Moberly et al. (Eds), 32, Washington (U.S. Gvt. Print. Off.), pp. 891-921.
54. Hattin, D.E. : 1971, Amer. Assoc. Petrol. Geol. Bull. 55, pp. 412-431.
55. Kauffman, E.G. : 1977, The Mountain Geologist 14, pp. 75-274.
56. Hattin, D.E. : 1975, Kansas Geol. Surv. Bull. 209, 128pp.
57. Arthur, M.A., Pratt, L.R., Kauffman, E.G., and Fischer, A.G. : in prep., "Cyclicity and paleoenvironmental changes through the Greenhorn Cyclothem of the Cretaceous Western Interior Seaway", U.S.
58. Arthur, M.A., and Natland, J.H. : 1979, in : M. Talwani, W.W. Hay, and Ryan, W.B.F. (Eds), Washington, Am. Geophys. Union, Maurice Ewing Series 3, pp. 375-401.
59. Arthur, M.A., Dean, W.E., and Stow, D.A.V. : 1983, in : "Fine-Grained Sediments : Processes and Products" , D.A.V. Stow, and D. Piper (Eds), Geol. Soc. Lond., in press.
60. de Graciansky, P.C., Auffret, G.A., Dupeuble, P., Montadert, L., and Müller, C. : 1979n in : "Initial Reports of Deep-sea Drilling Project", L. Montadert, D.G. Roberts et al. (Eds), 48, Washington (U.S. Gvt. Print. Off.), pp. 877-907.
61. Kennedy, W.J., and Garrison, R.E. : 1975, Sedimentology 22, pp. 311-386.
62. van Hinte, J.E. : 1976, Amer. Assoc. Petrol. Geol. Bull. 42, pp. 2696-2717.
63. Obradovich, J.D., and Cobban, W.A. : 1975, in : "The Cretaceous system in the Western Interior of North America",

W.G.E. Caldwell (Ed.), Geol. Assoc. Canada Spec. Pub. 13, pp. 31-54.

64. Harland, W.B., Cox, A.V., Llewellyn, P.G., Pickton, C.A.G., Smith, A.G., and Walters, R. : 1982, "Subdivisions of Phanerozoic Time", Cambridge Univ. Press.
65. Schwartzacher, W., and Fischer, A.G. : 1982, in : G. Einsele, and A. Seilacher (Eds), Springer-Verlag, Berlin, pp. 72-95.
66. Fischer, A.G., and Schwartzacher, W. : 1984, in : "Milankovitch and Climate", A. Berger, J. Imbrie, J. Hays, G. Kukla, B. Saltzman (Eds), Reidel Publ. Company, Holland. This volume, p. 163
67. de Boer, P.L., and Wonders, A.A. : 1984, in : "Milankovitch and Climate", A. Berger, J. Imbrie, J. Hays, G. Kukla, B. Saltzman (Eds), Reidel Publ. Company, Holland. This volume, p. 177.
68. Berger, W.H., and Heath, G.R. : 1968, J. Mar. Res. 26, pp. 134-143.
69. Guinasso, N.L., and Schink, D.R. : 1975, J. Geophys. Res. 80, pp. 3032-3043.
70. Berger, W.H., Johnson, R.F., and Killingley, J.S. : 1977, Nature 267, pp. 661-663.
71. Schlanger, S.O., and Douglas, R.G. : 1974, in : "Pelagic Sediments : On Land and Under the Sea", K.J. Hsü, and H.C. Jenkyns (Eds), Intern. Assoc. Sediment. Spec. Pub. 1, pp. 117-148.
72. Scholle, P.A., Arthur, M.A., and Ekdale, A.A. : 1983, in : P.A. Scholle, C.H. Moore, and D. Bebout (Eds), Amer. Assoc. Petrol. Geol. Memoir 33, Carbonate Environments, pp. 610-691.
73. Baker, P.A., Gieskes, J.M., and Elderfield, H. : 1982, J. Sediment. Petrol. 52, pp. 71.
74. Elderfield, H., et al. : 1982, Geochim. et Cosmochim. Acta 46, pp. 2259.
75. Neugebauer, J. : 1974, in : "Pelagic Sediments on Land and Under the Sea", K.J. Hsü, and H.C. Jenkynbs (Eds), Intern. Assoc. Sediment Spec. Publ. 1, pp. 149-176.
76. Land, L.S. : 1980, in : "Concepts and Models of Dolomitization", D.H. Zenger, J.B. Dunham, and R.L. Ethington (Eds), Soc. Econ. Paleontol. Mineral Spec. Pub. 28, pp. 87-110.
77. Arthur, M.A., and Scholle, P.A. : in prep., "Stable isotopic compositions of Cretaceous inoceramids : changes during chalk diagenesis".
78. Killingley, J.S. : 1983, Nature 301, pp. 594.
79. Savin, S.M. : 1977, Annual Revs. Earth and Planetary Science 5, pp. 319-355.
80. Irvin, H., Curtis, C., and Coleman, M. : 1977, Nature 269, pp. 209-213.

81. Scholle, P.A., and Arthur, M.A. : 1980, Amer. Assoc. Petroleum Geol. Bull. 64, pp. 67-87.
82. Anderson, T.F., and Arthur, M.A. : 1983, in : "Stable Isotopes in Sedimentary Geology", M.A. Arthur, T.F. Anderson, I.R. Kaplan, J. Veizer, and L. Land (Eds), Soc. Econ. Paleont. Mineral Short-Course Notes No.10, pp. 1-116.
83. Garrison, R.G. : 1967, Bull. Canadian Petrol. Geol. 15, pp. 21-49.
84. Ziegler, B. : 1958, Eclogae Geol. Helv. 58, pp. 265-278.
85. Ernst, G., Schmidt, F., and Klischies, G. : 1979, in : "Aspeker Kreide Europas", J. Wiedmann (Ed.), Intern. Union Geol. Series A, no. 6, pp. 11-46.

ICE-AGE ARCTIC OCEAN ICE-SHEETS : A POSSIBLE DIRECT LINK WITH INSOLATION

R.H. Fillon

Baruch Institute and Department of Geology
University of South Carolina, Columbia, South Carolina 29208, USA.

ABSTRACT

Aspects of the deep-sea paleoceanographic record can be satisfactorily explained by the assumption of two volumetrically important Northern Hemisphere ice masses, one centered at middle latitudes on the continents and the other centered in the Arctic Ocean. Insolation at the top of the atmosphere over a middle latitude ice mass would be dominated by precessional frequencies while insolation over the arctic would be governed primarily by obliquity. A new hypothesis of ice accumulation is presented to account for the formation of an Arctic Ocean Ice Sheet without the need for large pre-existing Northern Hemisphere continental ice sheets. In this model, a decline in obliquity decreases insolation at the sea surface in the Arctic. Low insolation then triggers the freezing of river water derived from warmer, southern landmasses directly onto Arctic Ocean sea ice. During periods of low heat input from the North Atlantic Ocean, the net effect would have been the creation and rapid expansion of ice shelves to form an Arctic Ocean Ice Sheet. Mass balance estimates indicate that such an ice sheet could have attained a volume of ca. 11.0 x 10^6 km^3 in less than 5 000 years. If the average $\delta^{18}O$ of this ice was ca. -25°/∘∘ , the approximate composition of the Ward Hunt Ice Shelf, it could have accounted for up to 0.2°/∘∘ or nearly one-fourth of the abrupt $\delta^{18}O$ enrichments seen in deep-sea cores.

A. L. Berger et al. (eds.), Milankovitch and Climate, Part 1, 223–240.

INTRODUCTION

The case for a partly grounded but mostly floating ice sheet in the Arctic Ocean during glacial periods has been forcefully presented in the literature (1, 2, 3, 4). Comparisons with the Antarctic Ice Sheet and theoretical considerations indicate that a glacial-period Arctic Ocean Ice Sheet is thermodynamically feasible. The concept of an Arctic Ocean Ice Sheet helps to explain a wide body of paleoglacial evidence from the surrounding continents (1) and is compatible with glacial-period foraminiferal barren zones in Arctic Ocean deep-sea cores (5, 6).

Published "direct snowfall" and "coalescing ice-shelf" theories of Arctic Ocean Ice Sheet inception (1, 2, 3) have in common the basic premise of two-phase (vapor-solid) aqueous accumulation. In this paper, I will pose an alternative hypothesis describing how Arctic Ocean sea ice, during periods of minimal heat input from the North Atlantic Ocean and reduced high latitude insolation could have been transformed by three-phase (vapor-liquid-solid) accumulation into a massive ^{18}O-depleted ice sheet. The proposed mechanism of Arctic Ocean Ice Sheet growth is appealing for two reasons : 1) unlike existing "coalescing ice-shelf" theories (e.g., 3), it does not require that the continents be extensively glaciated before Arctic Ocean Ice Sheet growth can begin ; and 2) it provides for a much higher rate of growth than can be accounted for solely by direct snowfall accretion onto Arctic Ocean sea ice.

The amount of heat input to the Arctic Ocean from the North Atlantic is a function of oceanic temperatures in the northern North Atlantic. Atlantic warmth is critical to the statibility of ice in the arctic (7). Fortunately for this attempt to model Arctic Ocean Ice Sheet formation, recent work by Ruddiman and McIntyre (8) has shown central subpolar North Atlantic sea-surface temperature to vary in a predictable way with the precession of the equinoxes (9). Changes in high latitude arctic insolation at the top of the atmosphere, on the other hand, are caused by variations in the tilt of the earth's axis. Tilt,or "obliquity", and precession are two of the three mathematically predictable orbital parameters which govern the intensity and distribution of caloric insolation at time scales of ca. 20 000 to 400 000 years (9, 10, 11).

The expected linkages between Arctic Ocean Ice Sheet growth and orbital parameters have been outlined elsewhere (12) and a method presented for assessing long-term trends in the growth of both mid-latitude Northern Hemisphere continental and high-latitude Arctic Ocean ice sheets during the last 5 million years. Using orbital variations as input, empirical equations were used to calculate the tendency for Arctic Ocean Ice Sheet growth and the tendency for continental ice sheet growth. It was assumed that there would have been strong feedback effects between the two ice masses contingent upon North Atlantic surface water heat transport. A correspondence between predicted increased tendency for Arctic Ocean Ice Sheet growth and cold paleotemperatures recorded in North Atlantic deep-sea cores spanning the last 2.0 m.y. is evidence of a long-term linkage with the North Atlantic. Alternatively, strong similarities were found to exist between the predicted record of continental ice sheet growth and the classical terrestrial glacial/interglacial record back to about 3.2 m.y. BP. A marked coincidence was found between the deep-sea $\delta^{18}O$ record which is thought to strongly reflect global ice volume changes (13) and the calculated combined tendency of continental and Arctic Ocean Ice Sheet growth.

The relationships elucidated by Fillon and Williams (12) imply that the Northern Hemisphere may periodically have been host to two volumetrically important ice masses each fluctuating in response to an orbital signal carrying a unique distribution of power within its frequency spectrum. Of course, it is possible that strongly negative feedback between decreased insolation at the top of the atmosphere and increased clould cover and storminess in the arctic would have increased air temperatures at sea level during obliquity minima thus ruling out a direct linkage between Arctic Ocean Ice Sheet growth and caloric insolation in the Arctic. However, one of the principal objectives of this paper is to provide insight into a key simplifying assumption inherent in computational ice-volume models which reasonably (although not perfectly) duplicate the deep-sea $\delta^{18}O$ signal using orbital parameters as input (14, 15, 16, 17). None of these models consider cloud cover and all take into account only Northern Hemisphere continental ice volume. By making an initial assumption that sea level insolationn in the arctic is directly proportional to caloric insolation at the top of the atmosphere, a potential Arctic Ocean Ice Sheet effect can be easily incorporated into existing continental ice sheet models for testing. In fact, today there is an excellent correlation in northern Canada (18) between low insolation at ground level, low average annual temperatures and high latitude (or low annual insolation at the top of the atmosphere). Moreover, the best dated episodes of peak ^{18}O enrichment in the deep-sea, those between about 230 000 B.P. and the present, closely correspond to intervals of reduced obliquity (Table 1).

HOW THREE-PHASE ICE-SHEET ACCUMULATION MIGHT WORK

The Arctic Ocean (Fig. 1) is a cold polar ocean surrounded on all sides by more southerly, less polar landmasses. In the summer months, it receives substantial runoff from rivers drain-

Table 1 The timing of recent obliquity minima and episodes of $\delta^{18}O$ enrichment in the deep-sea.

Obliquity minima (kyr BP) Orbital scale	Obliquity minima (kyr BP) Adjusted to $\delta^{18}O$ scale*	Deviation of Obliquity from Last Cyclic Maximum (9) (+)	Glacial Isotopic Stages	Estimates for the Beginning of Glacial Stages (13,29,38) (kyr BP)
29	32	-2.02°	2	32
70	73	-1.90°	4	75
112	115	-1.91°	5d	115
150	153	-1.77°	6(late)	153
191	194	-1.78°	6(early)	195
232	235	-2.18°	7d	230

+ obliquity minimum (A. Berger, pers. comm., 1982)

*The lead figure in this column was picked to correspond with Shackleton and Opdyke's (13) age estimate for the isotopic stage 3/2 transition. Obliquity at this time was within 0.1° of it cyclic minimum which occured ca. 29 kyr BP. Successive dates were dirived by adding the increments between corresponding minima in the first column.

Table 2 Isotopic, glacial to interglacial transitions corresponding to episodes of constructive interference between precession and obliquity-driven summer insolation.

Subartic Summer-Insolation Maxima due to Interference between obliquity and precession (9) (kyr BP)	^{18}O Glacial-Interglacial Transitions: ^{18}O Stage Boundaries	^{18}O Glacial-Interglacial Transitions: Age Estimates (kyr BP) (13,29,38)	Deviation of Closest Obliquity Maxima from from Last Cyclic Max. (9)
13	2/1	13	0°
83	5b/5a	85	0.05°
127	6/5e	128	0.03°
176	-	-	-0.13°
220	7b/7a	225	0.22°
243	8/7c	251	0.22

ing these warmer landmasses. Therefore, during a period of low obliquity, low caloric insolation at the top of the atmosphere in the arctic and presumed colder annual temperatures over the Arctic Ocean, seasonal discharges of ^{18}O-depleted river water spreading over the coastal sea ice would have been less likely to drain into the sea through holes in the ice as occurs presently (Fig. 2a) along the Beaufort Sea coast (19). Rather, with a shorter ablation period (fewer thawing degree days) shore-fast sea-ice would have been more stable (20) and the thin layers of river water emplaced on shore-fast sea-ice during the spring or summer might have become frozen onto the sea-ice surface (Fig. 2b) prior to (or after) the annual insolation maximum (June 21). The net effect would have been thickening of the ice cover. In this way, the winter and summer precipitation falling over most of arctic and subarctic North America, Europe and Asia including that ablating from continental ice sheets would eventually have been trapped and stored as ^{18}O-depleted ice or impounded in lakes dammed by thickening Arctic Ocean ice. The accumulation of a thick marine ice sheet under these conditions would have been rapid.

The modern Ward Hunt Ice Shelf of northern Ellesmere Island which has no tributary glaciers (21, 22) is situated at 83°N on a portion of coast that is near the pole and therefore has lower annual insolation than any other part of North America (Fig. 1). It is also subject to the coldest yearly average temperatures (ca. -20°C) on the continent (18). So, it seems that the WHIS depends for survival on low insolation and low ablation as would an ice sheet formed by three-phase accumulation.

Large glacial lakes in northward-draining Siberian river valleys are known to have been dammed to levels ca. 130 meters above present sea level by Arctic Ocean continental shelf-based ice of the Northern Eurasian Ice Sheet during the Late Wechselian (23). If portions of the Northern Eurasian Ice Sheet which grounded in the Arctic Ocean are considered to have been built by snowfall accretion in the normal "two-phase" manner of continental ice sheets, one has to ask what became of the north-flowing rivers during the early stages of ice sheet growth, i.e., before the ice sheet was high enough ($\geq$ 130 meters above present sea level in the river valleys) to divert Elster, Weichsel, Severnaya Dvina, Mezen, Pechora, Ob, Irtysh and Yenisei water southward toward the Caspian and Black Seas ? According to Grosswald (23), at its maximum, the Northern Eurasian Ice Sheet had a smaller area ($8.37 \times 10^6 km^2$) than the combined catchment basins of the northern Eurasian rivers (ca. $10.0 \times 10^6 km^2$). It follows that during the early stages of ice sheet growth, the discharges of the northern rivers must have far exceeded the volume of direct snowfall on the ice sheet. Surely, as the initial lobes of ice advanced into the broad ri-

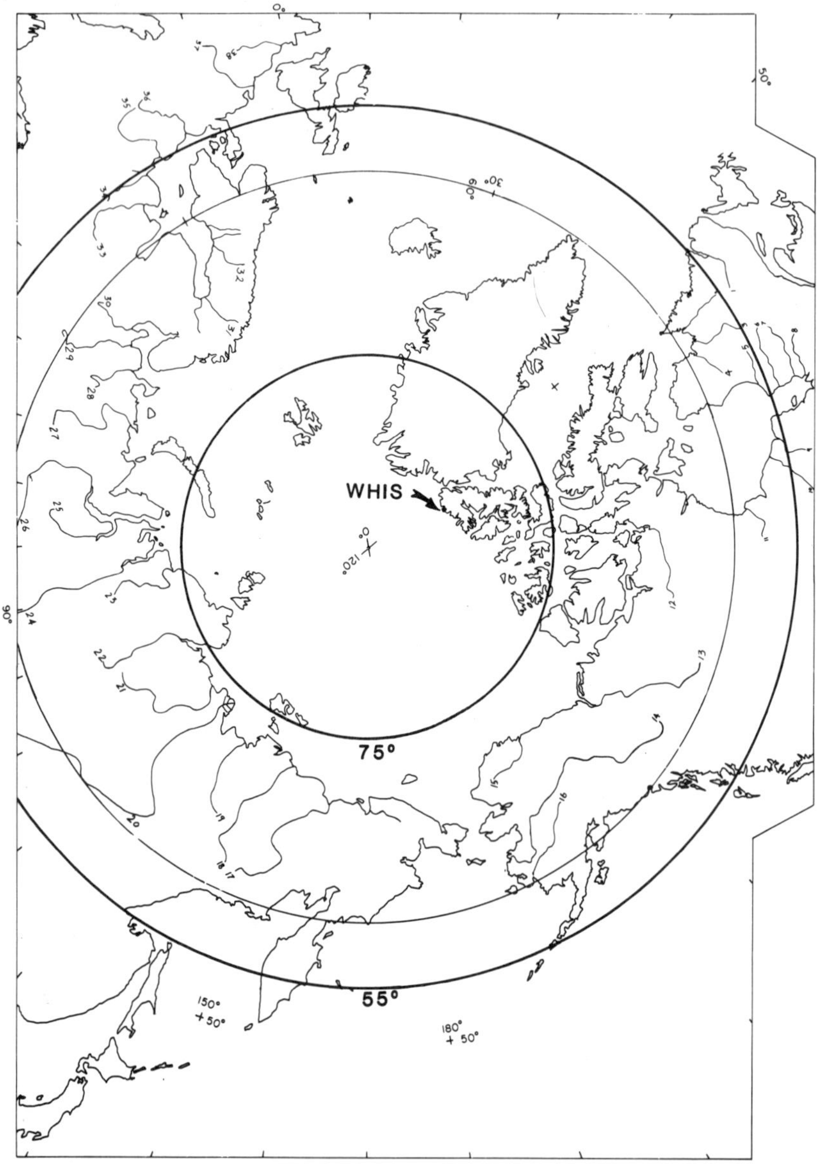

Figure 1 Map of the Arctic Ocean and surrounding areas showing 38 major arctic and subarctic rivers and the Ward Hunt Ice Shelf (WHIS).

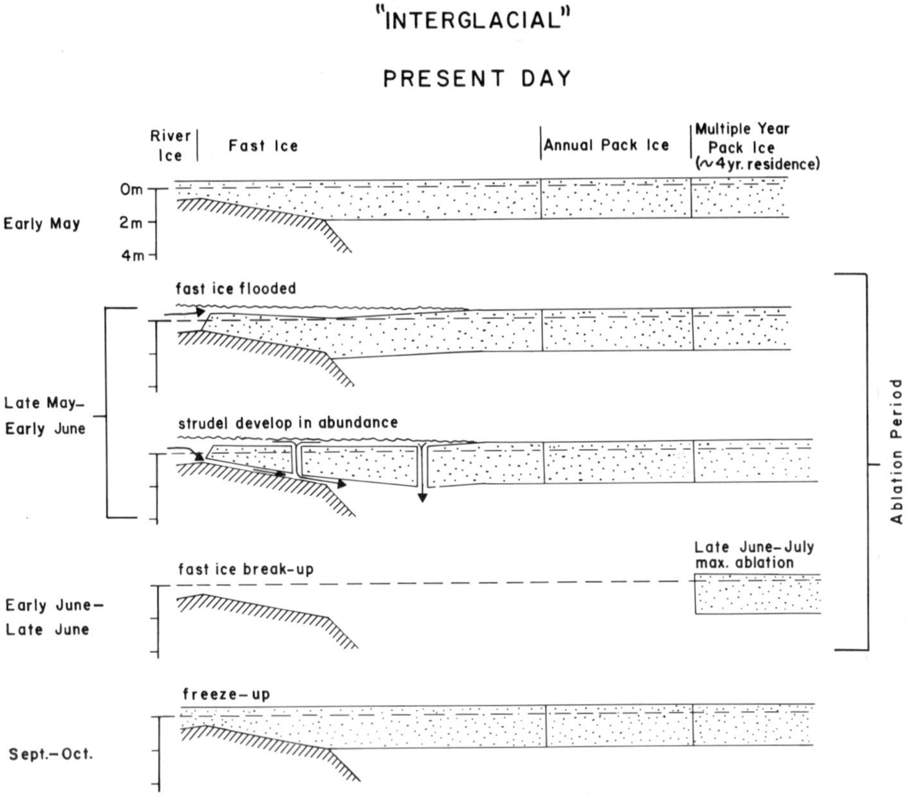

Figure 2a River/sea-ice interaction in the modern high insolation, high ablation Beaufort Sea environment (19).

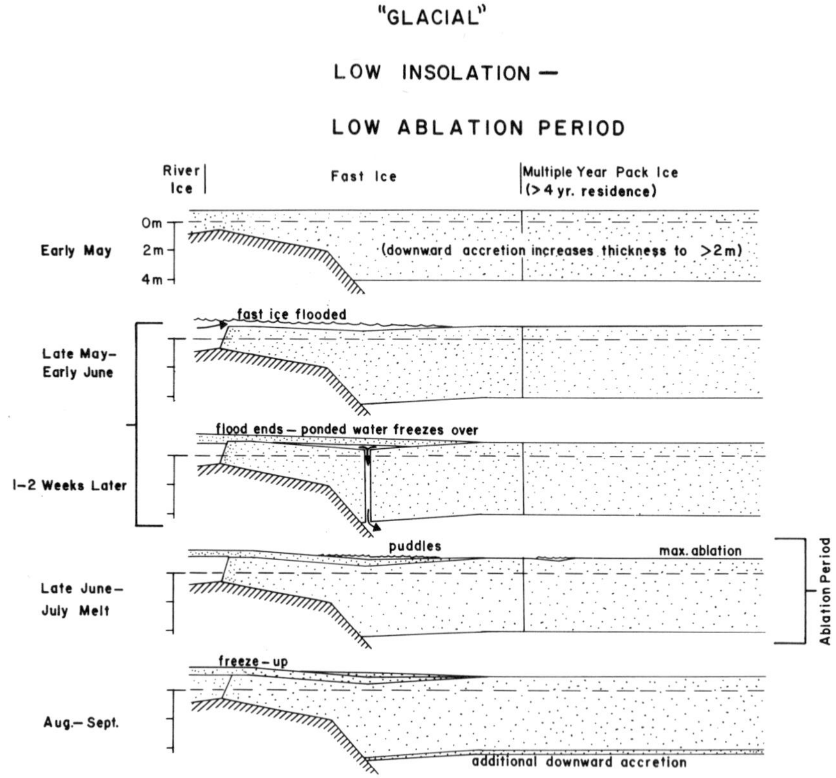

Figure 2b Schematic representation of three-phase ice-accumulation in the Arctic Ocean under conditions of continued run-off from subarctic rivers, low arctic insolation, and a relatively short sea-ice ablation period for the Beaufort Sea region.

ver valleys of the arctic coastal plain, the rivers would have continued to flow, spilling across (or under, 24) the ice sheet and melting the obstructing ice. That is, unless at some stage annual temperatures were cold enough to cause substantial amounts of river water to freeze in winter and to remain frozen during the short spring/summer ablation period. It is possible, then, that the freezing-on of river water would have contributed more than snowfall accretion to the rapid growth of marine portions of the early Northern Eurasian Ice Sheet. Once thickened sufficiently by freezing river discharge to divert river drainage to the south, the ice sheet may then have continued to expand and thicken, albeit at a relatively slower rate by the direct accumulation of snow on its surface. If the sea stood below its present level when the rivers were diverted, the height of ice dams above the contemporary sea level would have been higher than the ca. 130 meter level observed for lake deposits by an amount equal to the sea level lowering.

The reasoning set forth above in response to unanswered questions concerning the initial formation of the Northern Eurasian Ice Sheet can be extended to the entire Arctic Ocean by considering some possible geographical constraints and mass balances. Mercer (1) estimated the calving rate for a mature ice sheet covering the entire Arctic Ocean to be 3.0×10^5 km^3/1 000 yr ; but, the rate could well have been higher in a developing ice sheet which would have had a longer calving margin, ca. 6 000 km for the Northern Eurasian Ice Sheet compared to less than 2 000 km for a possible ice front between Greenland and Europe. If the modern export rate of sea ice, which amounts to 1.2×10^6 km^3/1 000 yr (25) is doubled and this figure taken as representative of a higher initial flux of freshwater ice out of the Arctic Ocean (eight time Mercer's estimate) and assuming that the volume of runoff into the Arctic Ocean was similar to today's ca. 4.0×10^6 km^3/1 000 yr (25), it is apparent that an ice sheet/glacial lake complex roughly 100 meters in height above sea level, ca. 3 000 meters thick over the deep basins, ca. 300 meters thick over the shelf areas and with a total volume of ca. 11.0×10^6 km^3 could have accumulated in about 4 000 years even if the export of ice from the Arctic Ocean continued at the very high initial rate. In fact, precipitation falling directly on the Arctic Ocean at the modern rate of 10 cm of water/yr (1×10^{-1} km/yr) (25) would have contributed another 8.0×10^5 km^3 of ^{18}O-depleted ice each 1 000 years. A steep, ca. 50%/1 000 yr exponential decrease in the export rate of ice over the period to reach Mercer's (1) estimate of 3.0×10^5 km^3/1 000 yr could have further speeded ice sheet growth, bringing the length of time necessary to build a 11.0×10^6 km^3 ice sheet down to a little less than 3 000 years.

The distribution of major rivers emptying into the Arctic Oean would have ultimately controlled the configuration of an ice sheet accreting from river runoff. It is likely that, at first, fan-shaped ice shelves wold have developed off major river mouths. These would have rapidly increased in area across the broad, shallow, continental shelves of arctic Siberia to form a coalescent ice sheet grounded to the shelf edge (Fig. 3). Next, the initially thinner ice over the deep, central Arctic Ocean basins would have begun to thicken. On reaching a thickness of ca. 1 000 meters, the ice sheet would have grounded on most of the Lomonosov Ridge which separates the American Basin from the Eurasian Basin, leaving only restricted passages for the flow of bottom water (1 000 m contour, and dashed arrows in Fig. 2). Reflection seismic records and cores indicating a very thin or non-existent layer of unconsolidated sediments on the Lomonosov Ridge above about 3 000 meters water depth and probable slumping dwn its flanks (26) are not inconsistent with grounded ice on the ridge in the relatively recent past.

During disintegration, the ice sheet would have been most vulnerable where it was thinnest, along its continental southern periphery. Insolation-driven ablation, strongest at low arctic latitudes, would have lowered the height of the ice surface near the coast diverting river runoff and meltwater drainage away from the colder, higher center of the ice sheet and into an ice marginal drainage system (23 - Urstromtal Warsaw-Berlin, his Fig. 7). The freshwater, a combination of river runoff and meltwater, would have eventually debauched into the sea at the thinnest margins of the ice sheet (black arrows in Fig. 3) to nourish meltwater layers in the marginal seas.

Once the continental shelves had been cleared of their relativey thin ice load and rivers had again begun to reoccupy their old valleys, the locus of sediment deposition would have shifted from ice marginal lakes to marine embayments dammed to seaward by a thick arctic ice plug remaining over the continental slope. When that ice too finally disintegrated, the seaward edges of sedimentary deposits on the shelf would have suddenly become unstable. High-resolution seismic studies of the Beafort shelf and slope, in fact, clearly document a period of massive slumping of unconsolidated sediments over relatively more competent deposits on the upper continental slope (27 and S.M. Blasco, pers. Comm., 1982).

SEQUENCE AND TIMING OF EVENTS IN THE ARCTIC

The probable interrelationships between obliquity and precession-dominated climatic/oceanographic parameters during the growth and decay of a marine ice sheet in the Arctic Ocean are

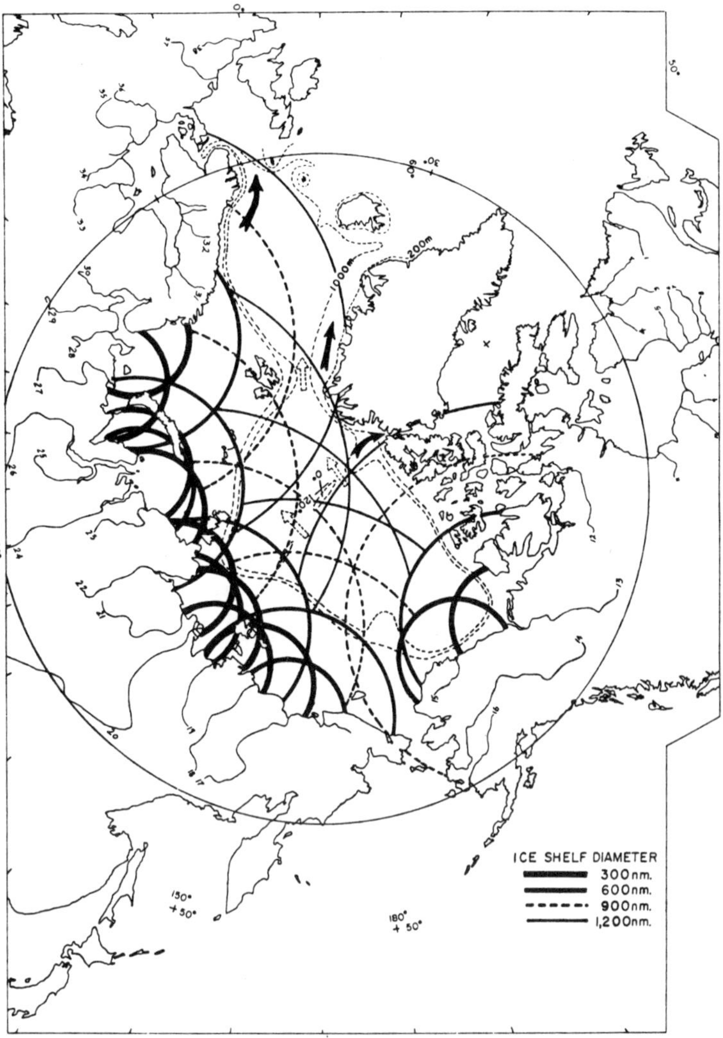

Figure 3 Schematic illustration of the growth of overlapping ice shelves fed by the direct conversion of river runoff into ice (hypothetical three-phase accumulation). The configuration portrayed here predicts that a large Arctic Ocean Ice Sheet would remain thinnest and its surface lowest off northern and eastern Greenland. Accordingly, during disintegration, these regions were probably loci for the escape of meltwater (black arrows). The expulsion of seawater from beneath the thickening ice sheet is depicted by the dashed arrows. Ice shelf diameters are given in nautical miles (nm.), 1 nm. = 1 minute of latitude = 1.853 km.

summarized in Figure 4. Because the periodicity of arctic insolation changes is just about twice that of mid-latitude North-Atlantic surface-water-temperature fluctuations (41 000 years and 23 000 years respectively), only two fundamentally different phase relationships can occur (Fig. 4a, b).

The foregoing suggests that fully interglacial $\delta^{18}O$ depletion in the deep-sea record would not appear at either the obliquity or precessional frequencies but would depend on an interference between these two cycles. This can be tested by searching Berger's (9) obliquity and precession cycles for intervals with the same relationship between obliquity and precession that obtained during the last glacial-interglacial transition, i.e., at 13 000 BP. At 13 000 BP, there was a maximum negative deviation of Berger's (9, 11) precessional term [$\Delta(e \sin \tilde{\omega})$] from its 1950 A.D. value coincident with high obliquity (greater than the 232 000 year mean of 23.3°). The results of this search (Table 2) are in good agreement with published benthic isotopic curves (8, 28, 29).

The only astronomically predicted date in Table 2 that does not closely correspond to a $\delta^{18}O$ change of more than -1.0‰ at a glacial stage-interglacial stage transition is 176 000 BP which does, however, coincide with a lesser change of ca. -0.5‰ (8). The relatively low value of the susequent cyclic obliquity maximum centered at 169 000 BP (9) which has an amplitude 17 percent below the average for cyclic obliquity maxima during the last 230 000 years (Table 2) may have been sufficient in itself to protect an Arctic Ocean Ice Sheet from complete destruction at 176 000 BP, and hence to abort a potential interglacial $\delta^{18}O$ depletion in the oceans.

Figure 5 summarizes the relationships outlined above for the last 220 000 years and suggests a possile sequence of Arctic Ocean events for that period.

IMPLICATIONS FOR THE $\delta^{18}O$ RECORD IN OPEN-OCEAN CORES

Very rapid ($\lesssim$5,000 yr) enrichments of over +1.0‰ are common in benthic $\delta^{18}O$ records obtained from high-resolution deep-sea cores (8, 30, 31) but have resisted a full explanation in terms of temperature change and continental ice volume by paleoceanographers (32) and modelers of continental ice growth. For example, Adrews and Mahaffy (33) computed a maximum sea level lowering of -2.5 meters during the first 5 000 years of North American ice sheet growth and -20 meters during the first 10 000 years of growth -equivalent to a ca. 0.2‰ $\delta^{18}O$ enrichment in the oceans. The <u>maximum</u> effect of bottom-water cooling (ca. 2°C) in the deep-sea <u>is likely</u> to have been an additional 0.5‰

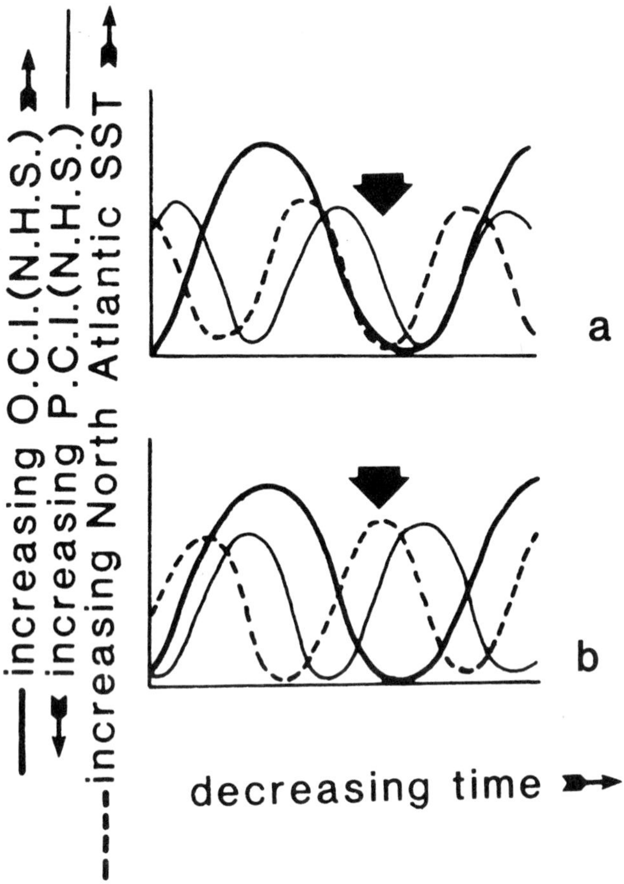

Figure 4 Two contrasting phase relationships between : the obliquital component of insolation (O.C.I.) for the Northern Hemisphere caloric summer and the filtered 23 000 year period component of North Atlantic summer sea-surface temperature (SST). In "a" (large arrow) the North Atlantic is cold late in the decline to an obliquity minimum (see Figure 5) while in "b" (large arrow), the North Atlantic is warm late in the decline to an obliquity minimum. The lag between P.C.I. maxima and SST maxima is about 9 000 years (8). The average period of O.C.I. is just about twice that of P.C.I., ca. 41 000 years and 23 000 years respectively.

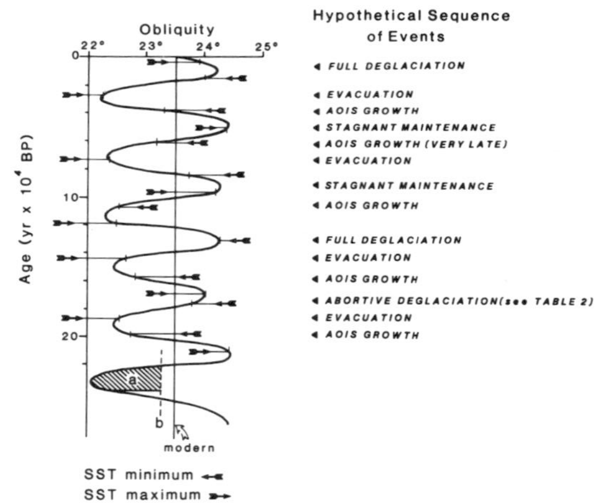

Figure 5 Obliquity variations plotted against time (9) with North Atlantic summer surface-water temperature (SST) maxima and minima (8) indicated for the last 211 000 years. "a", the shaded zone, is the period referred to in the text as beginning "late in an obliquity decline". If a North Atlantic sea-surface temperature minimum falls in this interval (Fig. 4a), marine ice sheets should be stable in the arctic. If a North Atlantic sea-surface temperature maximum falls in this interval (Fig. 4b), marine ice sheets in the arctic should begin breaking up with full removal being accomplished during the succeeding obliquity maximum. The precise limits of "a" are presently indeterminate. The upper limit depends on "b" - the critical level of obliquity (below the modern value) necessary to trigger widespread three-phase accumulation. The lower limit depends on the spacing between individual North Atlantic sea-surface temperature maxima and minima (23 000 years is only an average). The hypothetical sequence of events listed in the figure was constructed using the arbitrary but reasonable proportions for "a" given in the example. AOIS = Arctic Ocean Ice Sheet.

$\delta^{18}O$ enrichment (2) leaving ≥ 0.3 °/₀₀ of the observed "rapid" enrichments still unexplained in dep-sea cores. An ice sheet of ca. 11.0 x 10^6 km^3 volume in the Arctic Ocean could have produced a possible 0.3°/₀₀ oceanic $\delta^{18}O$ enrichment assuming an average isotopic composition of the ice sheet of ca. -40 °/₀₀ . This is probably too low an isotopic depletion estimate for a three-phase ice sheet. Present day average annual $\delta^{18}O$ (vs. SMOW) vaues for snow and rain in interior Canada (Alberta) which give an indication of the composition of river discharge are in the range of -20°/₀₀ (34). Snow and rain falling directly onto the ice sheet (which could have contributed up to one-third as much ice as river discharge - see earlier discussion) may have averaged only slightly lighter than -20°/₀₀ which is the estimated annual mean for precipitation falling near sea level in northeastern Greenland (34). Iced firn on the Ward Hunt Ice Shelf averages about -28°/₀₀ (35). If the mean $\delta^{18}O$ composition of precipitation falling during obliquity minima was also close to -25°/₀₀, an 11.0 x 10^6 km^3 Artic Ocean Ice Sheet would have effected only a 0.2°/₀₀ oceanic enrichment in $\delta^{18}O$.

The hypothesis of three-phase accumulation outlined in this paper requires less than 5 000 years in which to produce an Arctic Ocean ice volume of ca. 11.0 x 10^6 km^3. Accordingly, a combined 0.9°/₀₀ $\delta^{18}O$ enrichment in deep-sea would be possible after less than 10 000 years of bottom-water cooling, continental ice sheet growth and three-phase Arctic Ocean Ice Sheet accumulation even if the average isotopic composition of river runoff and snowfall which contributed to the Arctic Ocean Ice Sheet was only -25°/₀₀.

IMPLICATIONS FOR "GLACIAL" BOTTOM-WATER

Bottom-water cooling toward the final stages of Arctic Ocean Ice Sheet growth could have been stimulated by increased radiative cooling at the sea surface and sinking in the high latitude North Atlantic, brought about by higher surface salinities and decreased winter sea-ice cover. Somewhat earlier, however, water expressed from the upper 3 000 meters of the Arctic Ocean Basin by a thickening marine ice sheet would also have impacted on the nature of oceanic deep-water. In the upper 2 000 meters of the Arctic Ocean today, temperatures range from -1.8° to +0.5°C and salinities from ca. 33.0°/₀₀ in the uppermost 400 meters to a rather constant 34.9°/₀₀ below that (36). The O_2 content of this presently well-oxygenated watermass would presumably have been depleted by respiratory activity during the initial stages of ice sheet cover which, as mentioned earlier, would have been accompanied by cooler, lower salinity North Atlantic surface-waters and diminished thermohaline driven circulation between the Altantic and the

Arctic Oceans. The approximately 11 x 10^6 km^3 of this cold, potentially O_2-depleted water, which would have entered the world ocean during ca. 5 000 years of Arctic Ocean Ice Sheet growth, may thus have been a factor contributing to a "glacial period" deep bottom water cooling and to the proliferation of the benthic foraminifer Uvigerina peregrina which apparently favors low O_2 conditions (28). Major North Altantic abundance peaks of U. peregrina culminating in the early and latter parts of isotopic stage 3, in isotopic substage 5d, and in isotopic stage 6 (28) can be compared with Figure 5. North Atlantic U. peregrina maxima may well correspnd to periods favorable to Arctic Ocean Ice Sheet growth beginning at about 38 000 BP, 61 000 BP, 107 000 BP and 157 000 BP It will be interesting to see in future work if the frequency spectra (37) of U. peregrina abundance in cores with long time series differ from $\delta^{18}O$ spectra in a manner consistent with the contrasting time-series predicted for Arctic Ocean Ice Sheet and global ice volume (12).

CONCLUDING REMARKS

High resolution seismic and ^{14}C-calibrated core studies of Arctic Ocean continental margin sediments and the examination of isotopic and micropaleontological data bearing on the salinity and temperature histories of seas marginal to the Arctic Ocean will be the principal means of assessing the validity of the concept of an Arctic Ocean Ice Sheet in subsequent research. The idea expressed in this paper that Arctic Ocean Ice Sheet development would be enhanced at times of low obliquity and low North Atlantic sea surface temperature can also be tested. The concept of two partially independent ice masses, one at arctic latitudes with a relatively quick response time, and the other at subarctic/temperate latitudes with a longer response time can be incorporated in future attempts to model net cryospheric response to orbital variations. If this results in an improved prediction of deep-sea $\delta^{18}O$ records as preliminary experiments suggests (12) it can be taken as support for the hypothesis outlined above.

ACKNOWLEDGMENTS

Various aspects of this paper have benefited thanks to constructive discussions with R. Barry, W. Ruddiman and D. Williams. I would also like to thank R. Harmes for drafting assistance. J. Fillon provided indespensible encouragement. This work was supported by NSF grant AFM-8100424.

REFERENCES

1. Mercer, J.H. : 1970, Palaeogeography, Palaeoclimatology, Palaeoecology 8, pp. 19-27.
2. Broecker, W.S. : 1975, Science 188, pp. 1116-1118.
3. Hughes, T., Denton, G.H. and Grosswald, M.G. : 1977, Nature 266, pp. 596-602.
4. Denton, G.H. and Hughes, T. : 1981, in "The last great ice sheets", Denton, G.H. and Hughes, T, eds., New York, John Wiley & Sons, pp. 440-468.
5. van Donk, J. and Mathieu, G. : 1969, J. Geophys. Res. 74, pp. 3396-3407.
6. Larson, J.A. : 1975, Geology 3, pp. 491-492.
7. Crary, A.P. : 1960, Arctic 13, 32-50.
8. Ruddiman, W.F. and McIntyre, A. : 1981, Science 212, pp. 617-627.
9. Berger, A.L. : 1978, Quaternary Research 9, pp. 139-167.
10. Milankovitch, M.M. : 1941, in "Canon of insolation and the Ice Age problem", Royal Serbian Acadmey Special Publ. 133 (translation publ. by the U.S. Dept. of Commerce and the National Science Foundation, 1969, Washington, D.C.).
11. Berger, A.L. : 1977, Nature, pp. 44-45.
12. Fillon, R.H. and Williams, D.F. : 1983, Palaeogeography, -climatology, -ecology 42, pp. 7-33.
13. Shackleton, N.J. and Opdyke, N.D. : 1973, Quaternary Research 3, pp. 39-55.
14. Calder, N. : 1974, Nature 252, pp. 216-218.
15. Imbrie, J. and Imbrie, J.Z. : 1980, Science 207, pp. 943-953.
16. Birchfield, G.E., Weertaman, J. and Lunde, A.T. : 1981, Quaternary Research 15, pp. 126-142.
17. Kukla, G., Berger, A., Lotti, R. and Brown, J. : 1981, Nature 290, pp. 295-300.
18. Atlas of Climatic Maps, 1970, Series 1 to 10, Canada Department of Transport, Meteorological Branch, Ottawa, Canada.
19. Reimnitz, E. and Bruder, K.F. : 1972, Geological Soc. of America Bull. 83, pp. 861-866.
20. Barry, R.G., Moritz, R.E. and Rogers, J.C. : 1979, Cold Regions Science and Technology 1, pp. 129-152.
21. Crary, A.P. : 1958, Arctic 11, pp. 3-42.
22. Hattersley-Smith, G. : 1963, J. of Glaciology 4, pp. 415-424.
23. Grosswald, M.G.: 1980, Quaternary Research 13, pp. 1-32.
24. Blachut, S.P. and McCann, S.B. : 1981, Arctic and Alpine Research 13, pp. 63-74.
25. Mosby, H. : 1963, in "Water, salt and heat balance in the North Polar Sea : Proceedings Arctic Basin Symposium",

October 1962, Arctic Institute of North America, Washington, D.C. pp. 69-89.
26. Blasco, S.M., Bornhold, B.D. and Lewis, C.F.M. : 1979, in "Current Research", part C, Geological Survey of Canada, Paper 79-1C, pp. 73-83.
27. O'Connor, M.J. and Associates Ltd, 1981 : Morphology of the shelf edge : a report on the southern Beaufort Sea. (prepared for the Geological Survey of Canada) : unpublished manuscript.
28. Streeter, S.S. and Shackleton, N.J., Science 203, pp. 168-171.
29. Shackleton, N.J. and Matthews, R.K. : 1977, Nature 268, pp. 618-620.
30. Duplessy, J.C. : 1978, in "Climatic Change", Gribbin, J., ed., Cambridge, England, Cambridge University Press, pp. 46-67.
31. Ruddiman, W.F., McIntyre, A., Neibler-Hunt, V. and Durazzi, J.T. : 1980, Quaternary Research 13, 33-64.
32. Williams, D.F., Moore, W.S. and Fillon, R.H. : 1981, Earth and Planet. Sci. Lett. 56, pp. 157-166.
33. Andrews, J.T. and Mahaffy, M.A.W. : 1976, Quaternary Research 6, pp. 167-184.
34. Dansgaard, W. : 1964, Tellus 16, pp. 436-468.
35. Lyons, J.B., Savin, S.M. and Tamburi, A.J. : 1971, J. of Glaciology 10, pp. 93-100.
36. Kinney, P., Arhelger, M.E. and Burrell, D.C. : 1970, J. Geophys. Res. 75, pp. 4097-4104.
37. Hays, J.D., Imbrie, J. and Shackleton, N.J. : 1976, Science 194, pp. 1121-1132.
38. Ninkovitch, D. and Shackleton, N.J. : 1975, Earth and Planet. Sci. Lett. 27, pp. 20-34.

LATE NEOGENE ARCTIC PALEOCEANOGRAPHY: MICROPALEONTOLOGY AND CHRONOLOGY

Y. Herman[1], J.K. Osmond[2]

[1]Washington State University, Pullman, WA99164, USA
[2]Florida State University, Tallahassee, FL 3206, USA

ABSTRACT

Sediment cores from the Arctic Ocean yield evidence of three major oceanic-climatic regimes (represented by stratigraphic units) during the last 4.5-5 m.y. The evolution of these regimes appears to have been linked to global climatic, hydrologic and tectonic events. The oldest unit (III) comprises sediments deposited between ∿5 and 3 m.y. when the Arctic Ocean was cold but free of perennial ice. Unit II records a drastically altered oceanographic regime: a climatic threshold was crossed ∿3 m.y. ago with the development of sharp salinity-density stratification. Reduced planktonic foraminiferal production was due to decreased nutrients and low salinities during a warmer interval. Another oceanic-climatic threshold was crossed ∿ 0.9 m.y. ago with the inception of a perennial sea ice cover: this event marks the deposition of foraminifera rich sediments representing the third climatic-oceanic regime. The late Quaternary high amplitude long period (> 20 kyr) temperature fluctuations are probably also recorded in the Arctic sediments.

INTRODUCTION

The climatic history of the Arctic has been a matter of debate ever since the systematic sampling and study of sea-floor sediments commenced several decades ago. The early Soviet investigators (1) using "radium distribution" in sedimentary cores estimated that rates of sediment accumulation in the entire basin were 1.2 - 2 cm/10^3 years. These values are an order of magnitude higher than rates obtained by Ku and Broecker

A. L. Berger et al. (eds.), Milankovitch and Climate, Part 1, 241–250.

(2) based on uranium series isotope dates of one core. Linkova (3) was the first to determine the magnetic polarity of Arctic basin sedimentary cores. Her studies demonstrated conclusively that sediment accumulation rates on topographic highs such as the Lomonosov Ridge are extremely low, on the order of 1-3 mm/10^3 years. Similar results were obtained by Hunkins and others for the Alpha-Mendeleev Rise (4). The early (1) Russian geologists interpreted the uppermost 10-15 cm thick brown foraminiferal sandy-clay layer which covers vast areas of the sea floor to represent Postglacial deposits, while the underlying olive green and olive gray foraminifera-poor "glacial marine sediments" were thought to have accumulated during colder, glacial epochs (1). Subsequently, Clark (5) adapted the Russian interpretation and surmised that the Arctic has been covered continuously with perennial ice since middle Cenozoic time (~35 m.y. ago) to the present. According to Clark (5) the ice cover was much thicker during the deposition of the "foraminifera-poor" beds than today. In contrast, Herman (6,7) suggested that the foraminifera-poor zones were deposited during warmer global temperatures than those of today. These were deglacial periods when meltwater, ice shelves, and icebergs flooded the Arctic forming a low density surface layer (6) with salinities of 29 ‰ and temperatures of ~ +1.5°C based on the oxygen isotopic composition of Arctic planktonic foraminifera (8).

SEDIMENTARY RECORD

The sedimentary record representing roughly the last 4.5-5 m.y. is preserved in deep-sea cores raised by the Lamont-Doherty Geological Observatory (LDGO) from ice platforms drifting over the Arctic basin. In this article we discuss two Alpha-Mendeleev Rise cores sampled at 2-10 cm intervals for microfaunal analyses and uranium series isotope determinations (Figs. 1,2,3). These two cores are reprepsentative of the other sedimentary cores from the same physiographic province previously studied by one of us (Y.H.) (Table 1; 6,7,8). Uranium series isotopes, magnetic polarity time scale (4) and foraminiferal biostratigraphy provide the time framework for our paleoceanographic reconstructions (Figs. 1,2,3). Three major climatic regimes, here represented by three stratigraphic units, are recognized within this time interval. Age assignments beyond the Olduvai events are based on a small number of magnetic determinations and should be considered provisional and subject to modifications as additional determinations become available.

Rates of sedimentation were very low and variable ranging between ~ 5 mm - < 1 mm/10^3 yrs during the time interval represented by the studied cores. Ice rafted debris (IRD) is scatte-

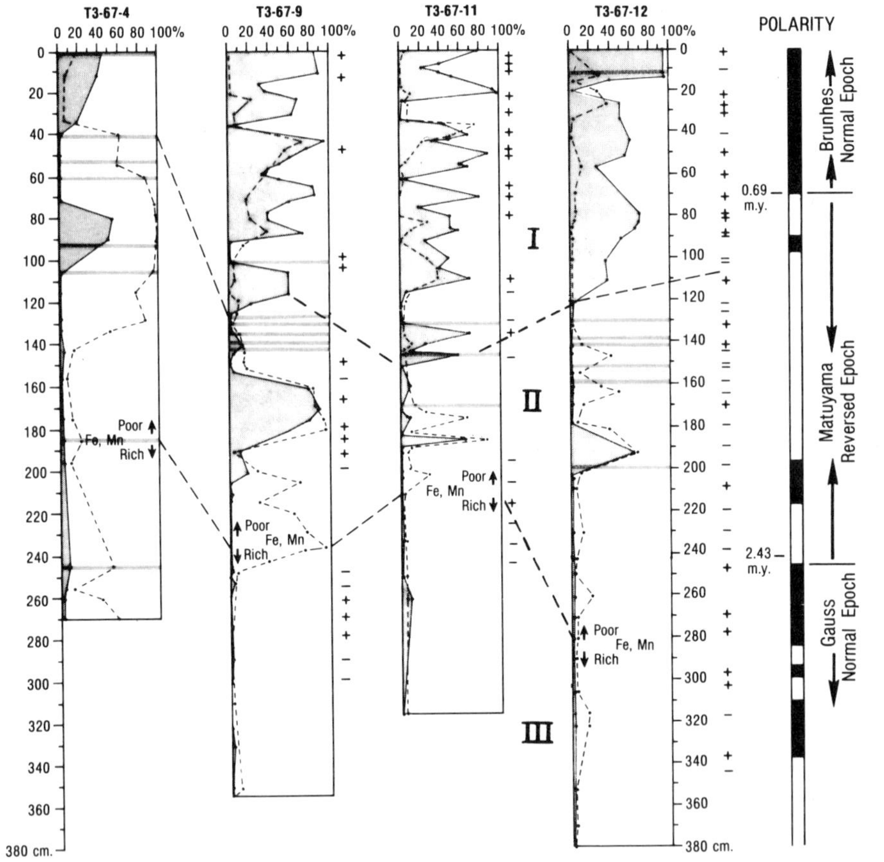

Figure 1 Paleomagnetic time scale (right) and percentage of micro-fauna in coarse fraction (>63μ) in cores T3-67-4, -9, -11, and -12. In core diagrams, shaded areas represent the microfauna, white areas the clastic particles. Dashed line represents the percentage of G. quinqueloba and G. egelida. Dark horizontal bands are zones in which benthonic foraminifers constitute >10% of the total fauna. Asterisk (*), low latitude planktonic foraminifera; plus and minus (+,-), are magnetic polarity determinations made in cores T3-67-9, -11 and -12. Figure modified after Herman, 1974 (7). Magnetic stratigraphy after Hunkins et al., 1971 (4). Long dashed lines indicate I/II and II/III unit boundaries.

red throughout the sediments in all three units. However, there is a marked increase in the abundance and size of the IRD in unit II as compared to unit III. There is evidence of extensive sediment mixing by deposit feeding infauna in all three units but burrow frequency is highest in unit III. Low latitude planktonic foraminifera occur infrequently, in low percentages (Fig. 1). Their presence has been discussed by Herman in numerous publications (6-10). It has been suggested that they may have been carried by currents and either deposited onto the sea floor or on Arctic shelves. Subsequently, they were incorporated into grounded ice. During periods of calving and drift over the Arctic, the incorporated debris was released to the sea floor. In sediments older than 3 m.y. they could have been transported by currents or were upwardly reworked. The oldest, unit III, comprising sediments deposited between 4.5 to 5 and 2.8 to 3 m.y. BP consists of fairly well sorted dark brown sandy-clays. Polar planktonic foraminifera dominate the preserved assemblages and exhibit evidence of dissolution, the benthonic/planktonic foraminiferal ratios are high and agglutinated shells prevail. Unit II sediments deposited between ∿3 and 0.9 m.y. ago consists of olive gray and green sandy-clays with rare faunal remains. The planktonic foraminifers are dominated by solution susceptible subpolar eurythermal, euryhaline Globigerina egelida (Cifelli and Smith) and Globigerina quinqueloba Natland (Fig. 1). The boundary between units II and I records another climatic threshold. The disappearance of G. egelida and the decrease in proportion of subpolar dextral (d) G.pachyderma (Fig. 2) and d. G. cryophila indicates that water temperatures dropped to present-day levels ∿ 0.9 m.y. ago. The base of unit I is identified by the deposition of the first foraminifera-rich bed dominated by sinistral, polar, G. pachyderma and G. cryophila complex (Figs. 1,2: T3-67-3: 230 cm; T3-67-9: 115 cm; T3-67-11: 145 cm; and T3-67-12: 110 cm) and is dated to about 0.9 m.y. (Figs. 1,2). Polar species are dominant, although G. quinqueloba attains peak abundances during short periods (Fig. 1) and is a valuable time marker.

Gamma Spectrometry

The ^{230}Th method of dating deep sea deposits is based on the accumulation with sediment of excess ^{230}Th ($T_{1/2}$=75 000 yrs.) derived from dissolved ^{234}U in the ocean water above (11,12,13). The gamma-ray variation of the ^{230}Th method measures, non-destructively, ^{214}Bi, a short-lived daughter in the ^{230}Th chain (14).

In cores T3-67-3 and T3-67-12, the ratio of the gamma radioactivity of ^{214}Bi to that of ^{40}K plus ^{208}Tl (daughter of

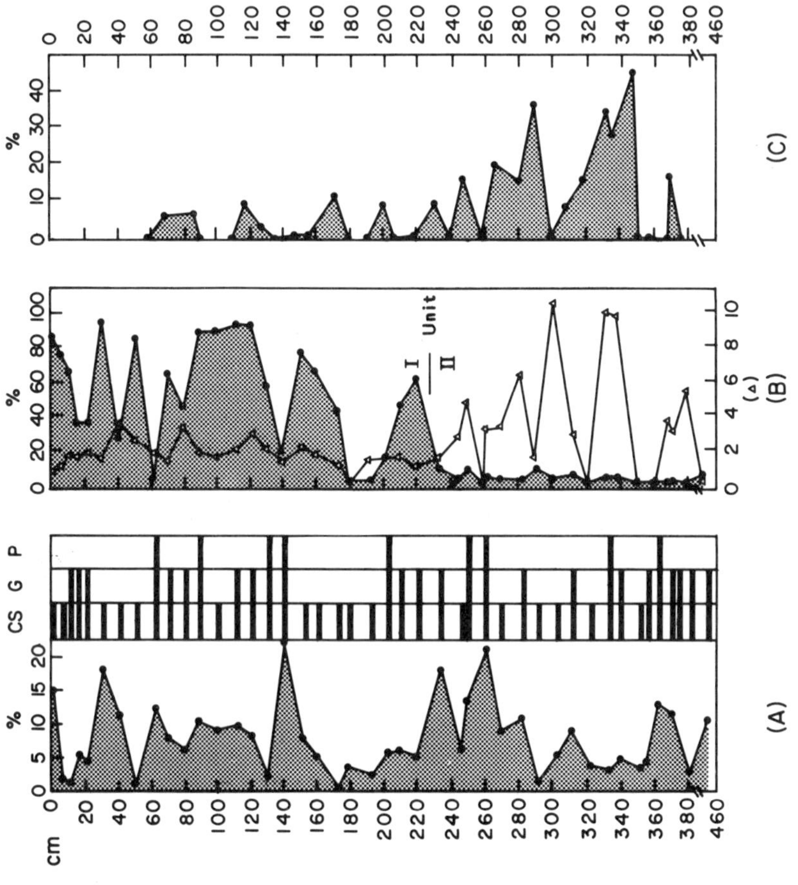

Figure 2 Core T3-67-3: (A) Percentage of coarse fraction (>63μ). CS-coarse sand; G=granules; P=pebbles. (B) Percentage of microfauna in the coarse fraction (>63μ). Shaded areas represent the microfauna, white areas the clastics; values are indicated at the top of the diagram. Open triangles - percentage of dextral G. pachyderma out of the toabcissa at the bottom of the diagram. (C) Percentage of Elphidium spp. out of the total benthonic foraminiferal fauna, an indicator of ice rafting. Core depth in cm.

^{232}Th) was determined at 5 to 10 cm intervals, and the amount attributable to unsupported ^{230}Th determined by substracting the

Table 1 Locations, depths and lengths of cores.

Core	Latitude	Longitude	Depth (m)	Length (cm)
T3-67-3	79°11'N	175°09'W	2285	380
T3-67-4	79°22.7'N	174°46'W	1760	272
T3-67-9	79°37.9'N	172°07'W	2237	356
T3-67-11	79°34.9'N	172°30'W	2810	250
T3-67-12	80°21.9'N	173°33'W	2867	374

relatively constant values for this ratio found lower in the core. Measurements were made with a 3x3" shielded NaI crystal coupled to a 256 channel pulse height analyzer, with 24 hours being the counting time per sample point. The excess ^{230}Th data are plotted in Figure 3. In both cores, the excess values decrease in a generally logarithmic fashion consistent with the excess accumulation model, and enabling reliable average sediment accumulation rates to be inferred. In general with respect to ^{230}Th dating, horizon ages and sediment accumulation rates are most accurately determined when such rates are on the order of a few mm per 10^3 yrs., as in the case of these Arctic Ocean cores. The observed variations about a smooth logarithmic decay (Fig. 3) are outside of the uncertainty range of counting statistics, and can be used to recognize changes in sediment accumulation conditions. The actual interpretation given to such variations, however, depends on the model of ^{230}Th accumulation one uses (12). If one assumes that the generation of ^{230}Th from dissolved uranium in the sea is less variable than the supply of sediment (constant flux model), then the horizons with higher than average ^{230}Th activity represent episodes when sediments were accumulating more slowly. Core T3-67-12 displays a near-uniform decay of excess ^{230}Th through the top 70 cm of core, with a fitted line corresponding to a sediment accumulation rate of 1.6 mm per 10^3 yrs. (Fig. 3). Deviations in the top 15 cm might be attributed to reworking by organisms or by other processes.

Core T3-67-3 is similar to T3-67-12 in that a best fit logarithmic line yields a sediment accumulation rate which is similar to that indicated by the magnetic and biostratigraphic

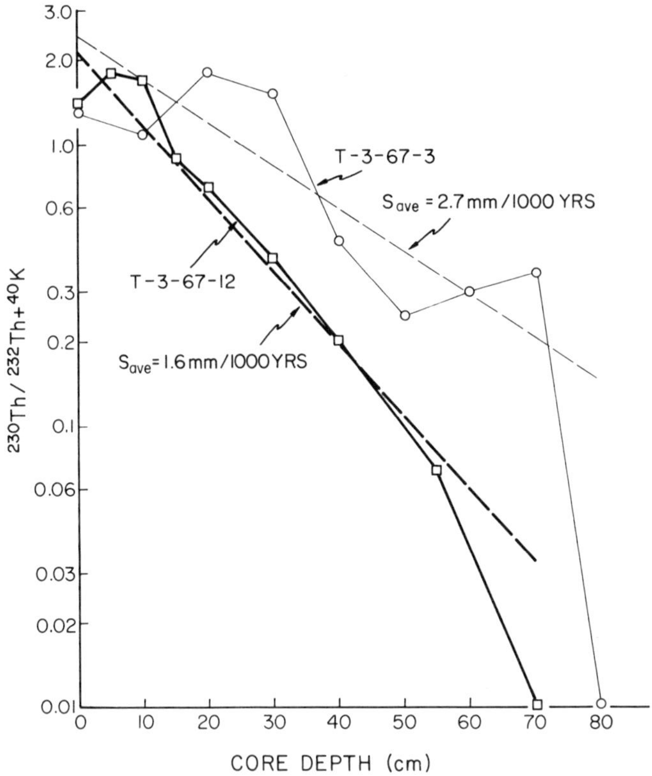

Figure 3 Average sedimentation rates in cores T3-67-12 and T3-67-3 obtained by gamma spectrometry. Discussion in the text.

data, and also in that the uppermost sample points may have been subjected to reworking. However, the more irregular pattern in T3-67-3 makes more plausible the application of a constant flux model, which would mean that the younger horizons were deposited more rapidly, and that horizons at 20, 30, and 70 cm were deposited more slowly. The break in the curve at 80 cm is quite pronounced, which may idnicate that sedimentation was interrupted at this level. The less regular activity ratio pattern of T3-67-3 means that sedimentation conditions were more variable over the last 300×10^3 yrs. than was the case with T3-67-12. Furthermore, because of the implied lesser time span allowed for the lower part of Brunhes, a hiatus is indicated below 80 cm.

DISCUSSION AND CONCLUSIONS

The evolution of the Arctic oceanic-climatic regimes during the last 4.5-5 m.y. appears to have been linked to major global climatic events (6,7,10). Our data as well as independent evidence (15) suggest that the Arctic water was cold but free of perennial sea-ice during the time represented by unit III. Faunal preservation and composition are interpreted to indicate elevated calcium carbonate compensation depth during this earliest oceanic regime. A major global cooling trend was recorded in other oceanic sediments between -4.4 and 2.9 m.y. ago (16,17). Northern Hemisphere local ice sheets and ice shelves over the circum Arctic shelves were probably developing at that time (10). This cold period was followed by a warm interval which commenced in late Gauss, approximately 2.9 m.y. ago (16,17). The low amplitude temperature fluctuations which characterize the late Gauss and Matuyama epochs (18) are not detected in the Arctic sediments. The initial warming, however, coincides roughly with the base of unit II in the Arctic. As discussed in previous publications (6,7), unit II records the inception of a pronounced salinity-density stratification in the Arctic as a consequence of the sudden dilution of surface water by the influx of large volumes of meltwater during an early deglaciation at high northern latitudes (6). The water temperatures indicated by the planktonic foraminifera of unit II are incompatible with the presence of perennial ice cover. The scarcity of planktonic foraminifers in this unit is attributed to their reduced production due to low surface water salinities and decreased nutrient levels (ibid.). Another oceanic-climatic threshold was crossed $\sim$ 0.9 m.y. ago with the inception of the perennial sea-ice cover, expressed by the earliest record of sediments similar to those being deposited today. The late Quaternary global high amplitude long period (> 20 kyr) temperature fluctuations are recorded in unit I sediments as alternating foraminifera-rich and foraminifera-poor layers. The lowest water temperatures and highest salinities correspond to the heaviest $\delta^{18}O$ in <u>G. pachyderma</u> tests of Arctic sediments. These enriched $\delta^{18}O$ values occur invariably in the foraminiferarich zones (7,8).

ACKNOWLEDGMENTS

We thank LDGO for making the Arctic basin cores available; R. Capo (deceased) and F.W. McCoy, Core Curators, for supplying core samples. Curatorial services were supported by LDGO grants NSF OCE78-25448 and OCE80-22109. This research was partially supported by W.S.U. fund 14N-2940-0020 and by the Smithsonian Foreign Currency Grant 33X0102-A20.

REFERENCES

1. Sacks, V.N., Belov, N.A., and Lapina, N.N. : 1955, "Priroda", translated in Canada Defense Research Board, translation no. T 196 R, 7, 13, Ottawa, Canada, pp. 1-14.
2. Ku, T.L., and Broecker, W.S. : 1967, "Progress in Oceanography", 4, M. Sears (Ed.), pp. 95-104, Pergamon Press, London.
3. Linkova, T.I. : 1965, in : "The Present and Past of the Geomagnetic Field", pp. 279-291, Moscow, Nauka, 1965, Directorate of Scientific Information Services, Publ. T. 463 R, Canada, 1966.
4. Hunkins, K., Be, A.W.H., Opdyke, N.D., and Mathieu, G. : 1971, in : "The Late Cenozoic Glacial Ages", K. Turekian (Ed.), Yale University Press, New Have, Connecticut, pp. 215-237.
5. Clark, D.L. : 1977, in : "Polar Oceans", M.J. Dunbar (Ed.), Arctic Inst. N. Am., Calgary, Alberta, Canada, pp. 603-615.
6. Herman, Y. : 1970, Science 169, pp. 474-477.
7. Herman, Y. : 1974, in : "Marine Geology and Oceanography of the Arctic Seas", Y. Herman (Ed.), Springer-Verlag, N.Y., pp. 283-348.
8. Herman, Y., and O'Neil, J.R. : 1975, Nature 258, pp. 591-595.
9. Herman, Y. : 1964, Nature 201, pp. 386-387.
10. Herman, Y., and Hopkins, D.M. : 1980, Science 209, pp. 557-562.
11. Ku, T.L. : 1976, Annual Rev. Earth Planet. Sci. 4, pp. 340-379.
12. Osmond, J.K. : 1979, Earth Sci. Rev. 15, pp. 95-150.
13. Osmond, J.K. : 1981, in : "The Sea, 7 : The Oceanic Lithosphere", C. Emiliani (Ed.), Wiley Interscience, N.Y., pp. 1329-1371.
14. Cochran, J.K., and Osmond, J.K. : 1974, Deep Sea Res. 21, pp. 721-738.
15. Einarsson, T., Hopkins, D.M., and Doell, R.R. : 1967, in : "The Bering Land Bridge", D.M. Hopkins (Ed), Stanford Univ. Press, Stanford, pp. 312-325.
16. Ingle, J.C.Jr. : 1973, in : "Initial Reports of the Deep Sea Drilling Project", 18, U.S. Government Printing Office, Washington, D.C., pp. 949-960.
17. Ciesielski, P.F., Ledbetter, M.T., and Ellwood, B.B. : 1982, Mar. Geol. 46, pp. 1-51.
18. Shackleton, N.J., and Opdyke, N.D. : 1976, Geol. Soc. Amer. Memoir 145, pp. 449-464.

[1]Note of the editors : there was a debate about the definition of the I/II boundary. Following Y.H., the base of unit I is defined by the first appearence of the polar fauna 0.9 m.y. ago. As mentioned in the text, and shown in Figure 1, in the sediments of unit II, subpolar _G. egelida_ and _G. quinqueloba_ dominate : T3-67-4 at 105-80 cm ; T3-67-9 at 180-160 cm ; T3-67-11 at 185 cm and T3-67-12 at 185-195 cm.

COMPLEX INTERACTION OF COSMIC AND GEOLOGICAL EVENTS THAT AFFECT THE VARIATION OF EARTH CLIMATE THROUGH THE GEOLOGIC HISTORY

N. Pantić[1], D. Stefanović[2]

[1]Serbian Academy of Sciences and Arts,
Knez Mihailova 35, Yu Beograd
[2]Rudarsko-geološki fak., Djušina 7, Yu Beograd

ABSTRACT

In order to understand the climate of any geological age it is necessary to identify a set of causes that shape the climate as a complex phenomena. The authors try to identify the specific role of orbital forcing, geodynamic phenomena and complex interaction of hydrosphere, cryosphere, atmosphere and biosphere through the geological history. This complex interaction can explain why there were no glaciations between Late Paleozoic and Neogene. Essentially, Milankovitch's hypothesis provides ground for interpretation of all data, particularly those related to orbital forcing.

INTRODUCTION

One could say that a new era in paleoclimatology started at the time when Milankovitch's theory of astronomical effect upon the Earth climate was experimentally proved (1976). In objective analysis of data pertinent to the variation of climate through the geological history, he had identified the first, clearly distinctive cause that played a decisive role in ice-age phenomena throughout the last half million years. Once the role of orbital forcing in climate variations was determined, it became much easier to identify other possile causes. Essentially, that was the route Milankovitch wanted to follow when trying to answer : why there were no glaciations between late Palaeozoic and Neogene ice-ages. It seems to us that the approach Milankovitch has in mind is good for a synthethic theory of climatic changes throughout the geological time (27).

A. L. Berger et al. (eds.), Milankovitch and Climate, Part 1, 251–264.

It is obvious nowadays that the climate of each timespan throughout the geologic past is a result of a complex interaction of many causes that simultaneously acted at this given geological moment. Throughout the geological past a set of causes could have produced a very complex and manyfold interactions and effects, each of them being different from the previous one, or the next to come. It should be pointed out that a variation of any of these causes could have been sufficient to trigger a whole chain of other variations (increase of CO_2 concentration, humidity, temperature variation, etc) that could have produced a noticable effect upon the global climatic system at any given geological time.

It has been proved that the Earth's orbital variations had effect upon global climates through geologic history, e.g. during Pleistocene ice-ages (13) as well as during the Mesozoic warm climate. A new task for the geosciences is to discover what causes acted at that time. A solution of the problem is somewhere among the curves describing the evolution of the climate through the geologic time.

Having in mind that a complex interaction of many causes produces the Earth's climate, M. Milankovitch (1941) pointed out that the geological knowledge (paleontological, geophysical, etc) could determine a relationship between his scheme and the real climate. It seems to us that future investigation should be oriented along the lines of modified principles of actualism, in particular when trying to reconstruct the climate of older geological eras. The background of the method was postulated by Russian scientist F.K. Rule (1818-1858) who used the term "comparative history method". His point was : "too many times we judge the past by the time we live in ... However, in the world we live, nothing is there from the very beginning : all had developed gradually". It is understable that no one could disregard the role of Lyell's principle of actualism. The point is to incorporate into his principles historicity in order to accomodate better the progress through the very long-lasting geologic time.

It seems to us that, among many others, there are four basic groups of causes that have shaped the global climate on the Earth. They are : 1) cosmic phenomena, 2) geodynamic phenomena, 3) interaction of hydrospheric and atmosheric phenomena and 4) the effects of biosphere, including human activities. One should try to find out how long the action of particular phenomena had lasted, when it was included into the global system, what was included into the global system, what was its intensity, etc.

Cosmic phenomena

We shall briefly review the effects of some of the cosmic phenomena that, according to modern knowledge, had played an important role in the global climate :

a) As discussed above, there is now good evidence that many features of the Pleistocene ice ages are caused by Milankovitch astronomical variation. Some recent investigations (30) do show that variation in solar output could be correlated with Cretaceous sequence of limestone and shale layers.

It seems that these could answer the question Milankovitch had asked himself : why the astronomic phenomena did not have obvious effect between Palaezoic and Tertiary ice-age.

b) Impact of celestial bodies at the Earth. During the last several years many authors (1), (14), (23) reported that the Earth had collided with many celestial bodies (asteroides, meteorites) during its long geological history. Those severe impacts had caused apparently short but drastic disturbances of global climate. Such findings were reported for the Devonian (365 m.y. ago), Middle Triassic (210 m.y. ago), Early Jurassic (180 m.y. ago), Late Cretaceous (65 m.y. ago), Late Eocene (38 m.y. ago), Early Oligocene (35 m.y. ago), Late Oligocene (28 m.y. ago), Middle Miocene (15 m.y. ago), Pleistocene (1 m.y. ago). Very probably there were many more but are not yet identified.

The meteorite that produced the Riss crater in Miocene had the diameter of approximately 20 km. It can be assumed that the colliding celestial bodies had diameter of that size,or sometimes bigger, even up to a hundred kilometer : if so their effects were substantial. However, there is a good ground for a conclusion that there was never such a catastrophic event during the Phanerozoic to cause global extinction of organic life. In other words there is no discontinuity within the complex, continual and permanent progressive evolution of the organic life.

c) Effects due to the Earth place in the Galaxy. There is a hypothesis that an ice-age could begin at a time when the Earth enters into the tail of a Galaxy. Such a hypothesis could not be disregarded, although an ice-age could start due to other circumstances.

Among the cosmic phenomena that play a role in global climate, one should not disregard a variable intensity of insolation due to the Sun evolution. Of course, the phenomenon is a long lasting one, commeasurable with the Earth age. In that sense solar flares and protuberances are something which counts.

Our conclusion is that the cosmic phenomena could cause cyclic, long period climatic variations (the tail of Galaxy), middle period variations (the Earth's orbital variation), short period variations (Sun-Earth's phenomena) as well as sudden, stochastic effects (impacts, etc).

Geodynamic phenomena

The history of the solid Earth is very long, dynamic and complex. The very first eons of the history are characterized by states and processes essentially different of those known from the latter time intervals, which we know and can anticipate. Some of those phenomena could have had substantial effect on global climate.

a) Variable heat-flow intensity at the Earth. No doubt the intensity of the heat-flow has played an important role in shapping the global climate, in particular during the oldest geological history. According to data published elsewhere (31), average annual temperature on the Earth was 40°C during Early Proterozoic, and around 30-32°C in Early Paleozoic. The average temperature decreases steadily since, according to some authors. However, there is also a hypothesis which anticipates a cyclic warming up and cooling down of the Earth through the process of its structural development and gaining rotation. If that was the case then it may have an important role in forming the Earth's climate.

b) Polar wandering. Intermittent ice-age phenomena is one problem. The other is the phenomenon of polar wandering. Milankovitch (21), (22) had found theoretical solutions for both problems, and new findings, when well incorporated and understood, should help to interpret the climate of the geological past, and to forecast its future trends.

Astronomical impacts on the climate were of different intensity during geologic times since the continents had position different from those they have now.

Paleomagnetic research has contributed toward the understanding of the geographical distribution of the continents at different geological times. Milankovitch had anticipated such possibility, together with his close coworker A. Wegener.

Polar wandering on a plastic Earth involves the pole of rotation, or geoidal pole and the pole of figure corresponding to the instantaneous shape of the Earth.

The vector of displacement of the pole of figure with regard to the geoidal pole triggers the polar wandering, but its velocity is not constant. According to Milankovitch, it is slowest at the ends of a possible paths, and fastest in the middle.

Milankovitch had calculated many possile paths of polar wandering, but had plotted only one for the present distribution of continents and oceans.

It is well known that the continents have changed their positions. Therefore, it is obvious that none of the possible paths of polar wandering was actually followed. Some preliminary results show that 40 to 200 m.y. would be necessary for the vector of displacement to become zero at the present distribution of continents. However, in the meantime new redistribution of the continents takes place, a new pole of figure is established, and the pole follows a new trajectory. The velocity of the polar wandering changes at the same time.

It can be assumed that astronomical effects have played a decisive role in climate during the time when the velocity of polar wandering was zero, and the effects of all the other phenomena constant or negligable. Such a hypothesis could be verified by finding a geological interval when the poles of figure and geoid coincided. A crosscorrelation of astronomical and paleoclimatological data could give an answer.

At the same time the orbital forcing probably was different at the geological time when the Earth's rotation was faster than at present.

c) <u>Horizontal and vertical movement inside the Earth's crust.</u> Polar wandering is closely related to the plate tectonics : horizontal and vertical displacement of large parts of the Earth's crust ; orogenesis and orogenic belt ; growing of the continents ; changes in its volume of the oceans etc. Each one of the mentioned phenomena effects the climate somehow. Those movements contribute that parts of the Earth's crust (either continent or oceanic crust) come closer to the poles. Milankovitch himself had emphasized (1941) that the ice caps of Antarctic and Arctic regions were closely related to the land masses at those regions. Any time when the horizontal movements or vertical uplift caused that a land mass appeared in the pole region, an ice cap was favored. However, one can not make a straight forward conclusion, that these two phenomena were sufficient to trigger a glaciation, because they act simultaneously with many other ones that could accelerate or slow down the process. Sometime the result is the introduction of the Earth into an era of "polyphase ice-ages" like the one during the Pleistocene.

d) Volcanism. The intensity of volcanism had varied markedly throughout the Earth's history, and its effect must have been substantial. On one side, there were periods when the explosive volcanism was pronounced. Such activity could obstruct the solar radiation, reducing its effects substantially, thus producing cooler periods. On the other side, long-lasting and intensive sub-oceanic volcanism could produce enormous amounts of vapor and long-lasting clouds, that could have acted as a green house.

Interaction of the Hydrosphere including Cryosphere and Atmosphere

Those systems are very closely related and many articles describe their interaction. The project of ocean drilling produced valuale data (Report of the 1981 Conference) which we would not discuss here.

Effect of the Biosphere

The remnants of flora and fauna found inside Late Mesozoic, Palaeogene and Neogene sediements (2), (7), (13), (19) do resemble the climate variation during corresponding geological ages. It is more important, however, to find out what the effect of biosphere was upon the climate throughout the Earth's history. It is well known that the long-lasting process of photosynthesis was essential for creating the oxygen-rich atmosphere. Further on, the same process gradually, approximately 440 m.y. ago, produced the terrestrial vegetation, and the whole set of activities that had obvious effects on climate. As an example : there are data that describe the relationship between the evolution of terrestrial vegetation, CO_2 concentration in the atmosphere and hydrosphere and its consequence on the chemical sediments. The close connection of the amount of biomass, cyclic variation of CO_2 concentrations in the atmosphere and the climate (10) was well described. It was proved that the phenomenom can be correlated with Milankovitch's astronomical mechanism.

It is obvious, from what we presented, that the climate of a given geological age is a result of complex interactions of many forces such as cosmic and geodynamic, with hydro-, bio-, and atmosphere.

CLIMATE VARIATION FROM THE LATE PALEOZOIC ICE-AGE TO THE NEOGENE ICE-AGE

The data on the Late Paleozoic ice-age are abundant. Using the palaeophytological, palaeomagnetic and other data it was possible to reconstruct the distribution of ice-caps, polar wandering and distribution of the continents at that age (20, 24, 25, 26). A large ice-cap in the Southern Hemisphere could have been as large as it was, due to the fact that great parts of the southern continents in Carboniferous and Permian were inside of the polar zone, and even at the Pole. The process of glaciation was probably stimulated by intensive volcanism during the Hercynian orogenesis, especially because the volcanic activity was of an explosive type. It would be of interest to study whether that ice-age was a polyphase one, because there are indication that the Carboniferous sedimentation do reflect the variation of the Earth's orbital parameters.

During the Triassic (approximately 220 m.y. ago) large parts of the southern continents drifted away from the polar zone. The new set of continents created a new regime that had a specific paleophytogeography with large equatorial realm with a dry climate, and with damp climates at the northern and southern margins. Investigations show that the specific vegetation developed at the time when the climate was very dry in some areas, which was synchronous with the rifting of the Pangea, followed by mentioned volcanism.

Jurassic terrestrial vegetation and climate

Intensive investigation of the oceans resulted in data on geodynamic evolution, as well as on the evolution of hydrosphere and atmosphere during Jurassic. The climate reflected the forcing caused by the opening of the Tethys to the west. The continents drifted further apart, subocean volcanism was very pronounced, ocean water level was very high and ocean currents very strong, and there were no ice-caps in the polar regions. Generally speaking the climate was warm although there were some variations. Results of investigations of Jurassic terrestrial flora in the Northern Hemisphere (9, 24, 25, 26) do confirm these conclusions.

Paleophytogeograpic and paleolclimatological rezoning in the Northern Hemisphere is illustrated in Figure 1.

Jurassic warm and equable climate is characterized by a broad tropical belt, broad subtropical belt, and rather limited temperate belt. More details are published elsewhere.

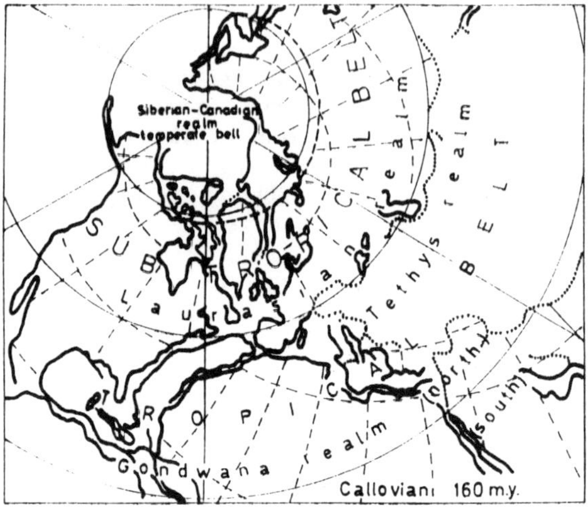

Fig. 1

Fig. 1 Phytogeography of terrestrial plants and distribution of paleoclimatic belts in Middle Jurassic

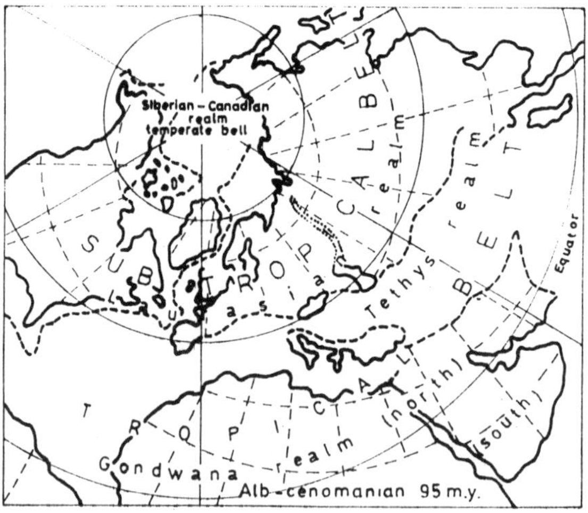

Fig. 2

Fig. 2 Middle Cretaceous (Alb-Cenomanien) phytogeography and distribution of paleoclimatic belts

A detail analysis of the Jurassic flora gives a more complex picture. Complex interactions of the geodynamic and other phenomena produced a steady variation of climatic zones causing migrations and alterations of plants. Those variation can be detected along the boundaries of two adjacent biogeographical realms. Such phenomena were reported as warming up at the Pliensbachian-Toarcian boundary, cooling down at the end of Toarcian and through Aalenian, and warming up again at the beginning of Bajocian which was followed by aridity sometime in the Callovian.

It would be useful to correlate the change in the spatial distribution of plants zones with the complex geodynamic events. The correlation can contribute to the understanding of the described concept.

Middle Cretaceous terrestrial vegetation and climate

In Lower Cretaceous, and in particular during Middle Cretaceous, the geodynamics was very intensive : the Tethys ocen closed, volcanism was pronounced, large transgression progressed, some meteoretic impacts occurred. All that caused drastic alteration of the plants. Intensive expansion of angiosperms through its Normapolles group came at first, while at the end of the Cretaceous, the animal world suffered badly.

The general aspect of the climatic belts during Lower Cretaceous, and to some extent during Middle Cretaceous, was similar to that during Jurassic age. The scheme is shown in Figure 2.

Some new findings (5), (24), (6), (12), (15) give interesting information about the changes of terrestrial plants and climate, most probably caused by desintegration of Tethys (large water barrier between the Laurasian and Gondwana phytogeographic realms).

In order to define, more precisely, the distribution of phytogeographic provinces and climatic belts at the time when the climate was still warm and equable (which was the case in the Jurassic and through much of Cretaceous) it is necessary to investigate terrestrial flora sensitive to variations of climate.

The following phytogeographic realms and climatic belts could be distinguished going down from the Pole toward the Equator :

REALM	CLIMATIC BELT
Siberian-Canadian	Temperate
Lauro-asian	Subtropical
Tethys	Transitional : tropical-subtropical
Gondwana (north and south of that time equator)	Tropical

Figures 1 and 2 show how the realms and belts were distributed at that time.

It seems that the most dramatic period began in the Cenomanian (Middle Cretaceous). At that time the terrestrial flora changed drastically : Normapolles group suddenly appeared and insects had developed explosively. Simultaneously, there were frequent periods of cooling (3), (4), (29) dated by radio isotopes (11). It is well known that the Cretaceous volcanism was very much pronounced, while the ocean level oscillated intensively. Concentration of CO_2 was variable partly due to evolution of the terrestrial plants and partly due to the exogenic carbon cycling. That effect played its role nevertheless (10).

Alterations of terrestrial plants as the indicator of global temperature decline during Tertiary

Recent paleo-oceanographic investigations (7), (8), (16), (28) have identified many climatic stepwise changes during Tertiary. It would be interesting to correlate those data with the evolution of terrestrial plants. There is no doubt that drastic variation of terrestrial plants produce some alteration of climate, and consequently a set of other events.

Throughout Tertiary period the climate was variable (Fig. 3a), but the mean temperature decline. As a response to the rapid variation of global climate, there was a corresponding rapid alteration of paleophytogeography : very wide tropical and subtropical vegetation realms and narrow realms with moderate-warmth vegetation, as they were at the time when the climate was warm, changed suddently as the climate changed. The tropical and subtropical belts contracted while temperate, boreal and polar realms expanded (Fig. 4). Step by step the Earth entered into periods of cold climate with Neogene ice-age and later, into present state.

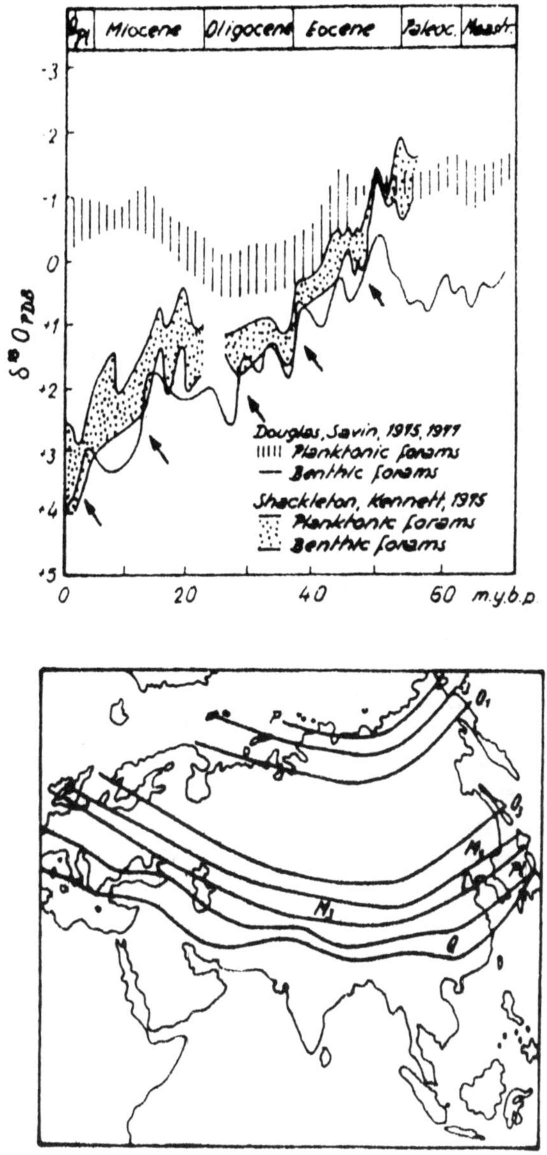

Fig. 3 Correlation of oxygen isotope trends in Cenozoic foraminifera from Pacific deep-sea sediments (a) - After Schwarzacher and Fischer (1982) and migration of the Northern boundary of palms during the Cenozoic (b), Sinitzin (1965).

P - Paleocene, O, O_3 - Oligocene, M_1 M_3 - Miocene, Pl - Pliocene, Q - Quaternary

Described processes are well illustrated (Fig. 3b) by the gradually southward move (31) of the palm tree boundary during the Cenozoic.

Some research done in the Northern Hemisphere (25), (26) have explained many detailds of the worldwide trend of the alteration of the terrestrial vegetation. The southward migration of a climatic belt that moved from Middle Europe down to Africa took place in time span from Middle Miocene to Late Miocene. The tracing of the migration was useful for understanding the salinity crisis in the Mediteranian basin. In

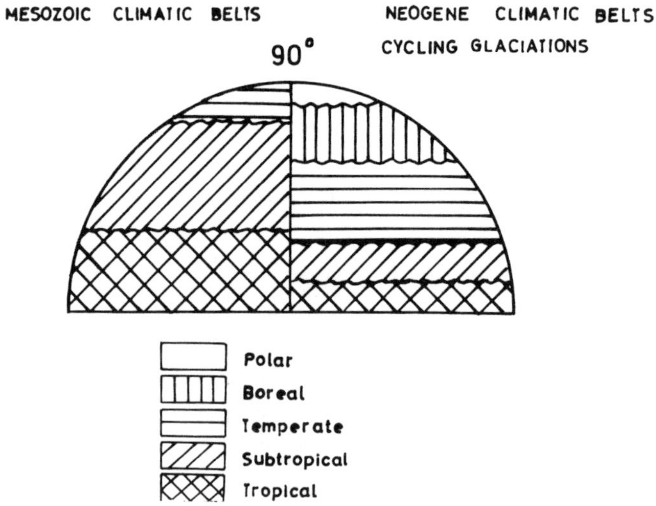

Fig. 4 Distribution of bioclimatic belts of continents.
a) when Mesozoic climatic epoch was warm and equable
b) when Neogene climatic epoch had cycling ice-ages

Messinian, the climate was dry and subtropical and it was neither humid nor cold. At that time, Tethys desintegrated, the ocean currents changed, and the oceans link shifted further north.

The Southern Hemisphere underwent similar shrinking of tropical and subtropical belts (18). Of course, the climatic belts had their own characteristics due to different geographic position of the continents and the fact that the ice-cap had developed earlier, was reflected in the ocean currents.

A general conclusion could be that the climate variation and the corresponding consequences in the geographic distribution of terrestrial plants, was the result of geodynamic events : the desintegration of Tethys ocean, the emergence of large parts of continents from the ocean. The continents drifted and split apart and the Pole wandered while the ocean currents changed their routes. Also some rather serious meteorite impacts occured (23) and there global effect must be considered.

CONCLUSION

What was the greatest and most important role of Milankovitch astronomical mechanism in climate ? It seems that he found a very reliable cause that acts all the time, synchronously with all other climate change variables at different settings at different geologic times.

It seems resonable enough to rate all events that shape the climate on the Earth as : high frequency (short-term variation) acting on a time scale of 10 to 1000 yr (according to R. Fairbridge) ; Milankovitch orbital forcing (long period variations) acting on a time scale of 10-100 thousand years, and low frequency geologic events acting on a time scale of million years. All of them act simultaneously and modulation can produce any apparant frequency.

By appreciating this principle it would be possible to trace the role of any event that either intensified or dampened te solar radiation (Milankovitch's effect). The greatest tribute to Milankovitch would be to follow his path, to the understanding of the past Earth's climate, and helping to forecast climatic future.

REFERENCES

1. Alvarez, L., Alvarez, W., Asaro, F., Michel, H.V. : 1980, Science 208, pp. 1095-1108.
2. Berger, W.H. : 1982, in : "Cyclic and Event Stratification", Springer-Verlag, pp. 121-161.
3. de Boer, P.L. : 1982, in : "Cyclic and Event Stratification", Springer, pp. 456-476.
4. Bolli, H., Krasheninkov, V. : 1977, Micropaleontology 23, pp. 436-452.
5. Brenner, G. : 1976, Origin and Early Evolution of Angiosperms, Col. Univ. Press. N.Y., pp. 23-44.

6. Chlonova, A.F. : 1981, Rev. Palaeobot. Palynol. 35, pp. 315-324.
7. Douglas, R.G., Savin, S.M. : 1975, in : Rep. DSDP, vol. 32, U.S. Gov. Pr. Office, Washington, D.C., pp. 509-520.
8. Douglas, R.G., Woodruff, F. : 1981, The Sea, 7, Wiley-Intersc. N.Y.
9. Erve van, A.W. : 1977, Ref. Paleob. Palynol. 23, pp. 130-177.
10. Einsele, G. : 1982, Cyclic and Event Stratification, Springer, 8-54.
11. Frerichs, W.E. : 1971, J. Paleontol. 45, 6, pp. 963-968.
12. Hallam, B. : 1981, Geol. Rundschau, 70, H.2, pp. 583-595.
13. Hays, J.B., Imbrie, J., Shackleton, N.J. : 1976, Science 1132.
14. Hsü, K.J. : 1980, Nature 285, pp. 201-203.
15. Hochuli, P.A. : 1981, Rev. Palaeb. Palyn. 35, pp. 337-358.
16. Imbrie, J., Imbrie, K.P. : 1979, "Ice Ages, solving the mystery", Enslow Publ., New Jersey.
17. Imbrie, J., Imbrie, J.Z. : 1980, Science 207, pp. 943-958.
18. Kemp, E.M. : 1978, Paleogeography, Paleoclimatology, Paleoecology 24, pp. 169-208.
19. Kennett, J.P. : 1977, J. Geoph. Res. 82, pp. 3843-3860.
20. Kremp, O.W. : 1982, Palynodata, Univ. of Arizona, Tucson, pp. 62-113.
21. Milankovitch, M. : 1930, Handbuch Klimatologie, 1A, pp. 176.
22. Milankovitch, M. : 1941, Acad. Roy. Serbe 133, Sec. Sc. Mat. et Nat. 33, pp. 633.
23. O'Keefe, IAA : 1980, Nature 285, pp. 309-311.
24. Pantic, N. : 1980, G.R. Soc. Serbe Geol., pp. 7-13.
25. Pantic, N. : 1981, Ann. Geol. Pen. Balk., XLV, pp. 157-171.
26. Pantic, N., Mihajlovic, Dj. : 1979/80, Ann. Geol. Pen. Balk. XLIII-XLIV, pp. 239-262.
27. Pantic, N., Stefanovic, D. : 1982, Serbian Acad. Sc., Conferences, XII, 3, pp. 217-229.
28. Savin, S.M. : 1977, Earth Planetary Science 5, pp. 319-355.
29. Scheibnerova, V. : 1971, Bios. Search 2, 7, pp. 251-254.
30. Schwarzacher, W., Fischer, A.G. : 1982, Limestone-shale Bedding and Per. Cyclic and Event Stratification, Springer, pp. 72-96.
31. Sinicin, V.M. : 1980, Introduction in Paleoclimatology (Russ.) Nedra, Lenjingrad, pp. 1-247.

CYCLIC VARIATIONS IN CALCIUM CARBONATE AND ORGANIC CARBON IN MIOCENE TO HOLOCENE SEDIMENTS, WALVIS RIDGE, SOUTH ATLANTIC OCEAN

W.E. Dean[1] and J.V. Gardner[2]

[1]U.S. Geological Survey, Denver, CO 80225, USA
[2]U.S. Geological Survey, Menlo Park, CA 94025, USA

ABSTRACT

The entire upper Miocene to Holocene sedimentary sequence recovered in a hydraulic piston core at DSDP Site 532 on Walvis Ridge shows distinct cycles in amount of $CaCO_3$ that correlate with dark and light cycles of sediment color. The average periodicities of the carbonate cycles for the Quaternary, upper Pliocene, and lower Pliocene are about 35 kyr, 46 kyr, and 28 kyr respectively, with an overall average of about 36 kyr for the last 5 Myr. Most minima in carbonate abundance correspond to dark parts of color cycles, and most maxima correspond to the lightest parts of color cycles. The darker parts of color cycles usually contain higher concentrations of organic carbon, but the organic-carbon record does not follow in detail the cyclicity of the color cycles. Organic-carbon cycles were only analyzed for the last 2.5 Myr, and for this interval they have an average periodicity of about 34 kyr.

The carbonate and color cycles persist through more than 5 Myr during which major changes in relative proportions of siliceous-biogenic, calcareous-biogenic, and terrigenous-clastic components occurred in response to climate change and the waxing and waning of the Benguela-Current upwelling system off southwest Africa. The cyclic nature of these sediments probably is the result of dilution by terrigenous clastic material and not dissolution of carbonate. We believe that the forcing mechanism that produced the cyclicity was external to the area of Site 532. Because of the similarity among the periodicities of the Walvis Ridge cycles and those of carbonate cycles in the northeastern Atlantic, Caribbean, and eastern equatorial Pacif-

A. L. Berger et al. (eds.), Milankovitch and Climate, Part 1, 265–266.

ic, these cycles probably are responses to global events. We conclude that fluctuations in global sea level with an average period of about 36 kyr over the last 5 Myr caused variations in influx of terrigenous clastic material from the African continental margin.

PART II

GEOLOGICAL EVIDENCE FOR LONG-TERM CLIMATIC VARIATIONS AT ASTRONOMICAL FREQUENCIES

SECTION 2 - MARINE PLEISTOCENE RECORDS OF CLIMATIC RESPONSE

THE ORBITAL THEORY OF PLEISTOCENE CLIMATE: SUPPORT FROM A REVISED CHRONOLOGY OF THE MARINE $\delta^{18}O$ RECORD

J. Imbrie[1], J.D. Hays[3], D.G. Martinson[5], A. McIntyre[3], A.C. Mix[3], J.J. Morley[3], N.G. Pisias[4], W.L. Prell[1], and N.J. Shackleton[2]

[1]Brown University, Providence, RI 02912, USA
[2]Cambridge University, Cambridge, England
[3]Lamont-Doherty Geological Observatory, Columbia University, Palisades, NY, USA
[4]Oregon State University, Corvallis, OR, USA
[5]Woods Hole Oceanographic Institution, Woods Hole, MA, USA

Observations of $\delta^{18}O$ in five deep-sea cores provide a basis for developing a geological time scale for the past 780 000 years and for evaluating the orbital theory of Pleistocene ice ages. The isotopic measurements are obtained from shallow-dwelling planktonic foraminifera at widely distributed, open-ocean sites in low- and mid-latitudes. The amplitudes of oscillations in this homogeneous set of isotopic records are highly correlated and must be strongly influenced by changes in the global volume of glacial ice. Three of the cores studied penetrate the Brunhes-Matuyama magnetic reversal, an event previously dated by K-Ar measurements at 730 KY BP. This date, and the assumption that variations in orbital precession and obliquity cause changes in global climate, are used to develop a new time scale for the $\delta^{18}O$ record. Displayed on this time scale, the isotopic variations are phase locked ($\pm$ 15°) and strongly coherent (> 0.9) with orbital variations --not only at the main periods of precession (19 KY and 23 KY) and obliquity (41 KY), but also in the 100-KY eccentricity band. This statistical evidence of a close relationship between the time-varying amplitudes of orbital forcing and the time-varying amplitudes of the isotopic response implies that orbital variations are the main external cause of the succession of late Pleistocene ice ages.

A. L. Berger et al. (eds.), Milankovitch and Climate, Part 1, 269–305.

INTRODUCTION

Since the pioneer work of James Croll (1864-1875) and Milutin Milankovitch (1920-1941), the central geological problem in testing the astronomical theory of the Pleistocene ice ages has been the difficulty of obtaining a chronology of climatic events that was sufficiently accurate to serve this purpose yet sufficiently independent of the theory itself to make the test credible (5,21,39). The advent of deep-sea piston coring in 1947 (40) opened the way for a fresh attack on this problem by providing sedimentary records of climate that were deposited at relatively constant rates over intervals of time long enough to be relevant to the astronomical theory. Paramount among such records are curves showing fluctuations in the ratio of ^{18}O to ^{16}O in tests of fossil foraminifera. These curves monitor major changes in global climate as the Earth shifts towards or away from an ice-age condition -- an approach to climate history that was pioneered in 1955 by Emiliani (8).

In the present study we analyze isotopic data from five deep-sea cores. Three of these penetrate the Brunhes-Matuyama magnetic reversal, an event dated radiometrically at 730 KY BP. We use this datum, as well as certain assumptions about the astronomical control of Pleistocene climate, to develop a time scale for the isotopic record. Finally, we present evidence that our chronology is sufficiently accurate to permit a meaningful evaluation of the Milankovitch theory.

The $\delta^{18}O$ Record

Measurements of the ratio of ^{18}O to ^{16}O are reported with respect to an international standard as $\delta^{18}O$ in parts per thousand (°/₀₀). In his initial study, Emiliani (8) argued that the dominant cause of Pleistocene $\delta^{18}O$ variations is a change in ambient water temperature. Later work by Olausson (23), by Shackleton (28) and by Shackleton and Opdyke (32) led to the conclusion now generally accepted that downcore variations in $\delta^{18}O$ reflect changes in oceanic isotopic composition, and that these changes are caused primarily by the waxing and waning of the great Pleistocene ice sheets. Fairbanks and Matthews (10), for example, estimate that 0.011 per mil of $\delta^{18}O$ variation is associated with 1 m of sea-level change. Subsequent work (6,7) has emphasized that a number of influences (in addition to variations in global ice volume) may have a significant effect on the shape of particular $\delta^{18}O$ curves. These influences include : (1) changes in ambient water temperature; (2) changes in the evaporation-precipitation ratio at the site of formation of the water mass under study; (3) vital and ecological effects of individual species; (4) differential dissolution; (5) sediment transport; (6) bioturbation; and (7) stratigraphic disturbance. With these influences in mind, we have designed a sampling strategy that will enhance the effect of ice-volume variations and suppress the effect of other influences.

Sampling Strategy

First, we choose cores from open-ocean sites in low- and mid-latitudes that accumulated relatively rapidly and at depths relatively unaffected by dissolution (Fig. 1, Table 1). Second, we limit our study to shallow-dwelling planktonic species. Four of our records are based on *Globigerinoides sacculifer*. One record (RC11-120) is based on *Globigerina bulloides*. Finally, after analyzing each core individually, we normalize and average the records to produce a stacked record in which most of the influences other than ice-volume will tend to cancel each other out. The benefits of stacking noisy, individual $\delta^{18}O$ records were recognized by Emiliani (9), who recast his observations in the form of a generalized isotopic curve.

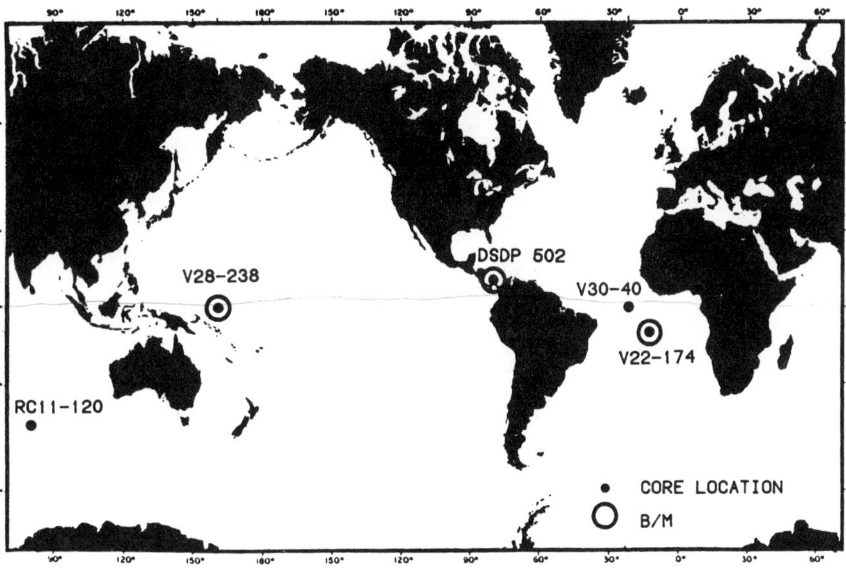

Figure 1 Location of cores used in this study. The symbol B/M indicates a core that penetrates the Brunhes-Matuyama magnetic reversal.

Standard Isotopic Stratigraphy

Like all stratigraphic records, $\delta^{18}O$ curves are subject to distortion by vagaries of the depositional process. Other dis-

Table 1 Location and description of cores.

Core	Ref.	Lat.	Long.	Water Depth (M)	Core Length (CM)	Ave. Acc. Rate (CM/KY)	Ave. Sampling Interval (KY)
RC11-120	(13)	43°31'S	79°52'E	3193	954	3.3	1.5
V22-174	(36)	10°04'S	12°49'W	2630	1566	1.9	4.8
V30-40	(42)	00°12'S	23°09'W	3706	755	2.8	1.1
V28-238	(30,32)	01°01'N	160°29'E	3120	1609	1.6	5.0
DSDP502b	(26)	11°30'N	79°23'W	3051	3584	2.2	4.7

tortions may result from the coring process itself. In order to identify and allow for such distortions before developing our time scale, we have made detailed comparisons between the isotopic events recorded in each core with events recorded in other cores. Toward this end, we have made extensive use of a stratigraphic study of a global set of $\delta^{18}O$ records conducted as part of the SPECMAP project (27). In essence, this study is an extension (9,29,32,33) of the concept of numbered isotopic stages initiated by Emiliani (8). In Emiliani's scheme, stages are numbered consecutively from the top of the record downward, with odd numbered stages corresponding to interglacial (isotopically light) intervals and even numbers corresponding to glacial intervals. In most cases, stage boundaries correspond to rapid, monotonic shifts in the curve. This scheme has proved very useful in describing and analyzing climate history back through Stage 22. As a result, earlier papers dealing with $\delta^{18}O$ chronology have presented their results in terms of stage boundaries. However, we consider that for purposes of detailed correlation this scheme should be supplemented by using the stratigraphic system proposed by Prell et al. (27).

The essential feature of this system is the identification of all negative and positive excursions (peaks and valleys) that are globally persistent. The stages previously defined are retained, and the isotopic events within stages are given a decimal notation such that negative (interglacial) and positive (glacial) excursions have odd and even numbers, respectively. For example, the negative events in Stage 5 previously called 5a, 5c, and 5e are designated 5.1, 5.3, and 5.5; the positive events previously called 5b and 5d are designated 5.2 and 5.4; and the boundary between Stage 5 and Stage 6 is designated 6.0. Clearly, this is a convenient and flexible notation. Our main reason for adopting it, however, is that the exact stratigraphic level of a peak or a valley can be defined unambiguously in one curve and recognized with a high degree of precision in another. This is often not true of stage boundaries. Most of the control points in our chronology have therefore been placed at the extremes of excursions recognized and numbered by Prell et al. (27).

A NEW LATE-PLEISTOCENE $\delta^{18}O$ CHRONOLOGY

Previous Work

Several recently published $\delta^{18}O$ chronologies have been based on a combination of radiometric control and astronomic theory (13,17,18,22). Broadly speaking, the results of these investigations are concordant over the past 400 KY, but discordant from 400 KY to 800 KY BP. Important discrepancies occur at the Brunhes-Matuyama boundary, dated radiometrically at 730 ±11 KY (20). In the time scales produced by Kominz et al. (18), Morley and Hays (22), and Johnson (17), this event is dated at 728 KY, 738 KY, and 790 KY, respectively. Some of these differences result from using different sets of basic data. However, most of them are the result of using different strategies to develop a time scale over a portion of the record for which only a small number of precise radiometric dates are available.

All of the studies cited above make an initial assumption that the sediment accumulation function (depth-in-core vs. age) is linear between radiometric control points. All then relax this assumption to produce a satisfactory match between the adjusted isotopic curve and one or more astronomical curves that have been designated as targets of the tuning procedure. As shown in Table 2, differences between one procedure and another can be described in terms of five elements of tuning strategy : (1) the choice of a target curve, i.e., an astronomical curve (or curves) assumed to represent the forcing function of the climate system; (2) an estimate of the phase lag between the assumed forcing function and the isotopic response; (3) the selection of a data processing technique to achieve a match between the astronomical and isotopic curves; (4) the number of control points allowed in the depth-vs.-age function; and (5) the criteria used to evaluate the postulated match between the astronomical and tuned isotopic curves.

A Revised Tuning Strategy

Target curves. Several investigators have used an insolation curve for a particular latitude and season as a tuning target. Instead, we follow Hays et al. (13) and Morley and Hays (22) by matching isotopic observations against curves showing variations in obliquity (ε) and variations in the precession index ($\Delta e \sin\omega$). This procedure has two significant benefits, one practical and one theoretical. On the practical side, the procedure is parsimonious: curves of ε and $\Delta e \sin\omega$ contain all of the information needed to calculate an insolation curve for any latitude and any season (2). In fact, to a high degree of accuracy, any insolation curve outside of the polar regions can be computed from these two orbital parameters by a simple linear transfer function involving only the ratio of the two parameters and the phase of ω, the longitude of perihelion (14). Theoretical benefits follow because there is widespread agreement on the general (if not the detailed) nature of the physical mechanisms by which the climate system responds to insolation changes driven by variations in obliquity (at periods of 41 KY) and precession (at 19 KY and 23 KY). In contrast, there is little agreement on the nature of the physical mechanisms responsible for the climatic oscillations around 100 KY that dominate the isotopic record.

Table 2 Elements of different tuning strategies

Reference	Astronomical Target Curve(s)	Phase Lag of $\delta^{18}O$ Response	Data Processing	Number of Non-radiometric Control Points within the Brunhes	Independent Evaluation Criteria
Emiliani (1955)	45°N summer insolation	5 KY	raw data		
Hays et al. (1976)	obliquity precession	9 KY 3 KY	41 K filter 23 K filter	2	
Kominz et al. (1979)	obliquity	10 KY	41 K filter complex demodulation	12	23 K filter COH (f)
Morley and Hays (1981)	obliquity precession	90° 90°	raw data	17	19 K filter 23 K filter 41 K filter
Johnson (1982)	35°N and 70°N	5 KY?	raw data	15	
This paper	obliquity precession	- arctan 2 f(17 KY)	22 K filter 41 K filter	56-72	COH (f) depth vs. age

As shown by Berger (3) and displayed in Figure 2, the obliquity signal has a simple spectrum with variance concentrated near periods of 41 KY. The spectrum of the precession index (which we will hereafter refer to as precession) is more complex, with variance concentrated near periods of 19 KY and 23 KY. In principle, one could follow Morley and Hays (22) and tune the isotopic curve separately against the 19 KY and 23 KY components of precession (Fig. 3). However, the length of a digital filter required to achieve the necessary resolution makes this strategy undesirable.

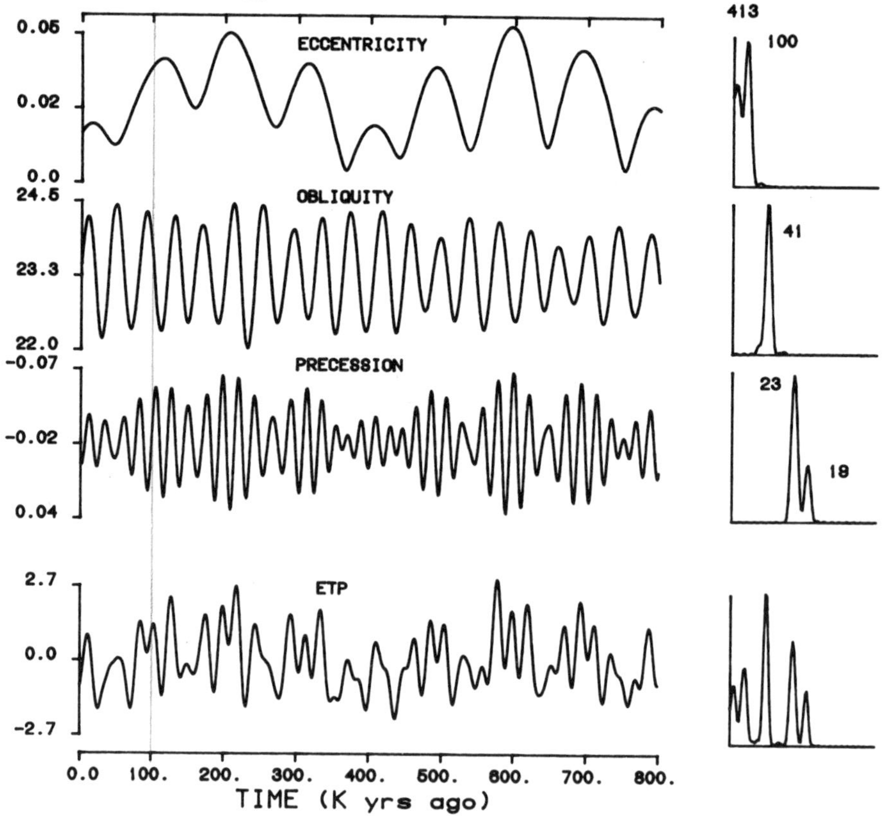

Figure 2 Variations in eccentricity, obliquity, and the precession index (Δ e sin ω) over the past 800 000 years. Left: The three upper time series are from the work of Berger (1). These have been normalized and added to form the curve labeled ETP. The scale for obliquity is in degrees; for ETP, in standard deviation units. Right: Variance spectra calculated from these time series, with the dominant periods (KY) of conspicuous peaks indicated.

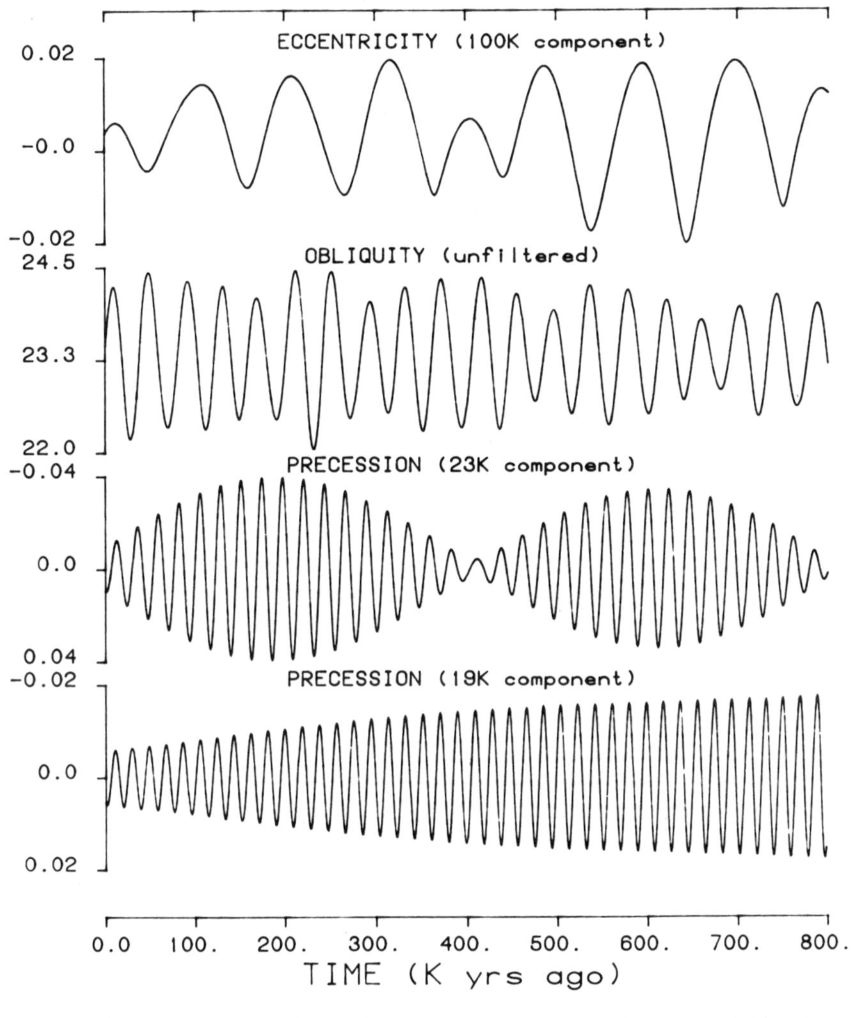

Figure 3 Narrow-band variations in eccentricity, obliquity, and the precession index (Δ e sin ω) over the past 800 000 years. The top curve consists of components of eccentricity variation having periods near 100 KY, and was obtained by digital filtering. Curves showing the 19 KY and 23 KY components of the precession index are obtained in the same way. The obliquity curve has not been filtered. Calculations made by the authors on primary orbital curves provided by A.L. Berger (1).

Phase Lag. Based on Weertman's ice-sheet model (38), the mean time constant of large ice sheets (expressed as an e-folding time) can be estimated to lie in the range 10 KY to 20 KY. Because these values are of the same order of magnitude as the periods of the astronomical forcing, the isotopic response to this forcing will exhibit phase lags that are significant fractions of the forcing periods. At each period the lag will be different, depending on the period, on the nature of the physical system, and on the magnitude of the system's time constant. The problem is to estimate these phase lags. We do this by assuming that climate is a time invariant, single-exponential system, i.e., we assume that the rate of the response at any instant is proportional to the magnitude of the forcing. The impact such a (linear) system has on phase (ϕ) is well known. For steady state, it is given by $\phi = -\arctan 2\pi f T$, where T is the time constant and f the forcing frequency (16,35). The problem of estimating phase lags therefore reduces to that of estimating T. Here we follow the work of Imbrie and Imbrie (14), who based their estimate of T on data spanning an interval of time over which radiometric control is reasonably good (the past 127 KY). This estimate of T is 17 KY$\pm$3 KY. As shown in Table 3, an error of 3 KY in our estimate of T introduces discrepancies in our estimates of time lags that are on the order of 400 years.

The assumption stated above could be employed in various ways to develop a tuning strategy. We choose to pass the obliquity and precession signals through a single-exponential system with a time constant of 17 KY, and use the output curves as our tuning targets (see Fig. 9). The phase of each frequency component in these output curves is shifted by an amount that is fixed by the assumed time constant.

Data Processing. Each of these phase-shifted orbital curves can be regarded as a prediction of the isotopic signal over a narrow frequency band. We therefore apply phase-free digital filters to extract the appropriate frequency components from the raw isotopic data, and match this curve of filtered data against the corresponding phase-shifted orbital curve. Specifically, we attempt to match the phase of each excursion of a filtered curve with the phase of a corresponding excursion in an orbital curve. Except for portions of the record which lie near radiometric control points, a reasonably good phase lock can be achieved fairly easily -- provided that attention is confined to one orbital curve at a time. If, however, one attempts to achieve a satisfactory phase lock with the obliquity and precession curves simultaneously, the degrees of freedom available to the investigator (and the simplicity of the tuning task) is substantially decreased, even at stratigraphic levels that are far re-

Table 3 Predicted phases of $\delta^{18}O$ responses at selected periods of orbital forcing, assuming a linear (exponential) system with time constants of 14 KY, 17 KY, and 20 KY.

Orbital Forcing	Period (KY)	Phase (°)			Time Lag (KY)		
		14 KY	17 KY	20 KY	14 KY	17 KY	20 KY
Obliquity	41	- 65	- 69	- 72	7.4	7.9	8.2
Precession	23	- 75	- 78	- 80	4.8	5.0	5.1
Precession	19	- 78	- 80	- 81	4.1	4.2	4.3

moved from radiometric time control.

In using this technique, the pass-band of a given filter must be wide enough to capture essentially all of the frequencies in the corresponding orbital curve. In the early phases of the tuning process, it must also be wide enough to capture isotopic frequencies which, although causally related to the orbital paprameter under study, have been shifted across the spectrum by inaccuracies in the chronology. Yet the pass-bands must not be so wide as to encroach on concentrations of isotopic variance related to orbital influences other than the one being investigated. For studies of the precession band, the filter that we have designed to meet these constraints passes more than 50 per cent of the signal at periods between 17 KY and 27 KY; for the obliquity band, our filter passes the same fraction of the signal between 35 KY and 50 KY (see Table 4 and Fig. 10).

In using filters to tune the geologic record we make a basic assumption, namely, that the only significant concentrations of isotopic variance which occur within the pass-band of our filters represent responses to orbital forcing.

Control Points. Previous attempts to tune the isotopic record against orbital curves have limited the number of control points in the depth-vs.-age function to 17. In order to allow for changes in accumulation rate that occur at many places in our cores, we expand the number of control points as required. For reasons discussed above, most of the controls are placed at isotopic events studied and named by Prell et al. (27). Additional controls are added between these events wherever there is evidence of a change in accumulation rate.

Independent Evaluation. Criteria independent of the tuning process are used to evaluate the final time scale. One such criterion is the extent to which orbital and isotopic variations are coherent, i.e., the extent to which the amplitudes of excursions in one signal (and in a given frequency band) are proportional to the amplitudes of corresponding excursions in the other signal (and in the same frequency band). This property is conventionally measured by a coefficient of coherency, which is essentially a correlation coefficient calculated at zero phase and over a narrow frequency band (16). Following the lead of Kominz et al. (18) we will evaluate the time scale by inspecting a coherency spectrum, and pay particular attention to coherencies at three periods: 19 KY, 23 KY, and 41 KY. As shown on Figure 3, each of these narrow-band variations in orbital geometry has a distinctive time domain pattern.

Table 4 Weights of band-pass filters used in this paper. See (11) and (13) for description of numerical procedures.

22 KY Filter		41 KY Filter	
Lag (±KY)	Weight	Lag (±KY)	Weight
0	.080	0	.077
2	.066	5	.055
4	.030	10	.003
6	-.016	15	-.050
8	-.054	20	-.073
10	-.072	25	-.055
12	-.064	30	-.008
14	-.036	35	-.039
16	.002	40	.061
18	.034	45	.047
20	.051	50	.010
22	.049	55	-.027
24	.031	60	-.045
26	.006	65	-.036
28	-.016	70	-.010
30	-.027	75	.016
32	-.027	80	.028
34	-.019	85	.022
36	-.006	90	.007
38	.004	95	-.007
40	.010	100	-.014
42	.011	105	-.012
44	.008	110	-.004
46	.004	115	.003
48	-.001	120	.006
50	-.002	125	.006
-	-	130	.001

Another way of evaluating a time scale is to calculate depth-vs.-age functions for different cores. Given the prevalence of stratigraphic disturbances, abrupt shifts in this function are to be expected in any given core. However, the occurence of abrupt shifts at the same time in cores from different sedimentary regimes would suggest that the shifts were artifacts of tuning.

Application of the Strategy

The application of this strategy to our cores can be summarized in terms of five sequential steps: (1) stratigraphic analysis; (2) development of an initial, radiometrically controlled time scale; (3) orbital tuning of individual cores; (4) inspection of depth-vs.-age plots; and (5) stacking.

Step 1 : Stratigraphic analysis. Inspection of the isotopic curves plotted as a function of depth in core (Fig. 4) reveals a number of inconsistencies that we interpret as evidence of stratigraphic disturbance. A conspicuous example occurs in Stage 5 (the isotopically light interval lying immediately above the 6.0 stage boundary). In three of our cores (V22-174, V30-40, and RC11-120), there are three conspicuous peaks, referred to in this paper as 5.1, 5.3, and 5.5. Because this pattern is consistent with dozens of high-resolution records previously analyzed, and inconsistent with the low-resolution records in cores V28-238 and DSDP502, we conclude that these two cores are disturbed in Stage 5. This conclusion is supported by independent evidence. In DSDP502, Prell et al. (26) report biostratigraphic evidence of a coring gap at this level; and in core V28-238 Prell et al. (27) report sedimentological evidence at this level of a disturbance associated with a coring gap. Another example of a stratigraphic inconsistency occurs in Stage 11 (the isotopically light interval near 700 cm in core V28-238). At depths from 723 cm to 753 cm in this core, there is a shelf of light values that has no counterpart in V22-174, in DSDP502, or in many other cores. A suspicion that the Stage 11 shelf in V28-238 is an artifact is strongly supported by sedimentological evidence of a disturbance at a core break (27). We conclude that this 30-cm section of core V28-238 represents a stretching of the record during core recovery, and have removed the corresponding data points from our files before tuning. Although we have not found it necessary to eliminate other raw data, the identification of stratigraphic inconsistencies played a crucial role in guiding our selection of control points.

Step 2 : Development of an initial time scale. Our initial time scale (Fig. 5) assumes that the accumulation rate was constant at each coring site between six stratigraphic levels. The first level is that of the core tops, where there is stratigraphic evidence of a near zero age. The remaining five control points are stratigraphic levels for which radiometric age estimates (Table 5) are available: two isotopic events in Stage 2 with radiocarbon ages of about 18 KY and 21 KY; the 6.0 isotopic stage boundary, taken as 127 KY; the Bruhnes-Matuyama magnetic reversal, taken as 730 KY; and the magnetic reversal at the top of the Jaramillo event, taken as 900 KY. Although the last-named event does not occur in any of the cores studied here, it nevertheless provides an important maximum age of the lowermost sample in V28-238. A biostratigraphic analysis of this core (37), indicates that the bottom of V28-238 is very close to the top of the Jaramillo interval. In our initial time scale we have therefore arbitrarily fixed the age of the bottom of this core as 890 KY.

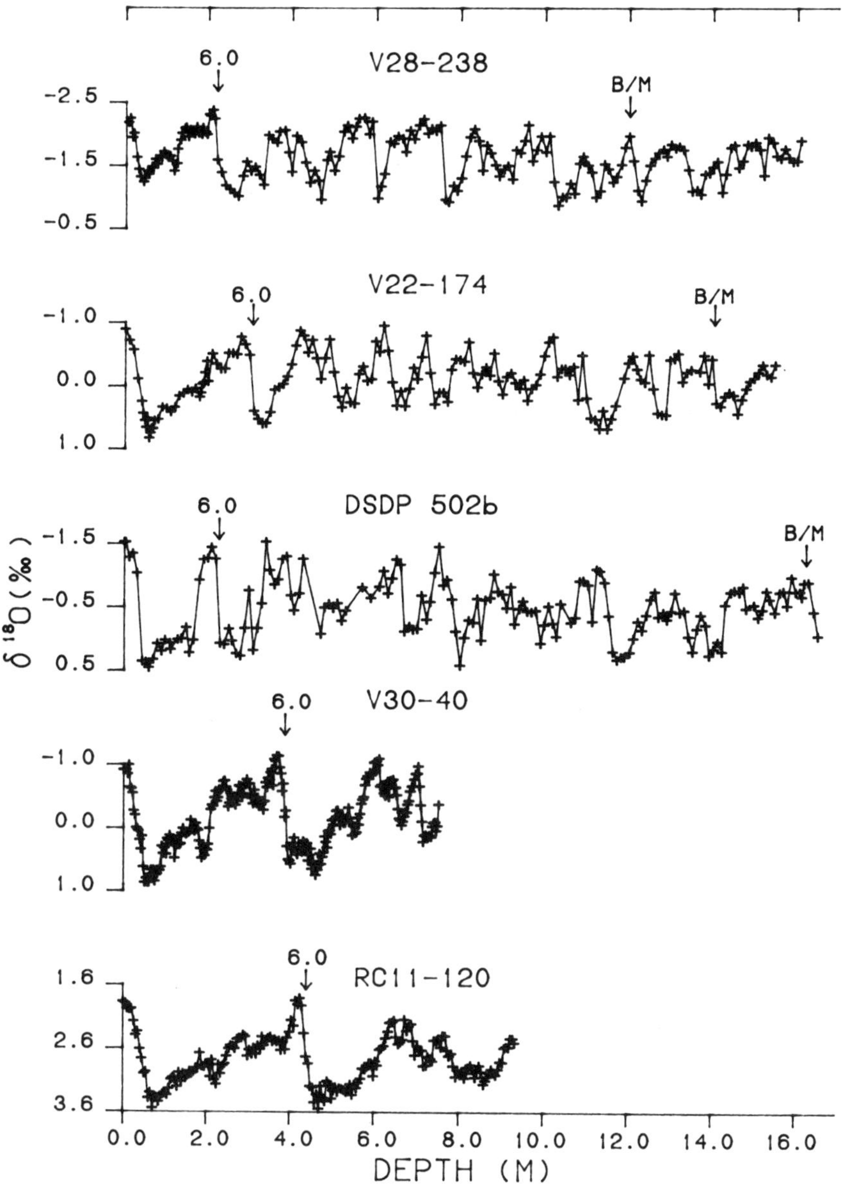

Figure 4 Variations in $\delta^{18}O$ as a function of depth in five deep-sea cores. Two important stratigraphic levels are labeled as follows : 6.0 for the boundary between isotope stages 5 and 6; and B/M for the magnetic reversal at the Brunhes-Matuyama boundary. See Table 1.

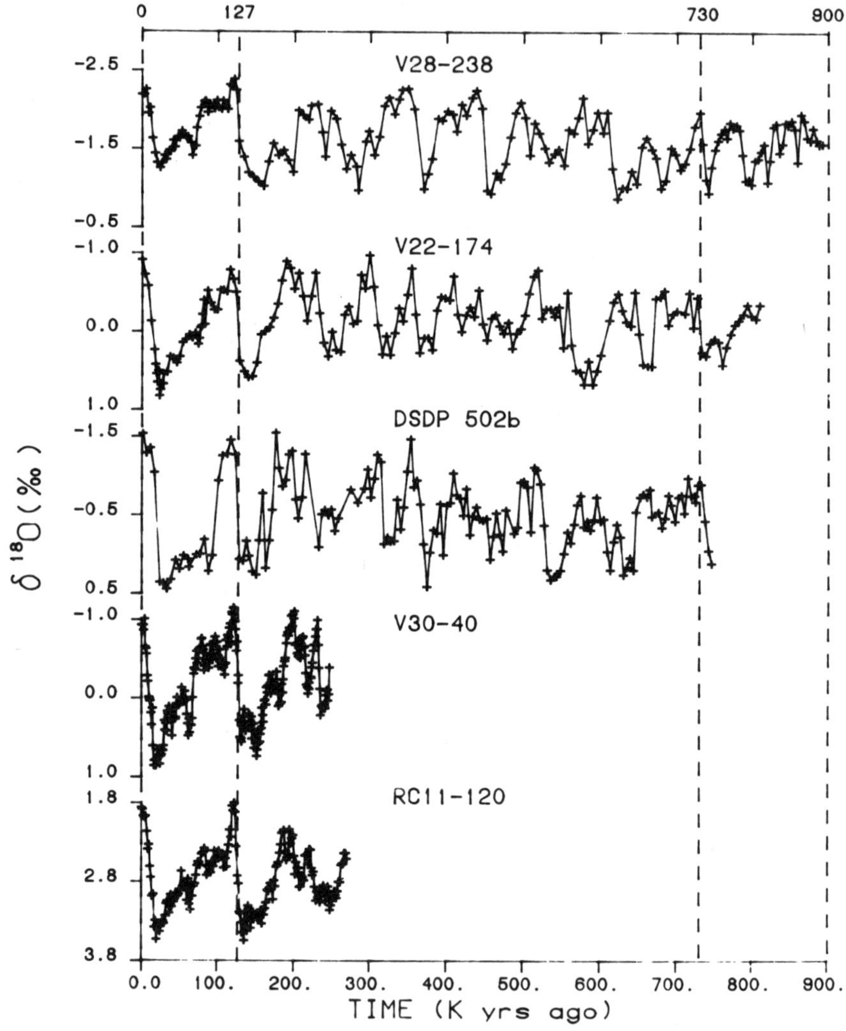

Figure 5 Variations in $\delta^{18}O$ as a function of estimated time in five deep-sea cores. The time scale is derived by linear interpolation between (and extrapolation beyond) control points at 127 KY, 730 KY BP. For details, see text and Table 5.

Table 5 Radiometric ages for stratigraphic levels used as control points in this study.

Level	Age (KY)	Core	Reference $\delta^{18}O$	Reference Dating
Upper $\delta^{18}O$ Stage 2 (2.22)	17.8 ± 1.5	V19-188	(25,43)	(25)
		CH22KW31	(24)	(24)
		V34-101	(43)	(43)
Lower $\delta^{18}O$ Stage 2 (2.24)	21.4 ± 2	V34-88	(43)	(43)
$\delta^{18}O$ Termination II (6.0)	127 ± 6	V12-122	(4)	(4,31)
B/M Magnetic Boundary	730 ± 11	V28-238	(30,32)	(20,44)
		V22-174	(36)	(20,44)
		DSDP502b	(26)	(20,44)
Top Jaramillo Event	900 ± 14	V28-238	(30,32)	(20,44)

Step 3 : Orbital tuning. The tuning process is iterative, and begins with the initial time scale just described. At each iteration, digital filters centered at periods of 22 KY and 41 KY are applied to the data, and the phase of each excursion in the resulting curves is compared with the phase of excursions in the corresponding target curves. If significant phase differences occur between either pair of curves, an appropriate adjustment is made in the age of one or more control points, and the filtering process repeated. Midway in this process, the radiometric time constraints at the 6.0 and B/M boundaries are removed. The process is continued until the investigator is satisfied that an optimum phase lock has been achieved in both frequency bands. In our final time scale (Fig. 6 and Table 6), the number of non-radiometric control points used within the Brunhes ranges from 56 in V22-174 to 72 in DSDP502; the tuned ages of the 6.0 and B/M boundaries are 128 KY and 734 KY, respectively; and the age of the bottom sample in V28-238 is 892 KY.

This procedure can fairly be described as ungainly, in that the results presented here required approximately 120 iterations. But the application of this chronology to any new core is quite straightforward. Having identified as many of the isotopic events listed in Table 6 as possible, the investigator simply uses our estimate of the ages of these events and interpolates linearly between them.

Step 4 : Depths-vs.-age plots. The set of depth-vs.-age functions shown in Figure 7 provides some welcome support for the assumptions used in tuning. Each curve is fairly smooth over considerable intervals, and the sharp inflections that are present do not occur in all cores simultaneously.

Step 5 : Stacking. After adjusting the record in each core to have zero mean and unit standard deviation, the normalized curves (plotted on the new time scale) were superimposed, sampled at intervals of 1 KY, and averaged (Fig. 8). To avoid averaging data that are known to be atypical of records having greater resolution, short sections of Stage 5 in V28-238, DSDP502, and V22-174 were removed before stacking. This signal was then smoothed with a 9-point Gaussian filter (Table 7).

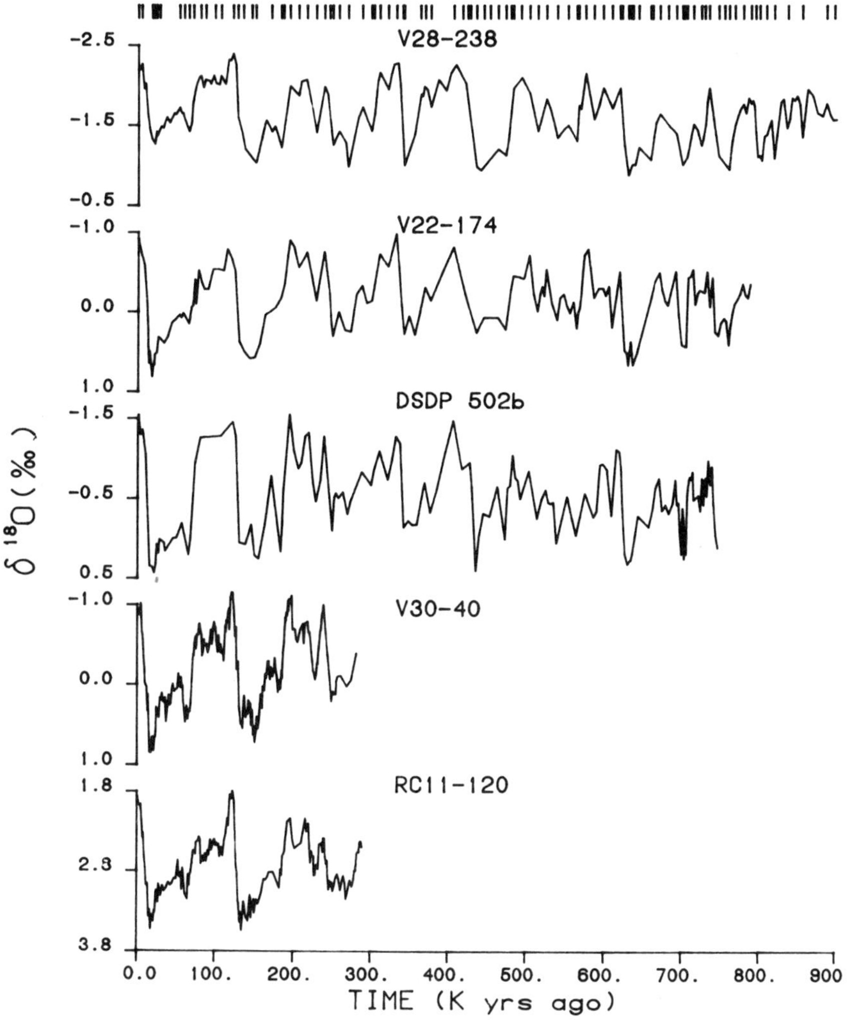

Figure 6 Variations in $\delta^{18}O$ plotted on the SPECMAP time scale in five deep-sea cores. On this time scale, the 6.0 and B/M boundaries shown on Figs. 4 and 5 are dated at 128 KY and 734 KY, respectively. Small vertical lines at the top of the figure indicate time-scale control points (Table 6).

Table 6 Control points for the SPECMAP time scale. Isotopic events labeled 2.0, 3.0, etc., are stage boundaries as defined by Shackleton and Opdyke (32) in V28-238. Other numbered isotopic events are local maxima and minima of $\delta^{18}O$ curves, as defined by Prell et al. (27). Unnumbered events are changes in sedimentation rate recognized in one core only. Zero age for core tops is an inference based on stratigraphic analysis. Ages marked (**) are based on radiocarbon measurements (Table 5). The age marked (*) relates to the isotopically heaviest excursion in the smoothed, stacked record for stage 2, as determined by interpolation between radiocarbon-dated levels. All other ages given without parentheses have been determined by orbital tuning methods. An age for a stage boundary given in parenthesis is determined by interpolation between adjacent ages with reference to the stratigraphic level of the corresponding event in V28-238. A depth given without parentheses represents an isotopic event recognized in a particular core and used there as time control. A depth in parentheses represents a stage boundary not used as time control in a particular core; this level has been determined by interpolation between adjacent levels with reference to the age of the corresponding event in column 2. Depths below 723 cm in V28-238 are 30 cm less than specified in (32) to allow for the effect of a core break.

Event	Age (KY)	Depth in Core (cm) V30-40	RC11-120	V28-238	V22-174	DSDP502b
Top	0	0	0	0	0	0
1.1	6	12	-	10	-	-
2.0	12	33	45	22	26	33
2.22	17.8**	58.5	70	-	-	47
2.2	19*	-	-	42	57	-
2.24	21.4**	75	85	-	-	59
3.0	24	91.5	110	55	80	74
3.1	28	-	135	-	100	99
3.3	53	162	185	91	150	-
4.0	59	183	215	111	175	154
4.2	65	195	225	115	180	157
5.0	71	208	250	128	192	178
5.1	80	241.5	290	145	-	191
5.2	87	261	-	-	235	-
-	94	-	335	-	-	-

Event	Age (KY)	Depth in Core (cm) V30-40	RC11-120	V28-238	V22-174	DSDP502b
-	95	279	-	-	-	-
5.3	99	297	-	-	255	-
5.4	107	-	380	-	-	202
-	110	-	-	-	270	-
5.5	122	370.5	420	210	-	210
6.0	128	387	440	220	307	227
6.2	135	399	470	-	-	235
6.3	146	-	490	-	-	252
6.4	151	462	550	271	-	275
6.5	171	522	592	302	-	300
-	176	540	-	-	-	-
6.6	183	555	600	332	-	310
7.0	(186)	567	612	(335)	395	330
7.1	194	606	645	343	420	340
7.2	205	627	665	364	440	360
-	212	633	-	-	-	-
7.3	216	642	675	384	450	386
7.4	228	666	722	399	470	408
7.5	238	705	760	410	490	430
8.0	(245)	(713)	788	(430)	500	450
8.2	249	717	808	443	520	472
8.3	257	742	828	452	530	500
8.4	269	747	860	468	545	520
-	281	753	-	-	-	-
8.5	287	-	928	489	570	570
8.6	299	-	-	501	-	591
9.0	(303)	-	-	(510)	595	611
9.1	310	-	-	531	600	622
9.2	320	-	-	543	610	631
9.3	331	-	-	565	620	651
10.0	(339)	-	-	(595)	(644)	668
10.2	341	-	-	603	650	671
11.0	362	-	-	630	(681)	709
11.1	368	-	-	658	690	711
11.2	375	-	-	671	700	722
-	395	-	-	691	-	-
11.3	405	-	-	710	720	752
11.4	416	-	-	-	-	762
-	420	-	-	723	-	-

Event	Age (KY)	Depth in Core (cm) V30-40	RC11-120	V28-238	V22-174	DSDP502b
12.0	(423)	-	-	(725)	(732)	(768)
12.1	426	-	-	-	-	771
12.2	434	-	-	733	740	801
-	439	-	-	741	-	-
12.31	443	-	-	-	750	822
12.32	451	-	-	-	-	831
12.33	461	-	-	752	760	842
12.4	471	-	-	761	770	851
13.0	(478)	-	-	(781)	780	(871)
13.11	481	-	-	792	790	882
13.12	491	-	-	-	-	912
13.13	502	-	-	812	820	922
13.2	513	-	-	821	840	931
14.0	524	-	-	830	880	951
14.2	538	-	-	860	900	993
14.3	552	-	-	880	-	1011
14.4	563	-	-	891	960	1031
15.0	(565)	-	-	(900)	(972)	1037
15.1	574	-	-	930	1015	1040
15.2	585	-	-	940	1030	1066
15.3	596	-	-	960	1050	1095
15.4	607	-	-	971	1080	1116
15.5	617	-	-	980	1090	1133
16.0	(620)	-	-	(985)	1095	1150
16.22	628	-	-	1000	1130	1176
16.23	631	-	-	-	-	-
16.24	634	-	-	-	1150	1206
16.3	641	-	-	1030	-	1226
16.4	656	-	-	1040	-	1236
17.0	(659)	-	-	(1045)	(1194)	(1243)
17.1	668	-	-	1060	1210	1266
17.2	679	-	-	-	1240	-
17.3	689	-	-	1080	1250	1313
18.0	689	-	-	1080	1250	1313
18.22	697	-	-	1090	-	1356
18.23	700	-	-	-	1280	-
18.24	703	-	-	1100	-	1426
18.3	711	-	-	1111	1320	1475

Event	Age (KY)	V30-40	RC11-120	V28-238	V22-174	DSDP502b
				Depth in Core (cm)		
18.4	721	-	-	1131	-	1512
19.0	(726)	-	-	(1150)	1372	1561
19.1	731	-	-	1171	-	1592
20.0	(736)	-	-	(1180)	1403	1640
20.22	743	-	-	1191	1420	1664
20.23	750	-	-	-	1440	-
20.24	756	-	-	1200	1460	-
21.0	(763)	-	-	(1220)	1490	-
21.1	774	-	-	1251	1520	-
21.3	784	-	-	1280	1550	-
22.0	(790)	-	-	(1310)	-	-
22.2	795	-	-	1331	-	-
22.3	804	-	-	-	-	-
22.4	814	-	-	1391	-	-
-	832	-	-	1433	-	-
-	851	-	-	1490	-	-
-	882	-	-	1540	-	-
-	892	-	-	1565	-	-

Table 7 The stacked, smoothed oxygen-isotope record as a function of age in the SPECMAP time scale. Ages in KY BP are given at steps of 2 KY. Isotopic variations expressed in standard deviation units around a zero mean.

0	-2.09	210	-1.12	420	-0.68	630	1.84
2	-1.91	212	-1.23	422	-0.53	632	1.77
4	-1.74	214	-1.35	424	-0.34	634	1.79
6	-1.41	216	-1.40	426	-0.10	636	1.69
8	-1.02	218	-1.27	428	0.25	638	1.49
10	-0.44	220	-0.01	430	0.69	640	1.25
12	0.29	222	-0.64	432	1.17	642	1.10
14	1.01	224	-0.31	434	1.50	644	1.05
16	1.58	226	-0.03	436	1.49	646	1.01
18	1.81	228	0.12	438	1.34	648	0.98

20	1.78	230	-0.02	440	1.19	650	0.94
22	1.65	232	-0.31	442	1.06	652	0.90
24	1.38	234	-0.68	444	0.97	654	0.86
26	1.14	236	-1.02	446	0.95	656	0.74
28	1.02	238	-1.18	448	0.93	658	0.51
30	0.96	240	-1.03	450	0.91	660	0.23
32	0.94	242	-0.65	452	0.87	662	-0.05
34	0.94	244	-0.20	454	0.79	664	-0.25
36	0.96	246	0.30	456	0.71	666	-0.38
38	0.94	248	0.70	458	0.64	668	-0.40
40	0.85	250	0.78	460	0.58	670	-0.23
42	0.77	252	0.66	462	0.61	672	-0.02
44	0.67	254	0.52	464	0.73	674	0.11
47	0.59	256	0.40	466	0.87	676	0.18
48	0.56	258	0.37	468	1.01	678	0.24
50	0.50	260	0.43	470	1.08	680	0.26
52	0.38	262	0.50	472	0.88	682	0.21
54	0.37	264	0.55	474	0.44	684	0.11
56	0.41	266	0.67	476	0.03	686	-0.01
58	0.50	268	0.85	478	-0.35	688	-0.12
60	0.68	270	0.89	480	-0.70	690	0.05
62	0.89	272	0.77	482	-0.86	692	0.46
64	1.00	274	0.60	484	-0.82	694	0.93
66	0.93	276	0.42	486	-0.79	696	1.33
68	0.66	278	0.21	488	-0.76	698	1.40
70	0.22	280	-0.01	490	-0.71	700	1.42
72	-0.24	282	-0.19	492	-0.68	702	1.36
74	-0.53	284	-0.35	494	-0.69	704	0.76
76	-0.69	286	-0.47	496	-0.74	706	0.08
78	-0.88	288	-0.46	498	-0.82	708	-0.21
80	-0.98	290	-0.31	500	-0.91	710	-0.32
82	-0.77	292	-0.15	502	-0.89	712	-0.16
84	-0.48	294	-0.05	504	-0.68	714	0.10
86	-0.45	296	0.02	506	-0.36	716	0.15
88	-0.47	298	0.05	508	-0.07	718	0.18
90	-0.46	300	-0.05	510	0.18	720	0.26
92	-0.52	302	-0.30	512	0.37	722	0.21
94	-0.71	304	-0.61	514	0.35	724	0.08
96	-0.80	306	-0.93	516	0.15	726	-0.14
98	-0.91	308	-1.20	518	-0.04	728	-0.43
100	-0.96	310	-1.34	520	-0.15	730	-0.55
102	-0.80	312	-1.31	522	-0.31	732	-0.49
104	-0.69	314	-1.19	524	-0.45	734	-0.42
106	-0.59	316	-1.06	526	-0.37	736	-0.18
108	-0.51	318	-0.95	528	-0.17	738	0.39
110	-0.50	320	-0.91	530	0.02	740	0.91
112	-0.73	322	-1.03	532	0.17	742	1.19
114	-1.19	324	-1.23	534	0.34	744	1.25
116	-1.53	326	-1.45	536	0.60	746	1.18
118	-1.72	328	-1.65	538	0.79	748	1.14

120	-1.98	330	-1.79	540	0.72	750	1.15
122	-2.12	332	-1.72	542	0.54	752	1.22
124	-1.89	334	-1.40	544	0.40	754	1.40
126	-1.19	336	-0.84	546	0.30	756	1.48
128	-0.26	338	-0.04	548	0.26	758	1.18
130	0.51	340	0.75	550	0.24	760	0.75
132	1.05	342	1.12	552	0.26	762	0.40
134	1.33	344	1.07	554	0.34	764	0.18
136	1.35	346	0.94	556	0.42	766	0.03
138	1.28	348	0.86	558	0.49	768	-0.10
140	1.32	350	0.86	560	0.64	770	-0.23
142	1.33	352	0.88	562	0.80	772	-0.36
144	1.26	354	0.86	564	0.65	774	-0.40
146	1.26	356	0.74	566	0.33	776	-0.30
148	1.41	358	0.53	568	0.08	778	-0.24
150	1.57	360	0.28	570	-0.27	780	-0.31
152	1.58	362	0.03	572	-0.68	782	-0.42
154	1.45	364	-0.18	574	-0.94		
156	1.30	366	-0.38	576	-0.93		
158	1.07	368	-0.50	578	-0.77		
160	0.85	370	-0.43	580	-0.51		
162	0.60	372	-0.25	582	-0.22		
164	0.40	374	-0.07	584	0.03		
166	0.25	376	-0.03	586	0.11		
168	0.15	378	-0.15	588	-0.01		
170	0.11	380	-0.30	590	-0.25		
172	0.12	382	-0.46	592	-0.51		
174	0.18	384	-0.61	594	-0.67		
176	0.27	386	-0.73	596	-0.71		
178	0.47	388	-0.82	598	-0.65		
180	0.71	390	-0.90	600	-0.57		
182	0.83	392	-0.98	602	-0.48		
184	0.62	394	-1.07	604	-0.23		
186	0.11	396	-1.19	606	0.11		
188	-0.42	398	-1.35	608	0.15		
190	-0.88	400	-1.51	610	-0.15		
192	-1.31	402	-1.66	612	-0.51		
194	-1.62	404	-1.77	614	-0.79		
196	-1.62	406	-1.77	616	-0.90		
198	-1.41	408	-1.64	618	-0.62		
200	-1.17	410	-1.46	620	0.09		
202	-0.99	412	-1.27	622	0.86		
204	-0.88	414	-1.08	624	1.42		
206	-0.88	416	-0.91	626	1.77		
208	-1.00	418	-0.79	628	1.92		

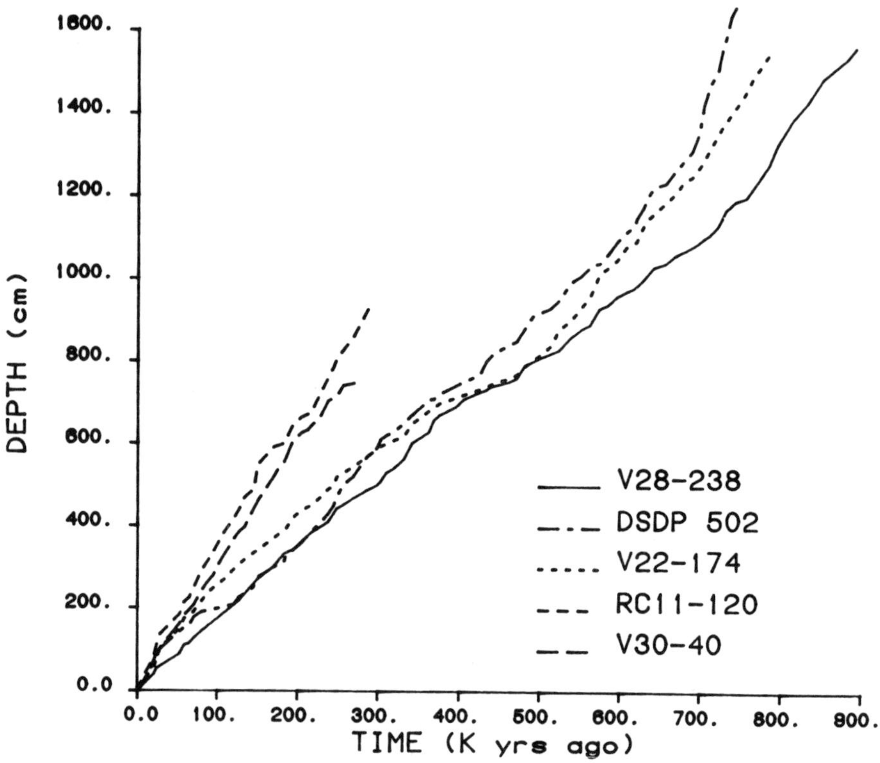

Figure 7 Depth vs. age in the SPECMAP time scale for five deep-sea cores analyzed in this paper.

DISCUSSION

The SPECMAP Time Scale

Filtered data. In each of the cores studied here, a time scale was developed by using digital filters to lock the phase of isotopic and orbital signals over two frequency bands. The stacked isotope record provides a convenient way of inspecting the result (41). As shown by the filtered data on Figure 9, a reasonably good phase lock has been achieved. Ninety per cent of the local maxima and minima of the obliquity curve lie within ± 3 KY of corresponding points on the filtered isotopic curve. A similar analysis of curves related to precession shows that the discrepancies do not exceed ± 2 KY. In both frequency bands, moreover, the discrepancies are considerably smaller away from the extremes of the excursions -- a point that will be emphasized below in our analysis of the phase spectrum.

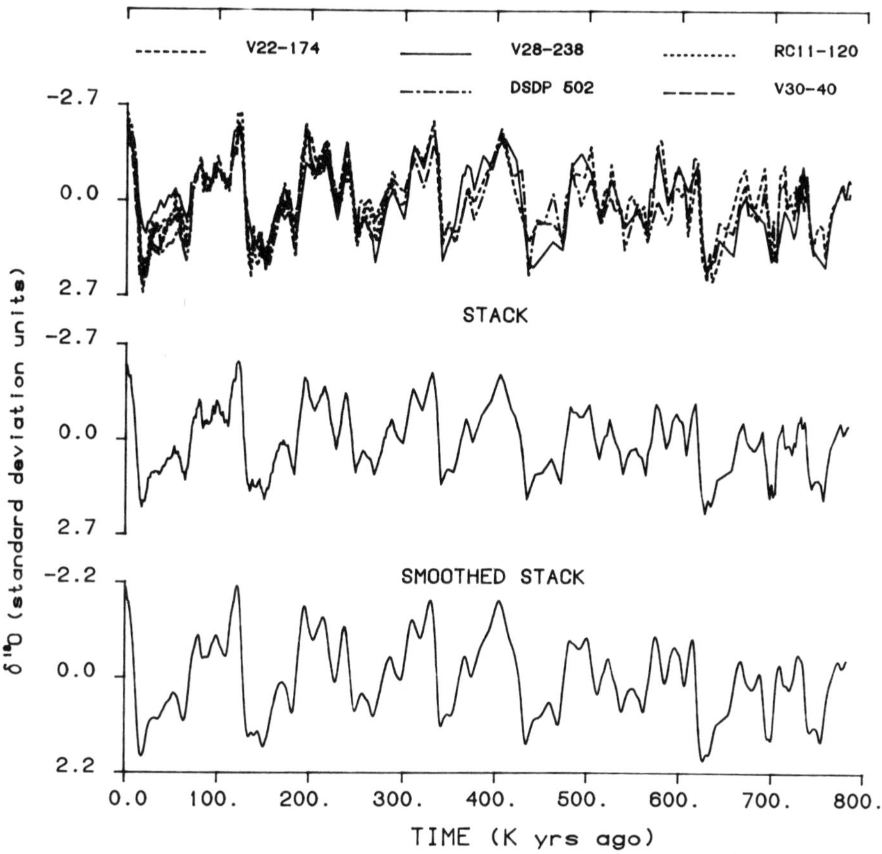

Figure 8 $\delta^{18}O$ variations in five deep-sea cores normalized and plotted on the SPECMAP time scale. In the top panel, data from each core has been normalized to zero mean and unit standard deviation. After interpolation at intervals of 1 KY, these curves have been averaged (middle panel), and smoothed with a 9-point Gaussian filter (bottom panel).

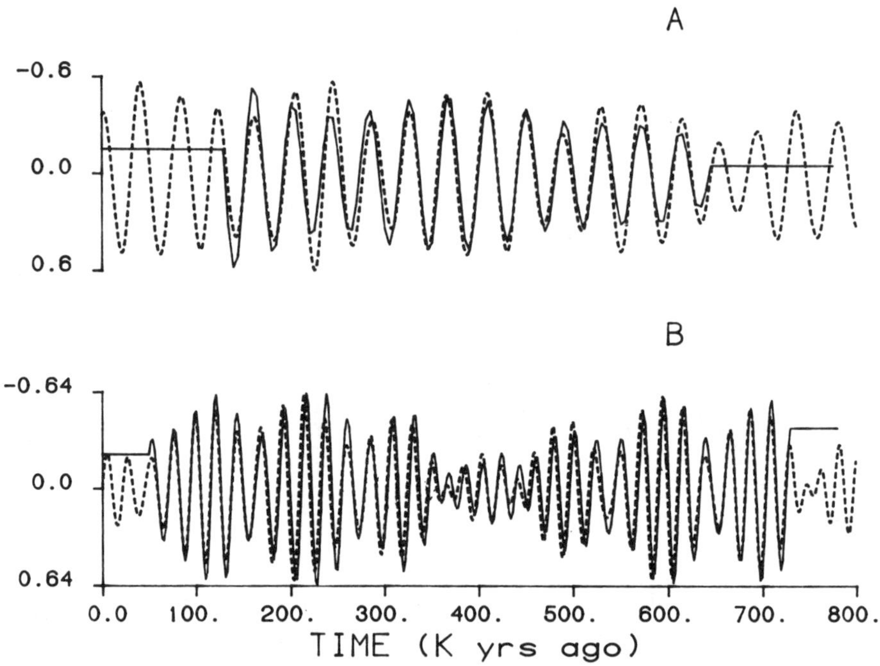

Figure 9 Variations in obliquity, precession, and the corresponding frequency components of $\delta^{18}O$ over the past 800 KY. Dashed lines are phase-shifted versions of obliquity (A) and precession (B) curves. Solid lines are filtered versions of the stacked $\delta^{18}O$ record plotted on the SPECMAP time scale. The filters used were centered on periods of 41 KY (A) and 22 KY (B). All curves have been transformed to have zero means with arbitrary scales.

An inspection of the filtered data on Figure 9 shows that the orbital and isotopic signals are strikingly coherent in both frequency bands. In other words, the magnitude of individual excursions in one curve tend to be proportional to corresponding excursions in the other.

Coherency spectrum. The techniques of cross-spectral analysis provide another way of analyzing the relationships between two signals. These techniques are more powerful than filtering because they make it possible to examine coherency (and phase) across the entire range of statistically visible frequencies, and to do so at a higher resolution than is practical with filters. We have performed such an analysis on two signals : (1) the raw, stacked isotopic data, plotted on the SPECMAP time scale; and (2) a signal constructed by normalizing and stacking curves of eccentricity, obliquity, and precession (Fig. 2). None of the individual components that make up this signal (which we will refer to as ETP) has been shifted in phase. However, we have reversed the sign of the precession index so that positive excursions in this core have the same climatic direction in the Northern Hemisphere as positive excursions in eccentricity and obliquity. Our object in performing cross-spectral analysis against the ETP curve, rather than against the individual orbital curves, is purely one of convenience, namely, to obtain a compact summary of orbital-isotopic relationships across the entire visible spectrum in a single diagram. Within each frequency band of interest, the results using ETP could be duplicated exactly by calculating a cross spectrum against the appropriate individual orbital curve.

In examining the coherency spectrum (Fig. 10), we first discuss the periods of variation in precession and obliquity (19 KY, 23 KY, and 41 KY), for it is over this part of the spectrum that the tuning was done. The measured coherencies (0.94, 0.97, and 0.93, respectively) are not only surprisingly high in absolute value, but lie well above the 5 per cent significance level (0.78). These peaks in the coherency spectrum coincide exactly with peaks in the isotopic and orbital spectra. Turning now to the low-frequency end of the spectrum, we find coherencies as high as 0.92 in the frequency band associated with the 100 KY eccentricity cycle. This peak in the coherency spectrum coincides approximately with conspicuous peaks in the isotopic and orbital spectra. Since the discovery of the 100-KY cycle (4,19), many investigators have been tempted to conclude that it is causally related in some way to variations in eccentricity (13,14,17). Our observation that variations in climate and eccentricity are strongly coherent in the 100-KY band is, we believe, the first compelling evidence in support of this idea.

These results -- and the fact that the tuned ages of 128 KY and 734 KY for the 6.0 and B/M boundaries agree with radiometric dates -- argue that the SPECMAP time scale is tightly constrained. To emphasize this point, we call attention to the diversity of the patterns of orbital variations in the 19 KY, 23 KY, 41 KY, and 100 KY frequency bands (Fig. 3). It is difficult to see how coherencies ranging from 0.92 to 0.97 could be achieved in all four frequency bands simultaneously as an artifact of the tuning procedure. We therefore conclude that the time scale presented in this paper is considerably more accurate than those developed earlier (13,17,18,22).

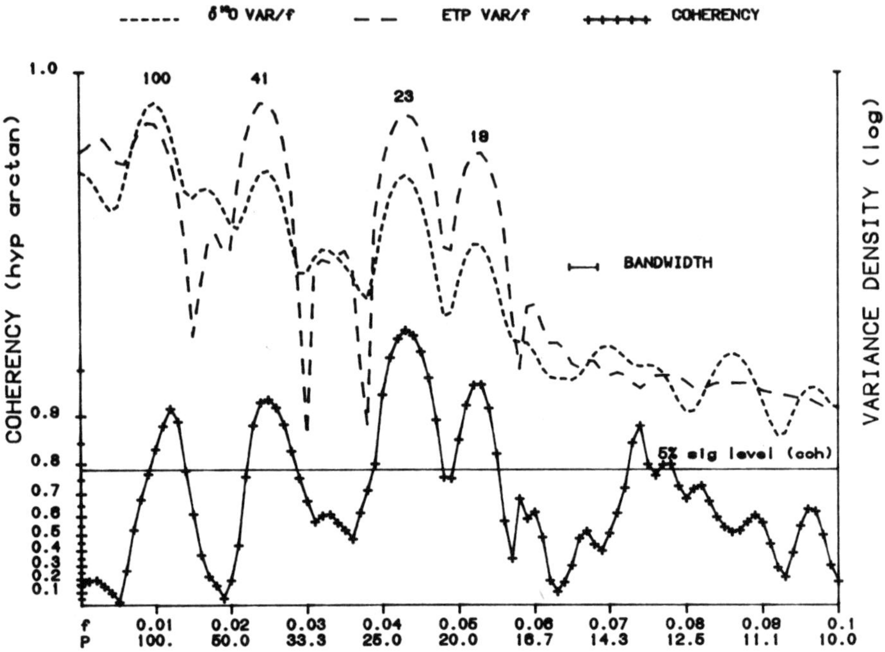

Figure 10 Coherency and variance spectra calculated from records of climatic and orbital variation spanning the past 780 000 years. Two signals have been processed: (1) ETP, a signal formed by normalizing and adding variations in eccentricity, obliquity, and precession; and (2) $\delta^{18}O$, the unsmoothed, stacked isotope record plotted on the SPECMAP time scale (Fig. 9). Top: variance spectra for the two signals are plotted on arbitrary log scales. Bottom: coherency spectrum plotted on a hyperbolic arctangent scale and provided with a 5% significance level. Frequencies are in cycles per thousand years.

Phase spectrum. The fundamental assumption used to develop our time scale is that isotopic phase lags at the frequencies of obliquity and precession are those of a single-exponential system with a time constant of 17 KY (Table 3). The extent that we have been able to adjust our time scale to fit this assumption has already been discussed in the context of plots showing filtered data and phase-shifted orbital curves (Fig. 9). Plots of this kind were crucial to the development of the SPECMAP time scale because they made it possible to examine phase relationships one cycle at a time. Having completed this iterative process, however, we can now extract additional information about phase by calculating a phase spectrum. Diagrams of this kind have a number of useful properties: they integrate phase information over the entire length of the geologic record; they provide statistical summaries of the information (means and standard deviations) over a wide range of frequencies; and they achieve a higher resolution in the frequency domain than is practical with digital filters.

Two phase spectra are shown in Figure 11. One of these is a theoretical phase spectrum calculated on the assumption that the steady-state response to orbital forcing can be modeled as a single-exponential system with a time constant of 17 KY. The other curve, given with 95 per cent confidence intervals, shows the observed phase spectrum between the ETP signal and the stacked isotopic data plotted on the SPECMAP time scale. Considering the assumptions we used in tuning, it is hardly surprising that the observed phases lie close to the predicted phases in narrow bands centered on the main frequencies of obliquity and precession. We are, however, somewhat surprised that the observed and predicted phases match so well over the entire range of periods from 16 KY to 45 KY; and that the 95 per cent confidence intervals over this range are as small as they are. Expressed in terms of time shifts, the 95 per cent confidence intervals in the obliquity and precession bands are ± 1.8 KY and ±0.6 KY, respectively.

At periods longer than about 50 KY, the observed phase spectrum in Figure 11 departs significantly from the predicted spectrum. One way of explaining this behavior is to postulate the existence of a resonance phenomenon acting near a period of 100 KY. This idea will be explored further in a later paper.

Accuracy. The phase spectrum of the stacked isotope record (Fig. 11) can be used as a basis for estimating the accuracy of the SPECMAP time scale. We start by assuming that the confidence intervals for the phase lags at the obliquity and precession frequencies (1.8 KY and 0.6 KY) reflect two types of uncertainty. Type 1 includes various kinds of observational error. Type 2 includes errors in our assumption that the climate system can be modeled over some 800 000 years as a time-invariant linear system. To these must be added our previous estimate of the error (0.4 KY) attached to the assumption of a 17 KY time constant (Type 3 error). In addition, errors in stratigraphic correlation caused by delay in ocean mixing (Type 4) must be considered. Here we use recent evidence that the mixing time of oceanic deep waters is about 500 years (34) to estimate the stratigraphic error as 0.25 KY. Assuming that these four types of error are independent and normally distributed, we combine them and estimate that the 95% confidence interval for control points in the SPECMAP time scale is ± 2 KY. However, our ability to identify any given isotopic event in any given core is limited to one half of the sampling interval used in the relevant part of that core (Type 5 error). In the records studied here, this uncertainty ranges from 0.5 KY to 2.5 KY (Table 1). Our final estimate of the error in our chronology for any given core therefore ranges from 3 KY to 5 KY, depending on the sampling interval.

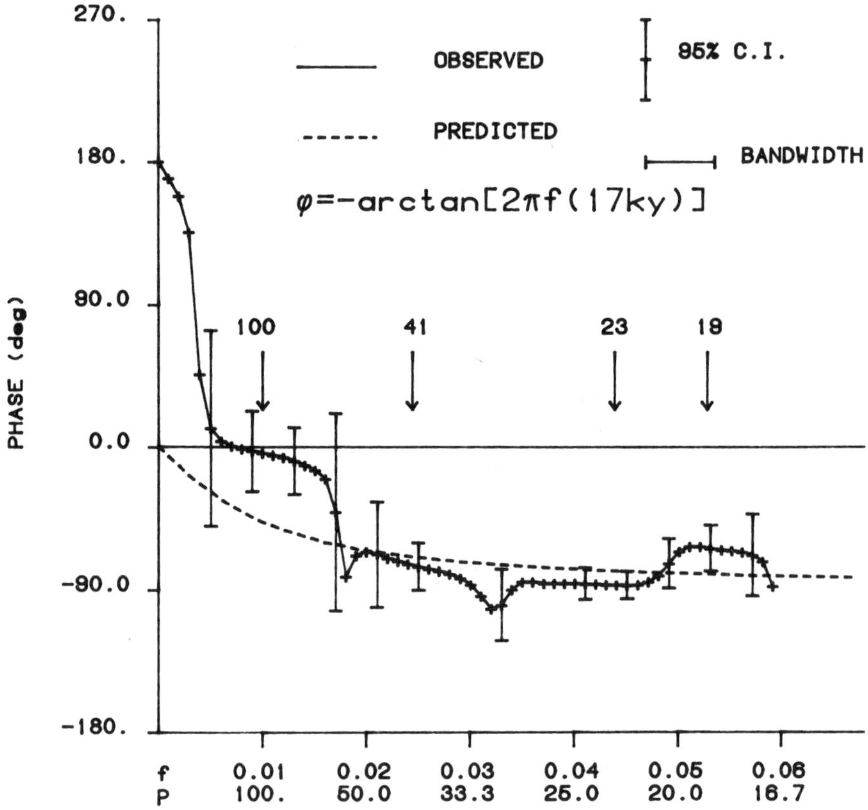

Figure 11 Theoretical and observed phase spectra relating climatic and orbital variation over the past 780 000 years. Negative phase indicates that climatic variation lags orbital variation. Dashed line: predicted phases (degrees) based on the response of a single-exponential system with a time constant of 17 KY. Solid line: observed phases calculated from orbital and $\delta^{18}O$ signals described in Figure 10. Frequencies in cycles per thousand years.

The B/M magnetic reversal is a non-isotopic event recorded at particular stratigraphic levels in three of our cores (45). Ages for these levels, calculated by interpolation in the SPEC-MAP time scale, lie in the interval 734 KY$\pm$3 KY. It seems likely that the differences in these estimates reflect the operation of Type 1, Type 4, and Type 5 errors. Allowing for the effects of errors of Type 2 and Type 3, we estimate that the age of the B/M boundary is 734$\pm$5 KY. On this basis, Johnson's 790-KY estimate (17) is 50 000 years too old.

The Astronomical Theory

Having developed a time scale that we believe is accurate to within 5 KY, we are now in a position to evaluate the astronomical theory empirically. Our main contribution to this goal is the coherency spectrum (Fig. 10). As discussed above, coherencies at the four main periods of astronomical forcing -- including the 100 KY eccentricity period -- are 0.92 or above. Since the square of any given coherency represents that fraction of the total observed variance that can be explained as a linear response to orbital forcing, we believe that as much as 85 per cent of the isotopic variance in each of four narrow frequency bands (centered on periods of 19 KY, 23 KY, 41 KY, and 100 KY) is forced in some way by orbital variation. By integrating the square of the coherency spectrum over the entire range of periods from 19 KY to 100 KY -- including frequencies at which no orbital variation occurs -- we estimate that some 60 per cent of the total isotopic variance observed over this part of the climatic spectrum is a response to orbital forcing. On average, therefore, Milankovitch mechanisms would explain at least 77 per cent of the amplitude of $\delta^{18}O$ excursions observed in the records under study here. It seems highly likely that a satisfactory account of the residual variance that is not explained by orbital theory will require the consideration of internal stochastic mechanisms (12,18) as well as a search for external causes that are unrelated to celestial mechanics. But a careful study of the marine isotopic record leaves little room for doubt that variations in the geometry of the Earth's orbit are the main cause of the succession of late Pleistocene ice ages.

CONCLUSIONS

1. Oscillations in five $\delta^{18}O$ records obtained from pelagic foraminifera at open-ocean sites in low- and mid-latitudes are strongly correlated over the past 780 000 years. We infer that changes in the global volume of glacial ice are the dominant influence on this pattern.

2. A geologic time scale can be developed from a simple model in which the isotopic record is considered as the response of a single-exponential system being forced by variations in obliquity and precession. With a time constant of 17 KY, this model satisfactorily accounts for the amplitudes and phases of the isotopic signal over a range of periods from 16 KY to 50 KY.

3. In this new time scale, the age of the isotopic Stage 5 - Stage 6 boundary is 128 KY ±3 KY, and the age of the Brunhes-Matuyama magnetic boundary is 734 KY±5 KY. Unlike some previously published time scales, the chronology presented here is consistent with radiometric dates for these boundaries (127 KY±6 KY and 730 KY±11 KY, respectively).

4. At each of the main orbital periods that are resolvable in a record of this length (19 KY, 23 KY, 41 KY, and 100 KY), coherencies between orbital and isotopic signals exceed 0.9 and are highly significant statistically. In narrow frequency bands centered on these four frequencies, therefore, at least 85 per cent of the observed isotopic variance is linearly related to orbital forcing.

5. This empirical study of the marine isotopic record leaves little room for doubt that variations in the geometry of the Earth's orbit are the main cause of the succession of late Pleistocene ice ages.

ACKNOWLEDGEMENTS

We wish to acknowledge our debt to several people whose efforts made it possible for us to complete this paper in its present form. André Berger provided us with the digital results of his orbital computations. Angeline Duffy carried out over half of the complex, iterative calculations required to develop our time scale. Gordon Start helped with the tuning process, particularly in DSDP502. Rosalind Mellor accurately processed the words in our text and the numbers in our tables. We also acknowledge the support of a National Science Foundation grant NSF ATM80-18897 (SPECMAP) through the Climate Dynamics Section, Division of Atmospheric Sciences, the Seabed Assessment Program, International Decade of Ocean Exploration, Division of Ocean Sciences; and the Division of Polar Programs. We are also indebted to the National Science Foundation for its support of the Lamont-Doherty Geological Observatory core laboratory.

REFERENCES

1. Berger, A.L. : 1976, Astron. Astrophys. 51, pp. 127-135; 1977, Celest. Mech. 15, pp. 53-74.
2. Berger, A.L. : 1978, Quaternary Research 9, pp. 139-167.
3. Berger, A.L. : 1977, Nature (Lond.) 269, pp. 44-45.
4. Broecker, W.S., and Van Donk, J. : 1970, Rev. Geophys. Space Phys. 8, pp. 169-197.
5. Croll, J. : 1864, Phil. Mag. 28, pp. 121-137; 1875, "Climate and Time", Appleton, New York.
6. Dodge, R.E., Fairbanks, R.G., Benninger, L.W., and Maurrasse, F. : 1983, Science 219, pp. 1423-1425.
7. Duplessy, J.C., Delibrias, G., Turon, J.L., Pujol, C., and Duprat, J. : 1981, Palaeogeog., -clim., -ecol. 35, pp. 121-144.
8. Emiliani, C. : 1955, J. Geol. 63, pp. 538-578.
9. Emiliani, C. : 1966, Science 154, pp. 851-857.
10. Fairbanks, R.G., and Matthews, R.K. : 1978, Quaternary Research 10, pp. 181-196.
11. Goodman, J. : 1960, J. Franklin Inst. 270, pp. 437-450.
12. Hasselmann, K. : 1976, Tellus 28, pp. 473-485.
13. Hays, J.D., Imbrie, J., Shackleton, N.J. : 1976, Science 194, pp. 1121-1132.
14. Imbrie, J., and Imbrie, J.Z. : 1980, Science 207, pp. 943-953.
15. Imbrie, J. : 1982, Icarus 50, pp. 408-422.
Imbrie, J., and Imbrie, K.P. : 1979, "Ice Ages : Solving the Mystery", Enslow, Short Hills, N.J.
16. Jenkins, G.M., and Watts, D.G. : 1968, "Spectral analysis and its applications", Holden-Day, San Francisco.
17. Johnson, R.G. : 1982, Quaternary Research 17, pp. 135-147.
18. Kominz, M.A., Heath, G.R., Ku, T.-L., and Pisias, N.G. : 1979, Earth Planet. Sci. Lett. 45, pp. 394-410. Kominz, M.A., and Pisias, N.G. : 1979, Science 204, pp. 171-173.
19. Kukla, G. : 1968, Current Anthropology 9, pp. 37-39.
Kukla, G.J. : 1970, Geol. Foren. Stockholm Forh. 92, pp. 148-180.
20. Mankinen, E.A., and Dalrymple, G.B. : 1979, J. Geophys. Res. 84, pp. 615-626.
21. Milankovitch, M. : 1920, "Théorie mathématique des phénomènes thermiques produits par la radiation solaire", Gauthiers-Villars, Paris; 1941, Royal Serb. Acad., Spec. Publ., 133, pp. 1-633.
22. Morley, J.J., and Hays, J.D. : 1981, Earth Planet. Sci. Lett. 53, pp. 279-295.
23. Olausson, E. : 1965, Progress in Oceanography 3, pp. 221-252.
24. Pastouret, L., Chamley, H., Delibrias, G., Duplessy, J.C., and Thiede, J. : 1978, Oceanol. Acta 1, pp. 217-231.

25. Peng, T.-H., Broecker, W.S., Kipphut, G., and Shackleton, N.: 1977, in : "The Fate of Fossil Fuel CO_2 in the Oceans", N.R. Andersen and A. Malahoff (Eds), Plenum Publ. Corp., New York, pp. 355-373.
26. Prell, W.L. : 1982, in : "Initial Reports of the Deep Sea Drilling Project", W.L. Prell and J.V. Gardner (Eds), LXVIII, U.S. Government Printing Office, Washington, pp. 455-464.
27. Prell, W.L., Imbrie, J., Morley, J.J., Pisias, N.G., Shackleton, N.J., and Streeter, H. : 1983, "Graphic correlation of oxygen isotope records : application to the late Quaternary", MS in prep.
28. Shackleton, N.J. : 1967, Nature (Lond.) 215, pp. 15-17.
29. Shackleton, N.J. : 1969, Proc. Roy. Soc. Lond. B 174, pp. 135-154.
30. Shackleton, N.J. : 1977, Phil. Trans. Roy. Soc. Lond. B 280, pp. 169-182.
31. Mesolella, D.J., Matthews, R.K., Broecker, W.S., and Thurber, D.L. : 1969, J. Geol. 77, pp. 250-274. Shackleton, N.J., and Matthews, R.K. : 1977, Nature (Lond.) 6, pp. 445-450.
32. Shackleton, N.J., and Opdyke, N.D. : 1973, Quaternary Research 3, pp. 39-55.
33. Shackleton, N.J., and Opdyke, N.D. : 1976, in : "Investigation of late Quaternary Paleoceanography and Paleoclimatology", R.M. Cline and J.D. Hays (Eds), Geol. Soc. Amer. Mem. 145, pp. 449-464.
34. Stuiver, M., Quay, P.D., and Ostlund, H.G. : 1983, Science 219, pp. 849-851.
35. Tse, F.S., Morse, I.E., and Hinkle, R.T. : 1978, "Mechanical vibrations theory and applications", 2nd ed., Allyn and Bacon, Boston.
36. Thierstein, H.R., Geitzenauer, K.R., Molfino, B., and Shackleton, N.J. : 1977, Geology 5, pp. 400-414.
37. Thompson, P.R., and Sciarrillo, J.R. : 1978, Nature (Lond.) 275, pp. 29-33.
38. Weertman, J. : 1964, J. Glaciology 38, pp. 145-158.
39. See (15) for historical reviews of the astronomical theory.
40. Bjore Kullenberg invented a piston-coring device that was used by scientists of the Swedish Deep-Sea Expedition (1947-48) to recover long sections of deep-sea sediment.
41. In a later paper, we will document the phase characteristics of the five individual cores, which are not significantly different from those of the stacked record.
42. Unpublished data of Alan Mix, Lamont-Doherty Geological Observatory.
43. Unpublished data of Warren Prell, Brown University.
44. Mankinen and Dalrymple (20) base their estimate of the B/M reversal on 23 K-Ar dates, and their estimate of the Top Jaramillo reversal on 13 K-Ar dates. The confidence

intervals given in Table 5 are pooled estimates of error made by the authors after discussing the matter with G. Brent Dalrymple.

45. In V22-174 and DSDP502b, the B/M reversal occurs at depths of 1405 cm and 1626 cm, respectively. In V28-238, it occurs at 1201 cm. As noted in Table 6, 30 cm must be substracted from this depth to be consistent with our tuning procedures.

MILANKOVITCH FORCING OF THE OCEANIC SYSTEM: EVIDENCE FROM THE NORTHWEST PACIFIC

N.G. Pisias[1], M. Leinen[2]

[1]School of Oceanography, Oregon State University, Corvallis, OR 97331, USA
[2]Graduate School of Oceanography, University of Rhode Island, Kingston, RI 02881, USA

INTRODUCTION

Some of the most important supporting data for the Milankovitch hypothesis of climate change has come from detailed studies of proxy paleoclimate records preserved in deep-sea sediment cores (1,2,3,4). Most of these studies have concentrated on oxygen isotopic records obtained from deep-sea sediments. The oxygen isotope data provides a measure of global ice volume and thus gives a record of the response of a major component of the climate system to variations in the orbital components of the Earth. However, only a few studies have presented detailed analysis of the variations of other paleoclimate indicators. The evidence of Hays et al. (1) from other paleoclimate indicators, including estimated sea surface temperature and abundance of the radiolarian, Cyclophora davisiona, also supported the Milankovitch mechanism. Ruddiman and McIntyre (5) have shown that in the North Atlantic several proxy oceanographic indicators support the presence of orbital frequencies in sedimentary variation. Their work has shown that the importance of any one orbital component can vary with geographic position.

However, a weakness of these studies is that the evidence presented is based only on the presence of peaks in the variance spectrum of paleoclimate records which coincide with the expected frequencies predicted by orbital forcing and on similarities in digitally filtered data series. As shown by Pisias (6) digital filtering of any data with a bandpass filter designed to extract "orbital" frequencies will produce records which superficially look similar to the orbital records. Thus, it is pos-

A. L. Berger et al. (eds.), Milankovitch and Climate, Part 1, 307–330.

sible that the observed spectral peaks may not be related in a simple, direct way to the orbital variation suggested by the estimated frequencies; or may not be related at all.

In the absence of physical models which can hindcast the temporal history of climate at individual localities, we must rely on multivariate statistical time series methods to show relationships between proxy paleoclimate records and orbital forcing. In this report we will present results from multivariate analysis of time series of paleoclimatic indicators from a deep-sea sediment core taken in the Northwest Pacific Ocean. Because these data represent the response of the ocean in a small geographic area, our analysis attempts to separate local and regional responses to climate change. We will show through univariate and bivariate time series analysis that Milankovitch frequencies are present in these paleoclimate records. However, two important results are that the presence of a spectral peak lying close to orbital frequency (23 kyr) is not a result of orbital forcing at that frequency, but instead arises as the second harmonic of orbital forcing at another frequency (41 kyr), owing to the local oceanographic setting.

Regional Oceanographic Setting

The location of the core used in this study and the general oceanographic features of the northwest Pacific are shown in Figure 1. Core RC14-105 is located at 39°41'N and 157°33'E in 5630 meters water depth. The core site is presently located in an oceanic frontal region where the warm northward-flowing Kuroshio Current meets the cold southward-flowing Oyoshio Current. This front, where the Kuroshio and Oyoshio currents merge and form the eastward flowing limb of the North Pacific gyre, is a region of intense mixing and high surface productivity. In addition, this complex oceanographic regime is a locus for the formation of the North Pacific intermediate water mass (7).

Analysis of sediments containing radiolarian and diatom microfossils deposited 18 kyr BP during the last glacial maximum show that the oceanic front in the northwest Pacific may have been as much as 10° further south than today (8,9,10,11). Thus, the core location is in an area which is extremely sensitive to oceanic variations during the late Pleistocene.

Paleoclimate Records

Core RC14-105 was studied by Robertson (8) who characterized the radiolarian microfossil population in 116 samples from this core (sampled at 10 to 20 cm intervals). We have used Robertson's data together with radiolarian microfossil date from an additional 60 samples to increase the total length of core

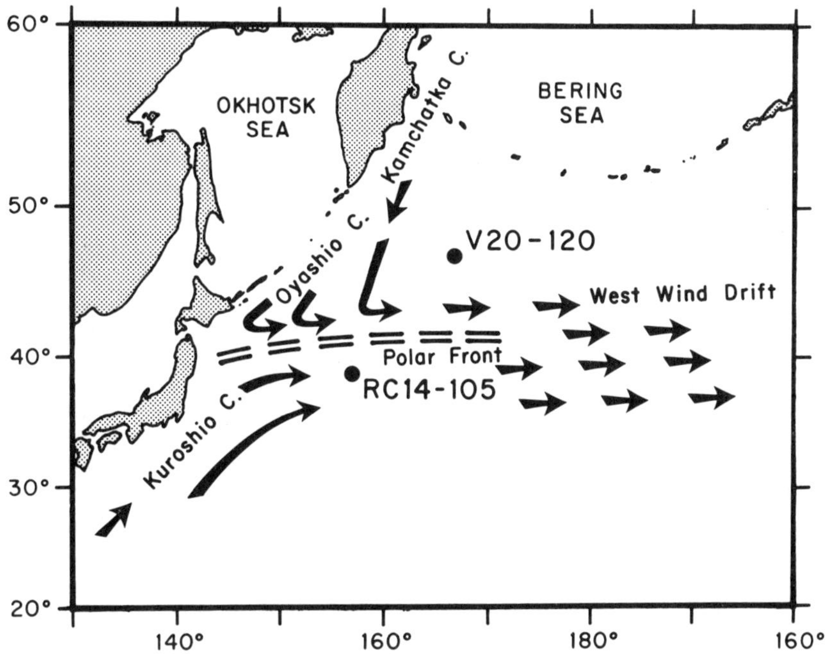

Figure 1 General oceanographic setting of northwest Pacific and locations of cores RC14-105 and V20-120.

sampled as well as to increase the sampling resolution. Together the two data sets provide a 500 kyr record with a sampling interval of 3 kyr.

The total radiolarian fauna in each sample has been partitioned into assemblages which were defined from a detailed study of surface sediments from the entire Pacific by Moore (9). Using Q-mode factor analysis of the radiolarian population data from over 300 surface sediment samples, Moore (9) identified seven assemblages with distinct geographic distributions. Of these seven assemblages, four are important components of the radiolarian fauna of the northwest Pacific: 1) a tropical assemblage, found in the warm subtropical regions of the western North Pacific; 2) a subarctic assemblage dominated by the species Cyclado-phora davisiana and found in the western subarctic Pacific (This factor is extremely important in the sea of Okhotsk where C. davisiana attains its highest abundances); 3) a transitional assemblage, found in the Kuroshio-Oyoshio frontal region of the northwest Pacific and in the eastern subarctic region of the Gulf of Alaska; 4) and a fauna which is called the temperate fauna by Moore (9), found south of the transitional assemblage and east of the area dominated by the tropical assemblage. This assemblage is important in the central gyre areas of the North Pacific where the number of samples containing abundant radiolarian tests is small and where dissolution of silica strongly affects the fossil assemblage. As noted by Moore, the poor definition of a central gyre assemblage may have been the result of this dissolution, but the temperate assemblage defined from the surface sediment samples is the best indicator of central gyre-type conditions available. Thus, variations in the importance of radiolarian assemblages in the samples from RC14-105 can provide a detailed history of water mass distribution in the Northwest Pacific.

In addition to the microfossil data, quantitative x-ray diffraction analyses of two sedimentary components in the samples, opaline silica and crystalline quartz, have been made using techniques described in Till and Spears (12), Ellis and Moore (13) and King and Leinen (14). The opaline silica concentration reflects the abundance of diatom and radiolarian remains in the samples. Expressed as a concentration, these data give the balance between production of silica in the surface water, dissolution of silica during transport and burial, and dilution by non-opaline sediments. Studies of equatorial Pacific sediments suggest that variations in opaline silica deposition strongly reflect surface production of silica (15,16). However, the effects of changing dissolution of silica during the last few hundred thousand years have not been adequately studied. Semi-quantitative estimates of radiolarian fossil dissolution in sediments from the Cascadia Basin in the northeast Pacific suggest that during the last glacial interval dissolution was much more important than during the Holocene (17). However, the total accumulation of silica during the last glacial was also much greater than today implying that silica supply was very high during the last glacial (17). In the Panama basin, opal accumulation rates were also higher during the last glacial maximum but a correlation with the dissolution of radiolarian tests and opal accumulation or climate change is not evident (15). Thus, our working hypothesis is that variations in opal content reflect, in part, surface ocean production and transport to the sediments of opaline silica.

There is no major source of crystalline quartz within the ocean basins and thus, the quartz in sediments reflects the supply and transport of terrigenous quartz to the deep sea. At the core location of RC14-105, 1300 km from land, seaward of the major trench systems of the North Pacific, and south of the area where ice rafting of terrigenous sediments is important (18), the major source of terrigenous material is atmospheric dust transport (19). Maps of the quartz concentration in surface sediments of the North Pacific clearly show the eolian control of quartz sedimentation at middle latitudes (20,21). The distribution of quartz is characterized by a maximum at 30-40°N which coincides with the southern boundary of the northern hemisphere westerlies. In the eastern Pacific a secondary lobe of high quartz concentrations extends west from Baja California reflecting trade wind of transport of eolian dust from the arid regions of the North American continent. This association of quartz content with atmospheric circulation patterns makes quartz in marine sediments a valuable tool to study past climatic states.

The amount of eolian material transported by the wind systems depends on both the supply of dust to the atmosphere and the efficiency of the winds in transporting particulate material away from the continental source areas. The supply of dust to the atmosphere generally reflects continental aridity because of the control of moisture on vegetation cover as well as the rainout of dust. The efficiency of transport is controlled by the intensity of atmospheric circulation. Global circulation models of the glacial world 18 kyr BP (22,23) suggest that both continental aridity and atmospheric circulation intensity were greater than today. Thus, given the location of core RC14-105, quartz content of sediments at this site should provide a detailed record of fluctuations in the factors controlling eolian transport to the western North Pacific.

Because the amount of biogenic opal and other non-eolian diluents is small (less than 15%), changes in the quartz content of the sediment actually reflect changes in the amount of quartz in the eolian aerosol. The ratio of opal-free quartz percent to the quartz and opal-free residual is essentially equivalent to the quartz content. The amount of other diluents like volcanic ash is negligible. This means that changes in the quartz percentage are actually reflecting changes in the mineral assemblage of the aerosol. The dominant control on the mineralogy cannot be wind intensity and must be weathering processes which are related to vegetative cover and aridity.

Thus the multi-parameter data set from core RC14-105 provides a detailed record of surface oceanographic conditions (radiolarian fauna), surface productivity (biogenic silica deposition), and atmospheric-continental climates (quartz) for the last 500 kyr.

Time Scale

Fundamental to any time domain study is the need for an accurate time scale. In deep-sea sediments, a time scale must often be established by indirect methods such as stratigraphic correlations of time horizons whose ages have been determined previously (often by indirect methods). In some cases, direct radiometric ages are available but even these age determinations often have errors on the order of 5 to 10% too large for time series studies. The major problem with deep-sea sediment cores is that few time control points are available during any given period of time. In the North Pacific, for example, there are three biostratigraphic datums for non-carbonate sediments during the last 500 kyr (the extinction of the radiolarian species *Stylotractus universus* and *Druppatractus aquilonious*, and the diatom species *Rhizosolenia curvesostris*). None have been associated with radiometric ages and only the *S. universus* extinction has been correlated to oxygen isotopic stratigraphy (24). This limited number of time horizons makes the definition of detailed changes in sedimentation rates impossible in the North Pacific.

Although the lack of calcareous microfossils in RC14-105 precludes the use of the oxygen isotope time scale, the strategy of using the Earth's orbital frequency components in the geologic record (2,3,6) provides an approach for estimating a time scale for non-carbonate records as well as for the isotopic data.

In the northwest Pacific sediments the dominant frequency component in variations of *C. davisiana* has a 41 kyr period. This periodic component has been shown to be related to orbital tilt (25). Using this observation the time scale for core RC14-105 was adjusted to maximize the cross-spectral coherence between *C. davisiana* variations and the tilt record. This using process is iterative and at each step the variance spectra and cross spectra were evaluated to determine whether the total coherence in the 41 kyr frequency band increased and whether the spectra continued to show a clear 41 kyr peak in the geologic data. Pisias (6) used similar techniques on random number series which had no statistical relationship to the Earth's orbital radiation and was unable to produce either an increase in coherence or to induce the presence of spectral peaks by "orbital tuning". This suggests that the spectral peaks from RC14-105 are not artificially produced by the time scale tuning technique. We also noted that throughout the tuning process the general shape of the geologic spectrum was not significantly altered with changes in the assigned time scale. Thus, conclusions drawn from the general slope, or the variance distribution with respect to frequency are very unlikely to change with improvement in the absolute time scale for North Pacific sediments.

RESULTS AND DISCUSSION

The time series obtained from core RC14-105 are shown in Figure 2. The good correlation between the temperature record from RC14-105 and the isotope record of core V22-174, especially in terms of the timing of major transitions, suggest that the time scale used for this North Pacific core is reasonable. The depth of the extinction of S. universus in core RC14-105 is correlated with the correct isotopic position using the derived time scale. Note that the last major cooling in the RC14-105 record coincides with the glacial transition (11 kyr BP) and not the last glacial maximum (18 kyr BP). The temperature response to climate change at the site is often much greater than the global ice volume response as indicated by the isotope record from V22-174, e.g., the cold interval at about 50-60 kyr BP (during isotope stage 4) is as cold as the more glaciated intervals of State 6 and 8 (Fig. 2).

Variance Spectra

Examination of Figure 2 shows that there is not a simple pattern of variation in the oceanographic, atmospheric, and global ice volume records. To gain further insight into the complex interactions between North Pacific circulation and late Pleistocene climate, we have used time series techniques. The variance spectra of the climate records from core RC14-105 can be divided into two groups (Fig. 3a,b). Detailed studies of oxygen isotope records from deep-sea cores have shown that the spectrum of global climate recorded in them is dominated by low frequencies and that superimposed on this "red" spectrum are spectral peaks which can be related to the Earth's orbital parameters (4). These parameters are the obliquity or tilt of the Earth's axis

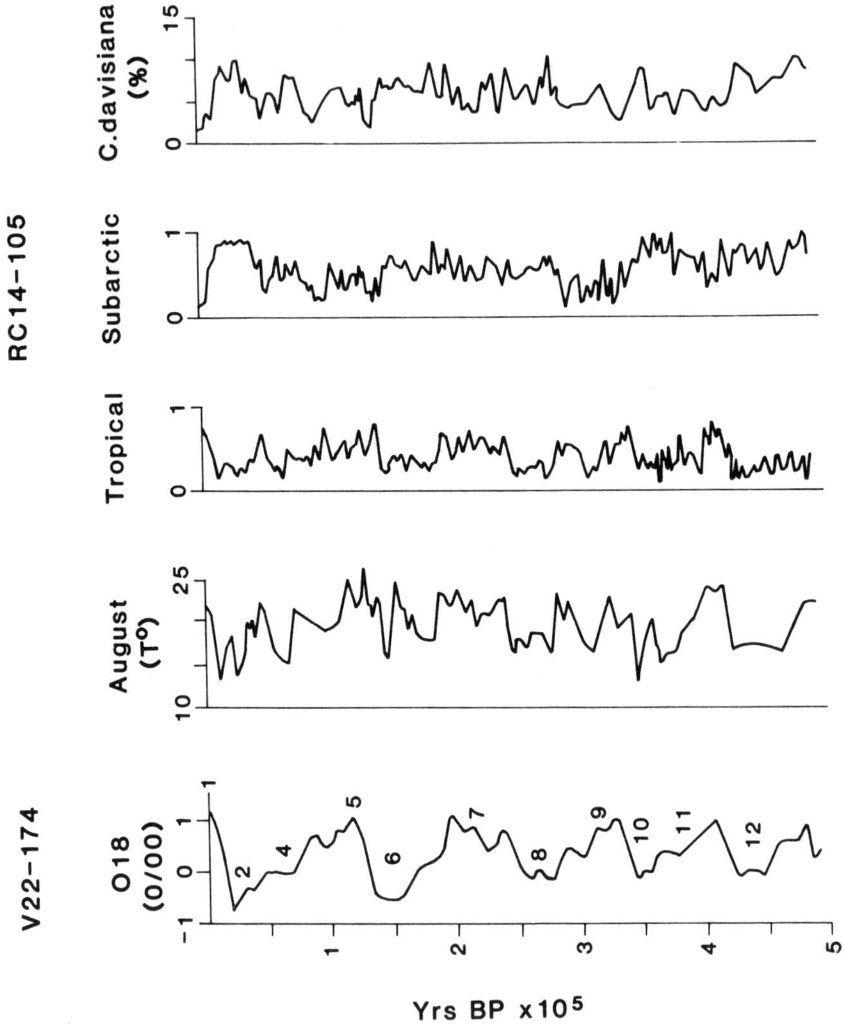

Figure 2a Time series for radiolarian data from core RC14-105. Summer temperatures were estimated using radiolaria data and regression techniques (8,27). Also shown are the relative importance of the tropical and subarctic assemblages and percent C. davisiana. Isotope data is from core V22-174 and is plotted versus age using the time scale developed by Imbrie et al. (28).

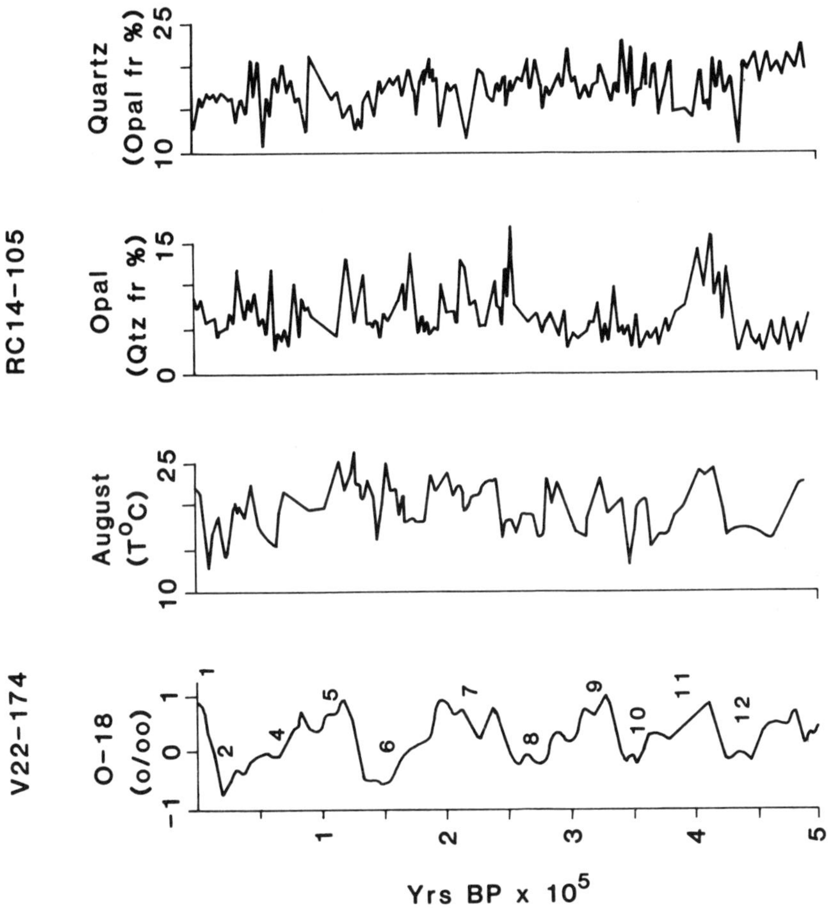

Figure 2b Time series for opal and quartz data plotted with radiolarian temperature estimates and isotopic data as shown in 7a. Quartz is expressed as percent of opal-free sediments and opal is percentage quartz-free.

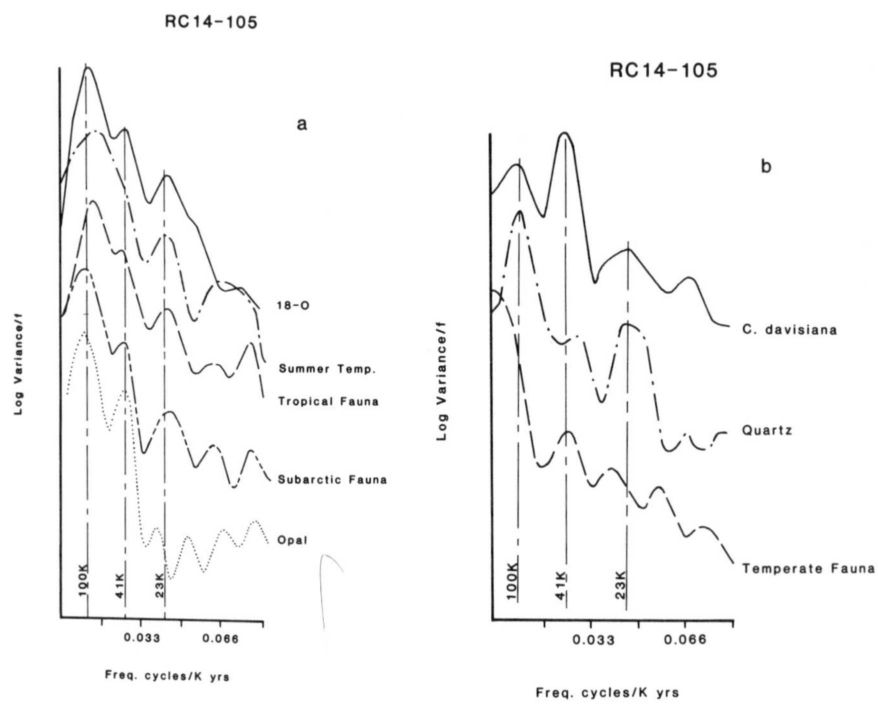

Figure 3 Variance spectra for time series data shown in Figure 2. Spectra are plotted on a log variance scale with variance normalized to 1. Spectra are offset vertically to illustrate general patterns in the frequency distributions. Figure 3a shows time series with variance spectra which are similar to the isotopic record of late Pleistocene ice volume change. Figure 3b shows spectra which show significantly different variance distributions.

with a 41 kyr period; the eccentricity of the orbit with a 100 kyr eriod; and the precession with 23 and 19 kyr periods (30). The variance spectrum of the isotope record from V22-174 is shown in Figure 3a and is typical of late Pleistocene isotopic records. Also shown in Figure 3a are the variance spectra of the data series from RC14-105 which show this "typical" low frequency response spectrum characteristic of late Pleistocene climate records. Most of the records, including sea surface temperature, the tropical and subarctic assemblages, and the opal record show this spectral pattern. The opal spectrum does, however, show a reduced response near the precession frequencies when compared to other data series shown in this figure. The 41 kyr frequency component in the sea-surface temperature spectrum is not clearly distinguished as compared to the other data sets. From these spectral distributions, we may conclude that most of the oceanographic proxy records reflect orbital forcing with responses at the 100 kyr, 41 kyr and 23 kyr periods. We will show later that the 23 kyr periodic components in these records are not totally a response to the precessional of the orbit.

The spectra for the time series from core RC14-105 which show distinctly different patterns are shown in Figure 3b. These include two faunal records and the quartz record. The temperate fauna (indicator of the central water mass) spectrum combines very long wave-length components with some evidence of a 41 kyr contribution. The spectrum of C. davisiana is dominated by variance concentration at the tilt frequency of 41 kyr. This dominance of the tilt frequency in a paleoclimate record has not been observed in other areas or other paleoclimate indicators. The quartz spectrum is dominated by a long period, 100 kyr peak, and shows a significant spectral peak at the 23 kyr period. Unlike the other spectra in Figure 3b, however, the variance in the quartz spectrum associated with the 23 kyr peaks is greater than that at the 41 kyr period.

Cross-Spectral Analysis

We have used cross-spectral analysis to examine the relationship between the spectral components of the paleoclimate records from core RC14-105, the global ice volume record from V22-174 and calculated values for the Earth's orbital parameters (30). Figure 4 shows coherence spectra (spectra of the linear correlation between each frequency component in two time series) for the tropical fauna compared to two other fauna (Fig. 4a), and for the isotopic record from core V22-174 and calculated orbital parameters (Fig. 4b). The variations in the tropical assemblage are strongly correlated with the subarctic assemblage at the precession and tilt frequencies, but less well associated with the temperate fauna. The frequencies with significant coherence are the 41 kyr period (tropical versus subarctic and tem-

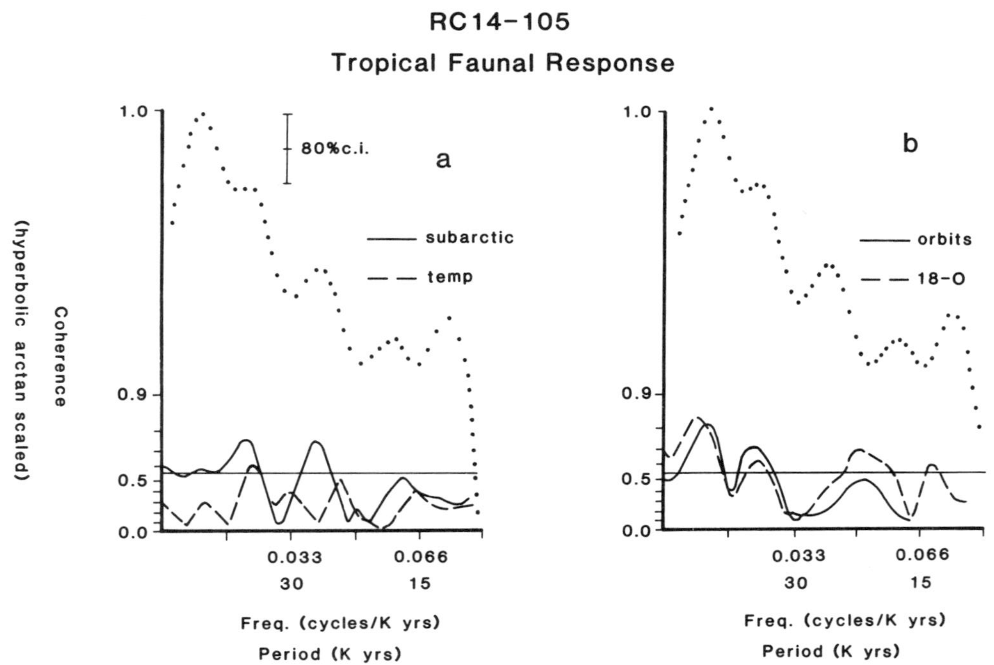

Figure 4 Coherence spectra comparing the tropical fauna from core RC14-105 with other faunal elements (Fig. 4a) and with the isotopic record from core V22-174 and the calculated orbital parameters (eccentricity, tilt and precession). The coherence spectra are scaled by the hyperbolic arctangent so that confidence intervals can be represented by a single interval (29). The 80% confidence interval for the coherence plots is shown (horizontal line is for non-zero values). The dotted spectrum in each frame is the original variance spectrum of the tropical fauna.

perate) and the 23 kyr period (tropical versus subarctic). At lower frequencies the coherencies between the tropical and the subarctic assemblage are significant but not as striking.

The coherence between the tropical assemblage and the orbital components shows strong correlations at the 100 kyr and 41 kyr periods. There is no coherence over the frequency band corresponding to precession of the Earth's orbit. This lack of coherence at the 23 kyr period is also characteristic of the tropical fauna versus the isotope data (Fig. 4b).

Other faunal indicators of surface water oceanographic conditions show similar coherence patterns. Both the subarctic fauna and biogenic silica show strong 41 and 23 kyr coherence with faunal elements and a very strong coherence with orbital tilt (Figs 5,6). The coherence between the subarctic fauna, orbital eccentricity and the isotope record is significant at the 100 kyr period but much less than that of the tropical fauna. The opal record shows no coherence at low frequency (Fig. 6).

The opal data show coherence at the 41 kyr period with various faunal components (Fig. 6), but have a different phase relationship with each component. Like correlation analysis, the calculated coherence between opal and transitional fauna and between opal and the subarctic fauna do not take into account the correlation between the two faunas themselves. The phase estimates between the opal time series and radiolarian assemblage time series suggest that, at the 41 kyr period the opal content is responding to changes in the importance of the transitional assemblage. This is true for the 23 kyr component as well. Figure 7 shows these two frequency components for the transitional assemblage and the opal records. These components have been extracted by using a 41 kyr and 23 kyr band pass filter. The 41 kyr component is in phase throughout the record and the changes in amplitude observed in the faunal data is also present in the opal record (Fig. 7a). The 23 kyr component of the opal and transitional assemblage is in phase where both display high amplitude variations (150-250 kyr BP). In the older interval, where the amplitudes of the 41 kyr components change, the phase between the opal and transitional fauna are intially in phase (350 kyr to 400 kyr BP) and then out of phase during the interval of 250 kyr to 350 kyr BP. Thus, the variation of opal deposition at the 41 kyr frequency is coherent with and therefore related to the transitional radiolarian fauna which Moore (9) has shown to be associated with the oceanic front between the Kurashio and Oyashio. Mixing at such fronts is conducive to high surface water biological productivity. This is not true of the 23 kyr frequency, however. The long period variations in opal content do not seem to be associated with

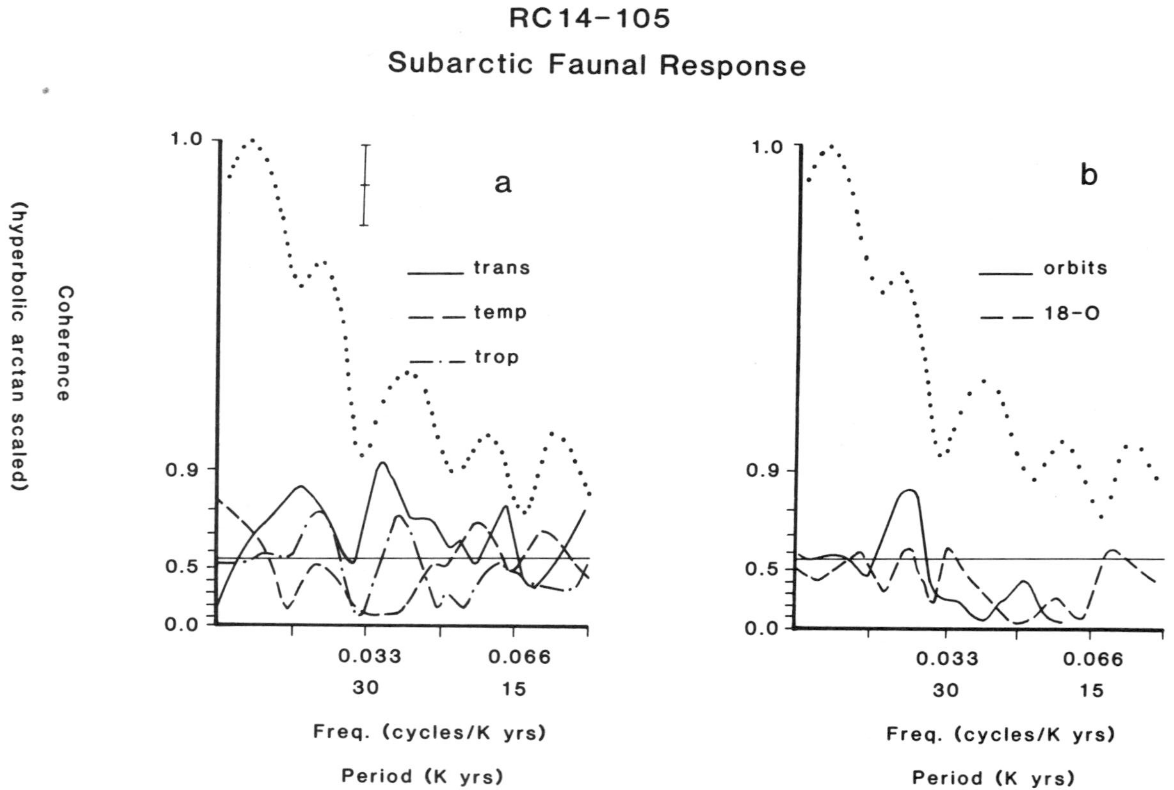

Figure 5 Coherence spectra for the subarctic fauna versus other faunal element (Fig. 5a) and versus the orbital parameter and isotope records (Fig. 5b). Scaling as in Figure 4.

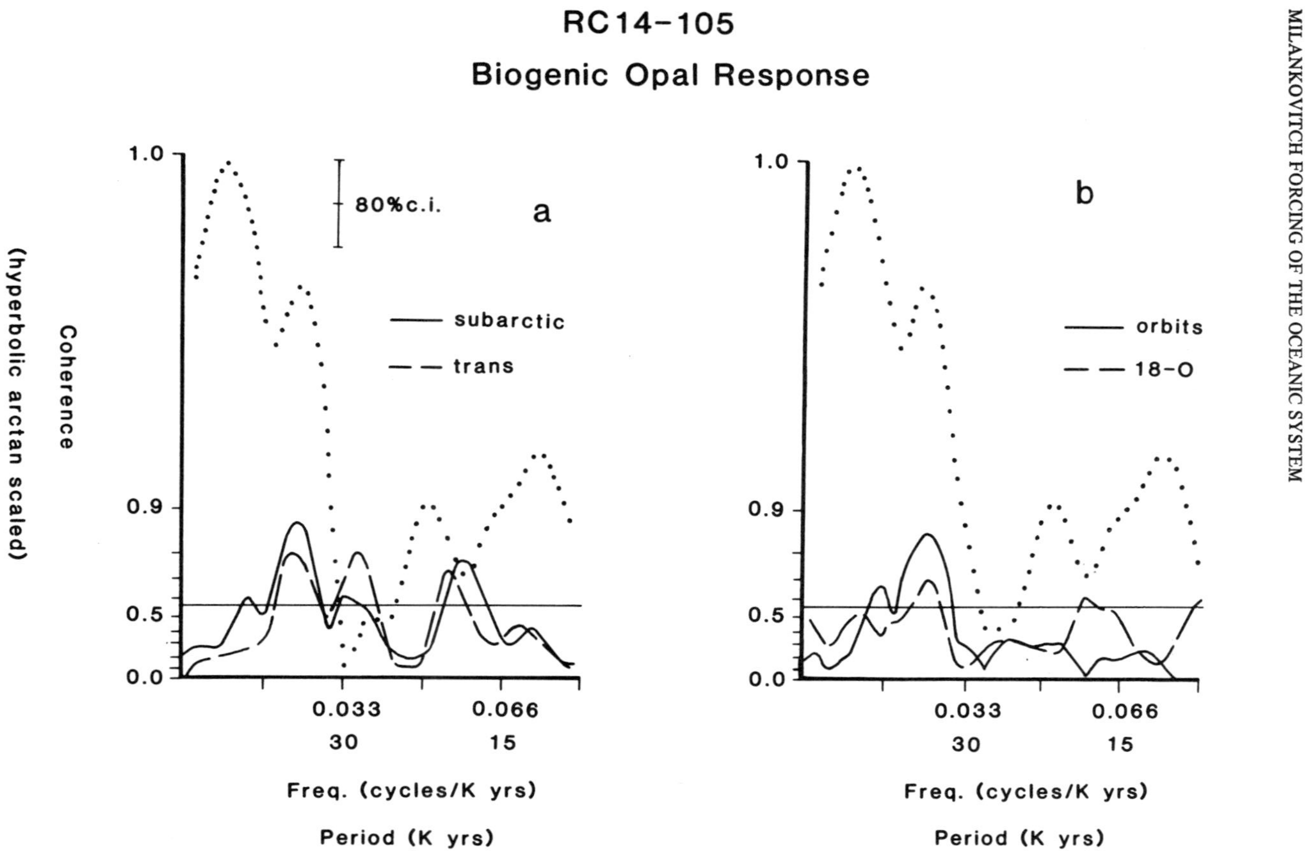

Figure 6 Coherence spectra for opaline silica. Scaling as in Figure 4.

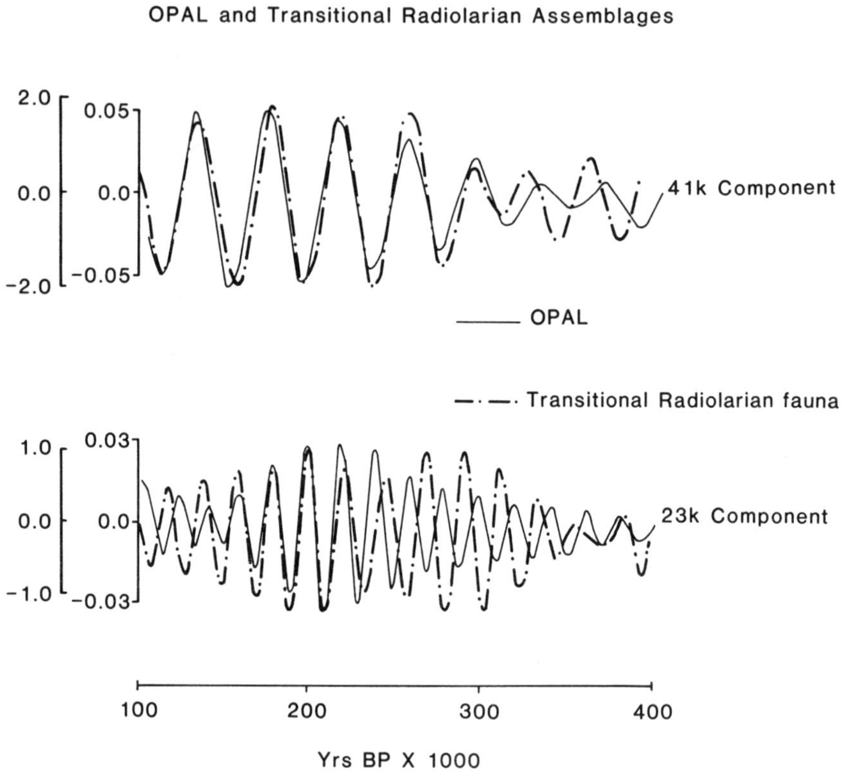

Figure 7 41 kyr and 23 kyr periodic components of the transitional assemblage and opaline silica derived from band pass filtering the time series of each record with 41 kyr and 23 kyr filters.

fauna assemblages or with indicators of global climate change (oxygen isotopes) or orbital forcing.

Since the 41 kyr component in the spectra of opal and radiolarian faunal assemblages is well correlated and in phase, the presence of a 23 kyr component, which is not coherent between this component in the opal data and either the orbital precession index or oxygen isotopic record, has important implications for the interpretation of the variance spectra There are a number of explanations to account for the low coherence between opal content and radiolarian fauna observed at the 23 kyr frequency:

1) Our data analyses are not precise enough to resolve the coherence.

2) The paleoceanographic records do not adequately reflect these frequencies due to bioturbation.

3) The coherence is low due to inaccuracies in the time scale.

4) A non-linear response to precession produces a frequency response at the dominant precession frequencies but the amplitude changes in precession are not seen in the geologic record.

5) There are other sources of the 23 kyr periodicity which are not associated with the orbital precession parameter.

The presence of the 23 kyr period in the quartz data and its close association with the precession index suggest that analytical problems or bioturbation are not the cause of the low coherence. Distortion and lack of resolution of the 23 kyr component as a result of bioturbation are possible, but the presence of the 23 kyr spectral peak in the faunal records and the quartz record suggest that this distortion is not complete ant that the resolution of this frequency component is possible. Also, the presence of the 23 kyr coherence in the quartz data suggests that if bioturbation was a problem, it would have to affect sediment components selectively, which is highly unlikely. Finally, with a sedimentation rate of over 5 cm/1000 years, 23 kyr are represented by 115 cm, an interval which would not be greatly affected by bioturbation based on simple bioturbation models (6).

Tuning experiments to adjust the 23 kyr period of the oceanographic records to better fit the precession frequency are possible but the strong coherence between quartz content and precession suggest that time scale inaccuracies are not responsible for the lack of coherence between opal and the faunal data. Tuning experiments were done, however, to adjust the time scale for core RC14-105 to better fit the 23 kyr component of the tropical and subarctic records to the precession record. Time scales were established by bandpass filtering each of these

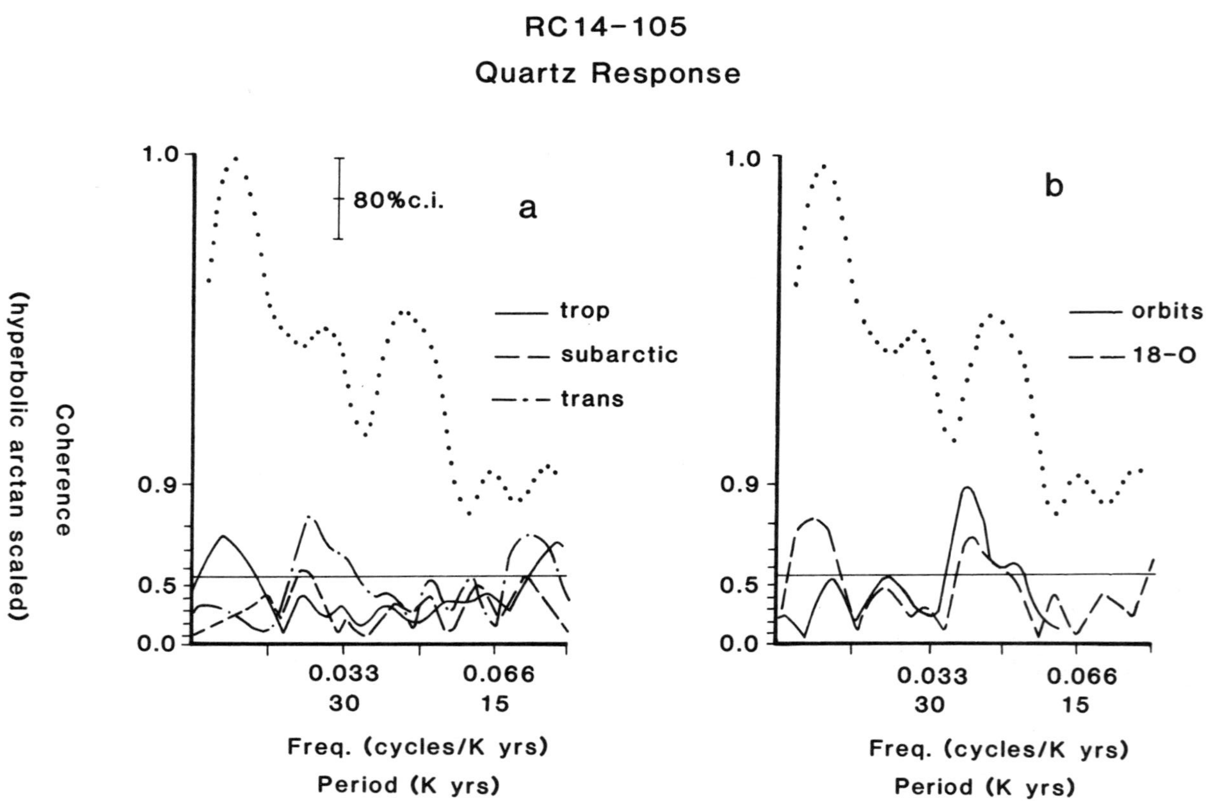

Figure 8 Coherence spectra for quartz data in RC14-105. Scaling as in Figure 4.

faunal records and adjusting the time scale to fit these components to precession. In this way two new time scales were produced. In both cases the coherence between the sediment records and precession never became significant and the new time scales reduced the coherence between the quartz record and the oxygen isotopic and orbital records. Thus, we conclude that the observed lack of coherence is not a function of time scale inaccuracies.

While the possibility of a non-linear response to precession cannot be ruled out, the time series of the 41 kyr and 23 kyr components suggest that an additional source of 23 kyr periodicity may be the reason for the low coherence between opal and the faunal data. The 41 kyr components of the tropical and subarctic assemblages and the 20 500-year component (the first harmonic of 41 kyr) of the transitional assemblage are plotted in Figures 9 and 10. Core RC14-105 is located in the zone dominated by the transitional fauna. To the north the subarctic fauna is dominant. If we allowed this three-zoned system to move north and south with a 41 kyr frequency, we would expect the subarctic fauna and the tropical fauna to vary, out of phase, with a 41 kyr frequency as indicated in Figures 9 and 10. However, the transitional fauna would be important at the core location twice during each 41 kyr cycle, just after the subarctic fauna was at a maximum and the oceanographic system began to move to the north, and again after the tropical fauna reached a maximum and the system began to move south. In our data the maximum in the 20 500-year component occurs when the tropical and subarctic fauna are at a cross-over point (e.g. Figures 9 and 10). Thus, the oceanographic setting of core RC14-105 results in the sediment components associated with the front recording the first harmonic of the tilt frequency. These results indicate that the presence of a spectral peak near an orbital frequency such as 23 kyr is not sufficient evidence to claim that the climatic indicator is responding to the changes in climate due to the precession of the Earth's orbit. Coherence estimates between the paleo-climate indicators and the orbital parameters are also necessary conditions to demonstrate orbital forcing.

The quartz content record shows a very different pattern in comparison to oceanographic and climatic change. Quartz content in RC14-105 shows strong coherence at long periods (100 kyr periods) with the tropical radiolarian assemblage and at 41 kyr with the transitional radiolarian assemblage (Fig. 8a). The most striking feature of the coherence spectra of the quartz data is the strong coherence near the precessional frequency with both the orbital precession and oxygen isotopes. Thus, unlike the surface water indicators in this site, the atmospherically controlled quartz record shows a very strong response to variations in the precession of the Earth. Also, unlike the surface water

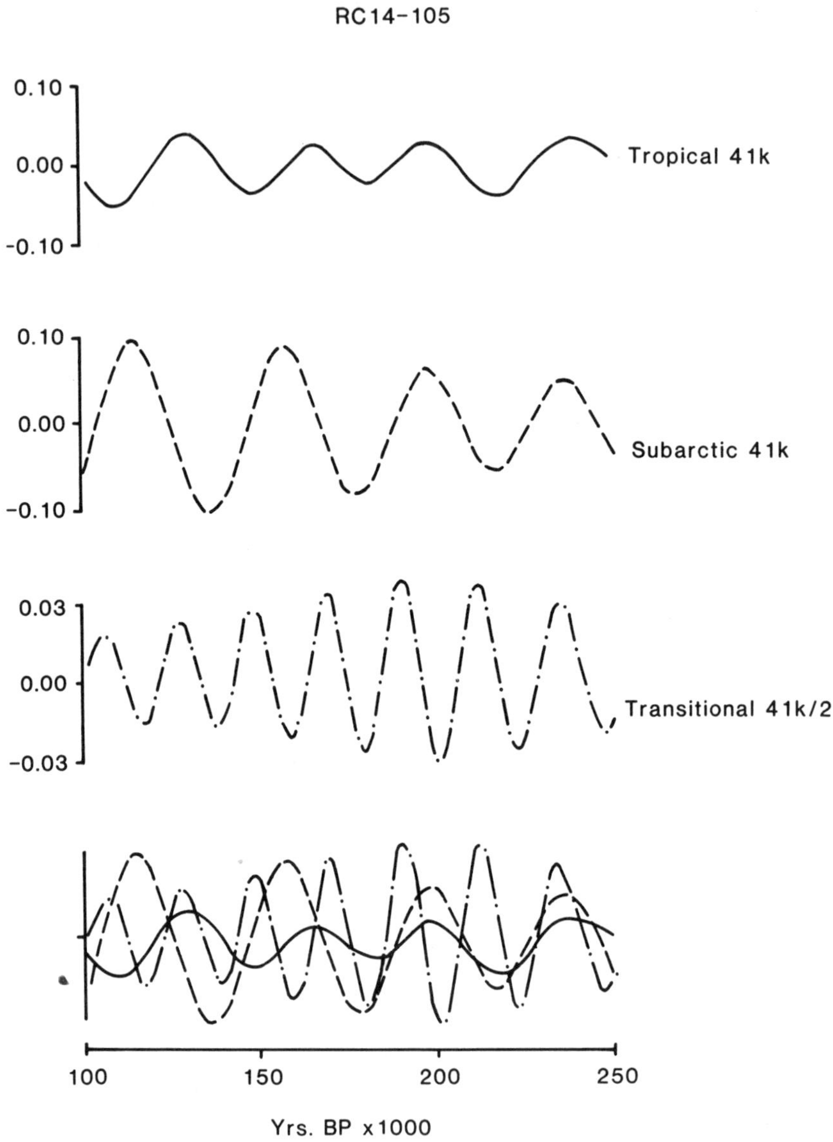

Figure 9 41 kyr period component of the Tropical and Subarctic assemblages compared to the first harmonic of the 41 kyr period in the Transitional assemblage for the interval 100 kyr to 250 kyr BP.

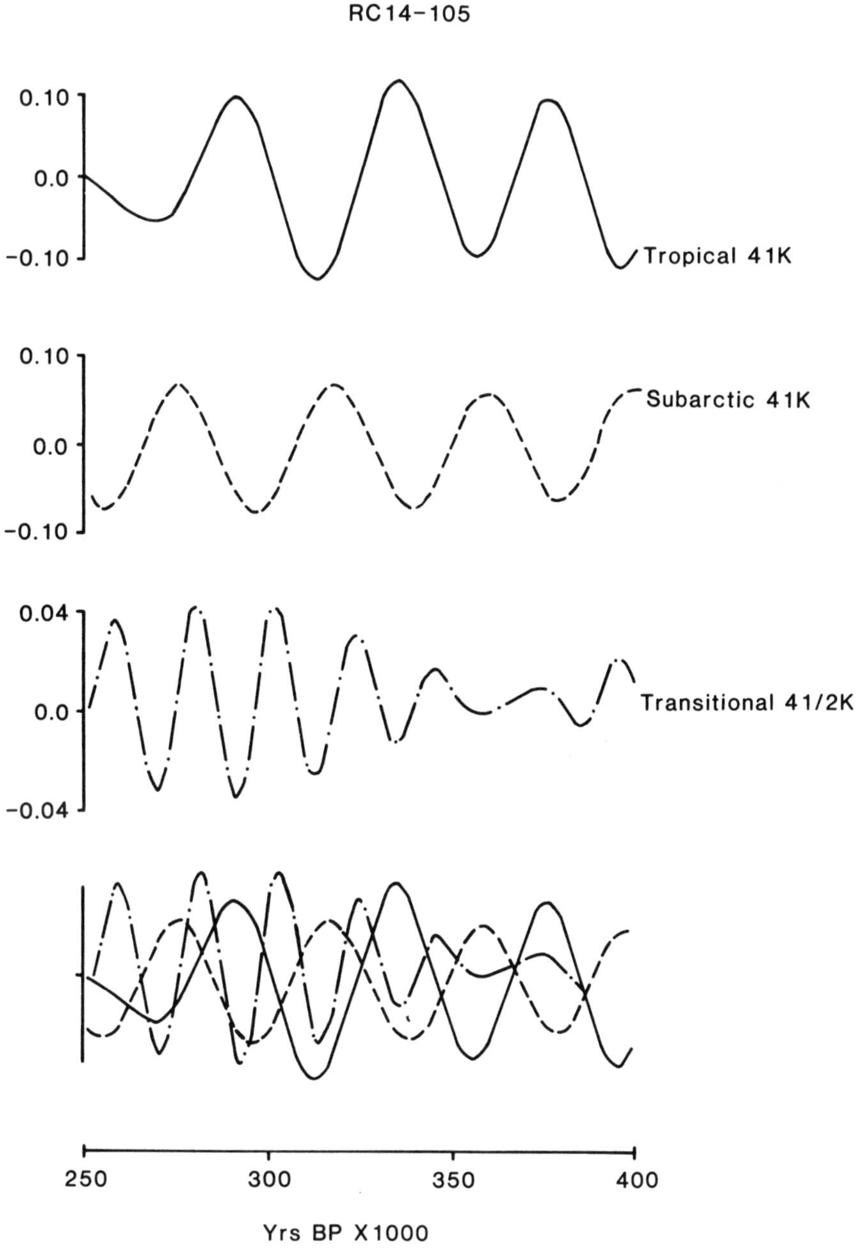

Figure 10 41 kyr period component of the Tropical and Subarctic assemblages compared to the first harmonic of the 41 kyr period in the Transitional assemblage for the interval 250 kyr to 400 kyr BP.

indicators, the quartz record shows a much smaller response to tilt than to the other orbital components. The phase relation of quartz with the oxygen isotopic record and orbital parameter records shows that quartz content increases with increased ice volume, with decreased eccentricity (which is associated with glacial intervals) and with increased precession index (which is characterized by increased Earth-sun distance during Northern Hemisphere summer and increased glaciation). The phase relation observed between this record of atmospherically transported quartz and eccentricity differs from that observed for atmospherically transported sediment from core KK75-02 located to the east (40°N, 179°W; (26)) where the 41 kyr frequency component dominated the record. This may reflect the different types of data being studied (total wind-borne accumulation rate in the case of the Janecek and Rea study compared with quartz content in this study) or the difference in the geographic location.

CONCLUSIONS

The late Pleistocene oceanic and atmospheric records in core RC14-105 display a complex history of climatic variations during the last 500 kyr. The detailed time domain analysis of these data allow us to draw the following conclusions :

1. The paleoceanographic variations recorded at the site of core RC14-105 strongly reflect the local oceanographic setting of this core as well as regional variations in oceanographic conditions.

2. The variance spectra for most of the paleoceanographic records in core RC14-105 are similar to the "red" spectra observed in late Pleistocene ice volume records and are dominated by the 100 kyr component but have spectral peaks at the frequencies equivalent to the 41 kyr and 23 kyr periods commonly associated with variations in the Earth's orbit.

3. Cross-spectral analysis indicates that while the 100 kyr and 41 kyr components in these data sets can be related to variations in the Earth's orbit, concentrations of variance near 23 kyr that are observed in some of the paleoceanographic records is not associated with precession but results instead from the local oceanographic setting of this core, as the second harmonic of the obliquity cycle.

4. At the frequencies of 41 kyr and 23 kyr, variations in opaline silica deposition are related to the transitional radiolarian assemblage indicative of the subpolar front and its associated high productivity. Thus, opal deposition over these time intervals reflects surface productivity. Long period chan-

ges in opal deposition as well as in some faunal elements suggest that a change in the character of proxy oceanographic indicators occurs at about 250 kyr BP.

5. Variations in eolian quartz, unlike other parameters studied, shows a clear relationship to the precession of the Earth's orbit. Comparisons with isotopic records suggest that eolian deposition at this site is highest during glacial advances at both long periods (100 kyr) and short period variations (23 kyr).

ACKNOWLEDGEMENTS

This study was supported by NSF grants ATM 7825304 and ATM 8116301 to the University of Rhode Island and grant ATM 8204127 to Oregon State University. We wish to thank T.C. Moore Jr. and Cindy Schramm for helpful discussions, and Dave Rea and Tom Janecek for discussions and access to their data on eolian sedimentation. Joe Morley kindly provided data from core C20-120 and also added much to our thinking about the North Pacific. To all we are grateful.

REFERENCES

1. Hays, J.D., Imbrie, J., and Shackleton, N.J. : 1976, Science 194, pp. 1121-1132.
2. Kominz, M.A., Heath, G.R., Ku, T.L., and Pisias, N.G. : 1979, Earth and Planet. Sci. Lett. 45, pp. 394-410.
3. Morley, J.J., and Hays, J.D. : 1981, Earth and Planet. Sci. Lett. 53, pp. 279-295.
4. Kominz, M.A., and Pisias, N.G. : 1979, Science 204, pp. 171-173.
5. Ruddiman, W.F., and McIntyre, A. : 1981, Science 212, pp. 617-627.
6. Pisias, N.G. : 1983, Mar. Geol. 51, pp. 99-113.
7. Reid, J.L. Jr. : 1965, "Intermediate waters of the Pacific Ocean", The John Hopkins Oceanographic Studies n°2, 85pp.
8. Robertson, J.H. : 1975, "Glacial to interglacial oceanographic changes in the northwest Pacific, including a continuous record of the last 400 000 years", Ph.D. Thesis, Columbia University, New York, 355pp.
9. Moore, T.C.Jr. : 1978, Mar. Micropaleontology 3, pp. 226-229.
10. Sancetta, C. : 1979, Mar. Micropaleontology 4, pp. 103-123.
11. CLIMAP Project Members : 1976, Science 191, pp. 1131-1137.
12. Till, R., and Spears, D.A. : 1969, Clays and Clay Minerals 17, pp. 323-327.

13. Ellis, D.B., and Moore, T.C.Jr. : 1973, J. Mar. Res. 31, pp. 210-227.
14. King, T.A., and Leinen, M. : 1981, "Measuring biogenic opal in sediments: an evaluation of the x-ray diffraction technique". Geol. Soc. Amer. 1981 Ann. Mtg., Abstracts with Programs 13, 487pp.
15. Pisias, N.G. : 1976, "Late Quaternary sediment of the Panama Basin: Sedimentation rates, periodicities, and controls of carbonate and opal accumulation", R.M. Cline, and J.D. Hays (Eds), Geol. Soc. Amer. Mem. 145, pp. 375-392.
16. Molina-Cruz, A., and Price, P. : 1977, Geology 5, pp. 81-84.
17. Heath, G.R., Moore, T.C.Jr., and Dauphin, J.P. : 1976, Geol. Soc. Amer. Mem. 145, pp. 393-410.
18. Ninkovich, D., and Robertson, J.H. : 1975, Earth and Planet. Sci. Lett. 27, pp. 127-136.
19. Windom, H.L. : 1975, J. Sed. Petrol. 45, pp. 520-529.
20. Moore, T.C.Jr., and Heath, G.R. : 1978, Chem. Oceanog. 7, pp. 75-126.
21. Leinen, M., and Heath, G.R. : 1982, Paleogeography, -climatology, -ecology 36, pp. 1-21.
22. Manabe, S., and D.C. Hahn : 1977, J. Geophys. Res. 82, pp. 3889-3912.
23. Gates, W.L. : 1976, Science 191, pp. 1138-1144.
24. Morley, J.J., and Shackleton, N.J. : 1979, Geology 6, pp. 309-311.
25. Pisias, N.G., and Leinen, M. : 1983, Quaternary Research, in press.
26. Janecek, T.R., and Rea, D.K. : 1984, in "Milankovitch and Climate", A. Berger, J. Imbrie, J. Hays, G. Kukla, B. Saltzman (Eds), Reidel Publ. Company, Holland. This volume, p. 331.
27. Moore, T.C.Jr. : 1973, J. Quat. Res. 3, pp. 99-109.
28. Imbrie, J., Hays, J.D., Martinson, D.G., McIntyre, A., Mix, A.C., Morley, J.J., Pisias, N.G., Prell, W.L., and Shackleton, N.J. : 1984, in : "Milankovitch and Climate", A. Berger, J. Imbrie, J. Hays, G. Kukla, B. Saltzman (Eds), Reidel Publ. Company, Holland. This volume, p. 269.
29. Jenkins, G.M., and Watts, D.G. : 1968, "Spectral Analysis and Its Applications", Holden-Day, 525pp.
30. Berger, A. : 1978, J. Atmos. Sci. 35(12), pp. 2362-2367.

PLEISTOCENE FLUCTUATIONS IN NORTHERN HEMISPHERE TRADEWINDS AND WESTERLIES

T.R. Janecek,[1] D.K. Rea

Oceanography Program, Department of Atmospheric and Oceanic Science, The University of Michigan, Ann Arbor, Michigan 48109, USA

The mass accumulation rate and grain size of the total eolian component isolated from pelagic clay from two North Pacific cores, one KK75-02 under the westerlies and another DSDP Site 503 under the tradewinds, have been used to evaluate changes in the intensity of atmospheric circulation over the past 700 000 years. The eolian grain size, a direct indicator of wind intensity, fluctuates at periodicities approximately equal to the earth's orbital parameters of precession, obliquity, and eccentricity suggesting the intensity of atmospheric circulation responds to changing solar insolation resulting from the earth's orbital fluctuations. Both sites display greater variability in eolian grain size and thus, wind vigor prior to 250 000 years ago. Lower eolian accumulation rates during colder (glacial) times most likely reflect glacial-age humidity at central Asian and Central American source areas.

INTRODUCTION

The intensity of atmospheric circulation in the geologic past is an important parameter in paleoclimatological and paleoceanographic models. Unfortunately, direct estimates of wind intensity in the past are lacking. Indirect estimates of past atmospheric circulation have been inferred from studies of past biological productivity under wind-driven circulation systems (1,2), the distribution of temperature sensitive marine microorganisms (3-5), and quartz distributions in the deep sea (6,7). However, recent work suggests that the non-authigenic, inorganic component of sediment recovered from the central portions of ocean basins is dominated by eolian material (8,9).

A. L. Berger et al. (eds.), Milankovitch and Climate, Part 1, 331–347.

Variations in the mass accumulation rate and grain size of this eolian material should provide direct estimates of source-area aridity and wind intensity during the past. This paper describes changes in wind intensity over the past 700 000 years as determined from eolian material isolated from two deep-sea cores in the North Central and Equatorial Pacific.

Eolian Sedimentation

Results of various sampling programs indicate that dust is a significant component of pelagic sediments (10). Away from the mouths of rivers, patterns of sediment mineralogy (11) parallel the zonal wind regimes and so are roughly perpendicular to boundary currents of the subtropical gyres. This observation serves to emphasize the rapid removal of small particles from the surface of the ocean (12). Up to 99% of the vertical mass flux from the epipelagic and mesopelagic zones is accomplished by fecal pellet transport (13,14). The process of ingestion of small grains by feeding zooplankton, incorporation of those grains into fecal pellets, and the rapid settling of those grains at hundreds of meters per day (15) quickly removes eolian material (16) and other particulates from the effects of ocean surface circulation resulting in little surface current smearing of sedimentary input patterns.

Pelagic sediments recovered farther than 1000 to 2000 km from land, seaward of the realm of hemipelagic sedimentation, and away from turbidites and ice-rafted debris, contain eolian material as their non-authigenic inorganic component. The grain size of this eolian material is determined by the intensity (we avoid the term velocity) of atmospheric circulation (17). Both air sampling (18,19) and theoretical calculations (8,20,21) show that beyond 1000 to 2000 km distance from the source, the size distribution of eolian grains changes very little. That is, the settling velocity of small eolian grains is some insignificant fraction of the vertical velocity inherent to the turbulence of the atmosphere and those grains, a minor portion of the initial dust load, remain in suspension indefinitely (17-22). These equilibrium grains are carried global distances in the upper troposphere and are generally removed by rainout (23).

In the simplest case, the intensity of the global wind systems should depend directly upon the pole-to-equator temperature gradient. As this gradient becomes greater, the velocity of the zonal winds should increase. Changes in the wind strength will result in a change in the size of the equilibrium grains, with stronger winds carrying coarser particles (24).

The flux of the wind-borne dust to the ocean basins depends in part on the strength of the zonal winds and on the distance from the source area but mostly upon the climate of the source area (25). Humid climates promote vegetation, thereby reducing the amount of dust available for wind erosion, transport, and subsequent deposition in the deep sea (26). High precipitation rates also increase the scavenging of eolian material by rain, thus decreasing the amount of dust deposition downwind (8,27). Thus, variations in the mass accumulation rate of the eolian debris represent changes in the source area climate and variations in the grain size of the eolian material record changes in zonal wind intensity (28).

Sediments and Analyses

We have examined the late Pleistocene eolian record in detail at two sites in the Pacific, one beneath the tradewinds, DSDP Site 503, and one beneath the prevailing westerlies, piston core KK75-02 (Fig. 1). KK75-02, at 38°37.4'N and 179°19.7'E, on the northeastern Hess Rise, is primarily a diatom-radiolarian bearing clay and should have the arid regions of Asia as the dominant source of eolian material. Hydraulic piston cores 503B-1 and 503B-2, at 4°03.0'N, and 95°38.3'W, contain Pleistocene to Holocene siliceous carbonate ooze alternating from white to light tan. The sight lies north of the Galapagos

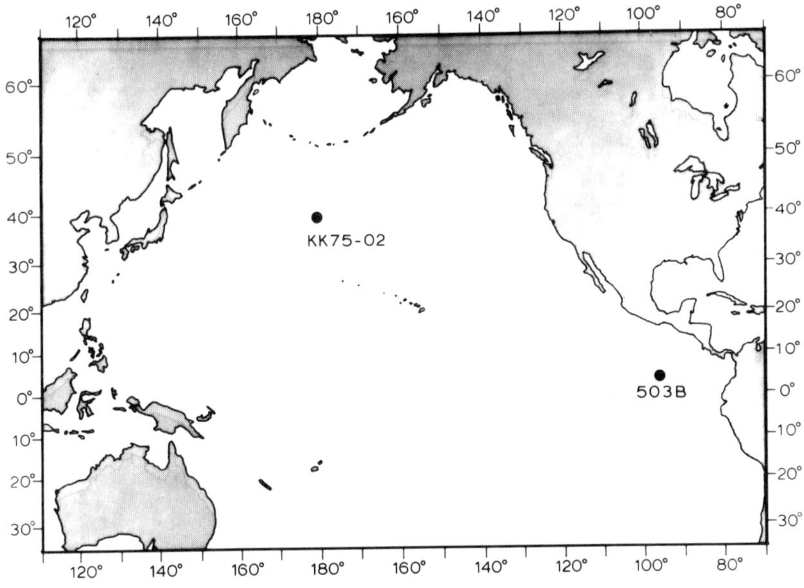

Figure 1 Location map of piston core KK75-02 and DSDP Site 503.

spreading center and east of the East Pacific Rise, between the zones of maximum influence of the northeast and southeast tradewinds (6). Eolian material should, therefore, have a Central American or perhaps South American source, depending on the position of the tradewinds.

A magnetic reversal and radiolarian biostratigraphic datum levels were used at KK75-02 to determine sedimentation rates and sample ages (Fig. 2, and Table 1). The sedimentation rates are relatively constant, varying between 1.18 and 1.41 cm/1000 years. Uniform sedimentation rates throughout the Brunhes, as seen in this core, are typical for cores in the Northwest Pacific (29) and suggest that no significant hiatuses occur in KK75-02. Samples used in this data set are spaced at approximately 6000 year intervals along the core.

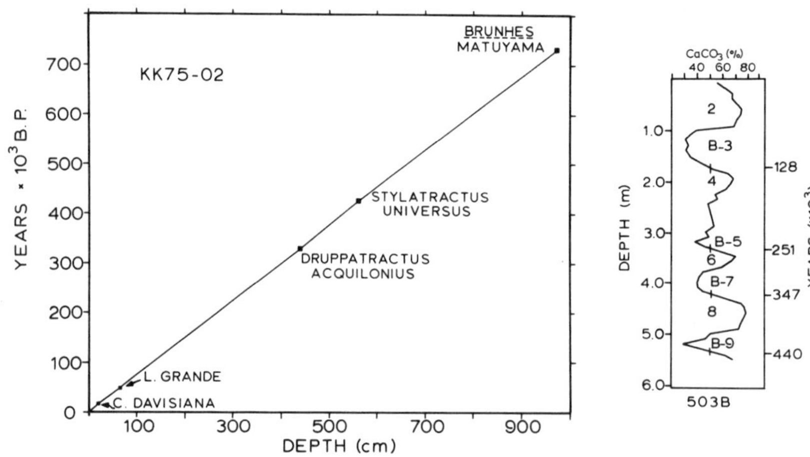

Figure 2 Left: Age-Depth plot for KK75-02. Right: Carbonate variations at DSDP Site 503, data from Gardner (30). Absolute ages for glacial terminations (defined as the 50% $CaCO_3$ level) from Shackleton and Opdyke (31). See Table 1.

The high quality record of carbonate dissolution cycles at Site 503 (30) provide a basis for determining accurate linear sedimentation rates for the uppermost portion of Site 503 (Fig. 2). Pacific carbonate cycles have not been dated directly, but they can be correlated to $\delta^{18}O$ fluctuations that have been dated elsewhere (31). Site 503 contains four transitions between high and low carbonate stages that correspond to Glacial Terminations II (Carbonate B3/4), III (B5/6), IV (B7/8), V (B9/10), which have been assigned the ages of 128, 251, 347, and 440 kyr, respectively (31). Linear sedimentation rates were calculated between age horizons and are presented in Table 1. Resulting linear sedimentation rates are reasonably uniform and vary from 1 to 1.3 cm/1000 years. Samples used in this date set are spaced at approximately 10 000 year intervals along the core.

Table 1 Determination of linear sedimentation rates : a) Site 503 sedimentation rates calculated from spacing of $CaCO_3$ peaks, data from Gardner (30) ; b) KK75-02 sedimentation rates calculated from a magnetic horizon (55) and radiolarian datum levels (29).

a) Glacial-stage Boundary	$CaCO_3$-stage Boundary	Depth (cm)	Age (kyr)	LSR of interval (cm/1000 y)
surface	surface	0	0	
5/6 T-II	B3/4	171	128	1.34
7/8 T-III	B5/6	330	251	1.28
9/10 T-IV	B7/8	422	347	0.96
11/12 T-V	B9/10	532	440	1.18
b) Horizon				
surface		0	0	
C. davisiana maximum		20	17	1.18
L. grande extinction		65	49	1.41
D. acquilonius extinction		440	329	1.34
S. universus extinction		560	425	1.25
Brunhes/Matuyama reversal		975	730	1.36

The detrital mineral or eolian component of pelagic sediments is isolated by treating the samples successively with 25% acetic acid to remove calcium carbonate, with a buffered sodium citrate-sodium dithionite solution to remove oxides, hydroxides, and zeolites and with warm sodium carbonate to remove opal. The residue, commonly a mixture of fine grained clays and quartz, is freeze-dried to give the weight percent of the eolian component. The mass accumulation of the eolian component is the product of the eolian weight percent and the total mass accumulation rate. Grain size analysis was carried out on the 6 to 10 ϕ (16 to 1 micron) size fraction at 0.5 ϕ intervals using a Coulter Counter Model Zb particle size analyzer. Precision of this analysis is $\pm$ 0.03 ϕ. A detailed description of the laboratory procedures is given by Rea and Janecek (32).

PLEISTOCENE EOLIAN SEDIMENTATION

Results

The eolian mass accumulation rate data from KK75-02 show high accumulation rates (greater than 400 mg/cm^2-1 kyr) centered at 750, 610, 430, 310, and 225 kyr ago (Fig. 3). The relative high at 30 000 years ago reaches 300 mg/cm^2-1 kyr. Two periods of severly reduced rates (less than 100 mg/cm^2-1 kyr) ocurred at 540 000 and 130 000 years ago.

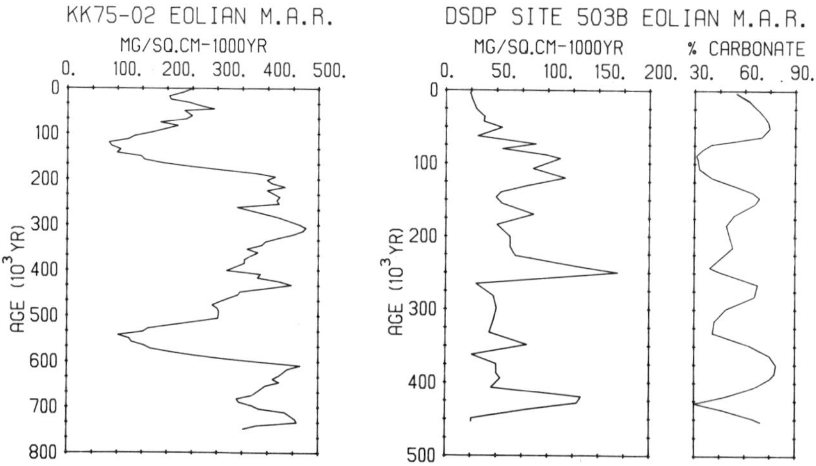

Figure 3 Left: Eolian mass accumulation rates for KK75-02 . Eolian mass accumulation rates and percent carbonate for DSDP Site 503. Right: Low carbonate values represent interglacial periods and high carbonate values represent glacial periods.

Eolian mass accumulation rates at Site 503 vary by nearly an order of magnitude, from 24 to 169 mg/cm^2-1 kyr (Fig. 3). Lower values, generally less than 60 mg/cm^2-1 kyr are associated with high carbonate stages 2, 4, 6 and 8. Higher values are associated with dissolution stages B-3, B-5, and B-9. Eolian mass accumulation rates from stage B-7 may or may not fit this pattern.

The grain size of eolian material at KK75-02 ranges from 8.81 ϕ to 8.37 ϕ (Fig. 4). At a constant grain density, this represents a factor of 2.5 range in grain mass. At Site 503 the grain size of the eolian material ranges from 8.79 to 8.25 (Fig. 4) which represents a factor of nearly 3.1 range in grain mass. The positions of the grain-size (wind-vigor) maxima in both cores do not correspond to times of glacial maxima; rather, both data sets show much higher frequency fluctuations which appear to be related to periodic variations in the earth's orbital parameters (see discussion section).

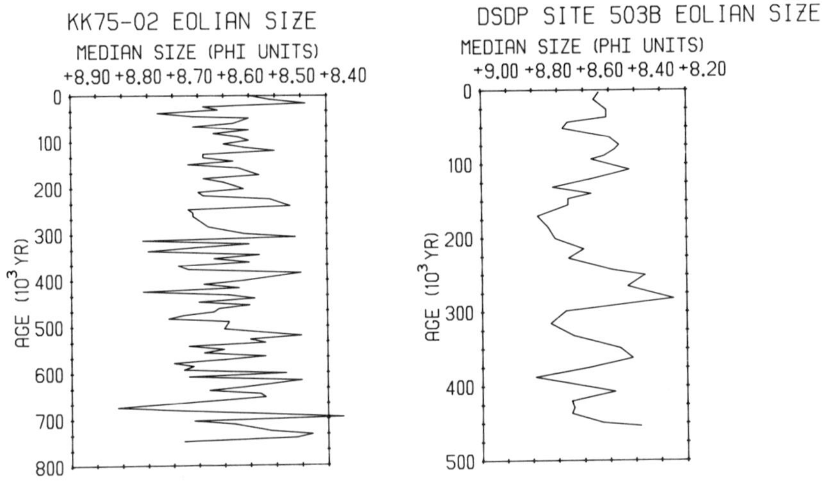

Figure 4 Eolian grain size for KK75-02 and DSDP Site 503.

The change in grain size can be used to quantify the relative change in strength of the wind. This calculation is based on the assumption that, far from the source, eolian grains have a size distribution in equilibrium with the average wind intensity (8,18,20). Changes in wind intensity can then be determined by comparing, in a ratio, the settling velocities in air of different sized particles. In such a ratio, the significant terms are the squares of the particle diameters; other terms cancel out. Thus, the ratio of high-to-low wind intensities, R_w, is the ratio of the squares of the grain sizes D^2 and D^2 : $R_w=D^2/D^2$. Wind intensity ratios can be calculated for every change in grain size (28,33).

At KK75-02, the average change in high-to-low intensities is about 22%. The amplitude of the intensity fluctuations decreased from 27% before 250 000 years ago to 17% more recently. In comparison, at Site 503 the average change in tradewind intensity during the Brunhes was 35%, and the amplitude of wind intensity fluctuations also decreased since 250 000 years ago from 47% to 26%.

DISCUSSION-CLIMATIC VARIABILITY

Eolian Accumulation Rates

Our previous work in eolian deposition in the deep sea (25,28, 32-34) has shown that the accumulation of eolian material depends more on source area climate than on wind intensity or distance to source. Site 503 records reduced eolian contributions during glacial times (Fig. 3) contrary to the trend of higher global aridity during glacial times reported form other regions (4, 35-37). This suggests that the source areas, Central America and northwestern South America, experienced greater humidity and vegetative cover during glaciations (38,39). Times of maximum eolian accumulation correspond to or are somewhat younger than carbonate-data indicators of glacial terminations which themselves are 5000 to 10 000 years younger than glacial terminations as expressed in $\delta^{18}O$ data (40-43). Thus, within eolian source regions, earlier portions of interglacial periods, which may last for 10's of thousands of years, may be more arid than latter portions.

The fluctuations in the accumulation of eolian material at KK75-02 do not correlate as well with glacial to interglacial transitions as at Site 503. The relative lows in the eolian accumulation curve, however, correlate with many of the "cold" intervals in the generalized curves calculated by Ruddiman and McIntyre (44) from forams for the equatorial Atlantic and the Polar Front in the North Atlantic (Fig. 5). This suggests that the climate of the now arid regions of Central Asia may have been more humid during these "cold" times.

An alternative explanation may be that the variations in eolian accumulation at KK75-02 resulted from changes in the position of the regions of greatest dust transport within the westerlies during these "cold" intervals. Rea and Janecek (33) have shown that there is a strong latitudinal gradient in eolian accumulation and grain size between 30° and 40°N in the North Pacific. Accumulation rates vary by a factor of 3 from south to north over these distances. KK75-02 is at the northern edge of this gradient, hence latitudinal displacement of the westerlies in response to alternating warm and cold intervals may have affected the accumulation rate of eolian material at this site.

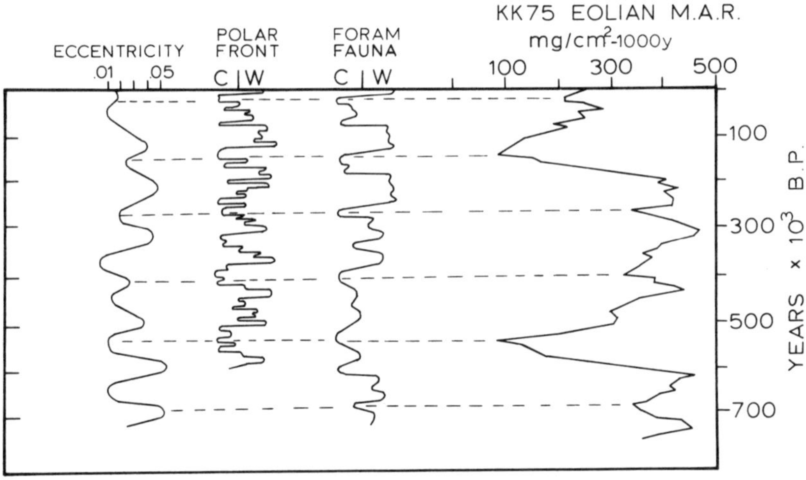

Figure 5 KK75-02 eolian mass rates plotted with generalized warm/cold climatic curves calculated by Ruddiman and McIntyre (44) for foraminiferal fauna in the equatorial Atlantic and for North Atlantic Polar Front oscillations. Variations in eccentricity for the past 700 000 years is also plotted for reference.

Eolian Grain size

The grain-size(wind-vigor) maxima in both cores do not correspond to times of glacial maxima; both exhibit much higher frequency fluctuations. To determine the nature of these fluctuations we used the technique of spectral analysis (45) to calculate spectra for our grain-size curves (Fig. 6). For KK75-02 (Fig. 6) the spectra is characterized by three peaks, significant at the 80% confidence interval, corresponding to periods of 104 kyr, 41 kyr, and 23 kyr. This is a further confirmation of the work of many investigators (42, 45-48) who have shown that frequencies similar to those for the orbital variables of eccentricity, obliquity, and precession are important components of climatic indicators recorded in deep sea sediments.

The climatic variance is mainly distributed in three discrete peaks. Unlike the spectra calculated by Hays et al. (45) for mid-latitude cores in the South Pacific, the low frequency (100 000 year period) peak does not contain more than half of the total variance. At KK75-02, a mid-latitude site in the North

Pacific, the low frequency 100 kyr peak contains 35% of the variance, the 42 kyr peak contains 38% and the 23 kyr peak 19%.

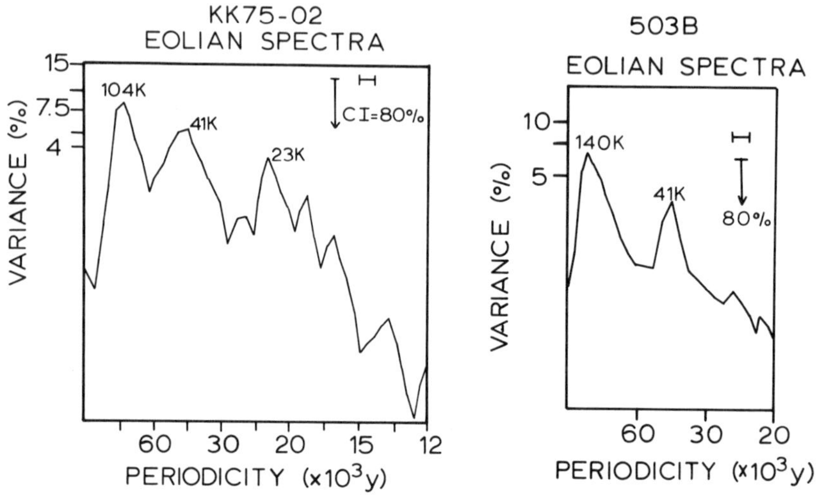

Figure 6 Spectra calculated for eolian grain size at KK75-02 (left) and DSDP Site 503 (right). Sample spacing is 6000 years for KK75-02 and 10 000 years for Site 503. Spectra for both cores is expressed as the natural log of the variance as a function of frequency (cycles/1000 years).

The spectra of the Site 503 eolian grain size record of the tradewinds is dominated by two discrete peaks, one corresponding to a period of 140 000 years and another corresponding to a period of 41 000 years. If present, the 21 000 year period would not be observed at the sample spacing utilized in this study. The 41 000 year period is very similar to that predicted for the orbital variable of obliquity (49). The low frequency peak is not well understood. It may be a harmonic of a much lower frequency or an alias of higher frequencies.

To further investigate the relationship between the frequency components of the eolian grain size records and orbital variations, we applied digital band-pass filters to the KK75-02 grain-size time series centered at 0.024 cycles/kyr (41 000 year period), at 0.043 cycles/kyr (23 000 year period) and at 0.0096 cycles/kyr (104 000 year period). A digital band-pass filter centered at 0.024 cycles/kyr (41 000 year period) was applied to the Site 503 grain size time series. The filtered components were plotted in the time domain with the calculated curves (49) for obliquity, precession, and eccentricity (Figs 7-9). The mean grain-size value was subtracted from the data during the filtering process. Thus, in Figures 7-9, positive deviations represent finer grain size, unlike normal phi units (Fig. 4) where larger positive numbers indicate finer grain size.

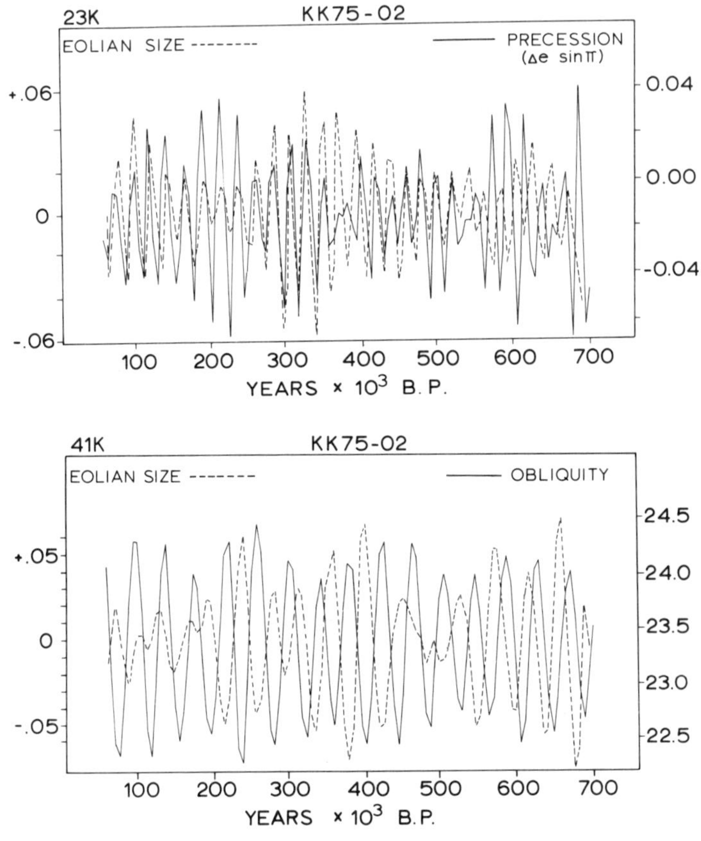

Figure 7 Variations in precession and obliquity along with corresponding eolian size frequency components plotted in the time domain for KK75-02. See discussion in text for details of the extraction of the filtered components.

Cross-correlation techniques were used to estimate the average phase shifts between the filtered geologic curves and the orbital curves. The 41 kyr cross-correlation results show maximum negative correlations at 0 lags and at multiples of 7 leads or lags (42 kyr) for KK75-02 and 0 lags and multiples of 4 leads or lags (40 kyr) for 503 indicating that the 41 kyr grain size curves are about 180° out of phase with obliquity. Times of lowest obliquity (low axial tilt) correspond to times of coarsest grain size (Figs 7 and 8).

Between 0 and 550 000 years ago, the 23 kyr cross-correlation results for KK75-02 show highest positive correlations at 0 lags and at multiples of 4 leads and lags (24 000 years). Thus, the two curves are approximately in phase. Times of coarsest grain size are associated with high positive values of precession - that is, when the earth-sun distance in June is greater than normal (Fig. 7). Between 550 000 and 700 000 years ago, the systematic phase relationships just described for the precession - 23 kyr component curves at KK75-02 do not exist. The two curves are approximately 180° out of phase. A major assumption in our calculations is that sedimentation rates are constant between stratigraphic control points. The change in phase relationships for the 23 kyr grain size component-precession curves may be the result of changes in the sedimentation rate between stratigraphic markers. Recent work has shown (47,50) that very detailed age control may be obtained for Pleistocene sediment sections by tuning an individual frequency component in a climatic record to a particular earth orbital parameter. The application of this technique to our data set may help resolve the phase problems in the lower portion of the core. Similarly, the

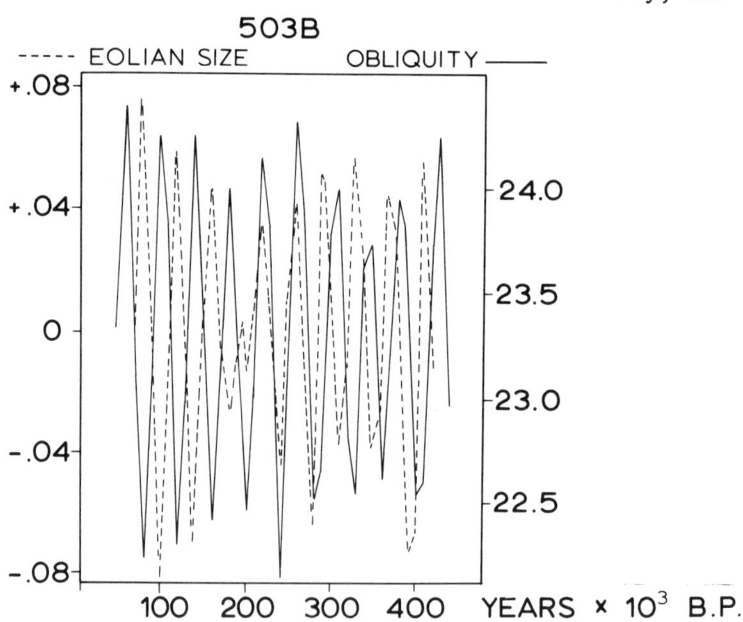

Figure 8 Variations in obliquity and corresponding eolian grain size frequency component plotted in the time domain for DSDP Site 503. See text for details.

change in phase relationships between 200 and 250 kyr at Site 503 may also be the result of changes in the sedimentation rate between stratigraphic markers (Fig. 8).

Our results show that times of minimum Northern Hemisphere summer insolation (low obliquity, high precession values) generally correlate with coarsest grain size and thus, most intense wind vigor. Such an orbital configuration is considered critical for rapid ice growth (glaciation) in the Northern Hemisphere (51,52). Gates (4) has shown that glacial times result in increased pole-to-equator temperature gradients and subsequently stronger zonal winds. This scenario is supported by our grain-size(wind-vigor) curves.

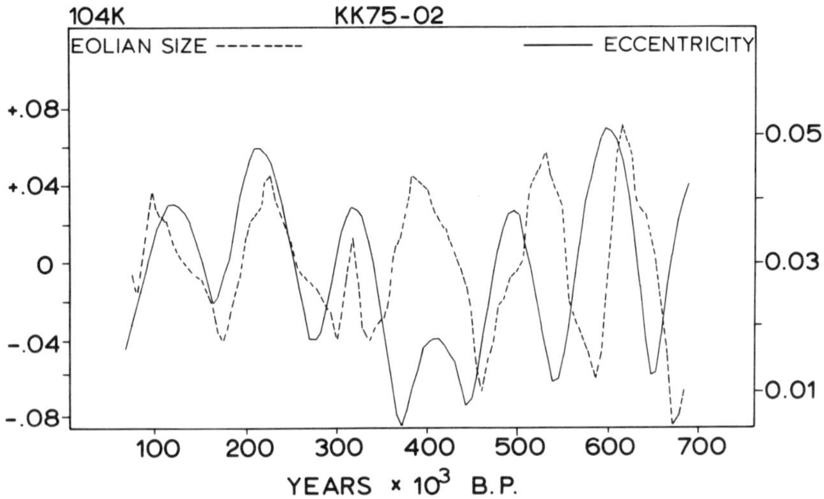

Figure 9 Variations in eccentricity and the corresponding eolian grain size frequency component plotted in the time domain for KK75-02. See text for details.

The 104 000 year filtered component of the eolian grain size at KK75-02 shows a confusing picture of phase relationships with eccentricity (Fig. 9). Eccentricity and the 104 kyr component are generally in phase for the first 4 cycles and the last cycle. The fifth cycle is clearly out of phase. As discussed earlier, this change in phase relationships may be the result of changing sedimentation rates in the lower portion of the core. In general, though, times of high eccentricity correlate with the coarsest grain size. However, several studies have shown that low eccentricity values correlate with geologic indicators of glacial periods (45,53,54). The 104 kyr component of our grain size data suggests stronger winds in interglacials (high eccentricity values) which conflicts with these studies and the results discussed earlier concerning the 41 kyr and 23 kyr components of the eolian grain size. The 104 kyr component may not be recording zonal wind intensity fluctuations but, rather, latitudinal shifts in the position of the westerlies. Gates (4) has shown that during the last glacial maximum the most intense portion of the westerlies shifted approximately 20° south in response to a southerly shift in the zone of the maximum meridional temperature gradient. Our data are in agreement with this model and suggest that the zone of maximum westerly intensity may have been south of KK75-02 during glacial times resulting in relatively less intense zonal winds over the site at these times. During interglacial times the zone of maximum intensity would shift northward (4) resulting in more intense winds at KK75-02 and subsequently coarser grain size of the eolian material. Thus, the 104 kyr component of the eolian grain size may be recording the greatest southerly shifts of the zonal westerlies during full glaciations and the 23 ky and 41 ky components may be recording the general intensification of the westerlies and tradewinds resulting from insolation and temperature gradient changes in response to obliquity and precession variations.

SUMMARY

Information derived from the analysis of the eolian component of pelagic sediments from the North Pacific Ocean reveals three important results. First, the intensity of atmospheric circulation responds to changing solar insolation resulting from the earth's orbital fluctuations. The eolian grain size, a direct indicator of wind intensity, reveals significant periodicities at 23, 41, and 104 kyr, the approximate periodicities of the earth's orbital parameters for precession, obliquity and eccentricity. Comparison of the three earth orbital parameters with the eolian grain size record shows: a) the 23 kyr component of the eolian grain size is in phase with precession, hence times of coarsest grain size correlate with maximum June earth-sun distance; b) the 41 kyr component of grain size is 180° out of phase with obliquity, hence times of coarsest grain size correspond to lowest obliquity (axial tilt) values; and c) the 104 kyr component is generally in phase with eccentricity. This last relationship suggests that times of coarsest grain size correspond to interglacial periods. Alternatively, the 104 kyr component of the eolian grain size may be reflecting the most southerly shifts of the westerlies during glaciations.

The mass accumulation rates of the eolian dust are higher during interglacial times. This suggests that the eolian source regions of Central Asia and Central America were more humid during glacial times over the past 700 000 years.

Finally, the fluctuations in eolian grain size beneath both the tradewinds and the westerlies show a significant change 250 kyr ago. Prior to that time the fluctuations in wind intensity, R_w, were 38% greater. This 38% decrease in wind intensity fluctuations may denote some important change in the parameters controlling global atmospheric circulation.

ACKNOWLEDGEMENTS

The authors would like to thank Chris Mato at the Hawaii Institute of Geophysics for supplying the samples for KK75-02 and Jim Gardner of the U.S. Geological Survey for supplying the DSDP Site 503 samples. We would also like to thank Nick Pisias for his assistance in radiolarian identification and his comments and suggestions regarding this manuscript. This work was supported by NSF Grant OCE80-24368.

REFERENCES

1. Ingle, J.C. : 1973, in : "Initial Reports of the Deep Sea Drilling Project", L.D. Kulm, R. von Huene et al. (Eds), 18, Washington, D.C., U.S. Gvt. Printing Office, pp. 949-960.
2. van Andel, Tj.H., Heath, G.R., and Moore, T.C.Jr. : 1975, Geol. Soc. Am. Mem. 143, pp. 1-134.
3. CLIMAP : 1976, Science 191, pp. 1131-1137.
4. Gates, W.L. : 1976, Science 191, pp. 1138-1144.
5. Moore, T.C.Jr., Burckle, L.H., Geitzenauer, K., Luz, B., Molina-Cruz, A., Robertson, J.H., Sachs, H., Sancetta, C., Thiede, J., Thompson, P., Wenkam, C. : 1980, Mar. Micropal. 5, pp. 215-247.
6. Molina-Cruz, A. : 1977, Quaternary Research 8, pp. 324-339.
7. Thiede, J. : 1979, Geology 7, pp. 259-262.
8. Windom, H.L. : 1975, J. Sed. Petrol. 45, pp. 520-529.
9. Leinen, M., and Heath, G.R. : 1981, Palaeogeography, -climatology, -ecology 36, pp. 1-21.
10. Griffin, J.J., Windom, H.L.; Goldberg, E.D. : 1968, Deep-sea Res. 15, pp. 433-459.
11. Windom, H.L. : 1976, in : "Chemical Oceanography", J.P. Riley and R. Chester (Eds), 5, pp. 103-135.
12. Berger, W.H. : 1976, ibid, pp. 265-388.

13. Bishop, J.K.B., Edmond, J.M., Ketten, D.R., Bacon, M.P., and Silker, W.B. : 1977, Deep-sea Res. 24, pp. 511-548.
14. Bishop, J.K.B., Ketten, D.R., and Edmond, J.M. : 1978, ibid 25, pp. 1121-1161.
15. Honjo, S. : 1980, J. Mar. Res. 38, pp. 53-97.
16. Scheidegger, R.F., and Krissek, L.A. : 1982, Geol. Soc. Am. Bull. 93, pp. 150-162.
17. Gillette, D.A., Blifford, I.H.Jr., and Fryrear, D.W. : 1974, J. Geophys. Res. 79, pp. 4068-4075.
18. Johnson, L.R. : 1976, Mar. Geol. 21, pp. 17-21.
19. Glaccum, R.A., and Prospero, J.M. : 1980, Mar. Geol. 37, pp. 295-321.
20. Schütz, L. : 1979, in : "Saharan Dust Mobilization, Transport, Deposition", C. Morales (Ed.), Wiley and Sons, New York, pp. 267-277.
21. Schütz, L., Jaenicke, B., and Pietrek, H. : 1981, Geol. Soc. Am. Spec. Pap. 186, pp. 87-100.
22. Gillette, D.A. : 1981, ibid, pp. 11-26.
23. Jackson, M.L., Gillette, D.A., Danielson, E.F., Blifford, I.H., Brysson, R.A., and Syers, J.K. : 1973, Soil Science 116, pp. 135-145.
24. Parkin, D.W. : 1974, Proc. R. Soc. London, Ser. A 337, pp. 73-100.
25. Rea, D.K., and Janecek, T.R. : 1981, Palaeogeography, -climatology, -ecology 36, pp. 55-67.
26. Prospero, J.M. : 1981, Geol. Soc. Am. Spec. Pap. 186, pp. 71-86.
27. Parkin, D.W., and Padgham, R.C. : 1975, Proc. R. Soc. London Ser. A 346, pp. 245-260.
28. Janecek, T.R., and Rea, D.K. : 1983, Geol. Soc. Am. Bull. 94, pp. 730-738.
29. Morley, J.J., Hays, J.D., and Robertson, J.H. : 1982, Deep-sea Res. 29, pp. 1485-1499.
30. Gardner, J.V. : 1982, in : "Initial Reports of the Deep Sea Drilling Project", W.L. Prell, J.V. Gardner et al. (Eds), 68, Washington D.C., U.S. Gvt. Printing Office, pp. 347-364.
31. Shackleton, N.J., and Opdyke, N.D. : 1976, in : "Investigations of Late Quaternary Paleoceanography and Paleoclimatology", R.M. Cline, and J.D. Hays (Eds), Geol. Soc. Am. Mem. 145, pp. 449-464.
32. Rea, D.K., and Janecek, T.R. : 1981, in : "Initial Reports of the Deep Sea Drilling Project", J. Thiede, T.L. Vallier et al. (Eds), 62, Washington D.C., U.S. Gvt. Printing Office, pp. 653-659.
33. Rea, D.K., and Janecek, T.R. : 1982, Mar. Geol. 49, pp. 149-167.
34. Rea, D.K. : 1982, in : "Initial Reports of the Deep Sea Drilling Project", W.L. Prell, J.V. Gardner et al.

(Eds), 68, Washington D.C., U.S. Gvt. Printing Office, pp. 409-415.
35. Williams, M.A.J. : 1975, Nature 253, pp. 617-618.
36. Manabe, S., and Hahn, D.C. : 1977, J. Geophys. Res. 82, pp. 3889-3912.
37. Sarnthein, M. : 1978, Nature 227, pp. 43-46.
38. Brakenridge, G.R. : 1978, Quaternary Research 9, pp. 22-40.
39. Peterson, G.M., Webb, T. III, Kutzbach, J.E., van der Hammen, T., Wijmstra, T.A., and Street, F.A. : 1979, Quaternary Research 12, pp. 47-82.
40. Shackleton, N.J., and Opdyke, N.D. : 1973, Quaternary Research 3, pp. 39-55.
41. Ninkovich, D., and Shackleton, N.J. : 1975, Earth. Planet. Sci. Lett. 27, pp. 20-34.
42. Pisias, N.G. : 1976, in : "Investigations of Late Quaternary Paleoceanography and Paleoclimatology", R.M. Cline and J.D. Hays (Eds), Geol. Soc. Am. Mem. 145, Boulder, Geol. Soc. Am., pp. 375-391.
43. Moore, T.C.Jr., Pisias, N.G., and Heath, G.R. : 1977, in : "The Fate of Fossil Fuel CO_2 in the Oceans", N.R. Anderson, and A. Malahoff (Eds), Plenum, New York, pp. 145-165.
44. Ruddiman, W.F., and McIntyre, A. : 1976, in : "Investigations of Late Quaternary Paleoceanography and Paleoclimatology", R.M. Cline and J.D. Hays (Eds), Geol. Soc. Am. Mem. 145, Boulder, Geol. Soc. Am., pp. 111-146.
45. Hays, J.D., Imbrie, J., and Shackleton, N.J. : 1976, Science 194, pp. 1121-1132.
46. Kominz, M.A., Heath, G.R., Ti-L, Ku, Pisias, N.G. : 1979, Earth. Planet. Sci. Lett. 45, pp. 394-410.
47. Morley, J.J., and Hays, J.D. : 1981, ibid 53, pp. 279-295.
48. Imbrie, J. : 1982, Icarus 50, pp. 408-422.
49. Berger, A.L. : 1976, Astron. Astrophys. 51, pp. 127-135.
50. Pisias, N.G., and Moore, T.C. Jr. : 1981, Earth Planet. Sci. Lett. 52, pp. 458-465.
51. Milankovitch, M. : 1941, K. Serb. Akad. Beogr. Spec. Publ. 132, translated by the Israel Program for Scientific Translations, Jerusalem, 1969.
52. Ruddiman, W.F., and McIntyre, A. : 1981, Science 212, pp. 617-627.
53. Mesolella, K.J., Matthews, R.K., Broecker, W.S., Thurber, D.L. : 1969, J. Geol. 77, pp. 250-274.
54. Broecker, W.S., and van Donk, J. : 1970, Rev. Geophys. Space Phys. 8, pp. 169-198.
55. Hammond, S.R., Seyb, S.M., and Theyer, F. : 1979, Earth Planet. Sci. Lett. 44, pp. 167-175.

[1]Present address : Lamont-Doherty Geological Observatory of Columbia University, Palisades, NY 10964, USA.

MONSOONAL CLIMATE OF THE ARABIAN SEA DURING THE LATE QUATERNARY: A RESPONSE TO CHANGING SOLAR RADIATION

W.L. Prell

Department of Geological Sciences, Brown University, Providence, Rhode Island 02912-1846, USA

ABSTRACT

A late Quaternary time series (164 kyr long) of wind-driven coastal upwelling in the western Arabian Sea documents variations in low-level monsoonal winds. The record of monsoonal upwelling is highly coherent with solar radiation at the frequencies of orbital precession (~22 kyr). This result, combined with GCM simulations of the monsoon, confirms that changes in solar radiation force changes in monsoonal circulation on time scales of 10^3 to 10^5 yrs. However, changes in upwelling lag changes in summer radiation suggesting that other processes, such as seasonal snow cover, alter the direct monsoonal response to radiational heating.

INTRODUCTION

Studies of planktic foraminifers from the Arabian Sea indicate that the strength of the Southwest Indian Monsoon has varied greatly during the Holocene and Late Quaternary (1,2,3,4,5). For example, CLIMAP studies of the western Arabian Sea indicate that relatively warm sea-surface temperatures (SST) occurred at the last glacial maximum (LGM). These enhanced SST's are thought to represent a decrease in coastal upwelling and hence weaker low-level winds during the summer monsoon. This inference of a weaker monsoon is supported by independent geologic observations such as lake levels from Africa (6) and pollen data from the Arabian Sea (7) and Pakistan (8). However, the same studies reveal that the monsoon was more intense during the early Holocene. Taken together, these investigations

A. L. Berger et al. (eds.), Milankovitch and Climate, Part 1, 349–366.

clearly indicate that the strength of monsoonal winds and precipitation has undergone major changes in the recent geologic past.

Theoretical studies also point toward the same conclusion. For example, high-resolution general circulation model simulation of the atmospheric circulation during LGM summers indicate a weaker surface flow over the Arabian Sea and less precipitation over India (9,10,11). Manabe and Hahn (11) also concluded that the increased albedo over Asia, rather than cooler Indian Ocean SST, caused the weaker glacial monsoon. Importantly, the earth's orbital parameters, and hence the summer distribution of solar radiation, were almost the same at the LGM as they are today.

Recently, Kutzbach (12) used a low-resolution global climate model to evaluate the effect of solar radiation patterns on the Indian Ocean monsoon. Specifically, he combined modern boundary conditions (continental location, elevation, albedo, SST) with a 9 kyr BP seasonal radiation pattern to simulate the climate of the early Holocene. His simulation of the Northern Hemisphere summer revealed greatly enhanced southwesterly surface winds over the Arabian Sea and increased precipitation over India. A later study (13), which included a residual North American ice sheet at 9 kyr BP also gave an intensified monsoon circulation. The basic meteorologic hypothesis confirmed by these simulations is that increased solar radiation during the Northern Hemisphere summer causes greater surface heating of Asia; that the enhanced heating results in lower surface pressure over central Asia and the Tibetan Plateau during the summer; and that the intensity of the Southwest Monsoonal surface winds also increases, as the pressure gradient between Asia and the Indian Ocean increases.

The geologic consequences of this mechanism can be tested in both the time and frequency domains. The basis for such a test requires : (a) an indicator of monsoon intensity, (b) a time series of the monsoonal indicator, and (c) a clear rationale for selecting the solar radiation parameters that are thought to force the summer monsoon. Here, I present data that fulfill these requirements and then discuss the covariation of monsoonal indicators and solar radiation.

A MONSOONAL UPWELLING INDICATOR

In the western Arabian Sea, coastal upwelling occurs only during the summer and is associated with the Southwest Monsoon winds (for example, 14,15,16) (Fig. 1). Coastal upwelling has been shown to be the dominant process controlling the SST and

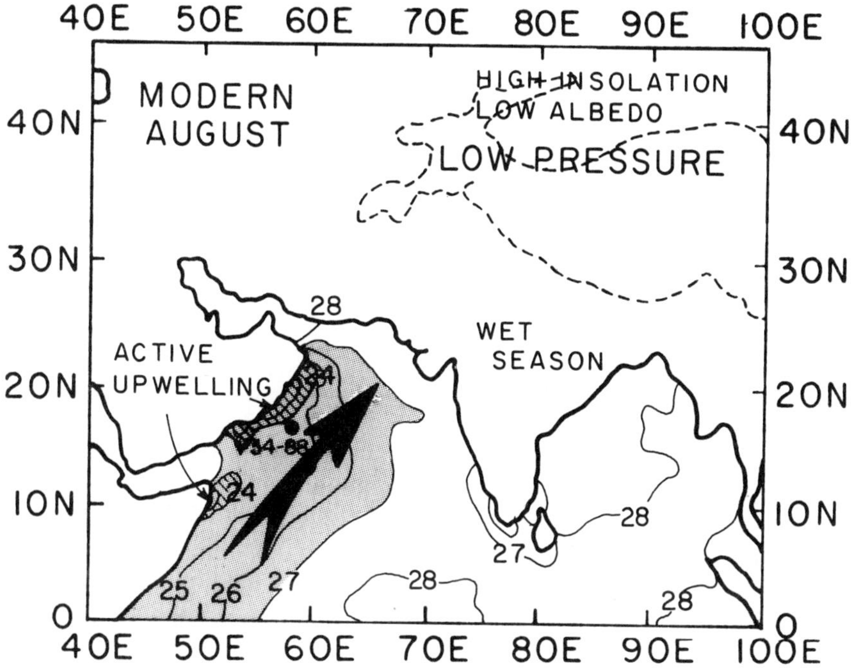

Figure 1 The location of V34-88 with respect to the area of active upwelling (cross-hatched), the low-level monsoonal winds (arrow) and low SST's (SSt's 27°C are shaded). Conditions represent the modern Indian Ocean-Southwest Monsoon.

heat budget of the Arabian Sea during the Southwest Monsoon (17). A direct forcing of the ocean by the wind field is illustrated by the observation that a simple Ekman upwelling model explains 66% of the variance in 60 yr mean monthly SST upwelling anomalies along the coast of Arabia (18). Hence, both the seasonal and spatial patterns of SST variation are explained as a response to the Southwest Monsoon surface wind field.

The abundance of a planktic foraminifer, G. bulloides, in the Arabian Sea is highly correlated with summer SST (r=-0.9) and nutrient concentrations, both of which reflect the effects of coastal upwelling along Arabia (3,19). The relationship of G. bulloides to upwelling is further documented by Prell (5). These studies indicate that the abundance of G. bulloides can be used as an indicator of the intensity of monsoonal upwelling and that variations in this indicator therefore reflect variations in the strength of the low-level winds during the Southwest Monsoon.

A TIME SERIES OF MONSOON INTENSITY

The abundance of G. bulloides in the western Arabian Sea over the past 180 kyr is recorded in the deep-sea sediments. Two cores, V34-87 and V34-88, were recovered from the Owen Ridge about 300 km off the coast of Arabia (16°32'N, 59°45'E) from a water depth of about 2000 m (Fig. 1). Although, the location is close enough to Arabia to record the effects of coastal upwelling, the cores are not in the area of maximum upwelling and G. bulloides abundance (5). Unfortunately, cores from the continental margin, which is the site of maximum upwelling, have discontinuous records. Sediments from the Owen Ridge are isolated from episodic sedimentologic processes which occur on both the Arabian margin and Indus Fan. The cores are composed of 60% to 80% calcium carbonate (by weight) and contain abundant planktic foraminifers for stratigraphic and paleo-environmental investigations.

Oxygen isotope stratigraphy for cores V34-87 and V34-88 was generated by analyzing a shallow-dwelling planktic foraminifer, Globigerinoides sacculifer (300-355 μm), at 10 cm and 5 cm intervals, respectively. All oxygen isotope data were generated in the Benedum Stable Isotopes Laboratory at Brown University and are reported in the standard per mil (°/₀₀) notation relative to PDB. For a description of laboratory procedures and calibration to PDB, see Prell and Curry (19). Analytical precision for oxygen, as indicated by the first acceptable analysis of the working carbonate standard run before each analytical session, is 0.08°/₀₀ (1) for oxygen. The analytical precision based on 24 blind duplicate analyses run on separate days is 0.11 ‰ (average 1/2 $\delta^{18}O$).

The oxygen isotope stratigraphy is distinct and extends to the stage 5/6 boundary in both cores and possibly into stage 7 in V34-88 (Fig. 2). Both cores are characterized by a $\Delta\delta^{18}O$ of 1.8 ‰ to 2.0 ‰ across Terminations I and II and by relatively enriched values in stage 3. Isotope stages and events are designated in Figure 2. On the basis of the age of various isotopic events (Table 1), the accumulation rates of these cores are about 4 cm/kyr and the resulting Δt between samples is about 1 kyr and 2 kyr in V34-88 and V34-87, respectively.

Table 1 Control points in age model for V34-88. The ages of datums are based on C-14 ages in V34-88 or by correlation to isotope stratigraphy. Isotopic events labeled 3.0, 4.0, etc. are stage boundaries as defined by Shackleton and Opdyke (29). Other isotopic events are local maxima and minima of the $\delta^{18}O$ curve as defined by Prell *et al.* (30) and assigned ages by Imbrie *et al.* (20).

	DEPTH(cm)	AGE(kyr)	EVENTS
1	0.0	0.0	
2	55.5	9.0	C-14
3	67.5	12.6	C-14
4	98.5	18.1	C-14
5	133.0	21.9	C-14
6	135.0	24.0	3.0
7	175.0	28.0	3.1
8	255.0	53.0	3.3
9	337.5	59.0	4.0
10	387.5	71.0	5.0
11	405.0	80.0	5.1
12	450.0	99.0	5.3
13	485.0	107.0	5.4
14	510.0	122.0	5.5
15	535.0	128.0	6.0
16	580.0	135.0	6.2
17	610.0	146.0	6.3
18	670.0	151.0	6.4
19	730.0	181.0	6.6
20	760.0	194.0	7.1

The faunal census data show that *G. bulloides* exhibits a quasi-periodic abundance that varies between 10% and 40% (Fig. 2). The maximum abundance of *G. bulloides* occurs in the lower portion of isotope stage 3 in both cores, whereas the minimum

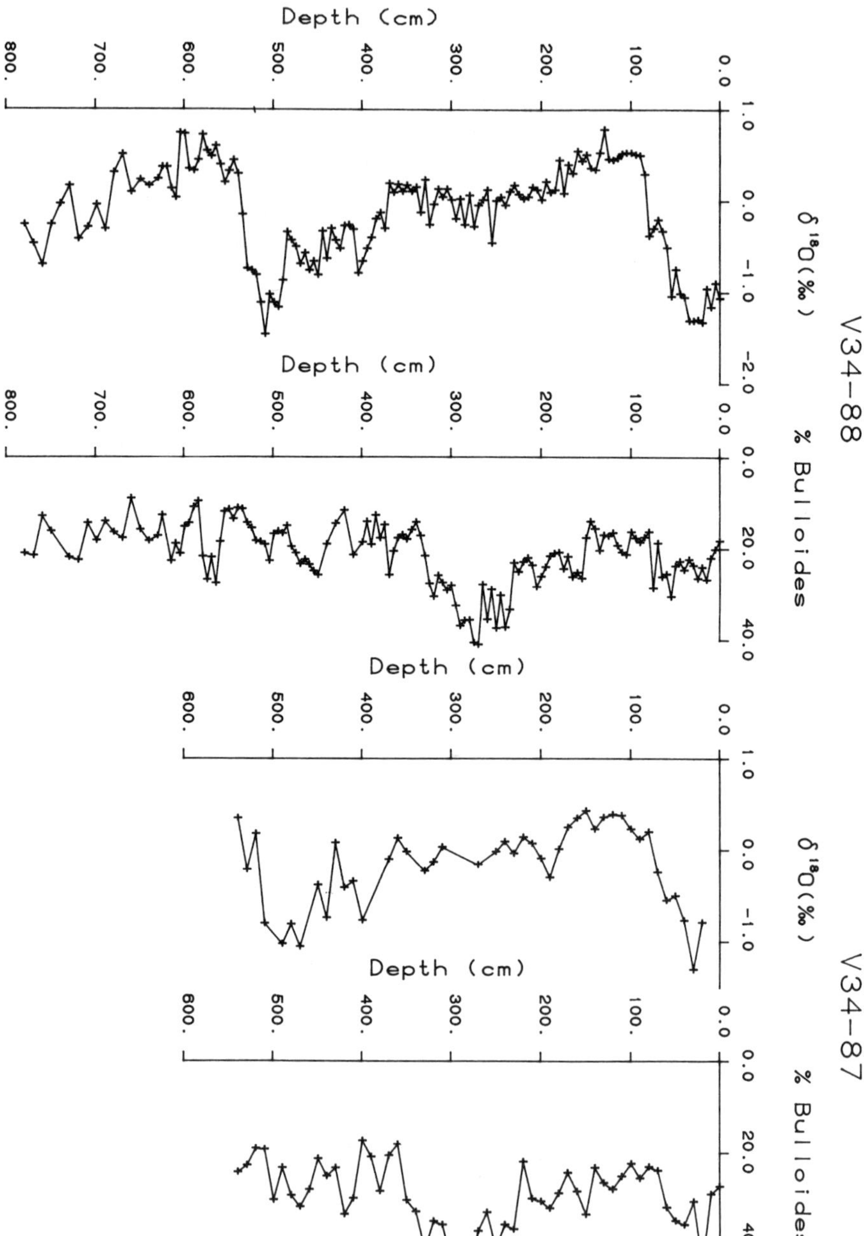

Figure 2 The isotopic composition of G. sacculifer and the percent abundance of G. bulloides vs. depth in cores V34-88 and V34-87.

abundances generally occur in glacial stages 2, 4, and 6. In a few cases, the abundance peaks of G. bulloides coincide with transitions between isotopic stages, rather than at interglacial extremes. For example, the clear maxima in the early Holocene, 10 kyr to 9 kyr (Fig. 1) is more pronounced in cores closer to the coast where upwelling is more intense and G. bulloides is more abundant. However, this relationship is not consistent at all deglacial trends. In summary, these two records of oceanic response appear to have similar periodicities and phases but are clearly different in amplitude.

To better understand the relation between G. bulloides variations and the isotopic record, I have converted the more detailed records of V34-88 into time series (Fig. 3) and examined their spectra. The age model (Fig. 3, Table 1) is derived from carbon-14 ages in V34-88 and correlation to dated isotopic boundaries and events (20). The time series has a Δt of 2 kyr and extends to 164 kyr BP. Lower in the core the correlations with standard records are unclear.

SPECTRAL ANALYSIS

A spectrum of the $\delta^{18}O$ time series (Fig. 4) reveals that most of the variance is at periods longer than about 20 kyr. A small but significant concentration of variance also occurs at about 12 kyr. The distinct 19 kyr and 23 kyr, and 41 kyr peaks, which are observed in other $\delta^{18}O$ records, are not resolved in this short time series. The somewhat damped signal in stage 3 may account in part for the lack of distinct spectral peaks in this frequency band.

The spectrum of G. bulloides (Fig. 4) also has most of its power in the lower frequencies (>15 kyr). However, the spectrum also displays a concentration of variance in the frequency band from 25 kyr to 21 kyr that is significant at the 0.8 level. Cross-spectra reveal that variations in $\delta^{18}O$ and G. bulloides are significantly coherent (0.80) and in phase (Fig. 4) over the frequency band from 20 kyr to 23.5 kyr (Fig. 4). This coherency exists in spite of the fact that no concentration of variance occurs in the $\delta^{18}O$ spectrum at that frequency band. High coherency also exists over the frequency band from 12.1 to 13.3 kyr, with G. bulloides lagging by about 90°.

COMPARISON OF MONSOONAL AND ORBITAL VARIATIONS

Numerous studies have documented that the periodicities associated with the earth's orbit (19 kyr, 23 kyr, 41 kyr, 100 kyr) are recorded in the isotopic and biotic composition of

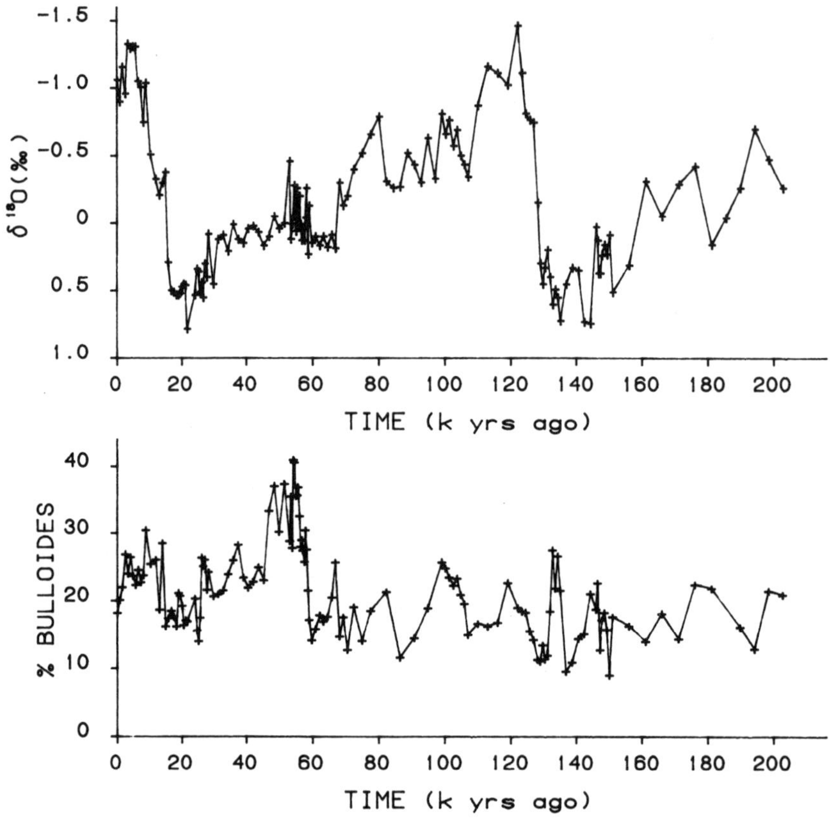

Figure 3 Time series of $\delta^{18}O$ and percent G. bulloides in V34-88. The age model used to construct this time series is given in Table 1. Time interval of samples is 2 kyr.

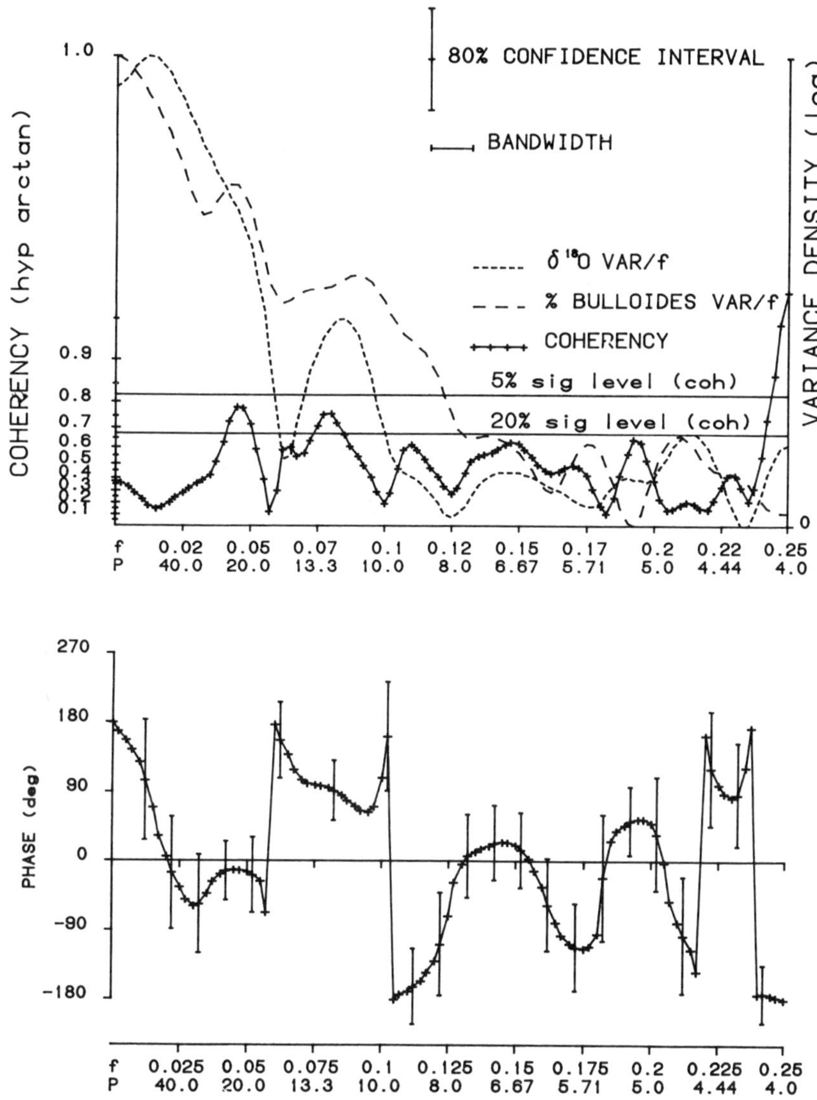

Figure 4 A. Normalized variance spectra of $\delta^{18}O$ (short-dash line) and percent G. bulloides (long-dash line) and the coherency spectrum between $\delta^{18}O$ and G. bulloides (crosses with solid line) for the interval from 0 kyr to 164 kyr. Variance spectra are plotted on arbitrary log scales and coherency spectrum is plotted on a hyperbolic arc tangent. Frequencies are in c/kyr. The sample interval is 2 kyr. Critical values of non zero coherence at the 80% and the 95% levels are shown. B. Phase spectrum of $\delta^{18}O$ vs. G. bulloides.

deep-sea sediments (22,23,24). According to the Milankovitch theory, these statistical correlations are caused by changes in the distribution of solar radiation, which is thought to be one important forcing function of climatic change. Because the orbital variations have known frequencies, amplitudes, and phases, they can be quantitatively compared to regional or local paleoclimatic records. The main purpose of this paper is to compare a geological record of monsoonal variation with astronomical curves of orbital variation.

Two possible strategies might be used to make this comparison. One strategy would be to compare the monsoon record with an insolation curve showing variations in incoming radiation for some particular latitude and season. Instead, I choose to make the comparison with a curve summarizing all of the relevant information about orbital variation. This curve, referred to as ETP (20) is produced by normalizing and summing time series of variations in eccentricity, obliquity, and precession (the latter with sign reversed). This curve is thus a compact description of information about the amplitude and phase of all of the frequencies of orbital variation. If ETP is coherent with a given geologic signal at a particular frequency, then the physical significance of that coherence - and the physical meaning of the observed phase at that frequency - can be analyzed in detail. For the purposes of this paper, the phase of the precession component of ETP is referenced to the earth-sun distance on June 21 (the summer solstice). In other words, the 22 kyr component of ETP is linearly related to variations in all Northern Hemisphere insolation curves for June 21.

The cross-spectra of $\delta^{18}O$ and G. bulloides versus ETP are significantly coherent in the main orbital frequency bands. $\delta^{18}O$ is coherent (0.95 level) with ETP over a broad band from 31 kyr to 18 kyr (Fig. 5). G. bulloides has significant coherence at the 0.80 level over frequencies from 20 kyr to 25 kyr and from 36 kyr to 40 kyr. G. bulloides is also significant at the 0.95 level at 22 kyr to 23 kyr (Fig. 6). At the precessional frequency band, both $\delta^{18}O$ and G. bulloides lag ETP approximately 90° or about 5.5 kyr (Figs 5, 6).

These results show that the time series of monsoonal upwelling has a high linear correlation with solar radiation over the precessional frequency band and confirms the link between orbital variations and the strength of the monsoonal upwelling and the strength of the monsoonal winds. Two questions remain : what is the mechanism that couples monsoonal upwelling to orbital variations ? And, what is the significance of the lag between them ?

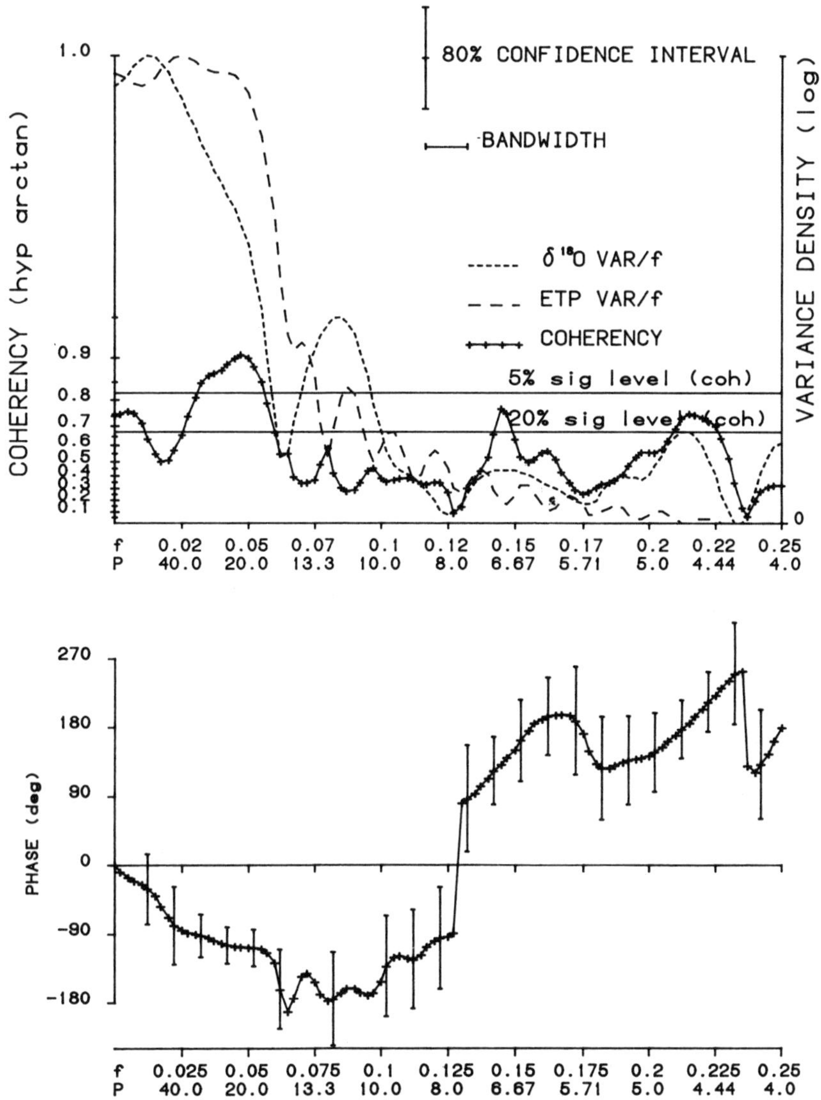

Figure 5 A. Normalized variance spectra of $\delta^{18}O$ (short-dash line) ETP (long-dash line) and the coherency spectrum between $\delta^{18}O$ and ETP (crosses with solid line) for V34-88 over the interval from 0 kyr to 164 kyr. Variance spectra are plotted on arbitrary log scales and coherency spectrum is plotted on a hyperbolic arc tangent. Frequencies are in c/kyr. Sample interval is 2 kyr. Critical values for non zero coherence at the 80% and 95% levels are shown. B. Phase spectrum for $\delta^{18}O$ vs. ETP.

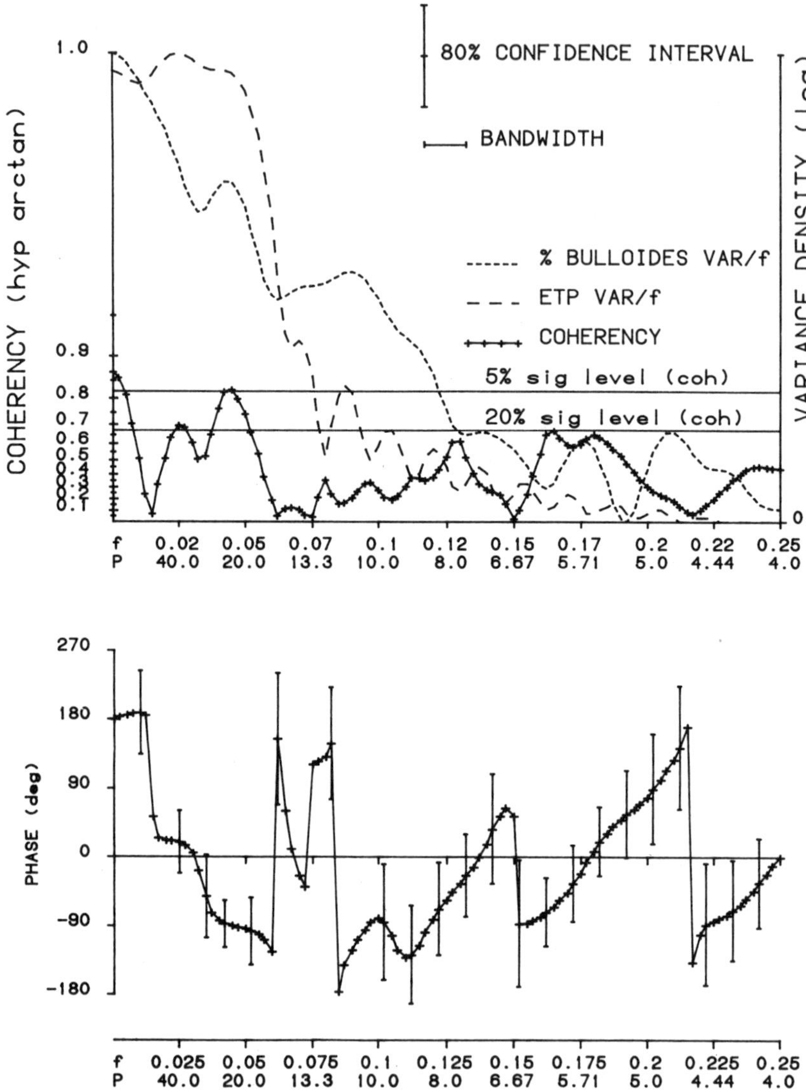

Figure 6 A. Normalized variance spectra of G. bulloides (short-dash line) ETP (long-dash line) and the coherency spectrum between G. bulloides and ETP (crosses with solid line) for V34-88 over the interval from 0 kyr to 164 kyr. Variance spectra are plotted on arbitrary log scales and coherency spectrum is plotted on a hyperbolic arc tangent. Frequencies are in c/kyr. Sample interval is 2 kyr. Critical values of non zero coherence at the 80% and 95% levels are shown. B. Phase spectrum of G. bulloides vs. ETP.

THE CLIMATIC MECHANISM

Thanks to the model experiments of Kutzbach (12) and Kutzbach and Otto-Bliesner (13), the large-scale climatic processes that couple variations in solar radiation and variations in monsoonal upwelling are relatively well known. These numerical simulations clearly demonstrate that increased solar radiation in the Northern Hemisphere summer (about 7% increase at 9 kyr BP) causes increased surface heating of the Tibetan Plateau and central Asia. The enhanced seasonal heating in turn creates lower atmospheric pressure at the land surface and increases the pressure gradient between the Asian continent and the Indian Ocean. Both the increase in summer monsoon surface winds of the Arabian Sea and the associated increase in upwelling intensity along Arabia are a response to the greater pressure gradient.

Although the above view of monsoonal dynamics is an oversimplification, it is consistent with the basic mechanism for the monsoon, it provides a clear link between orbital variations and monsoonal upwelling, and it confirms the Kutzbach model results. Clearly, a variety of complex feedback systems may alter any simple response of the atmosphere and the ocean to increase solar radiation over Asia. In fact, feedback systems probably cause the observed lag of the monsoonal upwelling relative to solar radiation.

THE PHASE LAG

Having identified with some confidence the basic physical mechanism by which secular changes in summer radiation cause changes in monsoonal intensity, and thus accounted for the observed coherency between orbital and geologic signals in the 22 kyr band, we can now turn our attention to the geologic evidence of a phase lag at these frequencies. As described above, the 22 kyr components of the <u>G. bulloides</u> and $\delta^{18}O$ curves both lag precession by about 90° (5.5 kyr). By definition, the phase of the precession curve is linearly related to incoming radiation on June 21. But because modeling and synoptic studies show that monsoon intensity is closely related to mid-summer radiation, the phase angle might be logically defined with respect to changes in radiation intensity on July 21. For the July 21 curve the phase angle is decreased by 30° to 60°. The corresponding time lag is 3.7 kyr. Hence, I conclude that the lag does have physical significance and is probably between 3 kyr and 5 kyr.

What physical mechanism might cause a phase lag of this magnitude in both the global ice sheet response ($\delta^{18}O$) and the local wind field (monsoonal upwelling)? Also, recall that spectra show the phase of the <u>G. bulloides</u> and the $\delta^{18}O$ records are virtually identical (Fig. 4). Unfortunately, the modeling experiments of Kutzbach (12) and Kutzbach and Otto-Bliesner (13) do not answer this question directly. The model results represent only the equilibrium response to a fixed orbital configuration, and do not tell us how the entire climate system, including the monsoon and the cryosphere and their associated time constants, would respond over time to a given change in this configuration (25). Fortunately, the phase relationship between the $\delta^{18}O$ record and orbital variations has been suggested by Imbrie and Imbrie (25) and Imbrie et al. (20) to be a function of the time constant (17 kyr) of the terrestrial ice sheets. They calculate approximately a 5-kyr lag over the precessional frequency band. The growth and decay of the ice sheets controls the ^{18}O time series of the ocean and therefore also controls the $\delta^{18}O$ of the planktic foraminiferal record.

But what feedback or process can retard the monsoonal response relative to its traditional forcing? The Kutzbach experiments (12,13) provide an important clue. Boundary conditions for the first experiment contain no Laurentide ice sheet, whereas the second experiment contains an ice sheet appropriate to the size of this feature at 9 kyr BP. In the second experiment, the intensity of the monsoonal winds over the Arabian Sea and precipitation over India were slightly reduced. This reduction is attributed to down-stream cooling effects of the Laurentide ice mass which inhibited the summer heating of the Asian continent and resulted in a weaker monsoon. This effect excludes the influence of ground albedo, which was specified rather than an interactive component of the model. These experimental results suggest a mechanism for weakening and possibly retarding the monsoonal response relative to the radiational forcing.

A related and most likely candidate for retarding or weakening the monsoon is the variation of albedo over Asia due to the seasonal extent and persistence of snow cover on the Tibetan Plateau and surrounding regions. If seasonal snow covered a larger area or persisted longer into the summer season, the low-level heating of the plateau region would be delayed. This delay in establishing the pressure gradient between the Asian interior and the Indian Ocean would be manifested as a weaker or delayed monsoon. This hypothesis is consistent with the simulation of a weaker monsoon at the last glacial maximum, which was attributed to increased albedo (11). Historical data also show that increased snow cover over Eurasia does lead to decreased precipitation over India (26) and later onsets of the monsoon (27,28).

The similar phase of the $\delta^{18}O$ and G. bulloides records therefore implies a connection between the volume of terrestrial ice sheets and the extent of snow cover over central Asia. Such a relationship is likely, but the details are not clear at this time.

If summer solar radiation and albedo are primary factors in determining the strength of the Indian Ocean summer monsoon, the strongest monsoon should be expected when solar radiation is at a maximum and albedo is at a minimum (Fig. 7). Alternatively, the weakest monsoon should occur when solar radiation is at a minimum and albedo is at a maximum (Fig. 7). This hypothesis is now being tested by varying the extent of snow cover and summer radiation in GCM simulations.

SEASONAL ALBEDO EFFECT

SOLAR RADIATION		
High	**Questionable balance between high energy input and less efficient heating.**	**Strongest Monsoon** **High energy input and an efficient upper tropospheric heating.**
Low	**Weakest Monsoon** **Low energy input and low efficiency of seasonal heating.**	**Questionable balance between low energy input and more effective heating.**

Figure 7 Conceptual interaction of solar radiation and albedo factors to produce strong and weak monsoonal circulations.

SUMMARY

This study shows that the variability of upwelling induced by monsoonal winds has a significant concentration at the 22 kyr frequency band and further that this variance is significantly coherent with orbital variations in the precessional frequency band. The study also reveals a phase lag of monsoonal upwelling relative to solar radiation (orbital variability) that is thought to be significant and caused by the retarding effects of snow cover over Asia, which is probably related to the extent of terrestrial ice sheets.

These results suggest that low- and mid-latitude radiation patterns (the precessional pattern) can force large-scale climatic features, such as the Southwest Monsoon. Here, I should note that no unique latitude of critical response can be identified in the radiation data. This observation rests on the fact that the response lies not in the radiation data as a function of latitude but rather in the interaction of the earth's surface with the incoming radiation. Hence, the great area and great elevation of the Tibetan Plateau and surrounding regions are the key dynamical link determining the strength of the monsoon. This study confirms that solar radiation forces monsoonal circulation during the late Quaternary, but also suggests that other processes such as seasonal snow cover cause the monsoonal response to lag behind solar radiation on time scales of 10^5 years.

AKNOWLEDGEMENT

This research was completed under funding from National Science Foundation Grant ATM 82-13296, Climate Dynamics Section, Division of Atmospheric Sciences and National Grant ATM 80-18897 (SPECMAP) through the Climate Dynamics Section, Division of Atmospheric Sciences ; the Seabed Assessment Program, International Decade of Ocean Exploration, Division of Ocean Sciences ; and the Division of Polar Programs.

REFERENCES

1. CLIMAP : 1976, Science 191, pp. 1131-1137.
2. CLIMAP Project Members : 1981, "Seasonal reconstructions of the earth's surface at the last glacial maximum", Geological Society of America Map and Chart Series MC-36.
3. Prell, W.L. : 1978, International Conference "Evolution of Planetary Atmospheres and Climatology of the Earth", pp. 149-156, Centre National d'Etudes Spatiales, Nice, France.
4. Prell, W.L., Hutson, W.H., Williams, D.F., Be, A.W.H., Geitzenauer, K., and Molfino, B. : 1980, Quaternary Research 14, pp. 309-336.
5. Prell, W.L. : 1983, "Variation of monsoonal upwelling : a response to changing solar radiation", submitted to Fourth Ewing Symposium volume.
6. Street, F.A., and Grove, A.T. : 1979, Quaternary Research 12, pp. 83-118.
7. Van Campo, E., Duplessy, J.C., and Rossignol-Strick, M. : 1982, Nature 296, pp. 56-59.
8. Bryson, R.A., and Swain, A.M. : 1981, Quaternary Research 16, pp. 135-145.
9. Gates, W.L. : 1976, Science 191, pp. 1138-1144.

10. Gates, W.L. : 1976, J. Atmos. Sci. 33, pp. 1844-1873.
11. Manabe, S., and Hahn, D.G. : 1977, J. Geophys. Res. 82, pp. 3889-3911.
12. Kutzbach, J. : 1981, Science 214, pp. 59-61.
13. Kutzbach, J.E., and Otto-Bliesner, B.L. : 1982, J. Atmos. Sci. 39, pp. 1177-1188.
14. Wyrtki, K. : 1971, "Oceanographic atlas of the International Ocean Expedition", National Science Foundation, Washington, D.C., 531pp.
15. Smith, R.L., and Bottero, J.S. : 1977, in : "A Voyage of Discovery", Angel, Martin (Eds), Pergamon Press, Oxford, pp. 291-303.
16. Duing, W. : 1970, "The monsoon regime of the currents in the Indian Ocean", East-West Center Press, Honolulu.
17. Duing, W., and Leetma, A. : 1980, J. Phys. Oceanog. 10, pp. 307-312.
18. Prell, W.L., and Streeter, H.F. : 1982, J. Mar. Res. 40, pp. 143-155.
19. Prell, W.L., and Curry, W.B. : 1981, Oceanologica Acta 4, pp. 91-98.
20. Imbrie, J., Hays, J.D., Martinson, D.G., McIntyre, A., Mix, A.C., Morley, J.J., Pisias, N.G., Prell, W.L., and Shackleton, N.J. : 1984, in : "Milankovitch and Climate", A. Berger, J. Imbrie, J. Hays, G. Kukla, B. Saltzman (Eds), Reidel Publ. Company, Holland. This volume, p. 269.
21. Here, I note that the character of the spectral peak in the G. bulloides record is somewhat sensitive to the age model. This sensitivity results from the relatively short record and the relatively large concentration of variance in stage 3 of the G. bulloides record. A concentration of variance always occurs in this frequency band, but its amplitude is sensitive to the age model. However, high coherency always exists in this frequency band. These data reveal that the upwelling index does contain a significant concentration of variance at about 22 kyr, which is coherent and in phase with the $\delta^{18}O$ record.
22. Hays, J.D., Imbrie, J., and Shackleton, N.J. : 1976, Science 194, pp. 1121-1132.
23. Pisias, N.G., and Moore, T.C. : 1981, Earth Planet. Sci. Lett. 52, pp. 450-458.
24. Ruddiman, W.F., and McIntyre, A. : 1981, Science 212, pp. 617.
25. Imbrie, J., and Imbrie, J.Z. : 1980, Science 207, pp. 943-953.
26. Hahn, D.G., and Shukla, J. : 1976, J. Atmos. Sci. 33, pp. 2461.
27. Lamb, H.H. (Ed.) : 1972, "Climate : Present, Past and Future", Methuen and Company, Ltd., London.

28. Dey, B., and Bhanu Kumar, O.S.R.U. : 1982, Amer. Meteor. Soc. 21, pp. 1929-1932.
29. Shackleton, N.J., and Opdyke, N.D. : 1973, J. Quat. Res. 3, pp. 39-55.
30. Prell, W.L., Imbrie, J., Morley, J.J., Pisias, N.G., Shackleton, N.J., and Streeter, H. : "Graphic correlation of oxygen isotope records : application to the late Quaternary", MS, in preparation.

IMMEDIATE CLIMATE RESPONSE TO ORBITAL INSOLATION: MEDITERRANEAN SAPROPELS AND THE AFRICAN MONSOON

M. Rossignol-Strick

Laboratoire de Palynologie, Faculté des Sciences USTL, F-3400 Montpellier, France,
and Lamont-Doherty Geological Observatory of Columbia University, Palisades, N.Y. 10964, USA

ABSTRACT

During the last 465 kyr, in the tropical Sudanese latitudes of Africa, the heaviest monsoonal precipitation over Ethiopia responded immediately to the seasonal pattern of highest orbital insolation for the northern summer. A record of the African monsoon is found in the subsurface of the East Mediterranean Sea. There, the Nile River discharge during the periods of heaviest monsoon resulted in the formation of organic rich sapropels, well dated by the $\delta^{18}O$ curve of the same cores.

After examination of the present African monsoon meteorology, including the 1972 drought, an "orbital insolation monsoon index" is devised, based on the insolation at tropical latitudes. Its computed variation shows a one-to-one correlation of the Mediterranean sapropels with periods of highest index, thus emphasizing the validity of the Milankovitch theory of climate. The strongest support comes from the correlation of the two sapropels which were formed during glacial periods, with highest values of the insolation index.

Thus, wettest North Tropics have been coeval with large Northern ice-sheets. Therefore, the African monsoon, when triggered by the very highest insolation over the N. Tropics, did overcome the aridifying influence of the ice-sheets, when these were somewhat smaller or less durable than during the Last Glacial Maximum. I suggest that the Late Pleistocene North tropical aridity, prolonged by albedo feed-back, was the consequence of the lowest summer insolation, which occurred at 22 kyr BP in

A. L. Berger et al. (eds.), Milankovitch and Climate, Part 1, 367–368.

the North Tropics, as its influence was cumulated in a still unevaluated balance with the Last Glacial Maximum ice-sheet expansion.

Under the opposite influence of the present minimum state of the N. tropical insolation and the minimum volume of the global ice, the present aridity in Africa is not as severe as during the Late Pleistocene. To which extent the albedo feedback effect will delay the moisture increase warranted by increasing tropical insolation in the millenium years range is open to study.

Southern Hemisphere Tropics display a ∿ 10 kyr dephasing with the N. Hemisphere Tropics for the initiation and peak of the Present Interglacial wettest conditions.

PART II

GEOLOGICAL EVIDENCE FOR LONG-TERM CLIMATIC VARIATIONS AT ASTRONOMICAL FREQUENCIES

SECTION 3 - NON-MARINE RECORDS OF PLEISTOCENE CLIMATE

A PALYNOLOGICAL REGISTRATION OF CLIMATIC CHANGE OF THE LAST 3.5 MILLION YEARS

H. Hooghiemstra

Hugo de Vries-Laboratory, Department of Palynology and Paleoecology, University of Amsterdam, 1018 BX Amsterdam, The Netherlands

ABSTRACT

A 357 m long Colombian palynological record, spanning the last 3.6 m.y., has been correlated with deep sea core V28-239 and with the European stratigraphical climatic subdivision.

The bore hole of Funza is situated almost in the centre of the sedimentary basin of Bogota, Colombia (lat. 4°50'N, long. 74°12'W), where over 800 m of unconsolidated Pleistocene and Pliocene sediments are present. A detailed palynological study of the upper 357 m of sediments has been carried out (1). This paper deals with some important aspects to test versions of the astronomical theory in the time domain.

Time control of the sequence is provided by the dating of 13 of the over one-hundred volcanic ash layers, which occur intercalated with the lake sediments. Fission track (ft) dating and/or K-Ar dating yielded the following 18 dates (in m.y.): 39.62 m(ft): 0.47; 39.62 m(K-Ar, glass): 1.05 ± 0.35; 40.23 m(ft): 0.56; 41.18 m(ft): 0.45; 77.77 m(ft): 0.39; 78.65 m(ft): 0.53; 80.15 m(ft): 0.79; 87.63 m(ft): 0.99 ± 0.08; 104.00 m(ft): 1.34 ± 0.39; 104.00 m(K-Ar, amphibole): 1.48 ± 0.48; 155.40 m(ft): 1.19 ± 0.31; 184.60 m(K-Ar, biotite): 1.99 ± 0.14; 272.03 m(K-Ar, biotite): 0.77 ± 0.46; 272.03 m(K-Ar, plagioclase): 1.99 ± 0.20; 293.80m(K-Ar, biotite): 0.64 ± 1.03; 293.80 m(K-Ar, plagioclase): 3.55 ± 0.93; 325.75 m(K-Ar, biotite): 5.62 ± 0.12 and 325.75 m(K-Ar, plagioclase): 19.92 ± 0.39.

A. L. Berger et al. (eds.), Milankovitch and Climate, Part 1, 371–377.

Some samples were very difficult to date, however, because of the poor quality of the material, while the biotite fractions generally yielded data which are difficult to interpret. The palynological records show a continuous rhythm of climatic cycles and, in conjunction with the stratigraphical column, does not give any evidence for a hiatus. We are, therefore, forced to accept a more or less linear accumulation of sediments. For the above-mentioned reasons the following dates are disregarded and omitted from the calculation of the depth-time curve:
39.62 m: 1.05 ± 0.35; 272.03 m: 0.77 ± 0.46; 293.80 m: 0.64 ± 1.03; 325.75 m: 5.62 ± 0.12 and 325.75 m: 19.92 ± 0.39 (for a detailed argumentation the reader is referred to Hooghiemstra (1)). Using a linear regression, the depth-time curve is

$$y = 16.78 + 85.30x \quad (r^2=0.83). \qquad [1]$$

By omitting also the dates 77.77 m: 0.39 and 78.65 m: 0.53, which are unacceptable on palynological grounds (see Hooghiemstra (1)), the resulting depth-time curve, using a linear regression, is

$$y = 6.30 + 90.10x \quad (r^2=0.84). \qquad [2]$$

Deep sea core V28-239 (2) yielded detailed isotope and paleomagnetic records for the last 2 m.y.. To facilitate a correlation with the Funza record the indicated, but unnumbered stages of core V28-239 were also given a number and the numbering of the not indicated but distinct stages was continued downwards to the bottom of the core (up to stage 64; see Hooghiemstra (1)). The 64 stages of core V28-239 could be correlated with the Funza record (Fig. 1), and the ages of the Funza stage numbers 1-64, as provided by depth-time curve (b), were substituted by the age of the corresponding V28-239 stage numbers, as assigned by interpolation. If the correlation and the V28-239 ages are correct, the resulting depth-time curve (Fig. 2) shows changes in the sedimentation rate of the Funza record. As this curve appears to coincide to a high degree with the depth-time curves of the Funza record, we may conclude that both records exhibit about the same linear character. A similar correlation with deep sea core V16-205 (3) proved to be possible. A tentative correlation with the stratigraphical climatic subdivision of the Quaternary in the Netherlands is provided in Figure 1. The age of the particular depth in the Funza record is substituted by the age of the corresponding boundary of the European subdivision and results in a depth-time curve for the Funza record (Fig. 2) which is also highly congruent with the previous ones. This strongly supports the validity of this correlation.

The Funza record is subdivided into 26 glacial cycles, most of which comprise two pollen zones. Figure 3 shows the duration of the glacial cycles, calculated from the ages provided by depth-time curve (b). A distinct change of the frequency occurs at the 250 m level (ca 2.8 m.y. BP), whereas major changes in the amplitude occur at the 40 m (ca 0.35 m.y. BP) and the 250 m levels. A statistical evaluation of the frequency domain is in preparation.

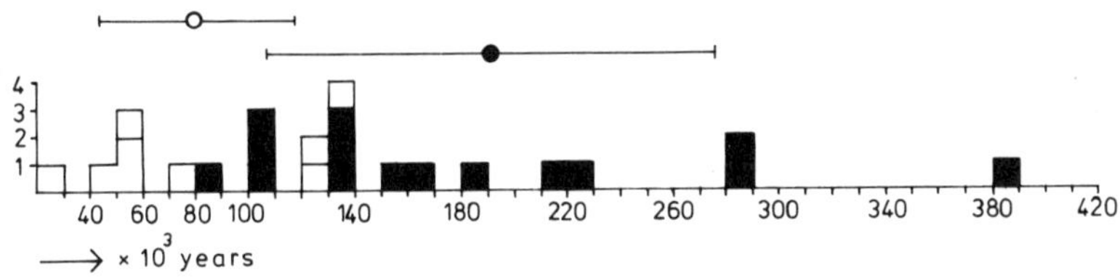

Figure 3 Duration of the glacial-interglacial cycles of the Funza record. Black squares indicate the 15 most recent cycles, covering the last 2.8 m.y. (x = 202 300 years, s = 84 100 years); open squares indicate the Pliocene cycles 16-26 (x = 91 500 years, s = 37 300 years).

ACKNOWLEDGMENT

Dr.L.G. Hogan (Corvallis, Oregon, U.S.A.) and Dr. J. Boellstorff (Tulsa, Oklahoma, U.S.A.) have taken care of the fission-track datings and K-Ar datings, respectively. The Nederlands Foundation for the Advancement of Tropical Research (WOTRO) supported this study financially (Grant W 75-168).

REFERENCES

1. Hooghiemstra, H.: 1984, "Vegetational and climatic history of the high plain of Bogota, Colombia; a continuous record of the last 3.5 million years", Thesis, University of Amsterdam. Diss. Bot., J. Cramer Verlag, Vaduz.
2. Shackleton, N.J., and Opdyke,N.D.: 1976, Geol. Soc. Amer. Mem. 145, pp. 449-464.
3. Van Donk, J.:1976, Geol. Soc. Amer. Mem. 145, pp. 147-163.
4. Zagwijn, W.H., and Doppert, J.W.C.: 1978, Geol.Mijnb. 57(4), pp. 577-588.
5. Berggren, W.A. et al.:1980, Quat. Res. 13, pp. 277-302.

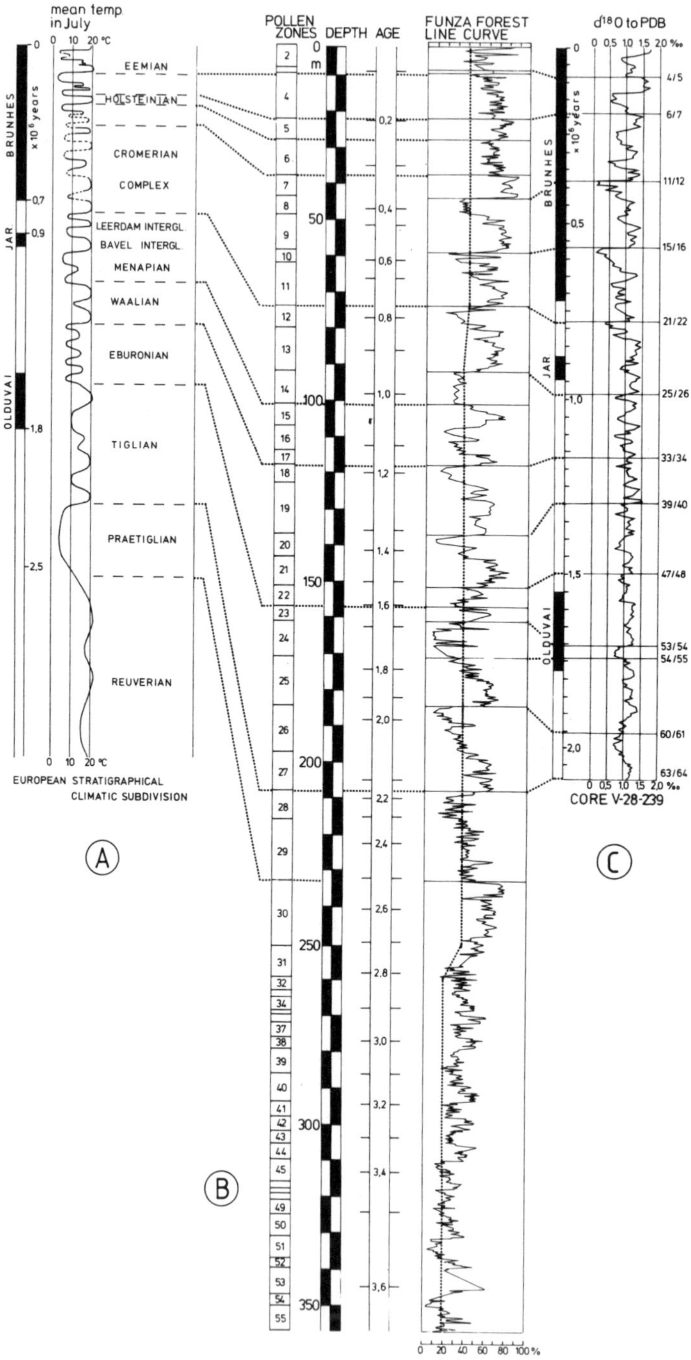
mean temp. in July
0 10 20 °C
BRUNHES
x 10⁶ years
JAR
OLDUVAI
EEMIAN
HOLSTEINIAN
CROMERIAN
COMPLEX
LEERDAM INTERGL.
BAVEL INTERGL.
MENAPIAN
WAALIAN
EBURONIAN
TIGLIAN
PRAETIGLIAN
REUVERIAN
EUROPEAN STRATIGRAPHICAL CLIMATIC SUBDIVISION
A
POLLEN ZONES
DEPTH
AGE
FUNZA FOREST LINE CURVE
0 20 40 60 80 100 %
B
d¹⁸O to PDB
0 0,5 1,0 1,5 2,0 ‰
4/5
6/7
11/12
15/16
21/22
25/26
33/34
39/40
47/48
53/54
54/55
60/61
63/64
CORE V-28-239
C

Figure 1 Correlation of section Funza with deep sea core V28-239 and the European stratigraphical climatic subdivision.

A. European stratigraphical climatic subdivision after Zagwijn and Doppert (4).

B. Section Funza (high plain of Bogotá, Colombia, alt.2547 m a.s.l.)(1). From left to right is presented:
a) a column with numbered pollen zones (2-55); b) the depth scale (m); c) the most reliable approximation of the time scale; d) the curve of the percentage of aboreal pollen (AP) of the general pollen diagram. The intersections of the AP curve with the dotted line indicate the moments in which the forest line passes through the high plain of Bogota and corresponds with a temperature of ca. 10°C at that altitude. The dotted line is situated on the 40% AP level during the pollen zones 2-11 (after a study of recent pollen rain; Grabandt, in prep.), on the 35% AP level during the pollen zones 15-30 (a correction is applied for the absence of *Quercus* (oak)) and on the 20% level during the pollen zones 32-55 (a correction is applied for the absence of *Quercus* and *Alnus* (alder)).

C. Oxygen isotope record V28-239 (2). The levels used for correlation are boundaries between stages (stage numbers are indicated; see also the text).

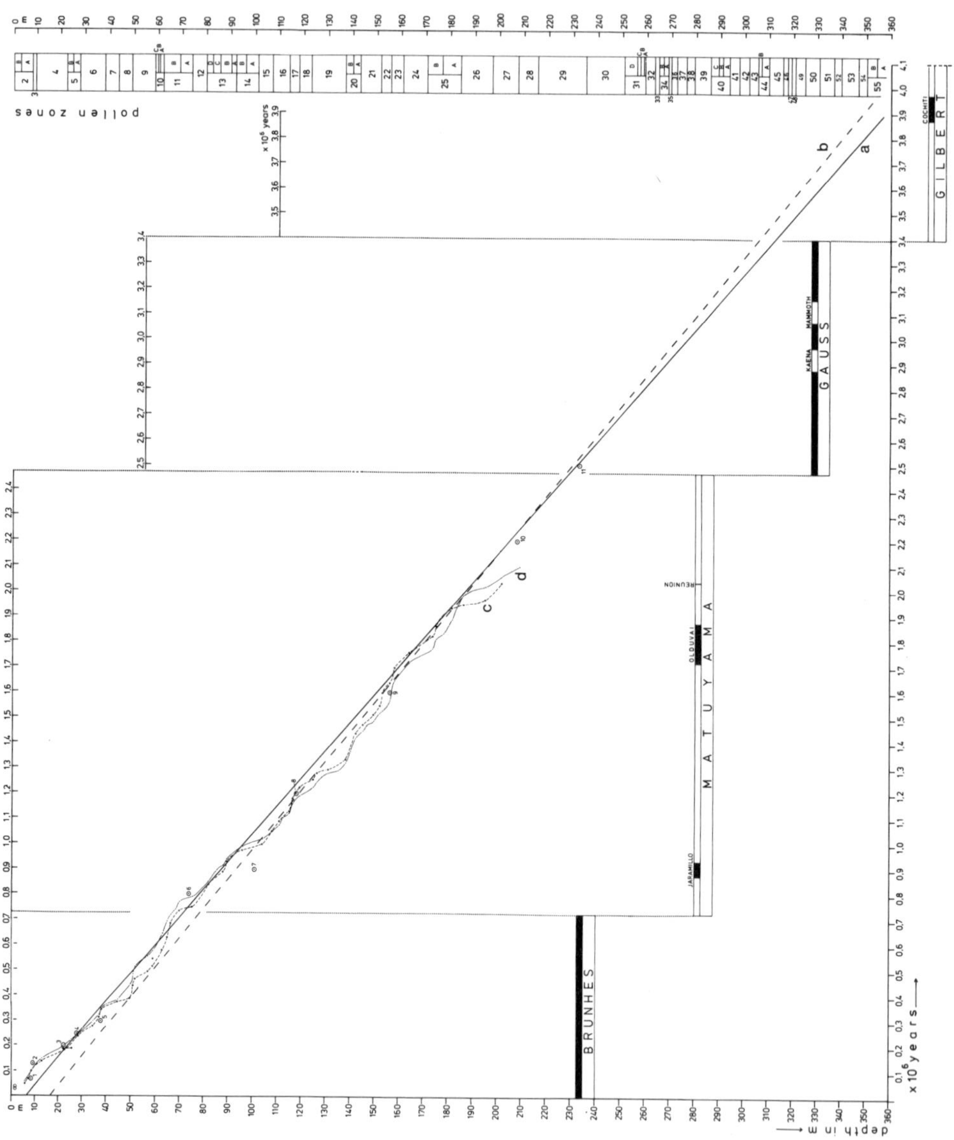
pollen zones
x 10^6 years
depth in m
x 10^6 years
BRUNHES
MATUYAMA
GAUSS
GILBERT
JARAMILLO
OLDUVAI
REUNION
KAENA
MAMMOTH
COCHITI
a
b
c
d

Figure 2 Depth-time curves for the Funza record. (a) : ages according to curves $y = 6.30 + 90.10x$ ($r^2=0.84$) for the Funza record ; (b) : ages according to the curve $y = 16.78 + 85.30x$ ($r^2=0.83$) for the Funza record ; (c) ages for the Funza record according to the correlated levels of core V28-239 (2) ; (d) ages for the Funza record according to the correlated levels of core V16-205 (3) ; $O^1 \ldots O^{11}$ ages for the Funza record according to the correlated levels of the European stratigraphical climatic subdivision. Vertically the depth and Funza pollen zones are indicated. Horizontally the time-scale and paleomagnetic reversals (after 5) are indicated.

IMPLICATIONS OF THE CORAL-REEF RECORD FROM NEW GUINEA CONCERNING THE ASTRONOMICAL THEORY OF ICE AGES

P. Aharon

Department of Geology
Louisiana State University
Baton Rouge, Louisiana 70803, USA

The raised coral-reef terraces in New Guinea yield a detailed record of $^{18}O/^{16}O$ and sea-level changes over the last 100 kyr. The combined utilization of both methods places a significant constraint upon the climatic variables and allows a quantitative evaluation of ice volume and of the temperature factor. The results contribute significantly in resolving the question as to the exact time-relationship between temperature change at low latitudes and ice accumulation at the latitude of the glacial ice caps.

Correspondence between the timing, frequency and intensity of climatic events recognized in the coral-reef record and the insolation intensity shifts predicted by the astronomical theory of ice ages at sensitive high latitudes implies that a cause and effect relationship exists between the two records. Important discrepancies that still persist between the predictions of the theory and the observations may be attributed to interactive processes between terrestrial energy reservoirs.

INTRODUCTION

The cause of climatic changes during the Quaternary demonstrably involves changes in solar radiation which is the primary source of energy on Earth. However, it is doubtful that the recorded climatic changes are due solely to variations in solar radiation. It is more likely that these changes also reflect the relative distribution with time of the energy sinks and the energy sources on Earth that ultimately control the climate. Prominent among the theories which attribute the cause of re-

A. L. Berger et al. (eds.), Milankovitch and Climate, Part 1, 379–389.

peated glaciations to periodic variations of solar radiation resulting from the Earth's orbital elements perturbations (i.e. eccentricity, obliquity and precession) is the Milankovitch astronomical theory of ice ages. The theory is presented in detail in numerous publications (1,2,3,4) and a thorough review of the historical evolution of ideas was recently published by Imbrie (5).

Two types of evidence support the astronomical theory of climatic changes. Firstly, a good correspondence exists between insolation intensities and climatic intensities taken from precisely dated paleoclimatic records (1,6). Secondly, spectral analyses of paleoclimatic time-series obtained from deep-sea cores yield significant peaks at just those frequencies at which insolation shifts occur at the high northern hemisphere latitudes (7). It must be noted, however, that the two types of evidence above implicitly bypass the search for solar-terrestrial-oceanic links in the climatic system and consequently do not answer the questions whether climatic changes were synchronous in time and space or whether there are leads and lags in the systems. These data are critical in evaluating the veracity of the astronomical theory and indispensable in sorting out causes from effects. In order to determine meridional sequences of changes, either extremely accurate time scales for the records of the tropical ocean and the continental ice from various sites, or records of the two systems from one site are required. Limitations imposed by the uncertainties of the dating methods and difficulties in stratigraphic correlation render the former inadequate. The last approach, however, eliminates problems of correlation or inaccuracies of time scales encountered in separate records.

It is the scope of this study to examine aspects of the astronomical theory of ice ages that are subject to verification in the paleoclimatic record from a sequence of late Quaternary coral-reefs in New Guinea. The record, spanning the last 100 kyr, offers distinct advantages in pursuing this investigation because (i) the coral-reefs are well dated by radiometric methods (8,9); (ii) the ice volume and ocean temperature are established independently by sea level data (9,10) and $\delta^{18}O$ measurements, respectively (11); (iii) the coupling of paleosea-level and $\delta^{18}O$ records on one site allows to simultaneously follow the thermal variations at high latitudes (indirectly inferred from sea levels) and in low latitudes (directly recorded by $\delta^{18}O$).

THE CORAL REEF CLIMATIC RECORD FROM NEW GUINEA

Two useful indicators of past changes in climate leave an imprint on uplifted coral reefs. Variations in the temperature of the marginal ocean and in the global ice volume leave a quantitative mark on the $^{18}O/^{16}O$ isotope ratios of biogenic carbonates associated with the reefs. The former changes the degree of ^{18}O-enrichment in the deposited carbonate relative to sea water (12). The latter affects the mean $^{18}O/^{16}O$ in the ocean because polar ice is significantly depleted in ^{18}O (13). The other climatic paleoindicator which leaves a quantitative mark on the coral reefs is the relative sea level. This is because transfer of water in the ocean-cryosphere system causes sea-level changes. The difference between the position of a coral reef unit of known age and present sea level provides a measure of past sea level changes if allowance is made for vertical motions of tectonic origin (9).

The radiometrically dated terraces on the northeast coast of Huon Peninsula, New Guinea (6°05'S; 147°36'E) provide relatively closely spaced "stratigraphic windows" into the past 100 kyr occurring at least every 20 kyr and on several occasions more frequently (Figure 1). The coral reefs, spaced between the modern and the last interglacial (VIIa and VIIb) represent ice-age interstadials and are considered to be time-equivalents of known episodes of the Laurentide ice partial retreats (14).

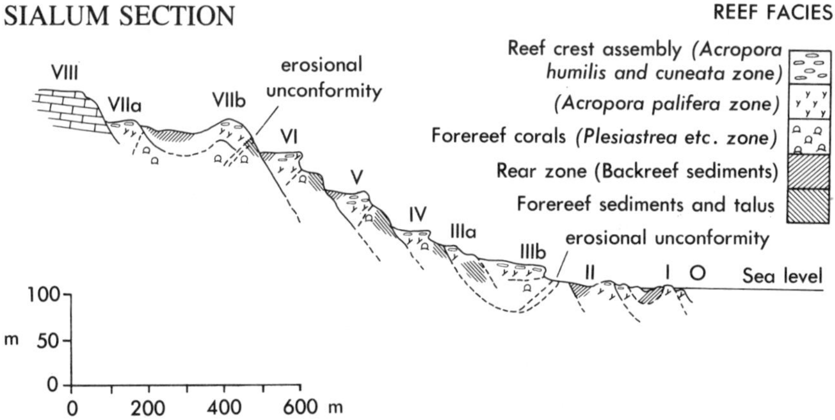

Figure 1 Geological elements illustrated in a cross-section of New Guinea coral reefs at Sialum spanning the last 10^5 years.

A close observation of the sea-level record and oxygen isotope data from the emerged coral reefs in New Guinea (Fig. 2a and b) reveals the existence of "cycles within cycles". The shortest cycle recognized in the sequence is that of an individual reef complex terrace. The duration of a hemicycle is roughly 10 kyr and its amplitude and frequency is related to the glacio-eustatic fluctuations induced by the land-based ice-volume changes. Only the high amplitude part of the cycle is exposed in the coral reef stratigraphy, that is, the portion related to the rise in sea-level. The upper half of the cycle is recognized in both the sea-level and oxygen isotope records, except for around the termination of the last interglacial, where sea-level and the oxygen isotopes moved in opposite directions. This exception is discussed in detail elsewhere (15). The second type of cycle recognized in the sequence has a lower frequency than the first and is present in the oxygen isotope data but not with the same amplitude in the sea-level data. The duration of a hemicycle is roughly 50 kyr and its amplitude and frequency are apparently related to the state of the oceanic thermal regime as shown below. The high amplitude segment of this cycle includes the interglacials and the early interstadials (VI and V), whereas the lower amplitude contains the late interstadials (IV, IIIa, IIIb, II).

ASPECTS OF THE ASTRONOMICAL THEORY OF ICE AGES THAT ARE SUBJECT TO VERIFICATION IN THE CORAL REEF CLIMATIC RECORD

The astronomical theory of ice ages has several distinct attractions which are not matched by other alternative hypotheses. Firstly, it has a built-in time-scale and is therefore subject to testing and verification by various dating methods (6). Secondly, the astronomical elements of the Earth's orbit are the only parameters outside the terrestrial energy reservoirs which can account directly and simultaneously for a decrease of insolation at high latitudes, and an increase of insolation in the tropical regions. This is considered by some (3,16) as a prerequisite during the initial phase of a glacial stage for a continuous transfer of water vapour from the warm tropical oceans to high latitudes in order to feed the growing polar caps on the continents.

The paleoclimatic data from New Guinea are correlated with the predicted seasonal insolation contrast (Figure 2c) at two distinct levels of correspondence. The first order correspondence to be searched for is the chronology of the two records. The second order correspondence equates climatic intensity ($\delta^{18}O$ and sea-level records) with insolation intensity.

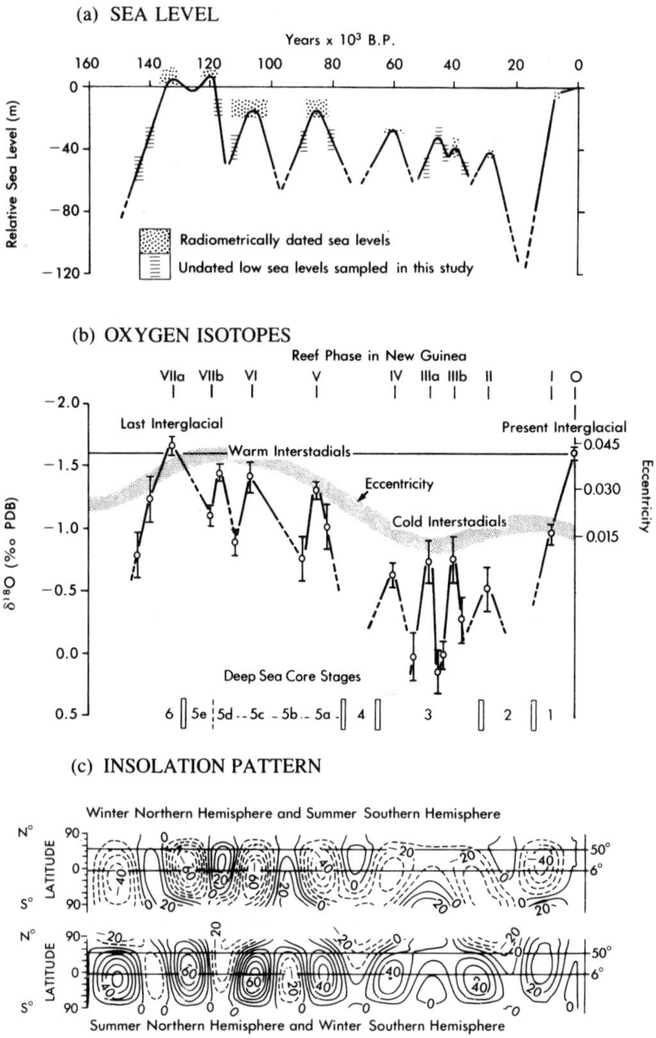

Figure 2 Sea levels, $\delta^{18}O$ and insolation changes over the last 10^5 years. a, b : Reconstructed sea levels and $\delta^{18}O$ records of the ice-age coral reefs (11). Bars represent the standard error estimate. Long term variations in the orbital eccentricity according to Berger (23). c : Deviations of spring and summer insolation from present values in langleys per days (3). The horizontal lines indicate the latitude of the coral reefs (6°S) and the latitude of 50°N considered as a key latitude in the Milankovitch theory (24).

The Chronological Link

A close comparison between the chronology of the northern hemisphere deviations of solar radiation from their present values, and the incidence of reef-building episodes in New Guinea (Fig. 2) illustrates the following points :

(i) The chronology of the reef terraces in New Guinea corresponds to intervals of enhanced seasonal insolation contrast, e. g. higher than present summer insolation and lower than present winter insolation. The agreement is excellent, particulary for the early part of the record (130, 107, 85, 60 kyr) and its last part (29, 10 kyr) but less obvious for reefs IIIa and IIIb around 45 and 40 kyr respectively.

(ii) Reduced seasonal insolation contrast, e. g. lower than present summer insolation and higher than present winter insolation, seems to correspond to the less known chronology of the glacial advances (low sea-levels), such as around 115, 95, 72 and 20 kyr.

The chronological correspondence between the glacial advances and retreats and the time-transgressive seasonal pattern of solar radiation follow closely the Milankovitch theory predictions. This is consistent with ice advances during cooler summer-warmer winter incidence, whereas enhanced seasonality resulting from warmer summer-cooler winter is consistent with ice-retreats. The close agreement suggests strongly that a cause and effect relationship exists between the two records.

Links between Insolation and Climatic Intensity

The second order correspondence implies a direct comparison between the (i) total solar radiation for half a year that contains spring and summer at the latitudes of late Quaternary ice sheets, (ii) paleoclimatic input data reported as $\delta^{18}O$ and sea-level shifts and (iii) temperature values decoupled from the oxygen isotope data according to Aharon (11). The salient results, listed in Table 1, lead to the conclusion that the second order correspondence indicates broad agreement between climatic intensity at low latitudes and insolation intensity at high northern latitudes. Some important divergences between the prediction of the theory and observations are discussed in the following.

During the early interval of the ice age (107-85 kyr), about the entire $\delta^{18}O$ signal can be ascribed to the land-based ice volume variations. However, the proportional importance of the ice volume factor declines dramatically to 30-40% during the late ice age stages (isotope stage 3) and is partly replac-

TABLE 1. Paleoclimatic input data obtained from the ice-age coral reefs in New Guinea and the predicted solar radiation shifts over corresponding time increments.

(1) Isotope Stage	(2) Reef-Phase in New Guinea	(3) Sea-level (m)	(4) $\Delta\delta^{18}O$ reef (‰ PDB)	(5) $\Delta T(\delta)$ (^{o}C)	(6) Excess Ice Volume ($x10^{6}$ km^{3})	(7) % Ice Volume in $\delta^{18}O$	(8) Milankovitch Factor (lyd^{-1})
5e	VIIa	5 to 8	0.3	0	0	100	+45
5c; 5a	VI; V	-13 to -14	0.2 to 0.3	0	5.2 to 5.6	100	+30
3	IV; IIIa; IIIb II	-28 to -42	0.8 to 1.1	-2 to -3	11.2 to 16.8	30 to 40	+5 to +15
1	I	-4 to -7	0.64	-3	1.6 to 2.8	6 to 11	+30

(1) Deep-Sea Cores isotope stages according to ref. 22.

(2), (3) Ref. 11.

(4) $\Delta\delta^{18}O$ reef = $\delta^{18}O$ ancient - $\delta^{18}O$ modern

(5) Isotope temperature difference from present values (28.2^{o}C) according to ref. 11.

(6) A transfer of <u>ca</u> 4 x 10^{6} km^{3} ice in the ocean-cryosphere system causes 10m of eustatic sea level change (11).

(7) $[(-\Delta T\ (\delta) \times 0.23 / \Delta\delta^{18}O) - 1] \times 100$

(8) Deviations of spring and summer solar radiation from present values in langleys per day at the latitude of 50°N (3).

ed by the isotopic effect of a 2-3°C cooling during the interstadial culminations (see Table 1). On this basis the evidence suggests that a considerable lag of ca 40 kyr occurred between the initiation of the continental ice and sea-surface temperature variations in the tropics.

The presence of persistent global cooling following the 72 kyr glaciation, compared to northern hemisphere high-latitude cooling prior to this interval, demands an explanation. On the one hand, the global cooling event which affected both the high and low latitudes coincides with the phase change from high orbital eccentricity to an interval of low orbital eccentricity (Fig. 2b). On the other hand, the Milankovitch theory of ice ages does not attribute any significant role to the orbital eccentricity in climatic change, other than modulating the precessional cycle (2,3). It should be stressed here that the only orbital element which can modify the total solar radiation received by the Earth is the eccentricity; all the other astronomical elements contribute only to a redistribution of that energy at various latitudes (3). In a search for the effect of the eccentricity alone on the insolation it is observed that "e" oscillated between 0.04125 during isotope stage 5 to 0.0125 during isotope stage 3 and Berger (17) has shown that the total variation in solar radiation received by the Earth during this period varied by no more than 0.009%.

Although these variations are small, they are positively correlated with the change in global temperature. It is instructive to note that among the quasi-periodicities found by Hays et al. and Imbrie and Imbrie (7) in the spectral analyses of deep-sea core paleoclimatic data, that of eccentricity (ca 100 kyr component) is significantly more pronounced than the Milankovitch theory predicts. The support from the deep sea-core data for a 100 kyr cycle with reference to eccentricity is particulary important, because the cores span the last half a million years and hence the repetition of this cycle in the geological record is confirmed.

Leads and Lags in the Climate System

In addition to the Milankovitch factor that has been shown to be important, there are two further implicit observations that have to be pointed out in relation to the mechanism of climatic changes. The first is related to conditions leading to glacial termination. As pointed out by Chappell (4), these are indicated by comparing the termination of the last ice age around 11 kyr with the glacial retreats at 107 kyr and 85 kyr. These climatic events stopped well short of complete deglaciation and yet were associated with summer insolation excesses greater than the summer excess of 30 $ly.d^{-1}$, 11 kyr ago. The second point refers to the question of why the warm oceans during the early part of the Holocene did not initiate a resurgence of ice growth, through abundant moisture supply, before the excess ice sheets disappeared entirely.

It is argued here that at least part of the answer can be found by studying the interactions between the thermal characteristics of the oceans and changes in albedo (16,18). For example, in order to accomodate the apparent discrepancies between the insolation levels and the climatic events leading to the present interglacial (the first point above), a negative feedback relationship between the excess glacier size and nourishment can be inferred. A glaciation terminates when on one hand the tropical ocean cools to the point that it cannot supply enough moisture to maintain the glaciers during the winter, and on the other hand the incidence of excess solar radiation during the summer (Milankovitch factor) increases the ablation factor.

In order not to refuel a new glaciation during the early part of the present interglacial (the second point above), Adam (16,18) argued that a significant lag must have occured between the complete warming of the ocean and the disappearance of the ice sheets. On the present argument, the evidence for the presence of surface water around New Guinea that was 2-3°C cooler than present, coupled with atmospheric temperatures a little warmer than present (e. g. no glaciers on the Highlands in New Guinea ref. 19), support the views of Adam (18) and Newell (20) that the heat now stored in the ocean above the thermocline cannot have suddenly appeared at the beginning of the Holocene. Rather it must have been accumulated gradually, and it may still be accumulating as a very slow deepening of the thermocline. This opinion is also supported by evidence from deep-sea cores suggesting a modern warming of the north Atlantic Ocean, following a mid-Holocene that was cooler than the present ocean by 1.5 to 2°C (21).

CONCLUSIONS

The coupling of $\delta^{18}O$ measurements with paleosea-level data obtained from ice-age coral reefs allows to follow simultaneously the thermal variations at high latitudes (indirectly inferred from the glacio-eustatic sea levels) and in the tropics (directly recorded by $\delta^{18}O$ data).

The timing, frequency and intensity of major climatic events over the last 100 kyr indicated by the observations in the coral reef sequence from New Guinea correspond to the predictions of the Milankovitch astronomical theory of ice ages.

Divergences between observations and theory may be ascribed to the effect of the terrestrial energy reservoirs. This assertion is supported by documented temporal divergences between the sea level variations and oxygen isotope data which indicate :

1. That in the early stages of the last ice age, the cooling of the surface ocean at low latitudes lagged significantly behind glaciation at high northern latitudes.

2. The initial warm period was followed by global cooling affecting both high and low latitude oceans.

3. That in the early Holocene the complete warming of the ocean lagged significantly behind the disappearance of the glacial ice caps.

The events outlined above may be attributed to time-dependent variations in the energy gradients between the tropical ocean and the ice caps.

ACKNOWLEDGEMENTS

I thank André Berger for the stimulus in writing this contribution and for his generous assistance with the digital data of caloric insolation variations for the past 140 kyr. Jana Kloss accurately processed several versions of the manuscript.

REFERENCES

1. Broecker, W.S., and Van Donk, J. : 1970, Rev. Geophys. and Space Phys. 8, pp. 169-198.
2. Berger, A.L. : 1978, Bull. Soc. Belge Geologie 87, pp.9-25.
3. Berger, A.L. : 1978, Quat. Res. 9, pp. 139-167.
4. Chappell, J. : 1978, in "Climatic Change and Variability", A.B. Pittock, L.A. Frakes, D. Jenssen, J.A. Peterson and J.W. Zillman (Eds), Cambridge Univ. Press, pp. 211-225.
5. Imbrie, J. : 1982, Icarus 50, pp. 408-422.
6. Mesolella, K.J., Matthews, R.K., Broecker, W.S., and Thurber, D.L. : 1969, J. Geol. 77, pp. 250-274; Chappell, J. : 1973, Quat. Res. 3, pp. 221-236; Kukla, G., Berger, A.L., Lotti, R., and Brown, J. : 1981, Nature 290, pp.295-300.
7. Hays, J.D., Imbrie, J., and Shackleton, N.J. : 1976, Science 194, pp. 1121-1132; Imbrie, J., and Imbrie, J.Z. : 1980, Science 207, pp. 943-953.
8. Veeh, H.H., and Chappell, J. : 1970, Science 167, pp. 862-865.

9. Bloom, A.L., Broecker, W.S., Chappell, J., Matthews, R.K., and Mesolella, K.J. : 1974, Quat. Res. 4, pp. 185-205.
10. Chappell, J. : 1974, Bull. Geol. Soc. Am. 85, pp. 553-570.
11. Aharon, P. : 1983, Nature 304, pp. 720-723.
12. Urey, H.C., Lowenstam, H.A., Epstein, S., and McKinney, C.R. : 1951, Bull. Geol. Soc. Am. 62, pp. 399-416.
13. Epstein, S., Sharp, R.P., and Gow, A.J. : 1970, Science 168, pp. 1570-1572.
14. Stuiver, S., Heusser, C.J., and Yang, I.C. : 1978, Science 200, pp. 16-21.
15. Aharon, P., Chappell, J., and Compston, W. : 1980, Nature 283, pp. 649-651.
16. Adam, D.P. : 1973, J. Res. U.S. Geol. Surv. 1, pp. 587-596.
17. Berger, A.L. : 1977, Nature 269, pp. 44-45.
18. Adam, D.P. : 1975, Quat. Res. 5, pp. 161-171.
19. Hope, G.S., and Peterson, J.A. : 1975, in "Quaternary Studies", R.P. Suggate, M.M. Cresswell (Eds), The Royal Society of New Zealand, Wellington, pp. 155-162.
20. Newell, R.E : 1974, Quat. Res. 4, pp. 117-127.
21. Ruddiman, W.F., Tolderlund, D.S., and Bé, A.W.H. : 1970, Deep Sea Res. 17, pp. 141-155.
22. Emiliani, C. : 1969, J. Geol. 63, pp. 538-578; Shackleton, N.J. : Proc. Roy. Soc. Lond. B174, pp. 135-154.
23. Berger, A.L. : 1977, Palaeogeogr., -climatol., -ecol. 21, pp. 227-235.
24. Imbrie, J., and Imbrie, K.P. : 1979, Ice Ages, Enslow Publ., N.J.

FREQUENCY COMPONENTS OF A GRANDE PILE POLLEN RECORD: EVIDENCE OF PRECESSIONAL ORBITAL FORCING

B. Molfino[1], L.H. Heusser[1], and G.M. Woillard[2]

[1]Lamont-Doherty Geological Observatory of Columbia University, Palisades, N.Y. 10964, USA
[2]Laboratoire de Palynologie, Université Catholique de Louvain, 1348 Louvain-la-Neuve, Belgium. Deceased

Empirical evidence of precessional orbital forcing is documented by pollen power spectra from the Grande Pile bog (France). The record is a composite of three Grande Pile Cores; it represents approximately 130 kyr, substantiated by stratigraphic correlations of indirect radiocarbon stratigraphy, lithostratigraphy and biostratigraphy. Relative abundance variations of herbs (an amalgam), pine and birch pollen are spectrally analyzed. Statistically significant periodicities of 23.4 kyr and 9.2 kyr are shown for herbs; 18.6 kyr, 9.3 kyr and 6.4 kyr are shown for pine; and 15.7 kyr, 8.8 kyr and 5.7 kyr are shown for birch. Only power spectra for herbs and pine pollen show statistically significant peaks at the 95% level. A perturbation study assessing the sensitivity of the spectral results to chronological errors shows only the herbs and pine spectra to be invariant. Their results support the presence of the major components of the precessional periodicities (23 kyr and 19 kyr) as well as possible harmonics of the 19 kyr. These data suggest a nonlinearity in the response of continental vegetation to orbital forcing.

INTRODUCTION

Proxy paleoclimatic data from the geologic record provide verification of the astronomical theory of climatic change proposed by Milankovitch (6). Empirical evidence supporting orbital forcing in two components of the climate system, the oceans and cryosphere, has been documented (3,8,10). These proxy data pri-

A. L. Berger et al. (eds.), Milankovitch and Climate, Part 1, 391–404.

marily consist of estimates of past sea-surface temperature and measurements of global ice volume ($\delta^{18}O$) variations derived from marine-microorganisms preserved in deep-sea sediment cores spanning time intervals of 200 kyr to 700 kyr.

It is the purpose of this paper to determine empirically whether orbital forcing plays a role in the response of yet another component of the climate system, the terrestrial biosphere. Our proxy data is pollen, an indicator of continental vegetation and presumably climate. The pollen record used is from Woillard (15). It is a composite of three Grande Pile Cores, Core I, XIV, and X (268 samples), representing a nearly continuous record over the last ~130 kyr. It is at present one of the few continuous continental pollen data sets available having sufficient chronostratigraphic detail to which spectral analysis techniques can be successfully applied.

This paper briefly describes the Grande Pile data set and its limitations. A stratigraphy is developed and a chronology adopted. Spectral analyses of variations in pollen percentages are presented together with a test assessing the sensitivity of the results to possible chronological errors. Finally the spectral results are briefly discussed with reference to the astronomical theory. We emphasize that neither eccentricity nor obliquity forcing are statistically verifiable due to the limited record length; however, precessional effects and the presence of higher frequency harmonics or combination tones (linear combinations of the orbital frequencies) are verifiable.

DATA

The Grande Pile beat bog is located on the southeastern edge of the Vosges Mountains in northeastern France (47°44'W, 6°30'E, 330m elevation). As this is a relatively large bog (25 ha), pollen variations at this site monitor local and regional vegetation changes (13). We infer these changes to be climatically induced and to reflect the dynamic paleoclimatic history of the adjacent North Atlantic Ocean. Ruddiman and McIntyre (9) have shown the North Atlantic polar front migrates through time with the largest amplitude along the European continental margin. CLIMAP (1) has shown the southernmost position of this polar front to be ~42°N during the last glacial maximum. If we presume that the position of the polar front is controlled by atmospheric circulation, it is reasonable to assume that the Grande Pile site would have responded to these major climatic changes.

Relative abundance variations of three pollen taxa extant in all three cores were analysed; (i) herbs (an amalgam of Artemisia, Rumex acetosella, and Chenopodiaceae); (ii) pine (Pinus); and (iii) birch (Betula) (Fig. 1). Of these, the herbs signal is the simplest to interpret: an increase in herbs implies cooler and dryer open upland conditions (5). The pine and birch signals are more problematical; they may incorporate alpine and forest-tundra species (eg. Pinus cembra and Betula nana) as well as the pioneering species (Pinus sylvestris, P. montana, and Betula pubescens) known to occur in the Vosges region (5,12). These uncertainties inhibit a precise interpretation of their spectra.

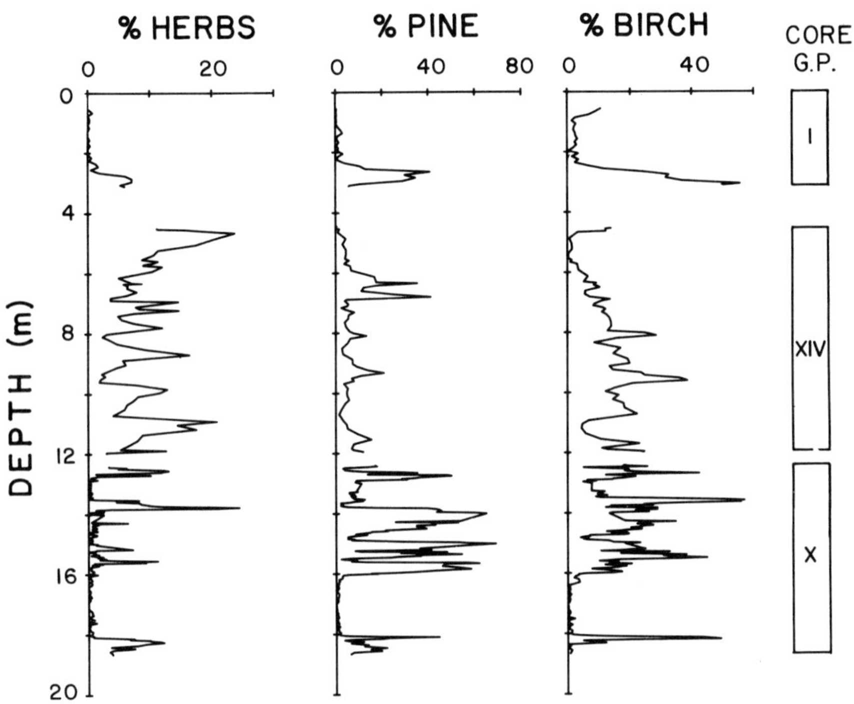

Figure 1 Depth plot of pollen relative abundances of herbs (an amalgam), pine and birch for Grande Pile Cores I, XIV and X. Note core gap positions in the record. Data from Woillard (15).

The simple assumption that pollen relative abundance variations can accurately represent vegetation change is debatable (2,7,11). The suggestion that they be rescaled to produce vegetational units has validity, and indeed should be tried. Currently, however, the necessary vegetation and pollen calibration data set for Northeast France is unavailable. Thus we content ourselves with an analysis of pollen relative abundance variations in a single record. This has the additional limitation of singularity; i.e. no strong conclusions can be made based upon an analysis of a single record (though composed of multiple taxa) at a single site. Although numerous cores have been collected from Grande Pile bog, none are continuous over a complete interglacial-glacial cycle. The percent tree and shrub pollen curve from another composite Grande Pile record (Cores I, XVIII, XIX and X) was published by Woillard and Mook (16) with detailed radiocarbon dates. Although their record is more continuous than this paper's data set over the last interglacial-glacial cycle, the raw pollen data were unavailable for spectral analysis. The published pollen curve is used here for chronostratigraphic correlation only.

CHRONOSTRATIGRAPHY

In order to develop a viable chronostratigraphy, it was necessary : (i) to make basic assumptions regarding the gaps between the cores comprising our composite record, to wit, how much time loss did they represent ; (ii) to use three correlation methods to define datum levels ; and (iii) to test two alternative age models, GP7 and GP8 (having 15 and 16 control points, respectively) (Table 1).

There are two gaps in the composite record. The first, 142 cm long between Cores I and XIV, occurs roughly at the Holocene boundary (oxygen isotope stage 2/1 boundary) and is assumed to represent approximately 2 kyr. This time loss is inferred from radiocarbon dates on Grande Pile Core XVIII which details the Holocene boundary (16) (Fig. 2). The second gap, 47 cm long between Cores XIV and X, occurs roughly at the penultimate interglacial-glacial transition and is assumed to represent a negligible time loss (15).

Approximately two-thirds of our datum levels are defined by one of the following stratigraphic correlation methods :

(i) indirect radiocarbon stratigraphy : C^{14} dates determined on Grande Pile Core XIX (16) are transferred to Core XIV (this paper) by correlating distinct fluctuations of the percent tree and shrub pollen (Fig. 2).

(ii) lithostratigraphy : The distinct lithologic contacts between silty-clay and gyttja in Core X (14) are assumed to occur at the $\delta^{18}O$ stage 6/5 boundary and substage 5 transitions

Table 1. Details of chronostratigraphy: control levels of Grande Pile Cores I, XIV and X for age models GP7 and GP8 (see text for discussion of age models) together with method of age determination. All C^{14} dates are from Woillard and Mook (16). Ages of the $\delta^{18}O$ stage boundaries are taken from SPECMAP (4); ages of the substage 5 transitions are taken from Table 2. Asterisk denotes a relative abundance peak in % birch coinciding with a lithologic change of clay to gyttja. See Figure 2.

G.P. Core	Depth (cm)	GP7 Age Model (KY)	GP8 Age Model (KY)	Method of Age Determination
I	55	1.0	1.0	arbitrarily defined
I	265	9.75	9.75	C^{14} date
I	310	12.0	12.0	correlation of % birch peak to $\delta^{18}O$ 2/1 boundary
XIV	452	14.0	14.0	assumed 2 KY time gap between Cores I and XIV
XIV	634	29.74	29.74	C^{14} controlled correlation of % tree and shrub curves
XIV	810	40.00	40.00	C^{14} controlled correlation of % tree and shrub curves
XIV	930	49.80	49.80	C^{14} controlled correlation of % tree and shrub curves
XIV	1070	59.0	59.0	correlation of % birch peak to $\delta^{18}O$ 4/3 boundary
XIV	1195	72.0	70.3	interpolated
X	1242	72.0	70.3	assumed 0 KY time gap between Cores XIV and X
X	1275.5	---	73.3	adjusted C^{14} date (analytical error added)
X	1357.5	84.0	84.0	* lithologic change correlated to $\delta^{18}O$ 5b/5a transition
X	1382.5	92.6	92.6	lithologic change correlated to $\delta^{18}O$ 5c/5b transition
X	1547.5	101.9	101.9	* lithologic change correlated to $\delta^{18}O$ 5d/5c transition
X	1562.5	112.0	112.0	lithologic change correlated to $\delta^{18}O$ 5e/5d transition
X	1817.5	128.0	128.0	* lithologic change correlated to $\delta^{18}O$ 6/5 boundary

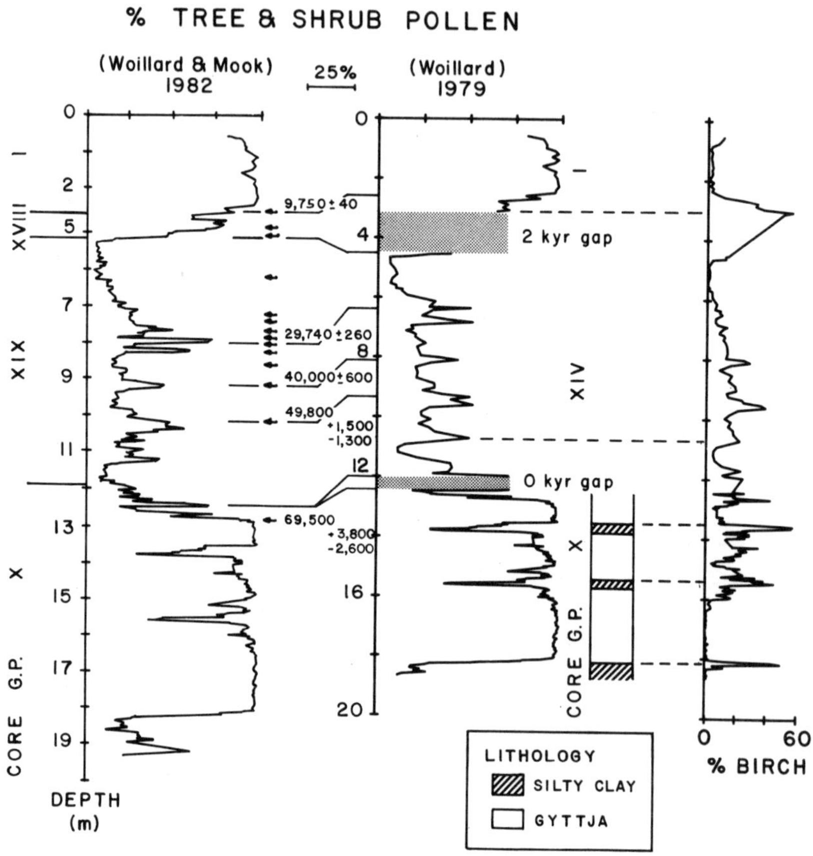

Figure 2 Stratigraphic correlations used to define stratigraphy of Grande Pile Cores I, XIV and X: (i) indirect radiocarbon dating is shown in solid horizontal lines; arrows denote C^{14} dates from Woillard and Mook (16) with specific dates used in age models GP7 and GP8 indicated; (ii) lithostratigraphy is shown for Core X, with contacts correlated to $\delta^{18}O$ substage 5 transitions; (iii) biostratigraphy is shown in dashed horizontal lines; correlation of peak abundances of birch at climatic ameliorations during $\delta^{18}O$ stage 5 is used as an analogue for younger deglaciations ($\delta^{18}O$ 4/3 and 2/1 boundaries).

(5e/d, 5d/c, 5c/b, 5b/a) (Fig. 2). As the average sample spacing is 0.5 kyr (see RESULTS), it seems plausible to assume that the sedimentary change occured within this timespan. The silty-clay layers themselves correspond to low percentages of arboreal pollen. (We are aware, however, that this interpretation requires that sedimentation rates differ between the cold substage 5 intervals (i.e. 5b and 5d) and younger glacial intervals (i.e. stages 2 and 4)).

(iii) biostratigraphy : These correlations are based solely on the relative abundance variations of birch pollen. It is noted that at climatic ameliorations during oxygen isotope stage 5 (the 6/5, 5d/c and 5b/a boundaries) the lithologic change of silty-clay to gyttja in Core X is coincident with a relative abundance peak in birch pollen. This fact was used as an analogue to corroborate the placement of the $\delta^{18}O$ stage 4/3 boundary at 1070 cm in Core XIV and the $\delta^{18}O$ stage 2/1 boundary at 310 cm in Core I, for which lithological information was lacking.

In addition to these correlations, two C^{14} dates are available in the sections of cores being studied: 9 750±40 Y at 265 cm in Core I, and 69 500 + 3 800/-2 600 Y at 1275.5 cm in Core X (16). The latter is a carbon enrichment date. Two age models, GP7 and GP8, are proposed, differing only in their inclusion or exclusion of the 69.5 kyr date (Table 1). Age model GP7 excludes this date and hence linearly interpolates the bottom of Core XIV (1195 cm) using the 59 kyr and 84 kyr datums. Age model GP8 includes the date but assumes it to be valid in its maximum age; hence its analytical error of +3.8 kyr is added giving an adjusted age of 73.3 kyr. The bottom of Core XIV is then linearly interpolated using the 59 kyr and 73.3 kyr datums. Either age model is plausible.

The chronology is based upon the SPECMAP time scale (4). Ages of the oxygen isotope stage boundaries are taken direct from Imbrie et al. (4); ages for the substage 5 transitions were obtained by applying the SPECMAP datums of 5.1, 5.3 and 5.5 (corresponding respectively to the lightest $\delta^{18}O$ values in substage 5a, 5c and 5e) to the oxygen isotope records in four deep-sea cores and linearly interpolating the ages for each of their substage transitions (Table 2). The average ages are used in both age models.

RESULTS

The original data (268 samples) are transformed into time-series via the chronostratigraphies given in Table 1, and then resampled at 0.5 kyr intervals by linear interpolation. The

Table 2 Determination of ages of $\delta^{18}O$ substage 5 transitions: average of interpolated ages obtained by applying the SPECMAP time scale for datums 5.1, 5.3 and 5.5 (representing the lightest $\delta^{18}O$ values of stage 5a, 5c and 5e, respectively) to each core (see (4)).

Geographic Area	Core	Ref.	Interpolated Ages (kyr) 5b/5a	5c/5b	5d/5c	5e/5d
Pacific	V19-29	(10)	86.3	93.6	101.5	111.7
N. Atlantic	V30-97	(10)	83.1	93.5	102.8	112.6
Eq. Atlantic	V30-40	(17)	82.9	91.7	101.8	112.7
S. Atlantic	RC13-228	(18)	83.7	91.6	101.5	111.1
	AVERAGE		84.0 ±1.6	92.6 ±1.1	101.9 ±0.6	112.0 ±0.8

Table 3 Perturbed age models: produced by randomly perturbing age model GP7 within the confines of its chronological errors (see text for details).

Age Model GP7 (cm)	(kyr)	Perturbed Age Models (kyr) GP7-1	GP7-2
55	1.0	1.0	1.0
265	9.75	9.70	9.97
310	12.0	13.1	11.6
452	14.0	15.1	13.6
634	29.74	29.64	29.69
810	40.00	40.19	40.28
930	49.80	48.84	49.79
1070	59.0	60.2	57.1
1195	72.0	72.1	70.9
1242	72.0	72.1	70.9
1357.5	84.0	83.1	83.6
1382.5	92.6	91.6	93.8
1547.5	101.9	101.3	103.9
1562.5	112.0	113.2	113.5
1817.5	128.0	125.8	127.5

resulting 261 samples are spectrally analyzed (Fig. 3) using the Blackman-Tukey technique as described in Hays et al. (3). As both age models show nearly parallel results for periodicities greater than 5 kyr (Fig. 3, Table 4), we discuss them together. The periodicities of statistically significant spectral peaks in Figure 3 are averaged results from the two age models.

Table 4 Periodicities (P) and corresponding percent of total variance (%) of statistically significant (80% level) peaks in power spectra of herbs, pine and birch using four age models. Power spectra plotted in Figures 3 and 4. Asterisk denotes statistical significance at the 95% level.

	Herbs		Pine		Birch	
Age Model	P	%	P	%	P	%
GP7	* 23.4	49.0	* 18.5	30.5	15.3	21.3
	* 9.3	13.2	* 9.2	13.9	8.7	11.9
			* 6.3	12.3	5.6	3.9
GP8	* 23.5	49.8	* 18.7	29.9	16.0	26.6
	* 9.2	13.5	* 9.4	14.2	8.8	10.6
			* 6.4	12.3	5.7	4.2
GP7-1	* 23.4	50.0	* 18.7	31.7	15.3	23.1
	* 9.4	14.5	9.6	9.9		
			6.7	15.0		
GP7-2	* 23.6	50.8	* 18.9	26.2	17.8	24.3
	* 9.3	10.6	* 9.5	14.8	9.8	13.4
			* 6.4	12.2	5.6	4.1

Herbs spectra show the strongest concentration of power at the 23.4 kyr periodicity, accounting for nearly 50% of the total variance. The 9.2 kyr periodicity accounts for 13% of the variance. Both are statistically significant at the 95% level.

Pine spectra show three statistically significant (95%) peaks: 18.6 kyr, 9.3 kyr and 6.4 kyr. These account for approximately 30%, 14% and 12% of the total variance, respectively.

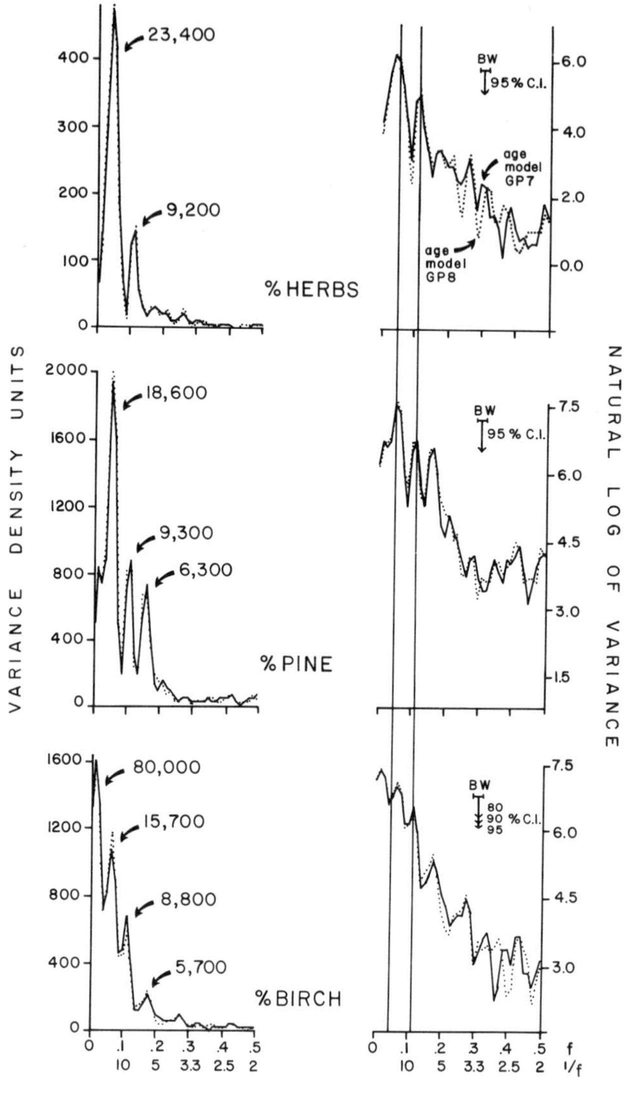

Figure 3 High resolution spectra of pollen relative abundance data from Figure 1, shown for age models GP7 (solid line) and GP8 (dotted line). Plots are of variance density units and ln of variance versus frequency (given to twice the nyquist frequency). Periodicities of statistically significant peaks shown are averages of the two age models (Table 4). Confidence intervals (C.I.) and bandwidths (BW) shown. Spectral techniques follow those described in Hays et al. (3) with n=261, m=80 and Δt=0.5 kyr. Solid vertical lines correspond to periodicities of 23 kyr and 9.3 kyr.

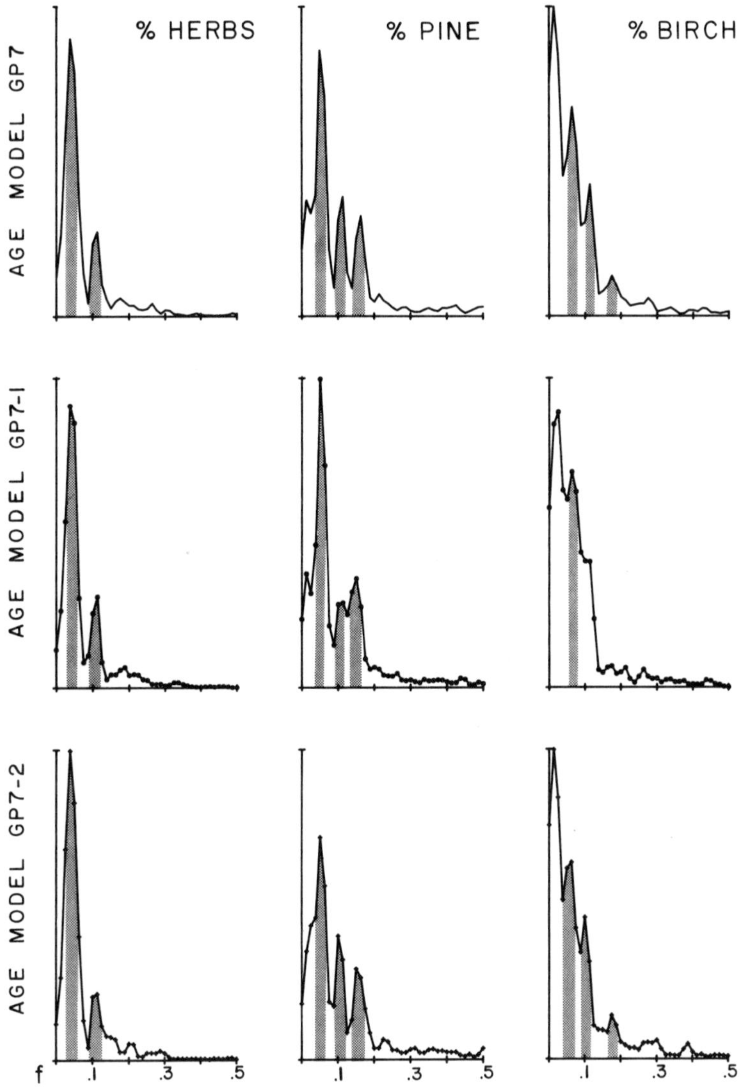

Figure 4 Comparison of high resolution variance density spectra produced using perturbed chronologies (age models GP7-1 and GP7-2) of age model GP7. Pollen spectra plotted as frequency versus equivalent variance scales (maximum values are 525, 2250 and 1600 variance density units for herbs, pine and birch, respectively) for each age model. Central frequency and variances of shaded spectral peaks are given in Table 4.

Birch spectra have power concentrated at 5.7 kyr, 8.8 kyr, 15.7 kyr and at lower frequencies (although shown to be 80 kyr, this is statistically irrelevant because of the shortness of our record). The corresponding variances are approximately 4%, 11%, and 23% respectively. The 15.7 kyr and 5.7 kyr peaks are statistically significant at the 90% level, the 8.8 kyr peak at the 80% level.

The herbs and pine spectra both contain at least one of the major precessional components (23 kyr and 19 kyr), and a higher frequency of $\sim$9.3 kyr, possibly the second harmonic of the 19 kyr. The 6.4 kyr periodicity of pine is suggestive of the second harmonic of 13 kyr, the combination tone of the 19 kyr precession and 41 kyr obliquity periodicities; it might also simply represent the third harmonic of the 19 kyr precessional periodicity. If the latter, the variations of pine pollen at Grande Pile would show a classic nonlinear effect to precessional forcing; i.e. its spectrum clearly defines the first, second and third harmonics of the 19 kyr precessional component. This could be due to a systematic migration lag of pine. The birch spectra do not contain the primary orbital frequencies of precession. However, the significant spectral peaks are suggestive of combination tones or harmonics of the primary orbital frequencies. The 15.7 kyr periodicity may be a linear combination of the 19 kyr precessional and 96 kyr eccentricity periodicities; the 5.7 kyr may represent a higher order harmonic of the 23 kyr precession. These periodicities infer a nonlinearity in the response of continental vegetation to primary orbital forcing.

How sensitive are these spectral results to chronological error? To assess this, we arbitrairly selected age model GP7 and randomly perturbed its chronology to produce two alternate age models, GP7-1 and GP7-2, within the confines of chronological error (Table 3). By chronological error we mean the analytical errors associated with each C^{14} date and the estimated SPECMAP time scale error (±3 kyr) (4) associated with each $\delta^{18}O$ boundary. A random number table was used to add or subtract proportions (ranging from 1%-99%) of these associated errors for each datum. Time gaps between cores and the age of the top of core I remained constant.

Two prominant results are shown (Fig. 4, Table 4). (i) The herbs and pine spectra are invariant. Although their percent variance values do differ, the periodicities of their central frequencies differ by at most 0.4 kyr. All peaks are statistically significant at the 95% confidence level with the exception of the 9.6 kyr and 6.7 kyr periodicities of the pine spectra described using age model GP7-1 (Table 4). (ii) The birch spectrum is most sensitive to induced chronological errors. The averaged

15.7 kyr periodicity is seen to have a perturbed range of 15.3 kyr to 17.8 kyr; the averaged 8.8 kyr periodicity, a perturbed value as high as 9.8 kyr. Hence the birch spectral results are equivocal; the cause may be the diversity of species comprising the birch pollen signal.

CONCLUSIONS

The major components of the precessional index (23 kyr and 19 kyr) are present in pollen power spectra from the Grande Pile : the herbs spectra show periodicities of ~23.4 kyr and ~9.2 kyr; the pine spectra show periodicities of ~18.6 kyr, ~9.3 kyr and ~6.4 kyr. These periodicities are statistically significant at the 95% confidence level and are invariant with respect to induced chronological errors in our chronostratigraphy. The ~9.3 kyr and ~6.4 kyr periodicities are suggestive of the second and third harmonics of the 19 kyr component of the precessional index. Hence, these results imply a nonlinearity in the response of continental vegetation to precessional orbital forcing.

ACKNOWLEDGMENTS

We thank Drs. Andrew McIntyre, Joseph Morley and Thompson Webb III for their critical reviews. This research was supported by National Science Foundation grants ATM80-19253S (SPECMAP) through the Climate Dynamics Section, Division of Atmospheric Sciences, the Seabed Assessment Program, International Decade of Ocean Exploration, Division of Ocean Sciences, and grant DEB81-09916 through the Division of Environmental Biology. Lamont-Doherty Geological Observatory contribution number 3493.

REFERENCES

1. CLIMAP Project Members, Coordinator and Compilation, A. McIntyre : 1981, Geo. Soc. Amer. Map and Chart Series, MC-36, R. Cline (Ed.).
2. Davis, M.B. : 1963, Amer. J. Sci. 261, pp. 897-912.
3. Hays, J.D., Imbrie, J., and Shackleton, N.J. : 1976, Science 194, pp. 1121-1132.
4. Imbrie, J., Shackleton, N.J., Morley, J.J., Hays, J.D., Martinson, D.G., McIntyre, A., Mix, A.C., Pisias, N.G., and Prell, W.L. : 1984, in : "Milankovitch and Climate", A. Berger, J. Imbrie, J. Hays, G. Kukla, B. Saltzman (Eds), Reidel Publ. Company, Holland. This volume.
5. Janssen, C.R. : 1981, Rev. Palaeobotany and Palynology 33, pp. 183-313.

6. Milankovitch, M. : 1941, Royal Serb. Acad., Spec. Bubl. 133, pp. 1-633.
7. Moore, P.D. : 1980, in : "Studies in the Lateglacial of North-West Europe", J.J. Lowe, J.M. Gray and J.E. Robinson (Eds), Pergamon Press, Oxford, pp. 151-155.
8. Morley, J.J., and Hays, J.D. : 1981, Earth and Planet. Sci. Lett. 53, pp. 279-295.
9. Ruddiman, W.F., and McIntyre, A. : 1977, J. Geophys. Res. 82, pp. 3877-3887.
10. Ruddiman, W.F., and McIntyre, A. : 1981, Science 212, pp. 617-627.
11. Solomon, A.M., West, D.G., and Solomon, J.A. : 1981, in : "Forest Succession", D.G. West, H.H. Shugart, and D.B. Botkin (Eds), Springer-Verlag, New York, pp. 154-177.
12. Walter, H. : 1973, "Vegetation of the Earth", Springer-Verlag, New York.
13. Webb III, T., Laseski, R.A., and Bernabo, J.C. : 1978, Ecology 59, pp. 1151-1163.
14. Woillard, G.M. : 1978, Quaternary Research 9, pp. 1-21.
15. Woillard, G.M. : 1979a, Nature 281, pp. 558-562.
Woillard, G.M. : 1979b, Bull. Soc. Belg. Geol. 88, pp. 51-69.
16. Woillard, G.M., and Mook, W.G. : 1982, Science 215, pp. 159-161.
17. Unpublished data of Alan Mix, L-DGO.
18. Unpublished data of Nicholas J. Shackleton, Cambridge. Morley, J.J. and Shackleton, N.J. : 1984, in "Milankovitch and Climate", A. Berger, J. Imbrie, J. Hays, G. Kukla, B. Saltzman, (Eds), Reidel Publ. Company, Holland. This volume.

THE PALEOCLIMATOLOGICAL CONSTITUENTS OF PALEOTEMPERATURE IN LAKE BIWA

S. Kanari[1], N. Fuji[2], S. Horie[3]

[1]Department of Geophysics, Hokkaido University
[2]Department of Earth Science, Kanazawa University
[3]Institute of Paleolimnology and Paleoenvironment on Lake Biwa, Kyoto University

ABSTRACT

Periodic constituents of the newly construed time series of paleotemperature fluctuations were analyzed by the maximum entropy method (MEM) developed by Burg (1). The peaks of the paleotemperature spectrum 104 kyr, 44 kyr and 25 kyr correspond well to Milankovitch's three periods of insolation variations. The predicted future temperature trend descends by about 2.4°C in the next 15 000 years.

INTRODUCTION

In 1971, a 200 m-long continuous sediment core was obtained in Lake Biwa, Japan by S. Horie. The core has been analyzed by many specialists in the fields of geology, geophysics, sedimentology, geochemistry, micropaleontology and other. Fuji (2) has derived a paleotemperature curve from the palynological data using a rigorous inversion method for transformation of pollen composition in the sediment core into paleotemperature fluctuations. Fuji's paleotemperature curve has been originally plotted as a function of core depth.

TRANSFORMATION OF POLLEN COMPOSITE SPECTRA INTO PALEOCLIMATIC TIME SERIES

The 200 m-long boring core was sampled at 5 m intervals for pollen analysis. Afterwards, sampling intervals were contracted

A. L. Berger et al. (eds.), Milankovitch and Climate, Part 1, 405–414.

to every 25 cm in the upper 110 m of the core (5). About 50 genera and/or families of fossil pollen grains found in the core samples were identified by Fuji and pollen diagrams have been constructed. In order to transform the pollen diagrams into a numerical index of climatic variation, the warmth index (6) and the pollen-distribution in modern deposits (7) were used. With the help of the warmth index, the pollen diagrams were divided into five climatic "levels", that is, Subpolar level, Cool Temperate level, Temperate level, Warm Temperate level and Subtropical level.

The analysis has shown that in the mid-latitudes, the environment ranged from Subpolar to Temperate levels.

The original core contains six horizons of volcanic ashes at the depth of 37, 62, 82, 99, 110 and 181 m. Nishimura and Yokoyama (3) have determined the ages of the above six ash horizons by the fission-track method. In 1978, Kanari has derived a simple consolidation model applicable to the deep lake bottom sediment assuming a constant sedimentation rate, which relates the depth in the sediment core to the age of the sediment by the following solution (4) :

$$Z(t) = H_0(1-\sigma_0)t + \frac{H_0\sigma_0}{\alpha}[1 - \exp(-\alpha t)] \qquad [1]$$

where t is the age of the sediment at depth Z, α the compression coefficient of sediment, H_0 the sedimentation rate at the lake bottom in cm/year, and σ_0 the porosity of sediment at the lake bottom surface.

The bulk coefficients, $H_0\sigma_0/\alpha$ and $H_0(1-\sigma_0)$, were determined on the basis of the fission-track data, and the sedimentation rate H_0 near the boring site was estimated to be 0.2 cm/year (8). Consequently, we obtained σ_0=0.83 and α=6.7x10^{-5} year^{-1}. Thus, the depth-to-time inversion curve was obtained, (Fig. 1 solid curve), by means of which we can transform Fuji's depth-based paleoclimatic curve into the paleoclimatic time series.

INTERPOLATION OF SAMPLING POINTS

The paleoclimatic curve by Fuji is originally made from a number of discrete sampling points spaced at unequal intervals. These were initially distributed at intervals of 5 m, but later samplings at every 25 cm interval and many additional supplemental samplings were made throughout the whole core length.

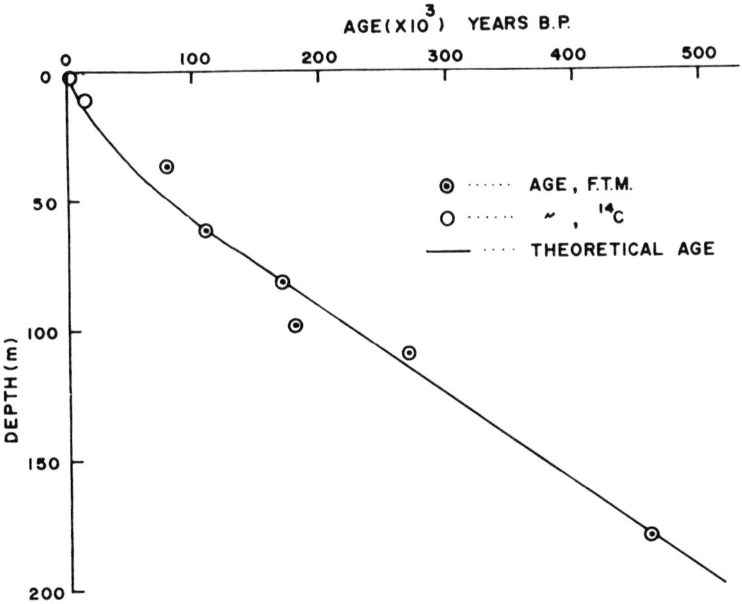

Figure 1 The solution of Kanari's consolidation model that relates the depth of sediments and its age (solid curve). Open circles are ages estimated by the ^{14}C method and dotted circles are ages estimated by the fission-track method (4).

The core length of 25 cm corresponds to the age interval of 250-500 years in the shallow part and 750-1 500 years in the deeper part of the core. For the sake of the power spectrum analysis, points at discrete, unequal intervals in the paleoclimatic curve were smoothly connected by the multi-point interpolation method and processed as 200 observation points of the paleoclimatic time series at every 2 500-year interval. The reconstructed climatic curve thus obtained is shown in Figure 2.

POWER SPECTRUM BY MEM

The power spectrum of the paleotemperature time series was calculated by a new spectral estimation method called the Maximum Entropy Method (MEM) which was presented by Burg (1). This technique enables us to calculate power spectra with comparatively high resolution even for short data series, frequently encountered in geological and geophysical records.

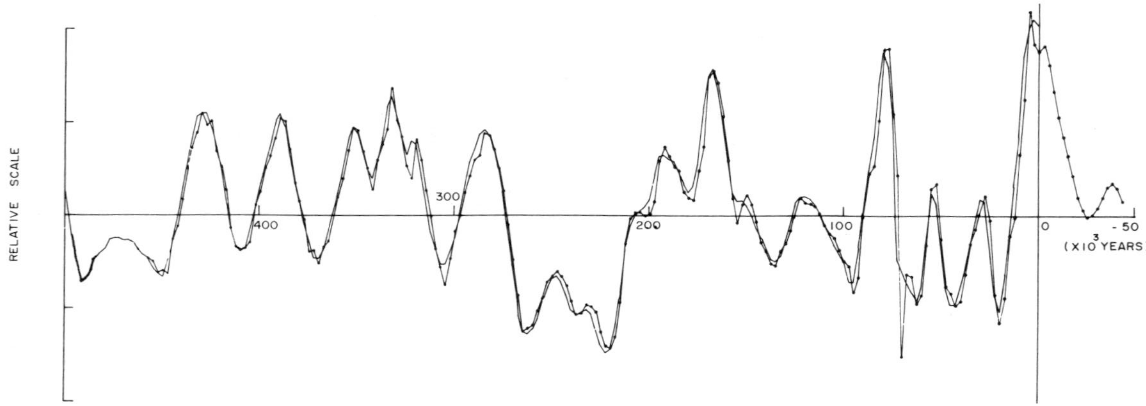

Figure 2 Time series of paleoclimatic variations during the last 500 kyr and the coming 50 kyr based on the 200 m-long core from Lake Biwa (solid curve). The abscissa in the curve were scaled by Kanari's consolidation model (4). The solid curve with black circles shows one-step-ahead autoregressive predictions by the 21 lags predictions error filter. In the past section of the curve (left-hand side of the origin of the time axis), the predicted value at every prediction step was replaced by the actual data before the next step prediction was made.

Let the Fourier transform of a time series x(t) be X(ω). If Z(ω) is the transfer function of a filter that whitens x(t), then, the power of x(t) can be given by

$$|X(\omega)|^2 = \frac{Q^2}{|Z(\omega)|^2} \qquad [2]$$

where Q is a constant noise amplitude.

Whitening of a given process can be accomplished by means of a prediction-error filter.

An estimate of the power spectrum for a discrete stochastic process is therefore given by

$$P(f) = \frac{P_{M+1}}{\left| 1 + \sum_{k=1}^{M} a_{Mk} \, e^{-i2\pi fk} \right|^2}$$

where P_{M+1} is the mean output power of the (M+1) point prediction-error filter, whose first coefficient is made equal to unity (9), and the prediction-error filter coefficient a_{Mk}'s can be determined by the Levinson algorithm and Akaike's method.

The estimated power spectrum of the paleotemperature time series is shown in Figure 3. The power is presented in a relative scale and the abscissa is frequency in 10^{-6} cycles/year unit (cpy).

The largest power is concentrated between the frequency range of 1.2×10^{-5} to 8×10^{-6} cpy, and the second and the third peaks are in the frequency ranges of $20 \sim 26 \times 10^{-6}$ cpy and $38 \sim 42 \times 10^{-6}$ cpy respectively. A comparatively lower peak is isolated at $76 \sim 82 \times 10^{-6}$ cpy.

The above mentioned frequency bands correspond to the periods of 125~83 kyr, 50~38 kyr, 26~24 kyr and 13.2~12.2 kyr. The median values of the peaks are 104 kyr, 44 kyr, 25 kyr and 12.7 kyr respectively.

Recently, the Milankovitch theory has been revived among paleoclimatologists. Milankovitch's ice age hypothesis is based on the idea that insolation variations received by the earth were caused by long-term variations of the distance between the sun and the earth as well as long-term variations of the inclinations of orbital plane and the axis of rotation. The period of variation of the eccentricity of the earth's orbit is 92 kyr, the period of obliquity change of the orbital surface of the earth is 43 kyr, and the period of precessional change of the axis of rotation is 21 kyr respectively. These periods are indicated by thin solid lines at the top of Figure 3.

The three peaks of paleoclimatic constituents correspond well to the periods of orbital disturbances. A similar periodicity has been obtained from the paleoclimatic curve based on the oxygen-isotope of ocean cores (10). Such correspondence does not necessarily mean that the insolation variations due to orbital disturbances directly cause the climatic changes on geological time scales. However, the crucial fact that the climatic curves derived independently from sediment cores taken at different sites in the world have similar periodicity to Milankovitch's insolation variations seems to suggest that the orbital insolation variations may play a role of trigger of the climatic change, received within an unknown nonlinear global thermal system (including ice sheets), and selectively amplified in sedimentary records.

FUTURE CLIMATIC TRENDS

Future temperature change can be estimated by using the prediction error filter already determined in the process of power spectrum estimation. This procedure is basically the same as the autoregressive prediction method.

In the predictional procedure, we have used the following equation :

$$\hat{x}(t+\Delta t) = \sum_{k=1}^{M} a_k x(t-k\Delta t)$$

where a_k is the k-th order prediction error filter, $x(t-k\Delta t)$ is the past k-th data of the time series, $x(t+\Delta t)$ is the one-step predicted time series.

By comparing with known time series, it is seen that the autoregressive prediction method of order 21 (M=21) predicts up to six steps of the future trend within a standard error of $\pm$ 13% without correction.

The solid curve with black circles in Figure 2 shows the predicted time series. If the maximum temperature range in the past 500 kyr is taken as 5°C, then the predicted future temperature decreases by 2.4°C from the present level during the coming 15 kyr. This is shown in Figure 2 by the solid curve with black circles and in details in Figure 4. Similar results were also obtained by Imbrie and Imbrie (11), Kukla et al. (12) and Berger

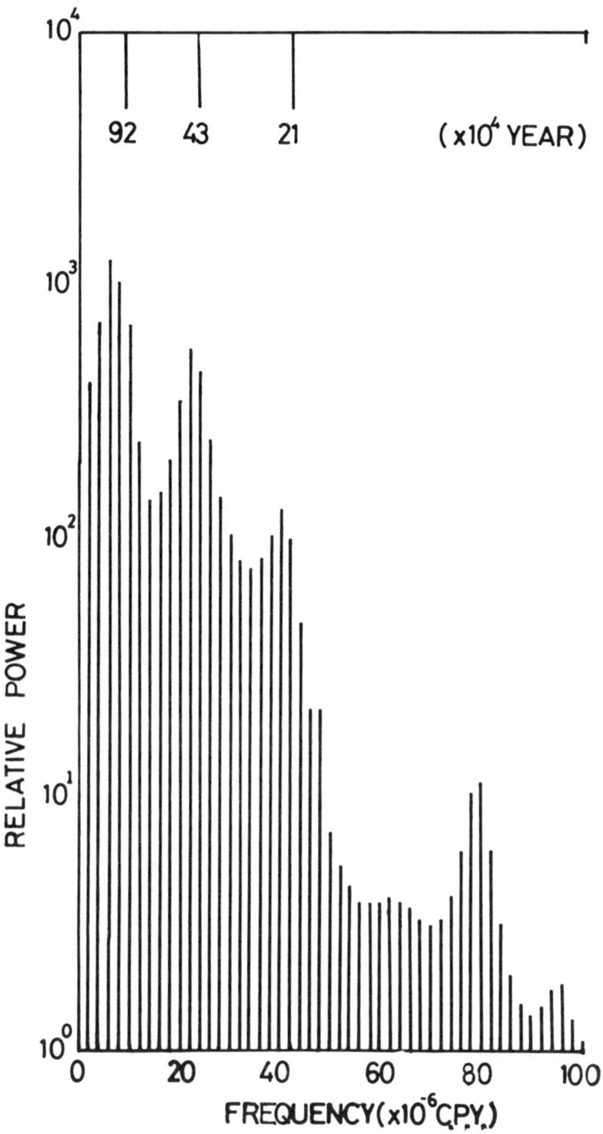

Figure 3 Power spectrum of the paleoclimatic time series estimated by the maximum entropy method. The solid lines in the top of the figure indicate the periods of astronomical disturbances; eccentricity, obliquity and precession of the earth's orbit.

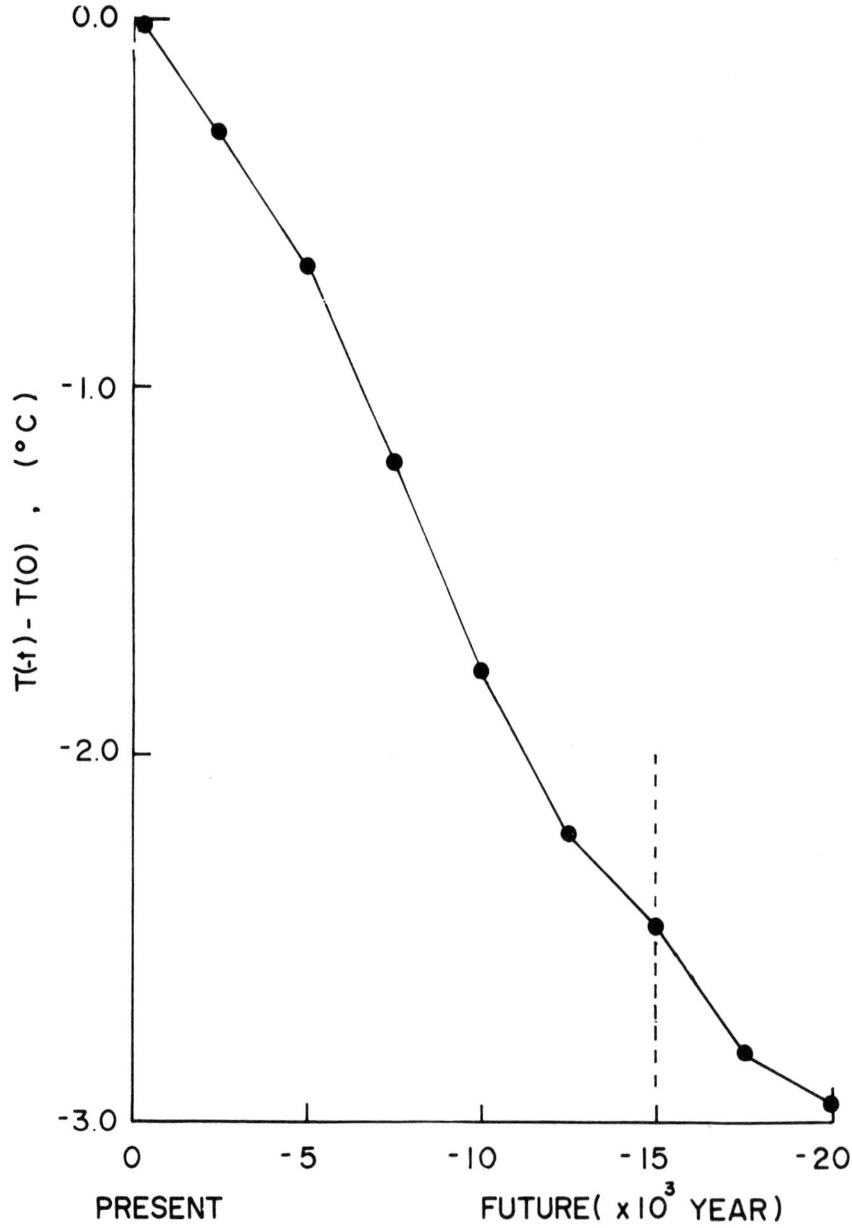

Figure 4 Predicted future temperature trend. The vertical broken line at 15 kyr shows a prediction limit without correction. The prediction error increases rapidly with the increasing prediction steps beyond the line.

(13). In this last model, however, a higher resolution in time was obtained.

CONCLUSION

Paleoclimatic variations reconstructed from the pollen analysis of the 200 m core from Lake Biwa were transformed into a paleoclimatic time series based on a relationship between depth and age derived from Kanari's consolidation model. The power spectrum of the climatic time series over 500 kyr shows four peaks at the periods of 104 kyr, 44 kyr, 25 kyr and 12.7 kyr respectively. The three longer periods correspond to the periods of Milankovitch orbital perturbations, that is, the eccentricity, obliquity and precession .

In the present stage, the mechanism that leads to climatic changes as an output of the Milankovitch insolation input is not clear. However, it seems to be beyond doubt that Milankovitch's insolation periodicity is registered world-wide in sediment cores recording climatic changes.

Autoregressive prediction of the future mean global surface air temperature shows a decreasing trend of 2.4°C/15 000 years, if 5°C amplitude is assumed between subpolar and temperate past climatic extremes.

REFERENCES

1. Burg, J.P. : 1967, Paper at 37th Ann. Internat. Meet., Soc. Explor. Geophys., Oklahoma City, Oct. 31.
2. Fuji, N. : 1976, Paleolimnol. Lake Biwa and Jap. Pleist. 4, pp. 316-356.
3. Nishimura, S., and Yokoyama, T. : 1975, Paleolimnol. Lake Biwa and Jap. Pleist. 3, pp. 138-142.
4. Kanari, S. : 1978, Jap. J. Limnol. 39, pp. 55-60.
5. Fuji, N. : 1978, Paleolimnol. Lake Biwa and Jap. Pleist. 6, pp. 235-262.
6. Kira, T., and Iida, K. : 1958, in : "Seibutsu to Kankyo", H. Tamiya et al. (Eds), Gendai Seibutsugaku Koza 5, Tokyo, Kyoritsu Shuppan, pp. 231-269.
7. Fuji, N. : 1976, Paleolimnol. Lake Biwa and Jap. Pleist. 4, pp. 357-421.
8. Yamamoto, A., Kanari, S., Fukuo, Y., and Horie, S. : 1974, Paleolimnol. Lake Biwa and Jap. Pleist. 2, pp. 135-144.
9. Ulrych, T.J. : 1972, J. Geophys. Res. 77, pp. 1396-1400.
10. Petersen, E.L., and Larsen, S.E. : 1978, Tellus 30, pp. 193-200.

11. Imbrie, J., and Imbrie, J.Z. : 1980, Science 207, pp. 943-953.
12. Kukla, G., Berger, A., Lotti, R., and Brown, J. : 1981, Nature 290, pp. 295-300.
13. Berger, A. : 1980, Vistas in Astronomy 24, pp. 103-122.

PART II

GEOLOGICAL EVIDENCE FOR LONG-TERM CLIMATIC VARIATIONS AT ASTRONOMICAL FREQUENCIES

SECTION 4 – ESTIMATION OF GEOLOGIC SPECTRA

AN OPTIMAL APPROACH TO THE SPECTRAL CHARACTERISTICS OF DEEP-SEA CLIMATIC RECORDS

P. Pestiaux and A. Berger

Université Catholique de Louvain, Institut d'Astronomie et de Géophysique Georges Lemaître, B-1348 Louvain-la-Neuve, Belgium

ABSTRACT

Presently existing spectral analysis techniques (SATs) are reviewed insisting on their main characteristics : i.e., the assumed underlying model, the discrete or continuous formulation, the computational cost and the advantages and disadvantages. Four of these SATs have been selected and described mathematically to justify our choice among those presenting a similar underlying time series model.

Their advantages and disadvantages are discussed after these SATs have been applied to the first 400 kyr of the deep-sea oxygen isotope record V28-239 leading to the conclusions that :

(i) The Blackman-Tukey (BT) spectral analysis (SA) estimates accurately the spectral amplitudes which have simple statistical properties. Three broad spectral peaks appear in the range of the astronomical frequencies.

(ii) The Walsh (WAL) SA is conceptually similar to the BTSA, but is more appropriate for records presenting abrupt changes in the amplitude or in the variance.

(iii) The Maximum Entropy (ME) SA has the advantages of high detection power and frequency resolution. The 100 kyr quasiperiodicity found in BTSA, is shown to be made of quasiperiodicities at 111 kyr and 62 kyr.

(iv) The Minimum Cross-Entropy (MCE) SA allows the posterior estimate of the Power Spectral Density given any a priori spectral shape. The four astronomical spectral peaks taken a priori are not only found to be consistent with

A. L. Berger et al. (eds.), Milankovitch and Climate, Part 1, 417–445.

the data, but when one or two astronomical peaks are taken *a priori*, the others apear clearly.

The complementarity of these SATs suggests a combined approach starting with the BTSA, allowing accurate spectral amplitude estimation and statistical testing with regard to an appropriate continuum background. The MESA and MCESA are then used in order to increase the frequency resolution, to detect peaks in the low frequencies, and to evaluate the irregularities of the detected quasiperiodicities.

Such a detection power, even with a restricted number of data, has been used to design an Evolutive Maximum Entropy (EME) SA and to study the time evolution of spectral characteristics of the whole record V28-239. The results of this EMESA show a progressive decay of the 100 kyr quasiperiodicity mainly if the time-interval 0-700 kyr BP is compared to 900-1300 kyr BP and to 1300-1900 kyr BP.

INTRODUCTION

According to the astronomical theory of paleoclimates, the variations in the insolation parameters are the fundamental cause of the succession of Quaternary ice ages. All these insolation parameters are pure quasiperiodic functions which can be very accurately approximated by a finite sum of sine functions. The largest amplitudes corresponding to these sine functions are centered around the 23-19 kyr and the 41 kyr quasiperiodicities, the amplitude ratio of these components being different for different insolation parameter (1).

This has been at the origin of an extensive use of spectral analysis techniques in order to evaluate the paleoclimatic variability around these astronomical frequencies. Taking the ice volume changes reconstructed from the oxygen isotope ratio ($\delta^{18}O$) of deep-sea sediment cores, a fairly large number of power spectra have been computed leading to the conclusion that there was evidence for orbital forcing (e.g., 2,3,4,5). It was thus recognized that spectral analysis was a very appropriate tool for the verification of the astronomical theory of paleoclimates.

The main purpose of this paper will be first to give an up-to-date review of the presently existing spectral analysis techniques (SAT), together with their main characteristics. A particular attention will be paied to their underlying assumptions, to justify the final choice of four complementary spectral analysis techniques. Each of them will be applied to a single deep-sea oxygen isotope record in order to illustrate his advantages and disadvantages. As a conclusion, an optimal combined approach will be suggested, allowing the most appropriate answer to the problem first, of statistical testing and amplitude estimation and second, of peak detection and splitting (with a minimal number of available data).

THE DATA

The equatorial deep-sea core V28-239 (6) has been chosen for its length (it covers a time range of roughly 2 millions years) together with its low and relatively constant sedimentation rate (1 cm kyr^{-1}).

The age model (Basic Chronology) is based for the first part of the record, on three unambiguous isotopic signatures, i.e. the maximum glacial extend at 18 kyr BP, and two of the three Barbados sea level rises dated respectively at 82 and 125 kyr BP, the other part being dated by magnetostratigraphy providing the Bruhnes/Matuyama and Jaramarillo/Olduvaï boundaries (7).

A constant sedimentation rate has been assumed between these dates (Fig. 1).

This assumption transforms the oxygen isotope data set sampled at a constant depth-increment into a time series of non-equidistant values. Cubic splines was then used to interpolate between these ^{18}O values for a constant increment of time (Fig. 1).

THE SPECTRAL ANALYSIS TECHNIQUES, THEIR ADVANTAGES AND DISADVANTAGES

Each SAT is based on an _a priori_ model which fits the observations. The performance of the various spectral technique is therefore attributed to how well the assumed model matches the process under analysis. This implies that different models may not necessary yield similar results, suggesting that a combination of several spectral techniques may be more appropriate when no reasonable _a priori_ assumption can be made about the data (8).

The spectral estimation can be reduced to the problem of fitting to N data, a time series model, having M parameters, and to evaluate its associated power spectral density for S discrete frequencies. Most of the existing SATs have been indexed in Table 1 with their main characteristics : the assumed underlying model, the discrete (D) or continuous (C) formula-

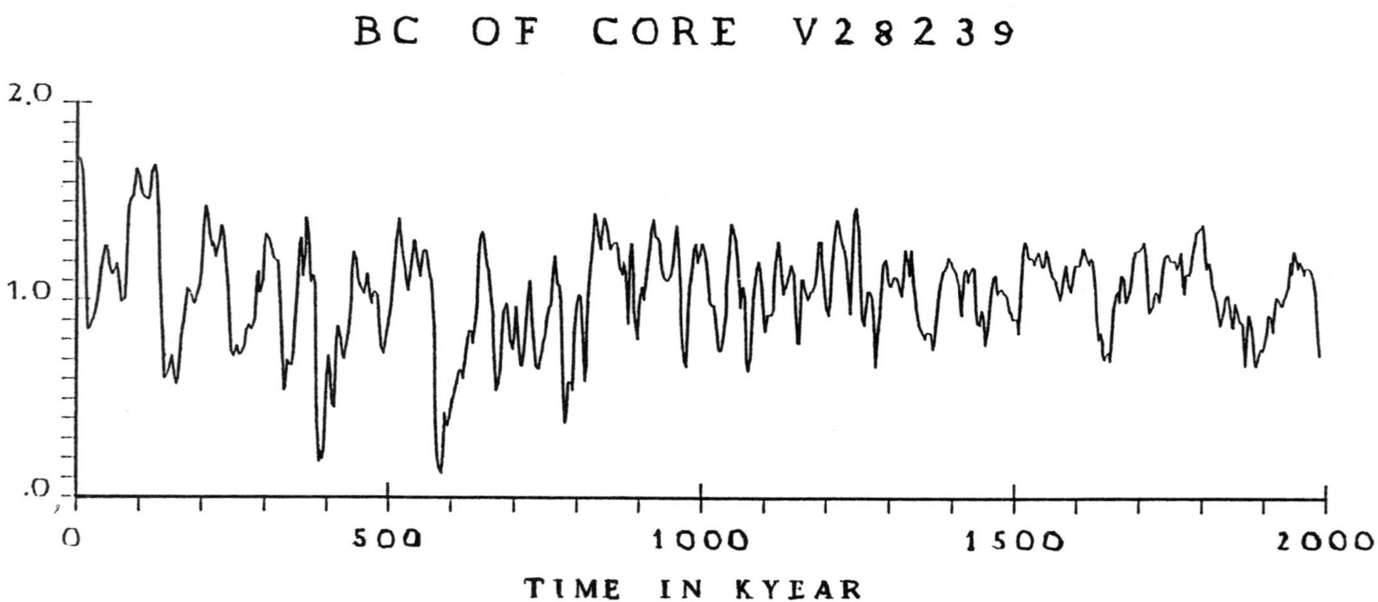

Figure 1 Basic Chronology of the oxygen isotope record V28-239 (6).

Table 1 Review of the main modern spectral analysis techniques. N is the number of data, M, the number of adjustable parameters, S, the number of spectral estimates. Est is the abreviation for estimates, coeff for coefficients and PSD for Power Spectral Density.

	DISCRETE OR CONTINUOUS SPECTRUM	COST IN ELEMENTARY OPERATIONS	MODEL	ADVANTAGES AND INCONVENIENTS	REFERENCES
Periodogram FFT algorithm	D	$N \log_2 N$	Sum of harmonically related sinusoids. Harmonic least squares fit.	Directly proportional to power. Computationally efficient Resolution $\frac{1}{N}$ Leakage distorsion Poor resolution-Short Data-Choice Window	Welch, 1967 (26)
BLACKMAN-TUKEY	C	Lag est N M PSD est M S	Identical to MA with windowing of the lags.	M N needed for computational efficiency Resolution $\frac{1}{N}$ Leakage distorsion Poor resolution-Short Data-Choice of window Possible negative PSD values Statistical properties	Blackman and Tukey, 1958 (27) Jenkins and Watts, 1968 (28)
MAXIMUM ENTROPY Yule-Walker Algorithm Y - W	C	Lag est N M AR coeff M^2 PSD est MS	Autoregressive (all pole) process	Amplitude strongly depends on the order p Better resolution than FFT or BT Spectral line Splitting No Side lobes	Ulrich and Bishop, 1975 (18)

Burg Algorithm		AR coeff $NM + M^2$ PSD est MS	Autoregressive (all pole) process	Amplitude strongly depends on the order p High resolution for low noise level Spectral line Splitting No Side lobes	Burg, 1975 (16) Fougères, 1977 (19)
Least Squares Mels		AR coeff $NM + M^2$ PSD est MS	Autoregressive (all pole) process	Amplitude strongly depends on the order p the sharpest response to narrow band processes NO SPECTRAL LINE SPLITTING OBSERVED	Marple, 1980 (22)
Walsh Square Waves FWT Algorithm	D	$N \log_2 N$	Sum of non harmonically related Walsh functions	Transient phenomena Shock waves with less harmonics	Ahmed and Rao, 1975 (30) Beauchamp, 1975 (14)
Moving Average	C	MA coeff Non linear simult. eq. set Lag est N M PSD est MS	Moving Average (all zero) process Can be reduced to high order AR	Amplitude strongly depends on the order p Low resolution Side lobes	Tong, 1976 (31)

ARMA Y - W Algorithm	C	Lag est NM Coeff M^3 PSD est M^3	ARMA process Rational Transfer Function MA order ≠ AR order Can be reduced to high order AR	Amplitude strongly depends on the orders p and q	Box and Jenkins, 1970 (9) Cadzow, 1980 (32)
Prony	C	AR coeff M^2 + NM Coeff M^3 PSD est MS	Sum of non harmonically related damped exponentials. ARMA with equal order MA and AR coeff (p=q)	Directly proportional to power Similar resolution as AR Methods No side lobes	Van Blaricum and Mittra, 1978 (33)
MINIMUM CROSS ENTROPY	D	Non linear simult.eq. set Lag est NM PSD est MS	Sum of non harmonically related sinusoids	Possibility to introduce any a-priori spectral information Choice of the a-priori spectral information	Shore, 1981 (25) Pestiaux and Berger, 1983 (23)
Capon Maximum Likelihood (MLSE)	C	Lag est NM Matrix Inversion M^3 PSD est MS	Optimal band pass filter of each spectral component MLSE related to AR Spectra as the mean of successive m order AR Spectra	Resolution better than BT not as good as AR Less variance in the estimates	Lacoss, 1971 (34) Burg, 1972 (35)

tion, the computational cost given by the approximate number of elementary operations, and finally, the advantages and disadvantages. Four of these eleven SATs have been selected on the basis of their computational cost and of the complementary spectral information that they provide. For each of these four SATs, we will briefly summarize their mathematical expression, justify our choice among the other ones presenting a similar underlying time series model, and comment their advantages and disadvantages when applied to the first 400 kyr of the deep-sea oxygen isotope record, V28-239. The sampling time interval, Δt, has been taken to the 1 kyr, the number of data, N, being 400.

The Energy Spectral Density, E(f), of an absolutely integrable function, x(t), is the squared modulus of its Fourier transform, X(f), i.e.

$$E(f) = |X(f)|^2 \quad [1]$$

If we consider a discrete time series, $\{x_i\}$, as not purely periodic, its Power Spectral Density, S(f), is defined as the time average of the Energy Spectral Density, E(f). In the case of a stochastic process, i.e. a realization of a time dependent random variable, the power is nothing else than the variance, σ^2, and the power spectral density, S(f), the continuous distribution of this variance as a function of frequency

$$\sigma^2 = \int_{-\infty}^{+\infty} S(f)df \quad [2]$$

The two main conditions required to allow a spectral analysis are :

(i) ergodicity, permitting the substitution of time averages for ensemble averages,

(ii) stationarity in the mean and the variance, implying that these two statistical moments only depend on the time lag. The non-stationarity in the variance can be removed by logarithmic transformation of the original data, the non-stationarity in the mean being attenuated by low order polynomial detrending or by filtering, if the number of data is sufficient.

Before starting the description and application of the four selected SATs, it is necessary to introduce the ARMA discrete time stochastic model (9) which has been recognized to approximate reasonably well most of the discrete time stochastic processes. In this model, a normal random (or white noise) input sequence $\{\varepsilon_i\}$ and the measured output sequence $\{x_i\}$ are related by the linear difference equation :

$$x_n = \sum_{k=1}^{p} a_k x_{n-k} + \sum_{l=0}^{p} b_l \varepsilon_{n-l} \quad [3]$$

where a_k, p and b_k, q are the coefficients and orders of the autoregressive and moving average contributions of the ARMA(p,q) global process.

Lagged Product (Blackman-Tukey) Spectral Analysis (BT)

This method is the indirect autocovariance approach commonly used under the name of Blackman-Tukey method (9). The estimated autocovariance function, r_k, is computed for M lags from the initial N discrete values, x_i, by the biaised estimate, r_k:

$$r_k = \frac{1}{N} \sum_{i=1}^{N-k} (x_i - \bar{x})(x_{i+k} - \bar{x}) \qquad [4]$$

and is smoothly truncated by multiplying it with a set of weights, λ_k, called a lag window, the Tuckey (Hanning) window in this case. The power spectral density is then obtained by taking the Real Discrete Fourier Transform (or Cosine Transform) of this modified autocovariance function (10,11,12) so that

$$S_{BT}(f) = \frac{1}{\pi} [r_0 + 2 \sum_{k=1}^{M-1} \lambda_k r_k \cos 2\pi fk] \qquad [5]$$

Since the spectral estimates are linear combinations of the autocorrelations, it has been possible to derive an approximate analytical expression for the confidence intervals (CI) of the spectral estimates. They are distributed as a Chi-Square, χ^2_ν, distribution, with a number of degrees of freedom, ν, depending on the used spectral window; in this case ν equals $\frac{8}{3}\frac{N}{M}$. The probability distribution of the possible spectral amplitude S'(f) is given by

$$P \left[\frac{\nu S_{BT}(f)}{\chi^2_\nu (1-\frac{\alpha}{2})} \leq S'(f) \leq \frac{\nu S_{BT}(f)}{\chi^2_\nu (\frac{\alpha}{2})} \right] = 1 - \alpha \qquad [6]$$

For practical reasons, a logarithmic transformation of the spectral density estimates, is often prefered because of the elimination of the frequency dependence of the confidence intervals. The variance of the spectral estimates which reflects the uncertainty in the height of the spectral peaks, increases with the number of autocorrelation coefficients, M, which, on the other hand, increases the frequency resolution. The best power spectral density estimate is therefore a compromise between frequency resolution, indicated by the bandwidth (BW), and the variance of the spectral estimates given by the confidence intervals (CI).

In the Lagged Product Spectral Analysis, the adjustable parameter is therefore the maximum number of lags, M, its optimal value being between one tenth and one third of the total number of data, N. The spectral peaks can finally be tested to be statistically different (two-sided CI) or superior (one sided CI) to a spectral density estimate, corresponding to a fitted stochastic model. The power spectral density estimates selected to be significant at the α-confidence level are those for which the α-confidence interval does not intersect the power spectral density corresponding to the fitted stochastic model.

Figure 2 illustrates the results of the Blackman-Tukey method (BT) applied to the first 401 data of V28-239, the maximum number of lags, M, is equal to 133, the autocorrelation function being assumed to be zero for the lags superior to M-1 (132). Three broad spectral peaks appear in the range of the astronomical frequencies, corresponding to frequencies around 100 kyr, 33 kyr and 22 kyr. These peaks being superposed to a strong autoregressive background, the statistical significance of the peaks has been tested against a first order autoregressive process (red noise).

Higher order autoregressive processes AR(p) or even autoregressive - moving average processes, ARMA (p,q), could also be fitted to the data, so that it is important to indicate the stochastic model against which the statistical significance is tested. When the statistical significance of the peaks seems questionable, it is strongly recommended to perform a Montecarlo simulation in order to confirm the appropriateness of the confidence intervals.

In summary, the main assumptions of the BT spectral analysis are :

(i) the linearity of the analytical expression of the power spectral density,
(ii) the annulment of the autocorrelations at lags greater than M-1, and
(iii) the structure of the stochastic model against which the significance test is performed.

The main advantages are the accuracy of the spectral amplitude estimation and the statistical properties of these estimates.

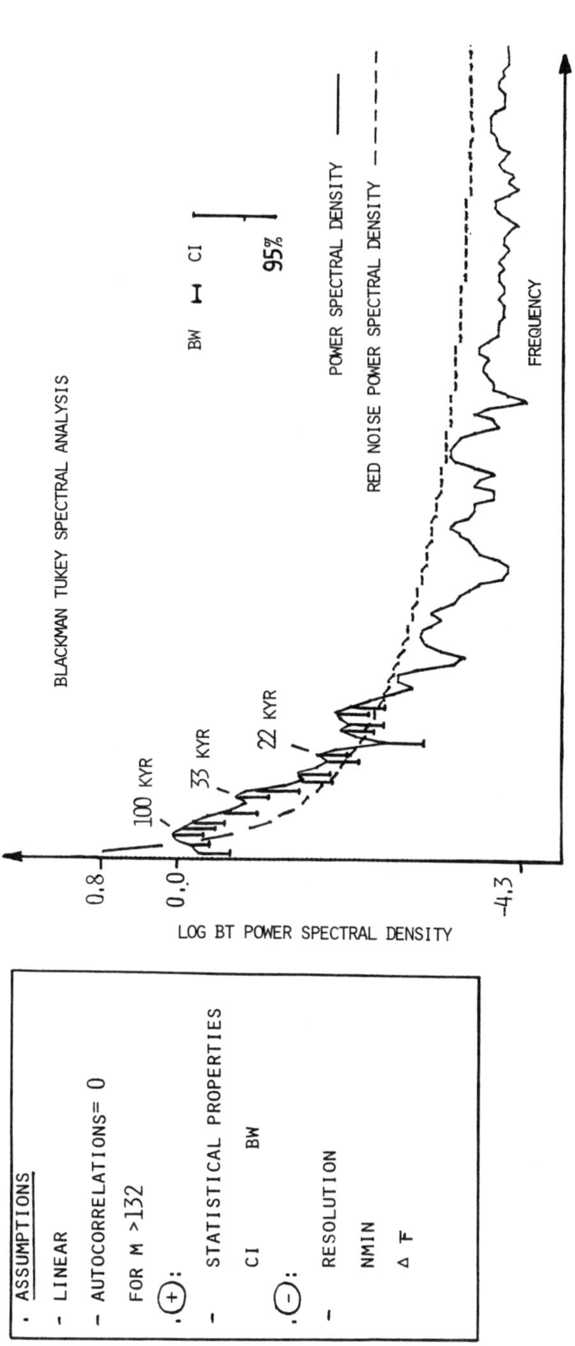

Figure 2 BT Spectral Analysis of the first 400 kyr of the record V28-239. The Power Spectral Density is in a logarithmic scale so that the confidence intervals (CI) are independent on the frequency.

However, the resolution in frequency is poor if we consider the minimum number of data necessary to identify a quasi periodicitiy in the low frequencies (NMIN) and in the ability to split close spectral peaks (ΔF).

An alternative to the Blackman-Tuckey method is the fast Fourier transform (FFT) which is used in order to evaluate the power spectrum of the discrete time series without computing the autocorrelations; this is the direct Periodogram method (Fig. 3). The only difference with the BT method is that the height of the spectral peaks gives directly the power while this power is given by the area under the power spectral density in the case of the BT method. The Periodogram method has the same advantages and disadvantages than BT method but is more computationally efficient when a large number of data must be analysed.

The three other methods will be selected to try to improve the frequency resolution of the statistically significant spectral peaks.

Walsh Spectral Analysis (WAL)

In 1923, J.L. Walsh (13) devised a new complete set of orthonormal functions. These functions denoted wal (k,t) bear a number of resemblances to the sines and cosines, appearing to be squared-up versions of them. They take only the values ± 1 and they change sign only when t is a multiple of a power of 1/2. The index k is the number of sign changes of wal (k,t) inside the unit interval.

In terms of these functions, a function f(t) can be expanded over the interval (0,T) so that

$$f(t) = \sum_{k=0}^{\infty} W(k) \, \mathrm{wal}\left(k, \frac{t}{T}\right)$$
$$W(k) = \frac{1}{T} \int_0^T f(t) \, \mathrm{wal}\left(k, \frac{t}{T}\right) dt \qquad [7]$$

The number of sign changes per unit time, $s = \frac{k}{T}$ is called the sequency. Similarly to the sines and cosines, the Walsh functions can be classified in terms of even cal $(k, \frac{t}{T})$, and odd, sal $(k, \frac{t}{T})$, waveform symmetry i.e.

$$\mathrm{wal}\left(2k, \frac{t}{T}\right) = \mathrm{cal}\left(k, \frac{t}{T}\right)$$
$$\mathrm{wal}\left(2k-1, \frac{t}{T}\right) = \mathrm{sal}\left(k, \frac{t}{T}\right) \qquad [8]$$

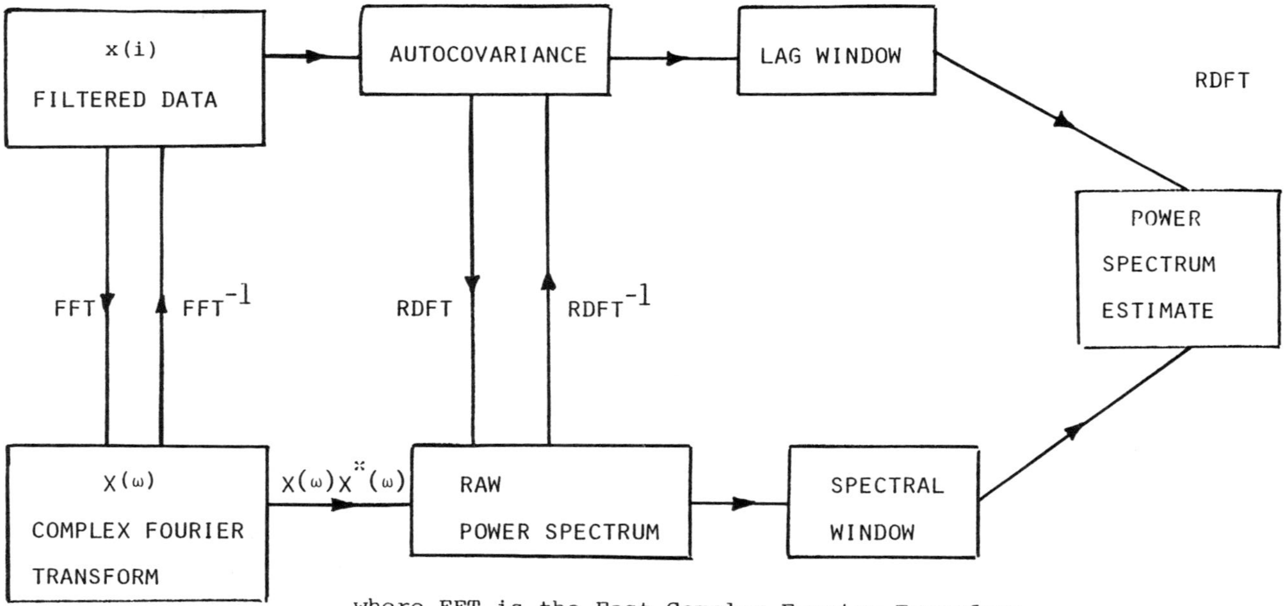

where FFT is the Fast Complex Fourier Transform.
RDFT is the Real Discrete Fourier Transform or Cosine Transform.

Figure 3 Flow chart diagram showing the equivalence between the BT (indirect) and the periodogram (direct) Spectral Analyses.

The general form of the Walsh Power spectrum $P_W(k)$ is given by

$$P_W(0) = W^2(0)$$
$$P_W(k) = W^2(2k-1) + W^2(2k), \quad k=1,2,\ldots, \quad -1 \qquad [9]$$
$$P_W\left(\frac{N}{2}\right) = W^2(N-1)$$

There exists also a fast Walsh Transform which has a similar computational efficiency as the Fast Fourier Transform. This method is perfectly similar to the Periodogram Spectral Analysis described before, allowing the use of analogous spectral windows to reduce the variance of the estimates. The main advantage of this square wave decomposition is that it is less sensitive to abrupt changes in the amplitude which reflect the non-stationarity in the mean and the variance (14).

Since the oxygen isotope record investigated here does not present the characteristics of abrupt changes in amplitude or variance, this method is not appropriate. However, in case of very sensitive paleoclimatic indicators, reaching strongly to changes in their environment, like particular species, abrupt changes may occur which deteriorate the spectral resolution of the Blackman-Tukey or Periodogram methods and which require the more efficient Walsh Spectral Analysis.

The Maximum Entropy Spectral Analysis by Least Squares (MELS)

As it has been mentioned before, one of the shortcomings of the Blackman and Tukey SAT is the assumption that the non computed autocorrelations are zero. However, the Maximum Entropy approach (MESA) does not make this assumption and chooses the Power Spectral Density which corresponds to the most random time series whose autocorrelation function agrees with the set of known autocorrelations computed from the data.

The realization of a random event always gives some "information". If the event is at first sight improbable, its realization brings much more information than if it was sure. The amount of information corresponding to the realization of one event is therefore a decreasing function of its probability. If N different events might happen with the probability p_i of occurence, the information I_i corresponding to the realization of the ith event may then be written by definition as :

$$I_i = k \ln \frac{1}{p_i} \qquad [10]$$

where k is a constant depending on the base of the logarithm. For an observation time T sufficiently large, we thus expect

$p_i T$ realizations of the ith event and therefore the total information I for this system is

$$I = k(p_1 \ T \ln \frac{1}{p_1} + p_2 \ T \ln \frac{1}{p_2} + \ldots + p_N \ T \ln \frac{1}{p_N}) \qquad [11]$$

The entropy, H, originally proposed by Shannon (15) is the information averaged over the time interval :

$$H = \frac{I}{T} = -k \sum_{i=1}^{N} p_i \ln p_i \qquad [12]$$

It is therefore obvious that the entropy is a measure of the uncertainty described by a given set of probabilities or, in other words, a measure of the disorder in the system.

The concept of entropy is particularly interesting for time series containing a high noise background as it is the case in paleoclimatic records. Defining the entropy rate, h, by

$$h = \lim_{M \to \infty} \frac{H}{M+1} \qquad [13]$$

it as been shown by Burg (16) and Smyrlie et al. (17) that if one assumes a Gaussian random process, then, the entropy rate, h, is proportional to the integral :

$$\int_{-1/2\Delta t}^{1/2\Delta t} \ln (S_{ME}(f)) \, df \qquad [14]$$

where Δt is the sampling interval, $S_{ME}(f)$, the Power Spectral Density, f the frequency and $\Delta t/2$, the Nyquist frequency. The Power Spectral Density $S_{ME}(f)$ is found by maximizing the entropy rate subject to the constraints that the M+1 known autocorrelations, r_k, satisfy the Wiener-Khinchin relationship given by :

$$r_k = \int_{-1/2\Delta t}^{1/2\Delta t} S_{ME}(f) \exp(-i2\pi fk\Delta t) \, df \qquad k=0,M \qquad [15]$$

This relationship express the fact that the autocorrelation coefficients can be recovered by the Inverse Fourier Transform of the Power Spectral Density. The solution found, for example, by the Lagrange multipliers method is equivalent to an autoregressive Power Spectral Density (18) given by :

$$S_{ME}(f) = \frac{\Delta t \, \sigma_M^2}{\left| 1 + \sum_{k=1}^{M} a_k \exp(-i2\pi fk\Delta t) \right|^2} \qquad [16]$$

When an ARMA (p,q) stochastic process, reduces to an autoregressive process of order M, its formulation becomes :

$$x_n = \sum_{k=1}^{M} a_k x_{n-k} + \varepsilon_n \qquad [17]$$

so that the a_k parameters of [16] are nothing else than the autoregressive coefficients and σ^2 is the variance of the residual noise, ε_n.

One of the major shortcomings of this spectral estimate is that, since the maximum entropy spectral estimate is non linear, it is impossible to obtain general analytical expressions for its statistical properties. The problem of the choice of the autoregressive order M is similar to the problem of the determination of the number of autocorrelations in the Blackman-Tukey method. Indeed, small values of M yield spectral estimates with insufficient resolution whereas for too large values of M, the estimates are statistically unstable with spurious details. It seems that an optimum value of M lies generally in the range from 5% to 50% of the number of data. But one of the more frequently used criteria consists of taking M to correspond to the minimum value of the final prediction error (FPE) or of more complex quantities as "informatic theoretic function" (AIC) or "autoregressive transfer function" (CAT), (19,20). Recently, Rovelli (21) suggested a more physical criterion based on the estimation of the characteristic time scale of the time series, leading to an optimal autoregressive order, M_{opt}, given by :

$$M_{opt} = \frac{\pi}{2} \frac{\sum_{k=0}^{M_{max}} c_k}{c_0} \qquad [18]$$

where the c_k are the autocovariances and M_{max} is an overestimated number of autocorrelations, say 0.5N.

The amplitude of the Maximum Entropy spectral estimates is very sensitive to the order and are therefore to be interpreted with caution. In this paper, the parametric methods are only used to increase the frequency resolution of the Power Spectral Density without according too much importance to the amplitude estimate. Since the Burg algorithm (16) has been found to introduce spurious line splitting and high dependence on the initial phase and on the signal to noise ratio, a new algorithm by least squares (22) has been used to avoid these problems.

The advantage of the high frequency resolution can be exploited in two ways. The first one is a more precise identification of the low frequency peaks with less data (NMIN) than required by the Blackman-Tukey method. In order to illustrate this property two pure sine waves having periodicities of respectively 41 kyr and 43 kyr have been analysed both by the

Blackman Tukey method and the Maximum Entropy method. The results (Fig. 4) show the power of MESA. In general, five to seven T-periods of data are necessary to identify a T periodicity with the Blackman-Tukey method, while two or three T-periods of observations are sufficient in the case of MESA.

The other advantage of the high frequency resolution is the splitting of close spectral peaks (ΔF) and the control of the regularity of the detected quasiperiodicities. A broad spectral peak detected by MESA indicates that this quasiperiodicity present in some part of the record has slightly changed with time, as it is often the case in deep-sea paleoclimatic records. Indeed, if one has a T_1 quasiperiodicity in one half of the record and another T_2 quasiperiodicity in the other half of this record, the two corresponding frequencies being sufficiently different, the resulting Maximum Entropy spectrum will have two distinct spectral peaks. However, if this irregularity is more variable with a mean quasiperiodicity around these two values, a broad bimodal peak will appear.

The results of the maximum Entropy Spectral Analysis when applied to the core V28-239 are shown in Figure 5. The main characteristic of this Maximum Entropy Power Spectral Density is a bimodal peak at quasiperiodicities of 111 kyr and 62 kyr, clearly suggesting a non-stationarity of the frequencies. This non-stationarity, probably coming from the uncertainty in the time scale, has produced a mixing of the 41 kyr and 100 kyr periods.

Going back to Table 1, the suggested MESA can be compared to the ARMA and to the maximum Likelihood Spectral Analyses. As far as any ARMA stochastic process can be reduced to an infinite order AR stochastic process, the frequency resolution of the ARMA spectral analysis can be obtained by increasing the order in the MESA equivalent to an AR Spectral Analysis. The Maximum Likelihood Spectral Analysis has generally less frequency resolution than MESA, its advantage being an easy extension to non equidistant data. However, the use of the expensive maximum Likelihood method can be avoided by interpolating the non uniform samples onto an uniform grid in order to allow MESA to be used.

The Minimum Cross Entropy Spectral Analysis (MCESA)

It has been shown that MESA introducing an *a priori* hypothesis about the unknown autocorrelations, was able to increase the frequency resolution. MESA chooses the spectral density which corresponds to the most random time series whose autocorrelation function is computed from the data. Since the most random time series is by definition, a white noise having

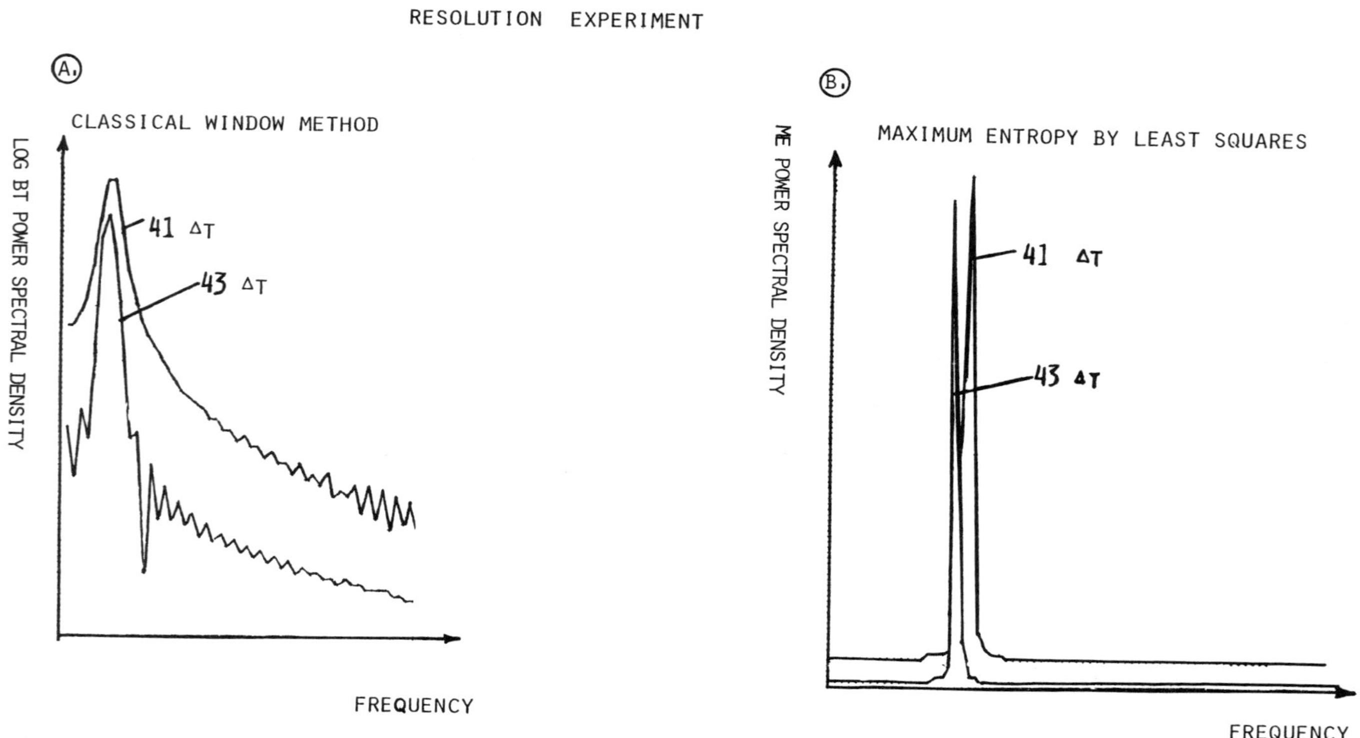

Figure 4 Resolution experiment with two sinusoïds having periodicities of 41 kyr and 43 kyr. The BT Spectral Analysis (Fig. 4a) does not make the difference while the ME Spectral Analysis detects precisely the two frequencies (Fig. 4b).

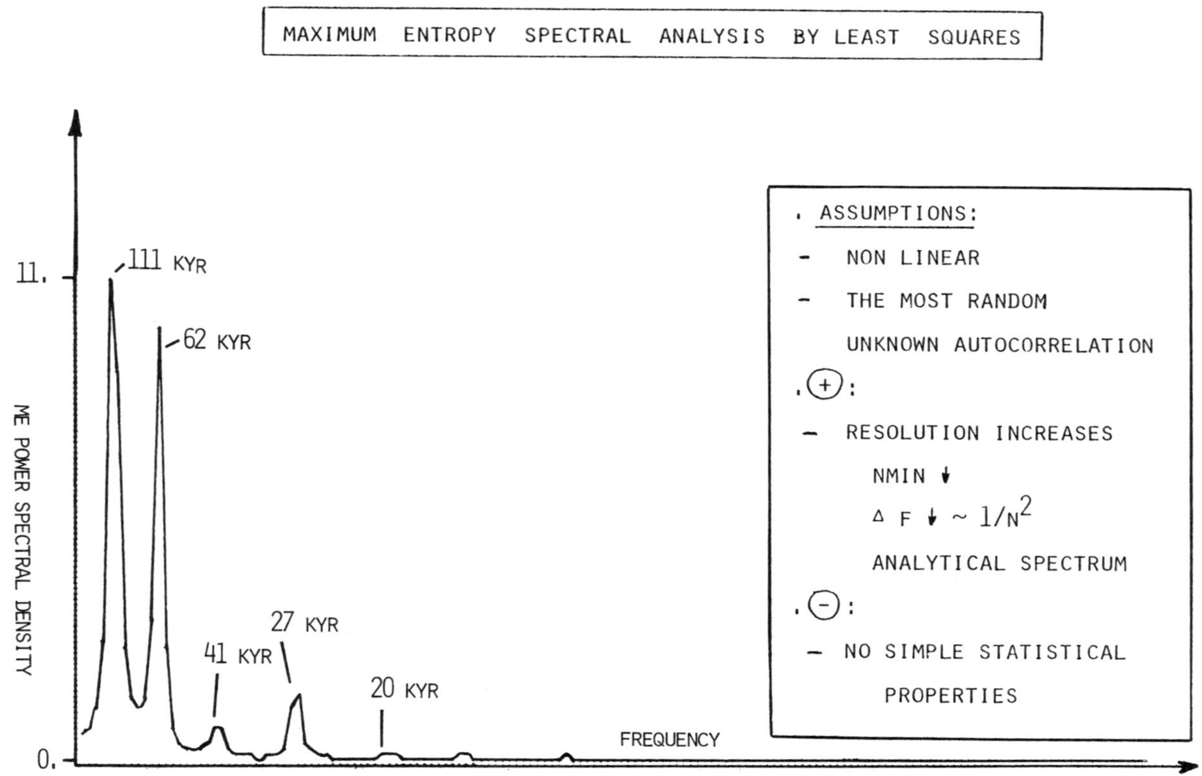

Figure 5 ME Spectral Analysis of the first 400 kyr of the record V28-239 with a number of AR parameters, M, equal to 120.

a constant spectral density, the implicit *a priori* assumption of MESA is a constant *a priori* spectral density.

The Minimum Cross Entropy Spectral Analysis (MECSA) can be viewed as a generalization of MESA allowing the posterior estimate of the Power Spectral Density, $S_{MCE}(f)$, given any *a priori* spectral shape. The concept of information, I_i, defined by [10] can be generalized so that the information gained over an *a priori* probability q_i is defined by :

$$I_i = - k \ln (p_i/q_i) \qquad [19]$$

If the sign of the information, I_i, is changed, the cross-entropy between a probability distribution p and an *a priori* distribution q may be defined by :

$$H(p,q) = \sum_j^N p_j \ln (p_j/q_j) \qquad [20]$$

so that the cross-entropy between the two probability distributions can be considered as a measure of the distance between these two distributions and the maximization of the information as a minimization of that distance.

The principle of minimum cross-entropy is to choose the distribution p that has the least cross-entropy with respect to the given prior q, among all distributions p that satisfy some fixed constraints. In our application, the probability distribution q_i, characterizes the preconceived spectrum which will be taken first as a white noise, and secondly as a "Milankovitch" one (23). The posteriori spectrum, characterized by a probability distribution p_i, will be computed in such a way that p_i will be the closest to the probability distribution q_i, with the autocorrelations of the data introduced as constraints. When the prior q is constant, H(p,q) differs from -H(p) only by a constant. The minimization of H(p,q) is equivalent to the maximization of H(p) and therefore the principle of maximum entropy is equivalent to minimum cross-entropy with a uniform priori distribution. The principle of minimum cross-entropy is therefore a generalization of maximum entropy allowing the use of a non-uniform probability distribution for the prior knowledge (24).

The principle of minimum cross-entropy applied to spectral analysis, given prior estimates of the spectrum $S_p(f_i)$ at S equidistant frequencies and with M+1 correlation constraints r_k gives for the posterior spectrum (25)

$$S_{MCE}(f_i) = [\frac{1}{S_p(f_i)} + \sum_{j=0}^{M} 2\beta_i \cos (2\pi t_i f_j)]^{-1} \qquad [21]$$

where the values of β_i are Lagrange multipliers and have to be chosen such that the following constraints are satisfied :

$$r_k = \sum_{j=1}^{S} 2S_{MCE}(f_j) \cos(2\pi t_i f_j) \qquad K=0,M \qquad [22]$$

The spectral estimates $S_{MCE}(f_i)$ are considered as random variables which have some probability distribution p_i and the constraints given by [22] relate $S_{MCE}(f_j)$ to the Fourier transform of the autocorrelations r_k calculated from the data.

In order to illustrate the frequency resolution of MCESA, two _a priori_ spectra have been chosen for a same number of frequency estimates. The first one is a pure white noise spectrum (each frequency has the same spectral amplitudes), the other is this white noise plus peaks at the astronomical frequencies. The amplitude of the _a priori_ peaks has been taken as a constant equal to a mean value of the power spectral densities detected in the spectral analysis with a pure white noise _a priori_ spectrum. MCESA re-estimates the amplitude of each of the _a priori_ spectral values such that the _a posteriori_ estimates are consistent with the known autocorrelations. The result, shown in Figure 6, has been performed by taking a white noise _a priori_ spectrum at the $0.3\ 10^{-2}$ level, three weak peaks being detected around quasiperiodicities of 120 kyr, 35 kyr and 22 kyr. Then assuming an _a priori_ spectrum taken as the superposition of the white noise and four astronomical peaks, the amplitude of the astronomical spectral peaks (Fig. 7) is reestimated confirming their consistency with the data. But one of the most significant results obtained from MCESA is that when only one or two astronomical peaks are taken _a priori_, the other ones are clearly detected.

THE COMBINED APPROACH AND THE EVOLUTIVE MESA

Considering the results presented in the preceeding section and summarized in Figure 8, it is clear that these spectral analysis methods are complementary, each of them having its own advantages and disadvantages. The suggested combined approach (Fig. 9) exploiting these advantages starts with the classical Lagged Product Spectral Analysis (non parametric method) because of its statistical properties and its accuracy in the spectral amplitude estimation. The statistical significance of the spectral peaks is tested with regard to a continuum (null hypothesis) background coresponding to the power spectrum of an adjusted low order ARMA (p,q) stochastic model. A parametric

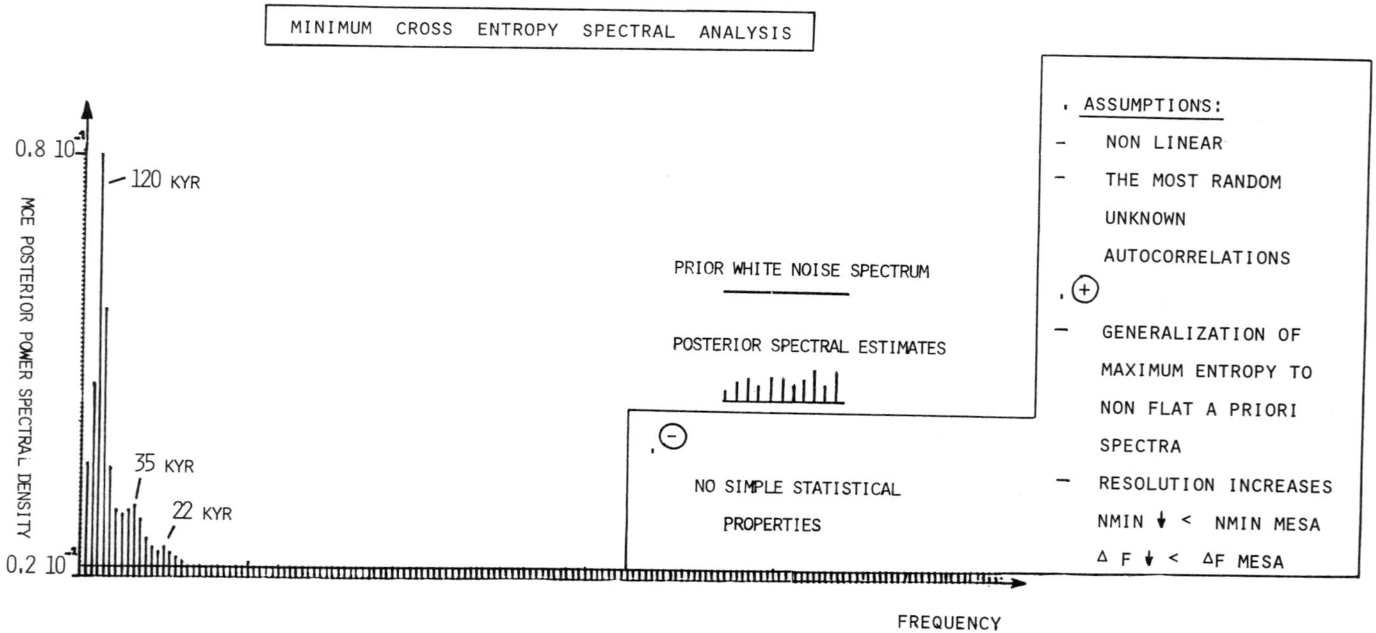

Figure 6 MCE Spectral Analysis of the first 400 kyr of the record V28-239 taking a white noise (WN) a priori Spectrum ( ) at the 0.3 10^{-2} level.

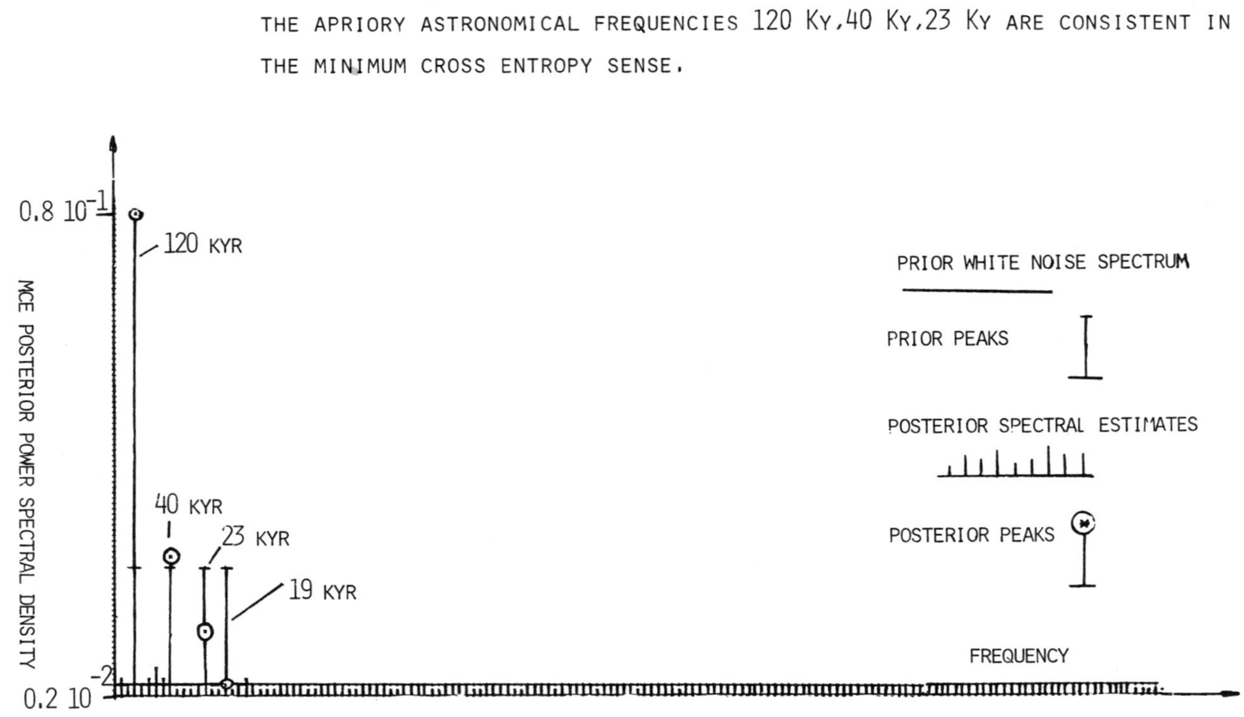

Figure 7 MCE Spectral Analysis of the first 400 kyr of the record V28-239 choosing the *a priori* spectrum as a superposition of a white noise (0.3 10^{-2} level) and an astronomical spectrum (0.5 10^{-1} level) with peaks corresponding to quasiperiodicities at 120 kyr, 40 kyr, 23 kyr and 19 kyr.

SPECTRAL ANALYSIS

BY

	TUKEY WINDOW	MAXIMUM ENTROPY	MINIMIM CROSS ENTROPY	WALSH TRANSFORM
DETECTION				
$N \geqq 3$ PERIODS	⊕	⊕	⊕	⊕
$N \simeq 2$ PERIODS	⊖	⊕	⊕⊕	⊖
$\Delta F > 1/M$	⊕	⊕	⊕	⊕
$\Delta F \leqq 1/N$	⊖	⊕	⊕⊕	⊖
STATISTICAL PROPERTIES	⊕	⊖	UNTIL NOW ⊖ ?	⊖⊖
GLOBAL NON STATIONARITY	⊖	LOCAL STATIONARITY ⊕	LOCAL STATIONARITY ⊕⊕	⊖
TRANSIENT	⊖	⊖	⊖	⊕

Figure 8 Summary of the main advantages ⊕ and disadvantages ⊖ of the four suggested Spectral Analysis Techniques.

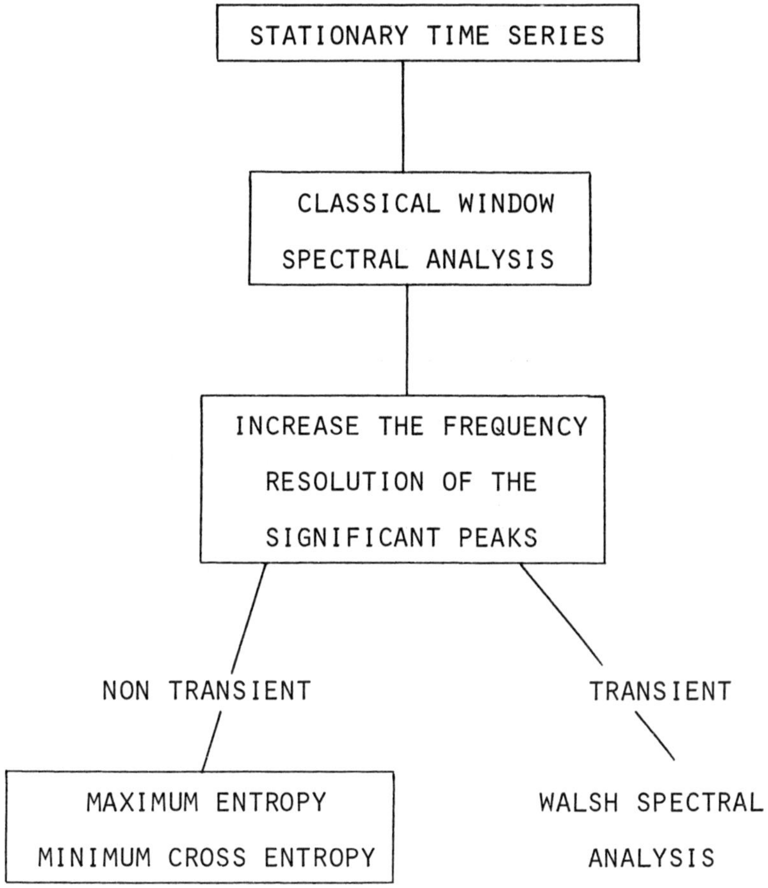

Figure 9 The combined approach, assuming a stationary time series, starts with the classical BT Spectral Analysis and refines the frequency resolution by ME or MCE Spectral Analysis in the case of a non transient record, or by Walsh Spectral Analysis in the case of a transient one.

method like the Maximum Entropy or the Minimum Cross-Entropy Spectral analyses is then used :

(i) to increase the frequency resolution of the statistically significant spectral peaks, allowing the splitting of close peaks,
(ii) the detection of peaks in the low frequencies (requiring less data than in the case of the non parametric methods) and, finally,
(iii) the evaluation of the irregularities in the detected quasiperiodicities, the most regular ones, being associated to sharper and higher spectral peaks.

Such a detection power with a restricted number of data, strongly claims for the use of the parametric methods to study the time evolution of the spectral characteristics of paleoclimatic records. This Evolutive Spectral Analysis is performed by a successive application of the parametric method on a restricted part of the record which will be called the "data window". The data window is then shifted from the beginning to the end of the global record giving a spectrum varying slowly at each step. The Evolutive maximum Entropy Spectral Analysis has been applied on the whole V28-239 oxygen isotope record with a data window covering 150 data points and shifted by 12 kyr at each step. Figure 10 is a three-dimensional diagram representing the power spectra corresponding to each of these time shifts. This diagram shows clearly a progressive decay of the 100 kyr quasiperiodicity, mainly if the time interval 0-700 kyr BP is compared to the 900-1300 kyr BP and 1300-1900 kyr BP ones.

CONCLUSION

Modern spectral methods, when used properly, are extremely valuable for paleoclimatic data analysis in the framework of the astronomical theory of paleoclimates. Each of the methods suggested here assumes an underlying time series model, the quality of the associated spectral estimates depending on the appropriateness of this model. For example, knowing that oxygen isotope deep-sea records present a strong red noise background which is characteristic of a low order autoregressive process, the Maximum Entropy Spectral Analysis is found to be particularly appropriate for high resolution spectral analysis of these records.

The suggested combination of spectral analysis methods provides an optimal information about the spectral characteristics of deep-sea paleoclimatic records. Indeed, the complexity of the statistical properties in the case of the parametric

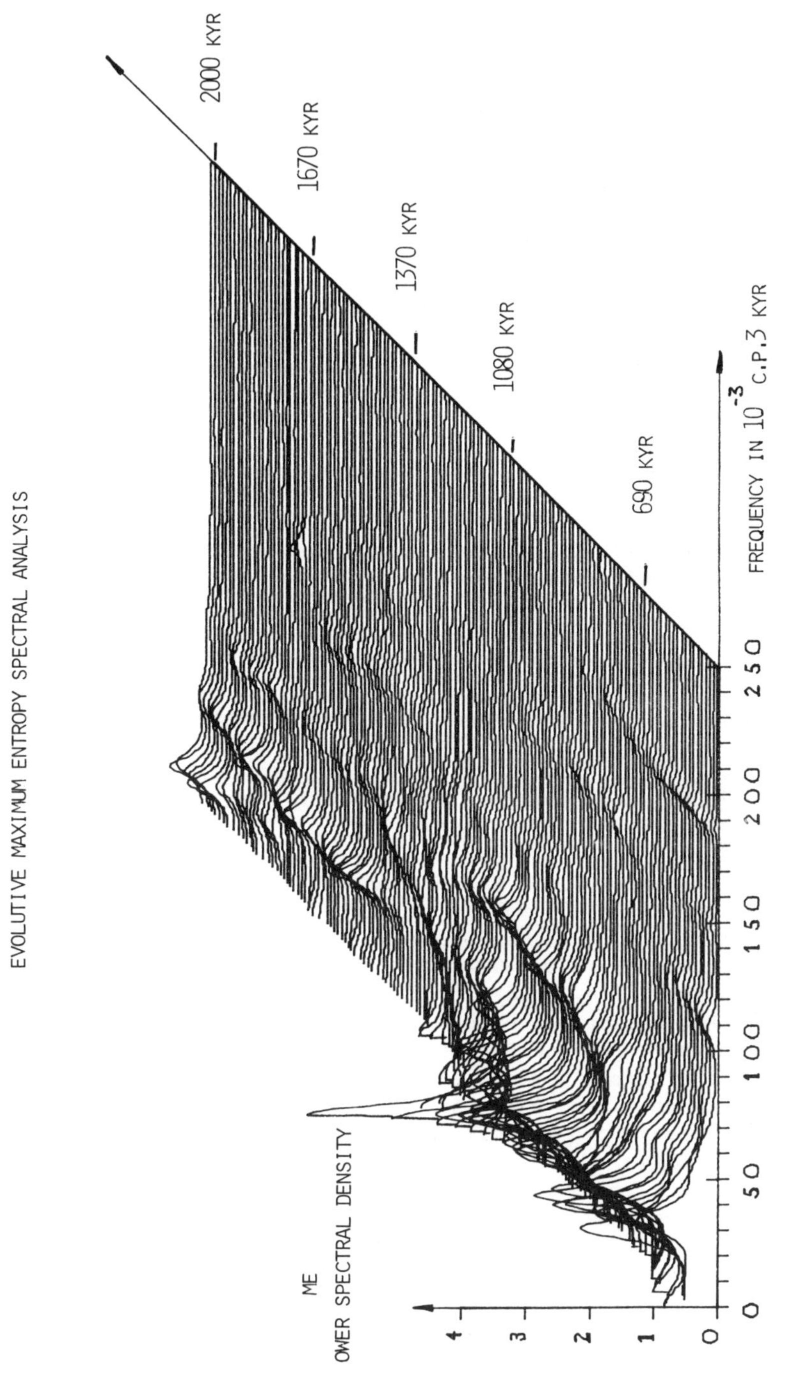

Figure 10 Evolutive ME Spectral Analysis of the whole record V28-239.

methods, and their high amplitude sensitivity require to start the analysis with the use of the classical Fourier techniques. Next, the parametric spectral analyses are able to detect the limitations of the data due to the non stationarity. Their applicability to a restricted number of data allows the study of the continuous time evolution of the power spectrum (Evolutive Spectral Analysis). The new Minimum Cross Entropy Spectral Analysis has not only a larger power of detection, but gives also indications on the interactions between the detected spectral peaks. For example, the imposition of a 100 kyr a priori spectral peak, allowing the refinement in the detection of the 40 kyr, 23 kyr and 19 kyr quasiperiodicities, would be an indication of a relationship between the 100 kyr cycle and the astronomical quasiperiodicities.

REFERENCES

1. Berger, A., and Pestiaux, P. : 1984, in : "Milankovitch and Climate", A. Berger, J. Imbrie, J. Hays, G. Kukla and B. Saltzman (Eds), Reidel Publ. Company, Dordrecht, Holland. This volume, p. 83.
2. Hays, J.D., Imbrie, J., Shackleton, N.J. : 1976, Science 194, pp. 1121-1131.
3. Kominz, M., Heath, G., Ku, T.L., and Pisias, N.G. : 1979, Earth and Planet Sci. Lett. 45, pp. 394-410.
4. Morley, J.J, and Hays, J.D. : 1981, Earth and Planet Sci. Lett. 53, pp. 279-295.
5. Imbrie, J., Hays, J.D., Martinson, D.G., McIntyre, A., Mix, A.C., Morley, J.J., Pisias, N.G., Prell, W.L., and Shackleton, N.J. : 1984, in : "Milankovitch and Climate", A. Berger, J. Imbrie, J. Hays, G. Kukla, B. Saltzman (Eds), Reidel Publ. Company, Dordrecht, Holland. This volume, p. 269.
6. Shackleton, N.J., and Opdyke, N.D. : 1976, Geol. Soc. Amer. Mem. 145, pp. 449-464.
7. Mankynen, E.A., and Dalrymple, G.B. : 1979, J. Geophys. Res.84, pp. 615-626.
8. Pestiaux, P., and Berger, A. : 1982, Numerical methods in the search for periodicities and quasi-periodicities. Contribution n°34, Institute of Astronomy and Geophysics, Catholic University of Louvain-la-Neuve, Belgium.
9. Box, G.E.P., and Jenkins, G.M. : 1970, Time Series Analysis Forecasting and Control, Holden Day, San Francisco.
10. Hannan, E.J. : 1958, J. of the Royal Statistical Society, serie B, 20, pp. 323-333.
11. Jenkins, G.M. : 1969, Tecknometrics 3, pp. 133-166.
12. Parzen, E. : 1961, Technometrics 3, pp. 167-190.
13. Walsh, J.L. : 1923, Amer. J. Math. 45, pp. 5-24.

14. Beauchamp, K.G. : 1975, Walsh functions and their applications, Academic Press, New York.
15. Shannon, C.E. : 1948, Bell Syst. Tech. J. 27, pp. 379-423.
16. Burg, J.P. : 1975, Maximum Entropy Spectral Analysis, Ph.D. dissertation, Dept. Geophysics, Stanford University, Stanford.
17. Smyrlie, D.E., Clarke, G.K., and Ulrych, T.J. : 1973, in : "Methods in Computational Physics 13, pp. 391-430, B. Alder, S. Fernbach, M. Rotenberg (Eds), Academic Press, New York.
18. Ulrich, T.J., and Bishop, T.N. : 1975, Rev. Geophys. and Space Phys. 13, pp. 183-200.
19. Akaike, H. : 1970, Ann. Inst. Statist. Math. 22, pp. 203-217.
20. Akaike, H. : 1973, Biometrika 60, pp. 225-265.
21. Rovelli, A. : 1982, IEEE Trans. on Geoscience and Remote Sensing, vol. GE-20, pp. 158-161.
22. Marple, S.R. : 1980, IEEE Trans. on Acoustics, speech and signal processing, vol. ASSP-28, pp. 441-454.
23. Pestiaux, P., and Berger, A. : 1983, Annales Geophysicae 1, 4-5, pp. 375-380.
24. Johnson, R.W. : 1979, Determining probability distributions by maximum entropy and minimum cross-entropy, proc. APL79, pp. 24-29.
25. Shore, J. : 1981, IEEE Trans. on acoustics, speech and signal processing, vol. ASSP-29, pp. 230-237.
26. Welsh, P.D. : 1967, IEEE Trans. Audio Electroacoust., vol. AU-15, pp. 70-73.
27. Blackman, R.B., and Tukey, J.W. : 1958, The measurement of power spectra from the point of view of communication engineering, Dover, New York.
28. Jenkins, G.M., and Watts, D.G. : 1968, Spectral analysis and its applications, Holden Day, San Francisco.
29. Fougère, P.F. : 1977, J. Geophys. Res. 82, pp. 1051-1054.
30. Ahmed, N., and Rao, K.R. : 1975, Orthogonal Transforms for Digital Signal Processing.
31. Tong, H. : 1966, IEEE Trans. Inform. Theory, vol. IT-22, pp. 493-496.
32. Cadzow, J.A. : 1980, IEEE Trans. on acoustics, speech and signal processing, vol. ASSP-28, pp. 524-529.
33. Van Blaricum, M.L., and Mittra, R. : 1980, IEEE Trans. Antennas Propagat., vol. AP-28, p. 949.
34. Lacoss, R.T. : 1971, Geophysics 36, pp. 661-675.
35. Burg, J.P. : 1972, Geophysics 37, pp. 375-376.

BRUNHES TIME SCALE: TUNING BY RATES OF CALCIUM-CARBONATE DISSOLUTION AND CROSS SPECTRAL ANALYSES WITH SOLAR INSOLATION

K. Herterich[1] and M. Sarnthein[2]

[1]Max-Planck-Institut fur Meteorologie
Bundesstrasse 55, 2000 Hamburg 13, F.R.G.
[2]Geologisch-Paläontologisches Institut, Universitat Kiel, Ohlshausenstrasse 40-60, 2300 Kiel 1, F.R.G.

ABSTRACT

To establish a more precise chronology of $\delta^{18}O$ stratigraphy during the Brunhes Epoch we examined the sedimentary record of Meteor-core 13519 (equatorial Atlantic, position of DSDP site 366), applying two different dating techniques. The time scale CARPOR is based on radiometric data and on the assumptions: that (i) the accumulation rate of aeolian dust has been fairly constant near the thermal equator (5°N), and (ii) differential porosity and calcium-carbonate dissolution have influenced the sedimentation rates in the short term. Cross spectral analyses between CARPOR and the solar insolation curve yields a significant coherence at 41,23, and 19 kyr, with 6% of the total climatic variance explained. Other model time scales were derived by adjusting the $\delta^{18}O$ record to the calculated record of solar insolation at 65°N during July (TUNE,STUNE) through a maximization of coherence (reaching up to 0.75). Additionally, some non-linear phase relationships between climatic variables are presented.

INTRODUCTION

An increasing number of different Pleistocene time scales have been proposed on the basis of the oxygen-isotopic stratigraphy of deep-sea cores, always with the claim for optimum accuracy (10, 13, 16, 23, 24). The somewhat limited reliability of these time scales may be attributed mainly to the absence of accurate radiometric dating methods covering the time range

A. L. Berger et al. (eds.), Milankovitch and Climate, Part 1, 447–466.

between some 150 kyr and the Brunhes-Matuyama boundary at 730 kyr BP (15). The $\delta^{18}O$ records of stratigraphy themselves are fairly generally accepted as a highly precise measure of climate stratigraphy. They can be reproduced worldwide with less than 1 000 years variation (the oceanic mixing time, (8)), apart from some sources of bias such as bioturbation, telescoping effects associated with different coring techniques, and hiatuses, or extremly reduced rates of sediment accumulation.

In principle, the existing age estimates of oxygen-isotopic curves were based on the following different techniques: (i) on a simple interpolation of core length between the few available radiometric ages, (ii) on an interpolation of core length averaging the intervals of different cores (23,24), (iii) on estimates of sediment accumulation rates based on sedimentology (13,20), and (iv) on cross spectral analyses between orbital parameters and the $\delta^{18}O$ curve, particularly by the use of tune-up techniques (10,13,16) including coherence tests.

All these efforts towards a global, high resolution deep-sea chronology basically served to provide a common time basis in order to calculate meaningful phase relationships of climatic signals from different parts of the globe and reliable rates of the chemical and organic flux in the ocean. We have tried to reassess the time scale problem by comparing the results from a number of different (partly new) statistical and sedimentological techniques. We were motivated to this analysis by the availability of a new broad set of detailed time series exceeding 750 kyr derived from the Meteor-core 13519 from the Sierra Leone Rise at 5°N (20). For the earth's insolation record we used Berger's (2,3) calculations.

Cross spectral analysis (12) was our basic tool used to derive information on the linear relationship linking the history of the earth's climate to the solar insolation record (2). Generally the following approaches (Fig.1) may be distinguished depending on the choice of input (solar insolation) and on the time scale used for the output (sedimentary record) :

1. The input may be prescribed through e.g., the set of orbital parameters of the solar insolation at 65°N, July, or a Legendre function and seasonal expansion of the global insolation, while the time scale of the output $\delta^{18}O$ record may either be fixed (case 1 of Fig.1) or subject to some optimization process (case 2a,b).

2. A subset of the complete global set of variables, describing the latitudinal and seasonal distribution of the solar insolation may be selected as input to yield the best simulation of the climatic record (case 3a). (4) used an "a posteriori" screening technique to select the most important prediction variables (which has problems in satisfying statistical signi-

MILANKOVITCH AND CLIMATE

(cross spectral approaches)

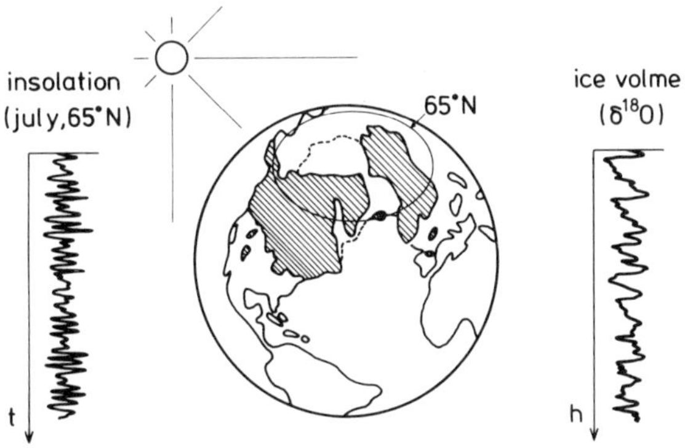

insolation S(φ,m) is initially	technique	stratigraphic timescales t(h) are initially	explained variance [%]
arbitrary fixed (φ=65°N, m=july)	(1) coherence tests → ? ←	fixed (CARPOR)	6
arbitrary fixed (φ=65°N, m=july)	(2) tune up experiments → t(h) ?	(a) undefined (TUNE) semi defined (STUNE) (b)	10 13
(a) undefined	(3) climate models φ,m ? ←	fixed (SIMPLEX)	≈ 50
(b) mainly fixed, degree of approximation undefined	? ← spherical harmonics expansion	fixed (CARPOR)	11

Figure 1 Comparison of different cross spectral techniques applied to the Milankovitch problem. For explanations of different terms see text. Arrows and questionmarks point to the conclusion to be drawn. The last column shows how much of the climatic variance of the output can be explained linearly by the input.

ficance criteria for a large number of variables, cf. (1), while we have used, in case 3b, an "a priori" ordering scheme based on an expansion of the solar insolation in terms of a series of seasonally dependent Legendre functions (5). The time scale of the climatic signal in either case is fixed.

The last chapter treats non-linear correlations between some major climatic variables which were derived from the sedimentary record of Meteor-core 13519 (25). These may add to the understanding of phase relationships between these variables and connect the underlying physical processes involved with the formation and the decay of large ice sheets.

OXYGEN-ISOTOPE STRATIGRAPHY OF METEOR-CORE 13519

The Meteor-core 13519 was taken from the Sierra Leone Rise (5°N,20°W) at 2 862 m water depth. The core is 10.67 m long and extends down to the base of oxygen-isotopic stage 21 at 10.52 m with an average sedimentation rate of 1.4 cm/1000 y. The following variables were determined from the sediment (25,20):

a) The $\delta^{18}O$ curve of the planktonic species <u>Globigerinoides sacculifer</u> (25). This signal is influenced primarily by the global ice volume, but to a minor degree also by sea-surface temperatures (23).

b) The $\delta^{18}O$ curve of the benthic species <u>Cibicidoides wuellerstorfi</u> (22). This signal basically represents the long-term record of the ice volume alone, because the deep-sea temperatures have changed very little during the Brunhes Epoch (6). Unfortunately, the sampling density is worse than for the plankton record because of the sparsity of benthic specimens in the sediment.

c) The percentages of $CaCO_3$ in the sediment. These vary between 30% and 90% (25).

d) The grain-size distribution of the terrigenous fraction (calcium carbonate-free insoluble residue minus opal fraction) (25).

e) The fraction of biogenic opal.

f) The clay-mineral composition which remained fairly constant (Lange, pers. com.).

g) The porosity of the sediment (65%-75%) as a measure to correct sediment accumulation rates (Koopmann,pers. com., (20)).

The variables a to d are presented in Figure 2. Figure 3 shows the abundance of biogenic opal during warm and cold stages.

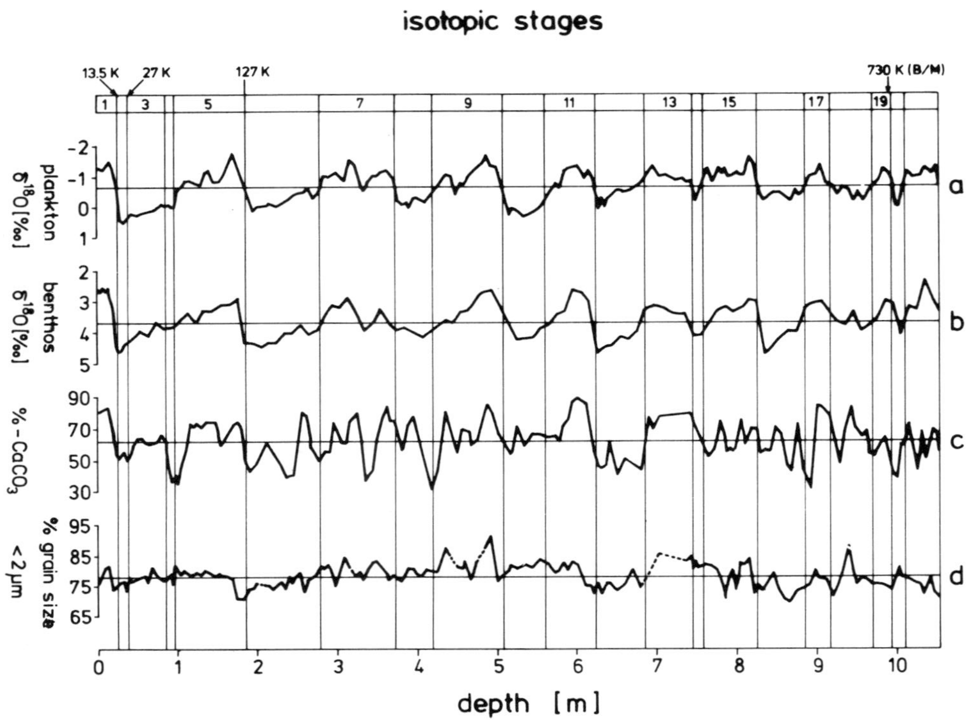

Figure 2 Climatic proxy data as derived from Meteor-core 13519 from the Sierra Leone Rise (5°N, 20°W) (25,20) : a) $\delta^{18}O$ of planktonic species Globigerinoides sacculifer, b) $\delta^{18}O$ of benthonic species Cibicidoides wuellerstorfi c) %-$CaCO_3$, d) percentages of grain sizes less than 2 µm in the terrigenous sediment fraction. Oxygen-isotopic stages after (23).

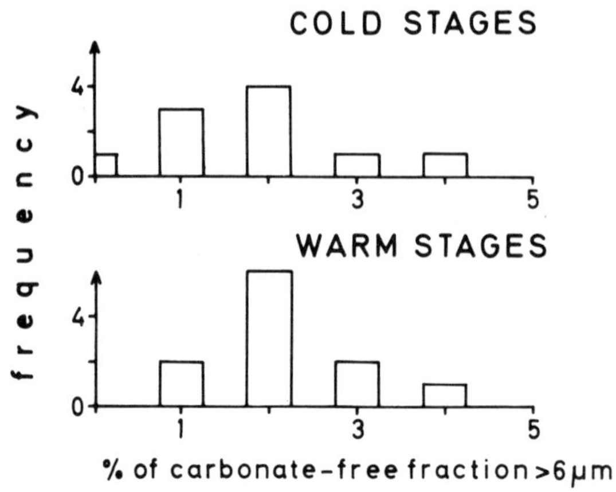

Figure 3 Frequency distribution of percentage of biogenic opal in the acid-insoluble sediment fraction.

SEDIMENTATION RATES AS A BASE FOR TIME SCALES OF THE OXYGEN-ISOTOPE RECORD

A first approximate age-depth relation "LIN" of Meteor-core 13519 was derived from the radiometric ages of the latest isotopic stage boundaries and extremes, together with the age of the Brunhes-Matuyama magnetic reversal (Table 1). Constant sedimentation rates were assumed in between. This linearly interpolated time scale LIN was used as a basic reference scale for the development of further time scales using additional assumptions.

As an improvement of the LIN time scale, the time scale CARPOR was developed by assuming that the accumulation rate of terrigenous clay and fine silt has been fairly constant near the thermal equator (5°N) during the Brunhes Epoch, but that fluctuations of the total sedimentation rates have occured on short time scales and are documented by changes of the calcium-carbonate content and the porosity in the sediment (25). This hypothesis is consistent with following observations:

i. Low percentages of $CaCO_3$ are in phase with low sedimentation rates where the $\delta^{18}O$ stage boundaries are radiometrically dated (Fig. 4).

ii. The ratio of biogenic opal to terrigenous matter is low (less than 5%) and nearly constant (Fig. 3). Thus both (independent) variables must have either fluctuated in phase or remained constant.

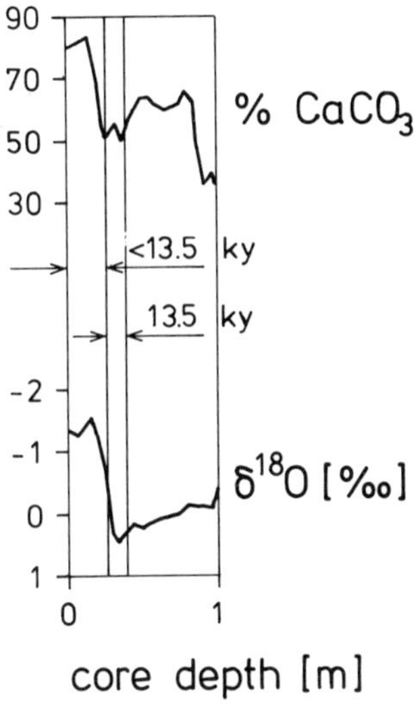

Figure 4 Comparison of %-$CaCO_3$ in warm and cold $\delta^{18}O$ stages 1 to 4. Low (high) sedimentation rate corresponds to low (high) %-$CaCO_3$.

iii. The grain-size distribution which is considered as a measure of wind speed, and possibly of the dust flux, is out of phase with $CaCO_3$ fluctuations (Fig. 2). Thus changes in $CaCO_3$ content cannot be related to varying dilution by the terrigenous input.

Accordingly we attribute differential percentages of calcium-carbonate to varying productivity and, more importantly, $CaCO_3$ dissolution. An improved chronology can now be derived in the following way:
Let h be the core depth, p(h) the porosity of the sediment, and t the time. Then the sediment mass accumulation rate is (1-p)dh/dt and is derived from two sources, the constant terrigenous input c_1 and the variable accumulation of calcium-carbonate $c_2(h)$. This is expressed by equation [1] :

$$(1-p)dh/dt = c_1+c_2(h) \qquad [1]$$

In terms of the observed percentages of calcium-carbonate $r = c_2/[c_1+c_2(h)]$, c_2 is given by $c_1 r/(1-r)$ and the differential equation [1] reads:

$$(1-r)(1-p)dh = c_1 dt \qquad [2]$$

Integration of equation [2] yields:

$$t = t_o + \frac{1}{c_1} \int_{h_o}^{h} (1-p)(1-r)dh \qquad [3]$$

The constant c_1 can be calculated from equation [3] for each section separately, with the upper and lower limits dated by radiometric ages (Table 1). The $\delta^{18}O$ record using the time scale CARPOR is shown in Figure 5, and the corresponding age depth curve in Figure 6. The ages of the isotopic-stage boundaries predicted by the different times scales of Figure 6 are listed in Table 2. In the following sections we attempt to intercompare and assess the different time scales by the application of cross spectral techniques.

COHERENCE TESTS

It was demonstrated by (10) that the oxygen-isotope and other records of climate exhibit statistically significant correlations with the earth's orbital parameters which control the input of solar insolation. Although the set of orbital parameter perturbations provides a complete description of the astronomical input to climate variations within the framework of linear response theory, we have preferred to use only a single scalar variable as input, since our optimal timing technique (see below) based on maximizing the coherence over the three principal astronomical frequency bands (19, 23, and 41 kyr), becomes very cumbersome when applied to a multidimensional input.

As input we selected the insolation curve for 65°N, July varying up to 10%. This insolation parameter is generally assumed to represent a particular critical climatic impact (11). Since the selected input contains energy in all three principal astronomical frequency bands, tuning with respect to this input can be equivalent to tuning with respect to the complete set of orbital variations as input, provided the transfer functions are allowed to adjust independently for the three different frequencies. Figure 7 shows the coherence between the solar insolation curve (July, 65°N) and the planktonic $\delta^{18}O$ record as a function of frequency for the time scales LIN and CARPOR.

For the linearly interpolated time scale LIN the coherence exceeds the 95 % confidence limit only near the 21 kyr period. However this frequency does not correspond to any of the dominant frequencies of solar insolation and the high coherence near 21 kyr is therefore presumably coincidental (5% of all frequency bands may be expected to exceed the 95% confidence level).

Table 1 Radiometric ages used for time scales LIN, CARPOR, and STUNE.

isotopic stage	core depth [cm]	age [ky]	ages based on
1/2	24	13.5	^{14}C, (14)
2/3	38	27	^{14}C, (19)
maxima of			
5a	115	82	$^{230}Th/^{234}U$,(24)
5c	140	105	$^{230}Th/^{234}U$, (9)
5e	169	118	
B-M boundary	987	730	K/Ar, (15)

Table 2 Ages of isotopic stages according to different time scales (see text).

isotopic stage	this work			other authors	
boundaries	CARPOR	TUNE	STUNE	(16)	(24)
1/2	14	17	10	11	13
2/3	27	31	18	27	32
3/4	56	73	49	58	64
4/5	70	86	63	72	75
5/6	127	139	127	128	128
6/7	209	195	184	188	203
7/8	277	260	244	244	262
8/9	312	290	269	279	310
9/10	374	348	332	334	362
10/11	410	381	369	347	383
11/12	444	420	409	421	459
12/13	510	478	475	475	492
13/14	540	526	527	505	524
14/15	551	537	539	517	565
15/16	608	591	598	579	617
16/17	657	635	644	608	654
17/18	678	658	668	671	675
18/19	712	701	712	724	712
19/20	733	720	730	744	736

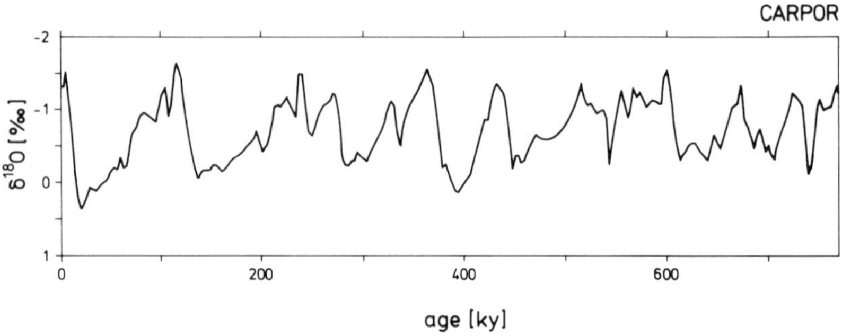

Figure 5 Planktonic $\delta^{18}O$ record as a function of time using the $CaCO_3$ and porosity corrected time scale CARPOR.

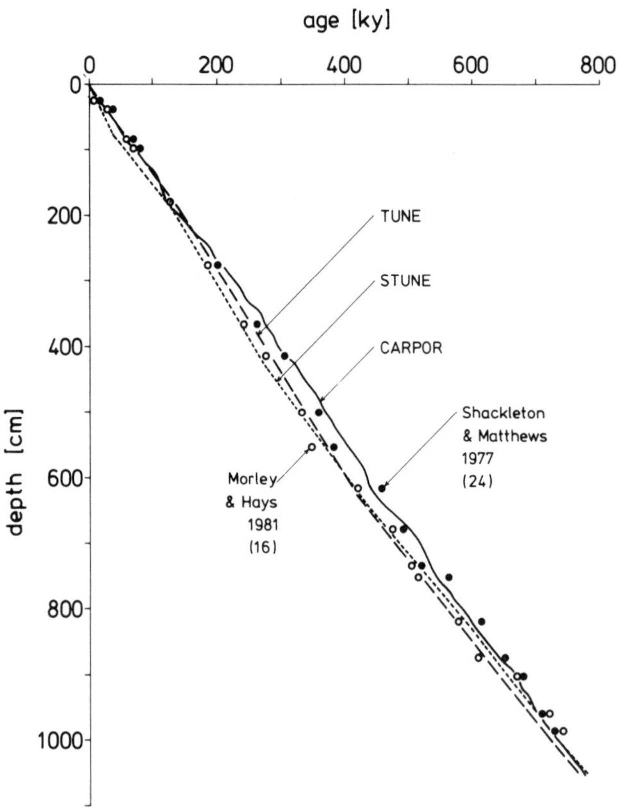

Figure 6 Age-depth curves of Meteor-core 13519 using different time scales derived in this paper (CARPOR, TUNE, STUNE) and proposed by the authors (16,24).

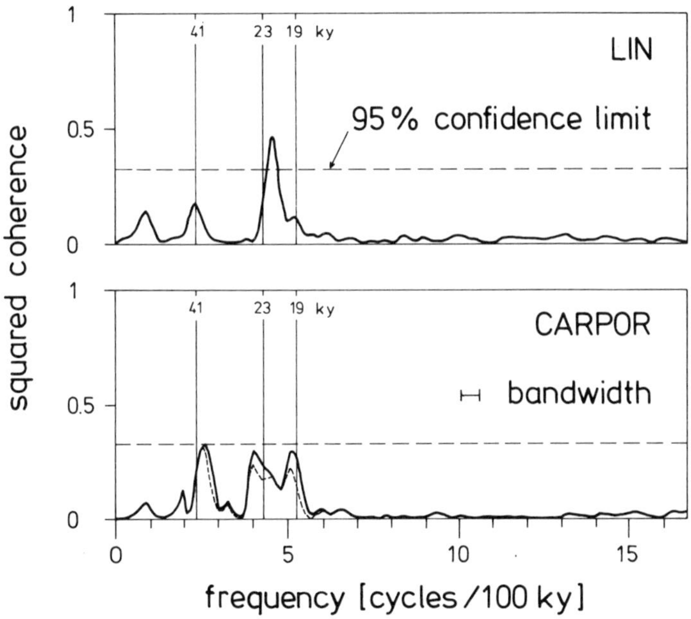

Figure 7 Squared coherence between the solar insolation curve 65°N, July and the planktonic $\delta^{18}O$ record dated by the time scales LIN and CARPOR (see text).

For the calcium carbonate corrected time scale CARPOR, coherence is near the 95% confidence limit for all three dominant solar insolation frequencies. This implies that :

i. A reasonably selected single solar-insolation curve can serve as calibration for the sedimentary time axis.

ii. Significant fractions of the energies in all three peaks at 41, 23, and 19 kyr in our $\delta^{18}O$ spectrum are linearly related to solar insolation. We may therefore anticipate an increasing coherence with increased precision in the dating of our sedimentary record. In fact, the omission of a hiatus-disturbance in a small sediment section close to the base of the investigated core (10.52 m) resulted in a pronounced increase of the coherence level (Fig. 7).

iii. The coherence at the 100 kyr period remains well below the 95% confidence limit. Thus there exists no detectable linear relation between the prominent spectral peak of the climatic record at 100 kyr and the (very small) insolation input at this frequency.

TUNE-UP EXPERIMENTS

The linear relation which exists between the variations of solar insolation (65°N, July) and the deep-sea climatic record as demonstrated by the coherence tests of the previous section, may be used for tuning the age-depth relation of the core stratigraphy. This technique was originally applied by (10) which used the orbital variables rather than the solar radiation as input. Their tuned time scale (TUNE-UP) covering the last 450 kyr was chosen such that phase relationships between the obliquity of the earth's axis and the deep-sea core record filtered at a period of 41 kyr, were constant throughout the core.

In our tuning approach (Fig. 1, approach 2a and 2b), the condition of constant phase in the time domain was replaced by the requirement of maximum coherence between solar insolation (65°N, July) and the (unfiltered) $\delta^{18}O$ record in the frequency domain. Starting with the linearly interpolated time scale LIN, the ages at 5 reference depths in the core (see Fig. 8) were allowed to vary, while constant sedimentation rates were assumed in between. The optimum age-depth relation (TUNE) was then defined as the one which yielded a maximum coherence, summed over the three frequency bands representing the three dominant insolation frequencies. This tuning resulted in an increase of the coherence at all three frequencies above the 95% confidence limit (Fig. 9).

In a further tuning experiment (STUNE), the age of the stage boundary 5/6 (127 kyr) and the age of the Brunhes-Matuyama magnetic reversal (730 kyr) were kept fixed. The ages at 5 other depths, indicated by dashed lines in Figure 8, were allowed to vary. The purpose of the STUNE experiment was to test whether it leads to a time scale more similar to the calcium carbonate corrected time scale CARPOR than the TUNE experiment, provided the same fixed age points were used as in CARPOR. Again coherence was increased above the 95% confidence limit. A particularly high value was found at the precessional period 23 kyr. However, this modified tuning exercise led to a time scale more similar to TUNE than to CARPOR (Fig. 6).

The different time scales derived in this paper are compared with the time scales of other authors in Table 2 and Figure 6. They show that both our time scales TUNE and STUNE are near to the time scale of (16). We also applied our tuning technique to the planktonic $\delta^{18}O$ signal of the combined cores RC11-120/E49-18 described by (10) and found that their TUNE-UP time scale indeed corresponds to the solution with the highest coherence. The agreement of these results based on somewhat differing methods may indicate that astronomical tuning is a rather robust technique. However, experiments with artificial

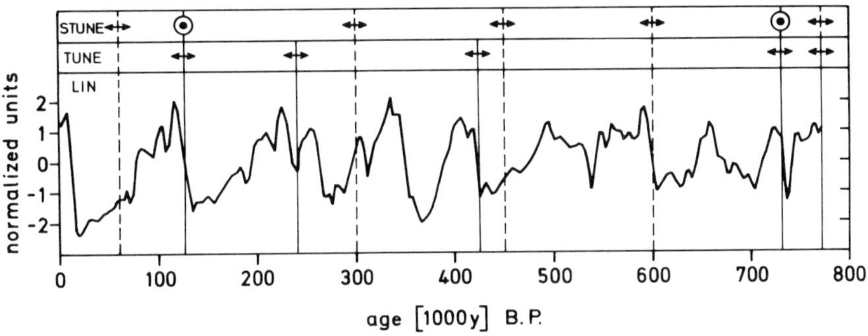

Figure 8 Sketch of the tuning techniques using coherence maximation applied to the $\delta^{18}O$ record time scale LIN (see text). Ages marked by vertical solid (TUNE) and dashed (STUNE) lines and arrows are shifted to obtain maximum coherence. Linear interpolation is applied in between. Ages marked by ⊙(STUNE) remain fixed.

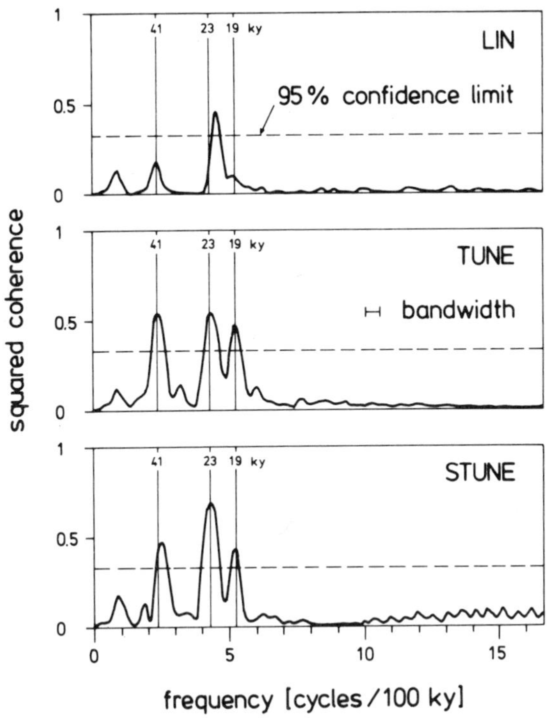

Figure 9 Squared coherence between the solar insolation curve at July 65°N and the planktonic $\delta^{18}O$ record dated by the time scales LIN, TUNE and STUNE.

time series reveal that tuning does not necessarily lead to the same time scales if coherence is maximized at different single frequencies.

The astronomically tuned time scales differ clearly from our carbonate corrected time scale CARPOR (Fig. 6) with a maximum deviation of 50 kyr corresponding to ± 8% relative to the absolute age. The CARPOR time scale, however, lies rather close to the time scale of (23,24), which is also based on assumptions on the sediment-accumulation rates.

At present, it is difficult to decide which of the two groups of time scales under discussion comes closer to reality. Only very few and mostly shaky radiometric, electron-spin resonance (ESR), and thermo-luminescence dates were published from the range older than 127 kyr by now as summarized in Table 3. The most reliable datum near 210 kyr and an ESR datum near 420 kyr support the timescale STUNE while the remaining three, but less reliable dates are in support of CARPOR. However, STUNE significantly deviates from the radiocarbon dates within the range of the last 50 kyr. It is generally rather consistent with astronomically tuned time scales of various other authors (16), while CARPOR is consistent with time scales based on the interpolation of sediment core sections (24). The difference of the percentages explained variance between STUNE (13%) and CARPOR (6%) cannot be used for discrimination because the high value for STUNE is partially an artefact inherent to the applied technique of coherence maximation. In summary, we suggest that both time scales be retained for study until more evidence is available. If CARPOR is more correct, non-linear and stochastic climatic forcing is more important for chrono-stratigraphy for example, as shown by the decrease of linearly explained climatic variance from 13% to 6%.

MODELLING CLIMATIC RESPONSE

So far we referred always to the same insolation curve (July, 65°N) for cross spectral analysis. However, for modelling the ice-age climate the complete latitudinal and seasonal distribution of solar insolation may be effective. For example (4) considered a linear combination of several solar insolation curves each corresponding to a certain month and latitude, as input in a simple response model. A subset of these insolation curves was then selected being able to explain a major part of the variance of the deep-core signal (SIMPLEX time scale based on linear interpolation of planktonic $\delta^{18}O$ curve). (5) has used a somewhat different approach in selecting the characteristic insolation functions. The latitudinal dependence was expressed by Legendre polynomials and the seasonal dependence

Table 3 Absolute ages for discrimination of time scales.

isotopic stage	core depth [cm]	age [ky]	ages based on
7a (top)	315	210 (+25, -21)	$^{230}Th/^{234}U$, (9)
7b (lower part)	335	250	K/Ar Dymond, in (17)
12 (center) LAD Pseudo-emiliania lacunosa	≈ 630 ≈ 630 ≈ 630	≈ 420 ≈ 460 ≈ 474	ESR, (21) ESR, (21) TL, (26)

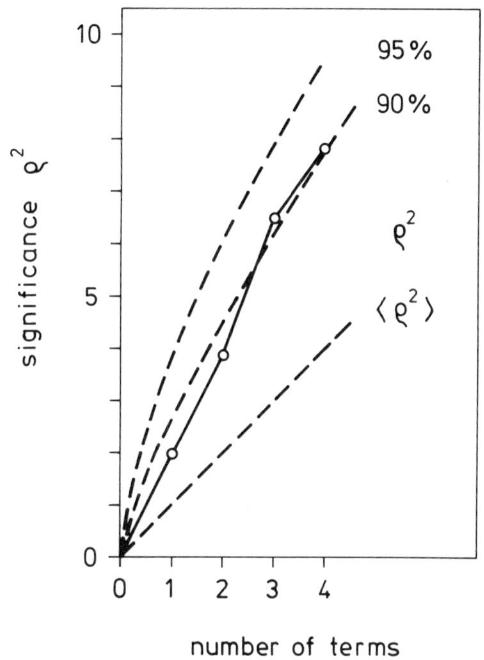

Figure 10 Significance measure ρ^2 as calculated for a simple response model (5) simulating the $\delta^{18}O$ curve. ρ^2 is a function of the number of terms retained in a series expansion of the global solar insolation input (equation [4]).

through a Fourier expansion. The variation of daily solar insolation $S(\phi,m,t)$ was then approximated by a truncated series

$$S(\phi,m,t) \simeq \sum_{i=1}^{N} \Phi_i(t) Y_i(\phi,m) \qquad [4]$$

in which the time dependence $\Phi_i(t)$ on the long time scales was separated from the latitudinal and seasonal dependence $Y_i(\phi,m)$.

The series of equation [4] truncated at the order N=3 can still explain more than 95% of the variance of the insolation changes. The time dependent coefficients $\Phi_i(t)$ ordered with respect to their contribution to the variance, were now taken as input in a linear regression model. The modelled output time series was CARPOR.

In Figure 10, the statistical significance of a linear regression model which has the solar radiation as input according to equation [4], is plotted as a function of the number of terms retained in the series. For N=3, the significance is above the 90% confidence limit.

The construction of a statistically significant model with three input time series $\Phi_1(t)$, $\Phi_2(t)$, $\Phi_3(t)$ corresponds to the existence of essentially three independent astronomical variables characterizing the orbital motion variations. To the extent that the insolation changes vary linearly with the orbital perturbations, the functions $\Phi_i(t)$ are mathematically equivalent to the orbital variables. However, the *a priori* ordering scheme has the advantage of representing a clearly identifiable physical forming function for model construction and interpretation.

PHASE RELATIONSHIPS BETWEEN DIFFERENT CLIMATIC SIGNALS

In the previous sections, we inspected the role of solar insolation for dating the deep-sea record and its significance for climatic modelling. We consider now briefly some qualitative phase relationships between other climatic signals derived from Meteor-core 13519, using a less rigorous event-type analysis which can be applied also to non-linear relations.

Firstly, we intercompare the $\delta^{18}O$ curve, mainly reflecting the global ice volume, and the percentage of $CaCO_3$, taken as an indicator of dissolution and thereby, of sea-ice extension in high latitudes of the North Atlantic (7). As shown earlier, the fluctuation in calcium-carbonate content on the Sierra

Leone Rise are mainly due to varying dissolution at almost 3000 m water depth. They are presumably related to changes in the bottom water regime. During phases of climatic cooling, we observe that the increase of $CaCO_3$ dissolution clearly leads the $\delta^{18}O$ isotopic signal. Figure 11 shows the times of the beginning and of the end of cooling phases. The mean lead of $CaCO_3$ vs. $\delta^{18}O$ amounts to 3.8 cm core length corresponding to 2700 y. This may possibly be explained by the development of an early sea-ice cover in the Norwegian and Greenland Seas blocking the formation of North Atlantic Deep Water (NADW). Thereby, the existing deep water becomes CO_2 enriched and more corrosive such as suggested by (7).

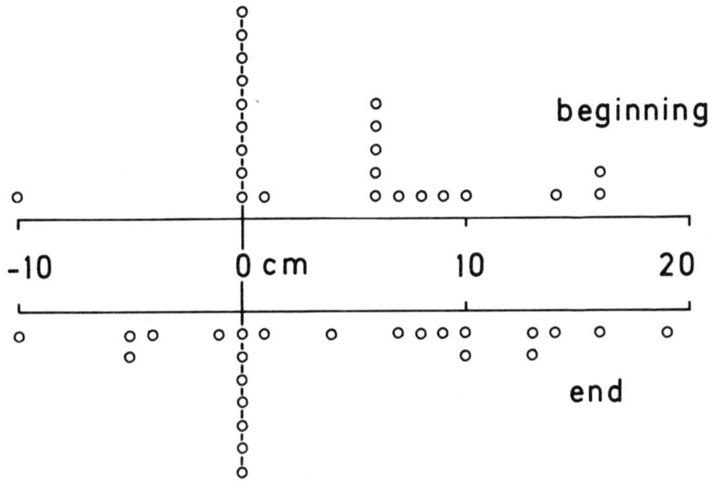

Figure 11 Frequency distribution of leads (positive depth values) observed for intervals of decreasing %-$CaCO_3$ relative to corresponding intervals of increasing $\delta^{18}O$ during the cooling phases of the last 750 kyr. Beginning and end of the intervals plotted separately.

Figure 12 shows a phase shift between a second pair of signals, the $\delta^{18}O$ record and the variation of the grain-size distribution of the terrigenous dust, a quantity which may be used to calculate fossil wind speeds (18). In most cases, the dust curve lags the $\delta^{18}O$ signal during phases of climatic warming. The mean lag is 7.6 cm or 5400 y. This might be explained by a lag of the reduction of the areal ice extent on land relative to the waning of global ice volume. Accordingly, a strong meridional temperature gradient and an associated rigorous atmospheric circulation can be maintained.

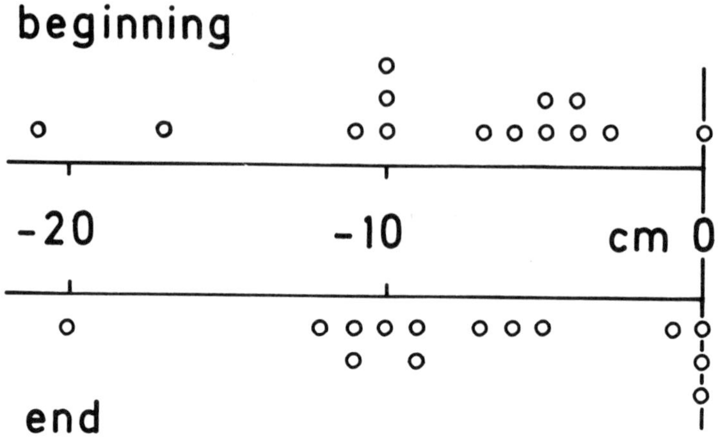

Figure 12 Frequency distribution of lags (negative depth values) observed for intervals of decreasing grain sizes of terrigenous matter relative to corresponding intervals of decreasing $\delta^{18}O$ during warming phases of the last 750 kyr. Beginning and end of the intervals plotted separately.

These examples suggest that although linear cross spectral analysis is clearly a useful tool in the Milankovitch problem, its applicability in calculating phase relationships of the kind shown in this last section may be limited. Linear models of climate do not distinguish between periods of cooling or warming, but a single linear mechanism is assumed to apply throughout the climatic history. Nevertheless, linear analysis can be applied as a first step to derive some first order insight into the temporal and spatial relationships between different climatic variables, for example a high coherence is found between the variations of $CaCO_3$ and the $\delta^{18}O$ curve. Further information may be obtained by calculating spatially dependent transfer functions using, for example, the spatially and seasonally dependent solar insolation functions of (5) as input. A necessary prerequisite for this approach is a generally accepted Brunhes time scale for which the Milankovitch forcing seems to provide a valuable calibration reference.

ACKNOWLEDGEMENTS

Our study was stimulated a lot by the diverging but gradually converging opinions of Klaus Hasselmann and John Imbrie on the principles of climatic forcing. We gratefully acknowledged discussions and their sympathetic support. André Berger kindly provided us with a computer program to calculate the variations of solar insolation. Thomas Bruns generously contributed to our paper by running his unpublished program of spherical harmonics expansion. Helmut Erlenkeuser permitted the use of $\delta^{18}O$ data prior to publication. This study is part of the German national program for climate research.

REFERENCES

1. Barnett, T.P., and Hasselmann, K. : 1979, Rev. Geophys. Space Phys. 17, pp. 949-968.
2. Berger, A. : 1976, Astron. Astrophys. 51, pp. 127-135.
3. Berger, A. : 1977, Celestial Mech. 15, pp. 53-74.
4. Berger, A., Guiot, J., Kukla, G., and Pestiaux, P. : 1981, Geologische Rundschau 70, pp. 748-758.
5. Bruns, T. : 1981, Unpubl. Diplomarbeit (Master Thesis), Universität Hamburg, 71 pp.
6. Duplessy, J.C. : 1978, "Climatic Change", John Gribbin (Ed), Cambridge Univ. Press, pp. 46-67.
7. Duplessy, J.C. : 1982, Bull. Inst. Géol. Bassin d'Aquitaine, Bordeaux, n°31, pp. 379-391.
8. Gordon, A.L. : 1975, "Numerical models of ocean circulation", Nat. Acad. Sci., Washington D.C., pp. 39-53.
9. Harmon, R.S., Ku, T.L., Matthews, R.K. and Smart, P.L. : 1979, Geology 7, pp. 405-409.
10. Hays, J.D., Imbrie, J., and Shackleton, N.J. : 1976, Science 194, pp. 1121-1132.
11. Imbrie, J., and Imbrie, J.Z. : 1980, Science 207, pp. 243-253.
12. Jenkins, G.M., and Watts, D.G. : 1968, in : "Spectral Analysis and its Applications", Holden-Day, San Francisco, 525 pp.
13. Kominz, M.A., Heath, G.R., Ku, T.L. and Pisias, N.G. : 1979, Earth and Planet. Sci. Lett. 45, pp. 394-410.
14. Koopmann, B. : 1979, Dissertation, Geologisches Institut der Universität Kiel, 107 pp.
15. Mankinen, E.A., and Dalrymple, G.B. : 1979, J. Geophys. Res. 84, pp. 615-625.
16. Morley, J.J., and Hays, J.D. : 1981, Earth and Planet. Sci. Lett. 53, pp. 279-295.
17. Ninkovitch, D., and Shackleton, N.J. : 1975, Earth and Planet. Sci. Lett. 27, pp. 20-34.
18. Sarnthein, M., Tetzlaff, G., Koopmann, B., Wolter,K., and Pflaumann, U. : 1981, Nature 293, pp. 193-196.
19. Sarnthein, M., Erlenkeuser, M.H., and Zahn, R. : 1982, Bull. Inst. Géol. Bassin d'Aquitaine, Bordeaux, n°31, pp. 393407.
20. Sarnthein, M., Erlenkeuser, M.H., von Grafenstein, R. and Schröder, C. : 1983, to appear in "Meteor" Forschungsergebnisse.
21. Sato, T. : 1982, Nature 300, pp. 518-521.

22. Schröder, C. : 1981, Unpubl. Diplomarbeit (Master Thesis), Universität Kiel, 31 pp.
23. Shackleton, N.J., and Opdyke, N.D. : 1973, Quat. Res. 3, pp. 39-55.
24. Shackleton, N.J., and Matthews, R.K. : 1977, Nature 268, pp. 618-620.
25. von Grafenstein, R. : 1982, Unpubl. Diplomarbeit (Master Thesis), Universitaet Kiel, 67 pp.
26. Wintle, A.G., and Huntley, D.J. : 1980, Can. J. Earth Sci. 17, pp. 348-360.

THE EFFECT OF ACCUMULATION RATE ON THE SPECTRUM OF GEOLOGIC TIME SERIES : EVIDENCE FROM TWO SOUTH ATLANTIC SEDIMENT CORES

J.J. Morley [1] and N.J. Shackleton [2]

[1] Lamont-Doherty Geological Observatory of the Columbia University, Palisades, New York 10964, USA
[2] Godwin Laboratory for Quaternary Research, Cambridge, CB2 3RS, ENGLAND

ABSTRACT

Late Pleistocene climatic signals from two nearby subtropical South Atlantic piston cores (with accumulation rates of 2.0 and 3.7 cm/kyr) are examined to determine the degree to which the different accumulation rates at these sites affect (1) the correlation between each of three different geologic signals; (2) the spectra and cross-spectra of these signals; and (3) the coherency between signals and orbital curves. The geologic signals investigated are time series of oxygen isotope measurements, sea-surface temperature estimates, and C. davisiana abundance. A nearly identical oxygen isotope signal is recorded at these two sites despite differences in sedimentation rate. At periods longer than about 15 kyr, the isotopic signals are significantly coherent and the spectra are essentially the same. For the temperature and C. davisiana signals, this is true only at periods longer than about 25 kyr and 20 kyr, respectively. Thus our ability to record primary information about geological signals is a strong function of frequency, and depends not only on the accumulation rate but also on the variability of the specific signal in a given frequency band.

INTRODUCTION

Spectral analyses of geologic signals recording variations in ice volume, sea-surface temperature, wind and current patterns as preserved in marine sediments show that many of these

A. L. Berger et al. (eds.), Milankovitch and Climate, Part 1, 467–480.

variables have frequency peaks with periods similar to those of the earth's orbital components of eccentricity, obliquity and precession (1-5). A recent study by Pisias (6) suggests that a high proportion of these climatic signals, in this case variations in oxygen isotope ratios, are retained in marine sediments accumulating at rates $\geq$ 2 cm/kyr. The purpose of the present study is to extend this line of investigation by examining three climatic variables that are recorded in two cores taken from the same region but having distinctly different sediment-accumulation rates. The data from analyses of these three variables in the time and frequency domain show the possible effects of a relatively slow accumulation rate on the recording resolution of three distinctly different climatic signals.

MARINE RECORDS

The late Pleistocene marine sediments examined in this study are from two piston cores taken from the southeastern subtropical South Atlantic. Core RC13-228, an 11 m core, was located at the base of the continental slope in the northeastern corner of the Cape Basin in 3200 m of water (Table 1). The other core, RC13-229, was taken on the continental rise downslope from core RC13-228 in 4200 m of water (Table 1). Core RC13-229 is longer than core RC13-228, 16 m as opposed to 11 m, although sediments accumulated at a slower rate at this site (2.0 cm/kyr versus 3.7 cm/kyr). Because of its lower accumulation rate, the variations in the three climatic signals in only the upper six meters of core RC13-229 will be examined, since this is the portion of the record which coincides in time with that recorded in core RC13-228.

Table 1 Location and identification of piston cores containing climatic signals.

Core	Location		Water Depth (m)	Core Length (cm)
RC13-228	22°20'S	11°12'E	3204	1120
RC13-229	25°30'S	11°18'E	4191	1637

Calculations of the oxygen isotope ratio, the percentage of a particular radiolarian species, <u>Cycladophora davisiana</u>, and sea-surface temperature were made at 5 cm intervals in core RC13-228 and at 10 cm intervals in core RC13-229. Since the sediment in core RC13-228 accumulated at almost double the rate in core RC13-229, the time interval between successive samples is approximately 1250 years in core RC13-228 compared to 5000 years in core RC13-229.

The oxygen isotope measurements were generated using benthic foraminifera. The error for these isotopic analyses is +0.07 per mil. Estimates of sea-surface temperature were produced with transfer functions based on variations in siliceous microfaunal (radiolarian) assemblages. The standard error of estimate for these transfer functions is ±1.36°C (7). The third variable, abundance of radiolarian *C. davisiana*, was calculated relative to all other radiolaria. At these mid-latitude sites, this species, whose abundance variations are not directly related to sea-surface temperatures, is probably responding to variations in local phenomena such as upwelling or intensity of the Benguela Current. Reproducibility of counts of this particular species in these cores is about ±0.50 percent.

Examining the variations in these three climatic parameters enables us to monitor three different aspects of the climate system, with oxygen isotope variations reflecting changes in northern hemisphere ice volume, sea-surface temperatures reflecting local changes in ocean temperature, and *C. davisiana* abundance reflecting variations in upwelling and/or oceanic currents related to changes in atmospheric wind patterns.

Figure 1 shows the oxygen isotope, summer sea-surface temperature and percent *C. davisiana* curves in the upper portion of core RC13-229. The location of the globally synchronous extinction of the radiolarian *Stylatractus universus* in this core confirmed preliminary identification of specific isotopic stages since this datum has been shown to coincide with the oxygen isotopic stage 11/12 boundary (8-9). Estimates of summer sea-surface temperature range from a minimum of 16.9°C to a maximum of 26.4°C. The estimated temperature of 19.1°C at the top of the piston core corresponds closely with today's observed summer temperature of 20.2°C at this site. The abundance of *C. davisiana* remains low (10%) through most of the upper 4 m of this record. Higher relative abundances as well as large-amplitude variations are recorded in older sediments coinciding with isotopic stages 7 through 9.

The downcore variations in these same three climatic signals as recorded in core RC13-228 are shown in Figure 2. Because the variables in this core were calculated at a significantly higher sampling density than in core RC13-229 (1250-yr versus 5000-yr time increment), all three records contain more detail than their low-density counterparts. The three ^{14}C dates in addition to the absence of *S. universus* in bottom sediments

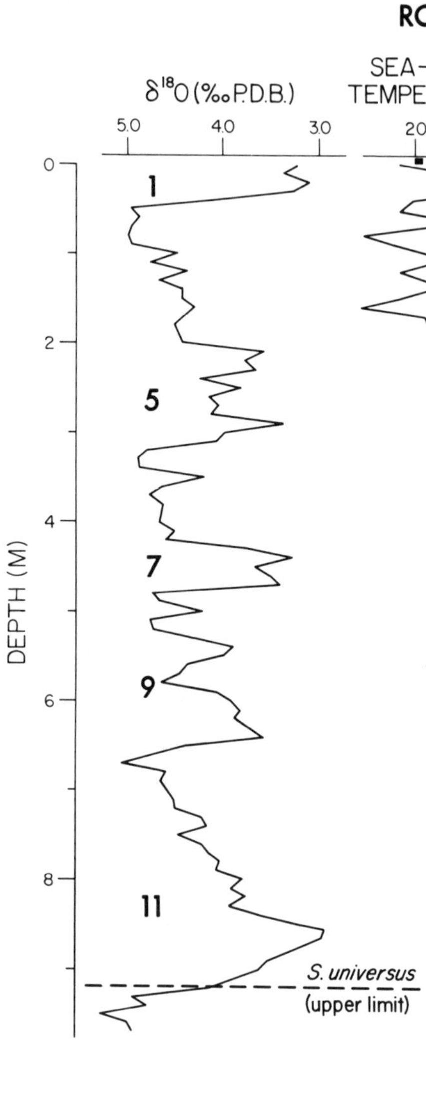

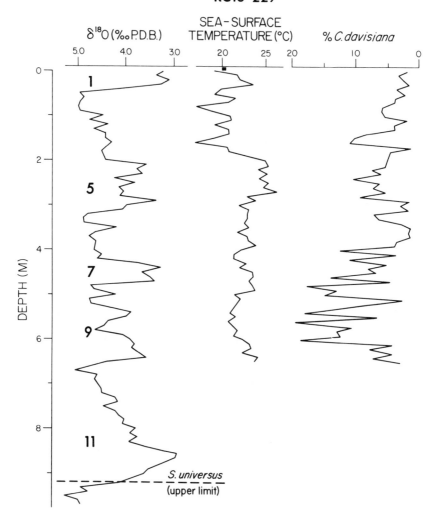

Figure 1 Oxygen isotope, summer sea-surface temperature and *C. davisiana* abundance curves in core RC13-229. Light isotopic stages and extinction level of *S. universus* are identified as well as today's (observed) summer sea-surface temperature (solid square symbol).

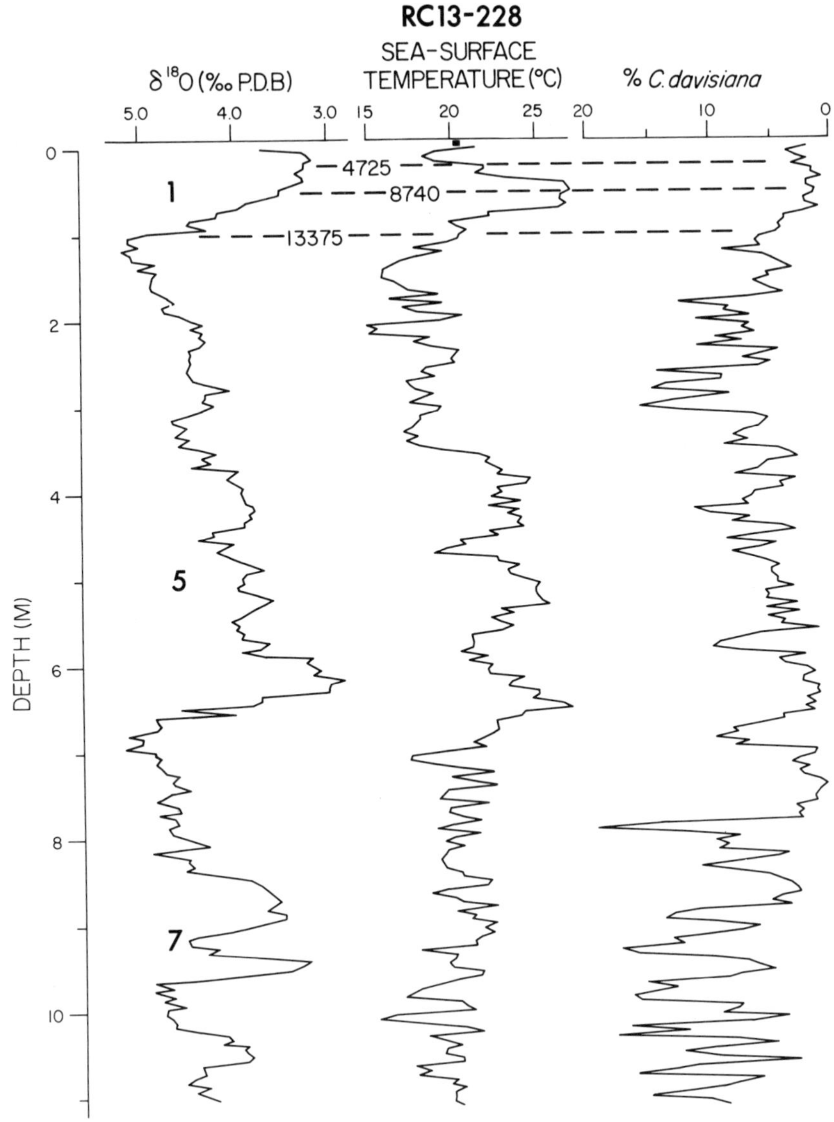

Figure 2 Oxygen isotope, summer sea-surface temperature and <u>C. davisiana</u> abundance curves in core RC13-228. Light isotopic stages and ^{14}C dates are identified as well as today's (observed) summer sea-surface temperature (solid square symbol).

from this core make it possible to identify isotopic stages 1 through 9. The range of summer sea-surface temperatures is larger in core RC13-228 than in core RC13-229 with a slightly lower minimum and a higher maximum. The estimated sea-surface temperature at the core top of 21.4°C compares favorably with today's observed summer-surface temperature of 20.4°C.

TIME AND FREQUENCY DOMAIN ANALYSES

If the sediments at these two sites retained similar records of each climatic variables, then the correlation coefficients and phase relationships between the three signals should be similar in both cores. For this experiment, the interval between successives samples in both cores was 5000 years.

Prior to the cross-correlation analyses, time series of the three variables were generated using ages from the SPECMAP age model (10) for as many of the characteristic features common to the oxygen isotope curves in both cores RC13-228 and RC13-229. The time series in both these cores are based on 30 datum levels common to both records. Comparison of the results from cross-correlation analyses (Table 2) shows that the correlation coefficients between the three variables in core RC13-228 (when sampled at 5000-yr increments) are twice as high as those in core RC13-229. Since there are major differences in correlation coefficients, even though the two cores were sampled at identical time increments, it would appear that the lower accumulation rate in core RC13-229 may be responsible for producing some of the disparity between the three sets of variables at the two sites.

To examine what effect, if any, sampling interval had in determing correlation coefficients and phase relationships between climatic variables in a sedimentary record, we decreased the spacing between consecutive data points in the core with the higher sedimentation rate (RC13-228) from 20 cm (5000-yr increment) to 5 cm (1250-yr increment). The correlation coefficients and phase relationships are similar to those resulting from analyses of core RC13-228 using a lower sampling density (Table 2). Maxima and minima in oxygen isotopes lag minima and maxima in sea-surface temperature by an average 3750 years with a correlation coefficient of 0.62. Changes in C. davisiana abundance are in phase with changes in sea-surface temperature. Maxima and minima in oxygen isotopes lag corresponding maxima and minima in C. davisiana abundance by about 2500 years. The similarity of the correlation coefficients and phase relationships between the three variables in core RC13-228 at different sampling densities suggests that variations in the sampling interval (time/depth), on the order used in this experiment, do not significantly alter the results of cross-correlation analyses.

Table 2 Correlation coefficients and phase (+ = lead, - = lag) between climatic signals.

Data Set (ΔT)	Oxygen Isotopes versus Temperatures (phase in years)	Oxygen Isotopes versus *C. davisiana* (phase in years)	Temperatures versus *C. davisiana* (phase in years)
RC13-229 (5000 years)	0.37 (-000)	0.07 (-000)	0.15 (-000)
RC13-228 (5000 years)	0.60 (-5000)	0.23 (-2500)	0.39 (-000)
RC13-228 (1250 years)	0.62 (-3750)	0.30 (-2500)	0.45 (-000)

It follows that if the degree of recording resolution is similar in the two cores, then each of the three variables should be in phase with its counterpart and have a relatively high correlation coefficient. In the frequency domain, the signals should also be significantly coherent.

Cross-correlation analysis between each of the three variables with its counterpart in the two cores using an identical time increment of 5000 years between consecutive samples showed that of the three variables, the oxygen isotope records exhibited the highest degree of similarity with a correlation coefficient of greater than 0.9 at zero lags. Altough the summer sea-surface temperature curves as well as the *C. davisiana* abundance patterns are also in phase (zero lag), their correlation coefficients are only 0.58. This indicates that there are some differences in the character of the respective sea-surface temperature and *C. davisiana* curves in these two cores which could be the result of different degrees of recording resolution of these variables at the two sites.

Frequency domain analyses of the three sets of variables show that the two oxygen isotope records (Figure 3) are significantly coherent (above the 20% significance level) at all dominant frequencies with periods greater than 15 000 years. The two sea-surface temperature signals (Figure 4), however, are

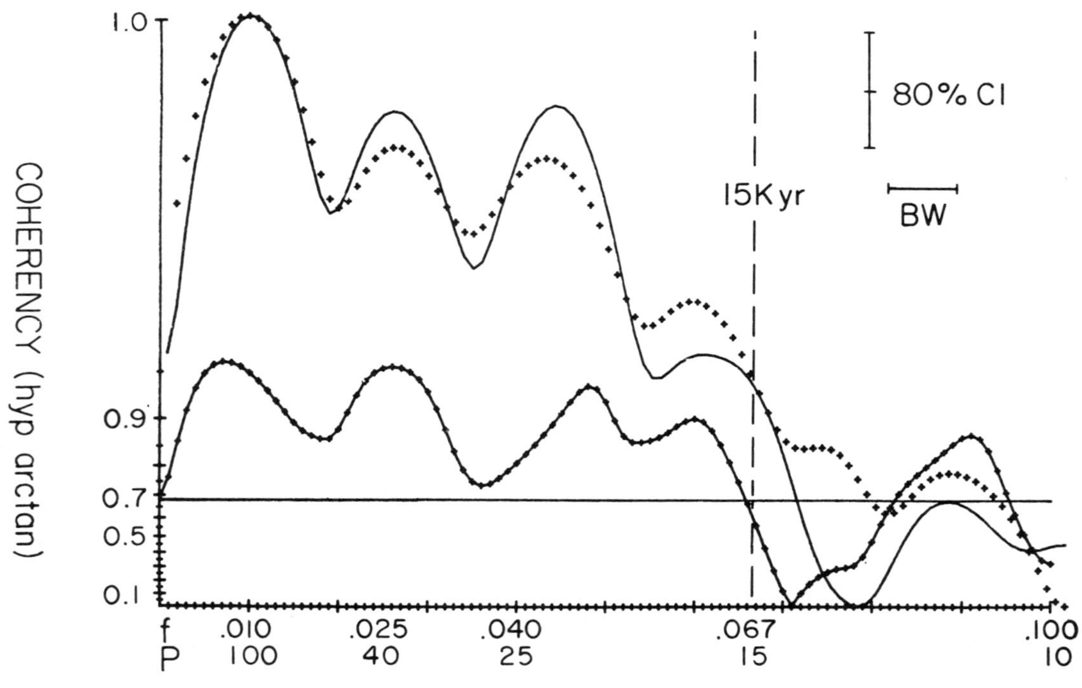

Figure 3 Variance oxygen isotope spectra from cores RC13-228 (solid-curved line) and RC13-229 (dotted-curved line) plotted on arbitrary log scale with indicated bandwidth (BW) and confidence interval (CI). Coherency spectrum (connected-dotted line) plotted on a hyperbolic arctangent scale provided with a 20% significance level (horizontal line). Frequencies (f) and periods (P) along x-axis are in cycles per thousand years and in thousands of years, respectively.

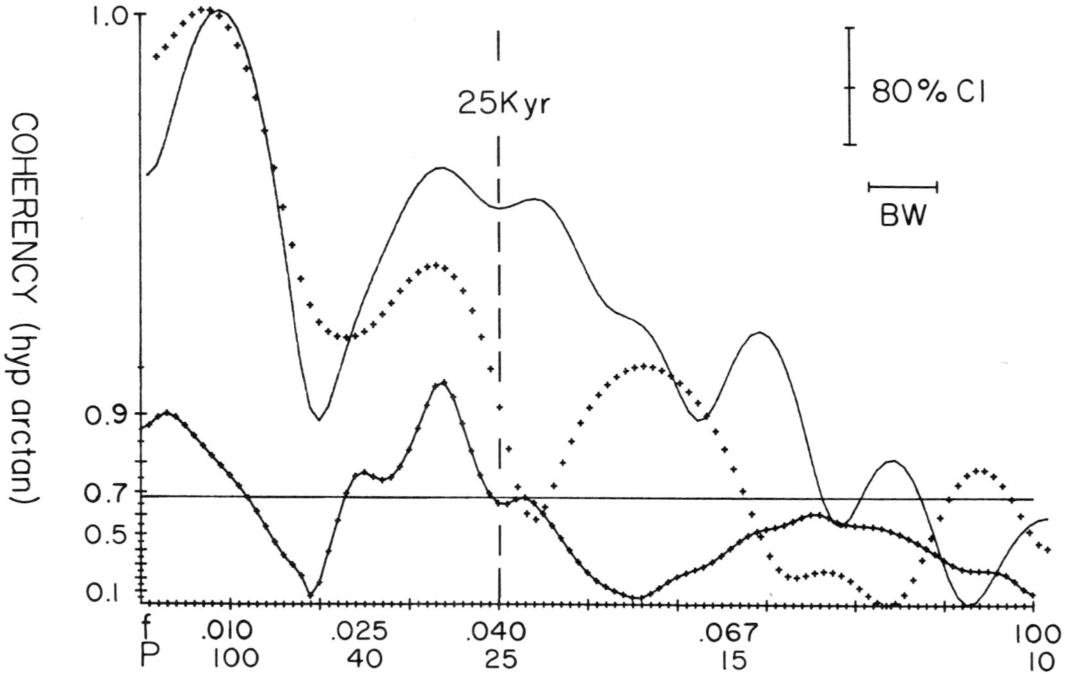

Figure 4 Variance summer sea-surface temperature spectra from cores RC13-228 (solid-curved line) and RC13-229 (dotted-curved line) plotted on arbitrary log scale with indicated bandwidth (BW) and confidence interval (CI). Coherency spectrum (connected-dotted line) plotted on a hyperbolic arctangent scale provided with a 20% significance level (horizontal line). Frequencies (f) and periods (P) along x-axis are in cycles per thousand years and in thousands of years, respectively.

significantly coherent only at dominant frequencies with periods greater than 25 000 years. Significant coherence exists between the two C. davisiana abundances curves (Figures 5) only over periods longer than 20 000 years.

Another way to assess the degree of similarity between the climatic signals in the two cores is to compare the dominant frequencies and the percent of total variance under these frequency peaks. For this experiment, we examined the frequency distribution of each of the three variables as recorded at 5000 year increments in core RC13-229 and in core RC13-228, and at 1250 year increments in core RC13-228. The values of each signal were normalized prior to generating the spectrum. As the results in Table 3 show, all three oxygen isotope curves have dominant frequency peaks at similar frequencies. The oxygen isotope record in the core with the lower sedimentation rate (RC13-229) contains lower percentages of total variance at all the dominant frequencies with periods less than 100 000 years. Comparison of the summer sea-surface temperature spectra (Table 4) shows that not all the dominant frequencies are in common to all three records. Of the dominant frequencies with periods less than 100 000 years which are in common to the three data sets, those in core RC13-229 contain the lowest percentages of total variance. Each of the three C. davisiana abundance curves displays a somewhat unique frequency distribution making it difficult to compare the percentage of total variance at specific

Table 3 Period (x 1000 years) and percentage of total variance of dominant frequency peaks in oxygen isotope spectra.

RC13-229 (ΔT=5000 years)	RC13-228 (ΔT=5000 years)	RC13-228 (ΔT=1250 years)
100 - (64%)	110 - (48%)	100 - (53%)
40 - (18%)	40 - (23%)	41 - (21%)
23 - (14%)	23 - (25%)	23 - (23%)
11.5 - (0.5%)	11.5 - (1%)	11.5 - (1%)
		6 - (1%)

frequencies common to all the data sets. At the dominant frequencies which are in common in the three data sets, the lower percentage of total variance at medium to high frequencies in the core with the lower accumulation rate (RC13-229) suggests that the total character of variability in the climatic signals was not recorded in the sediments at this site.

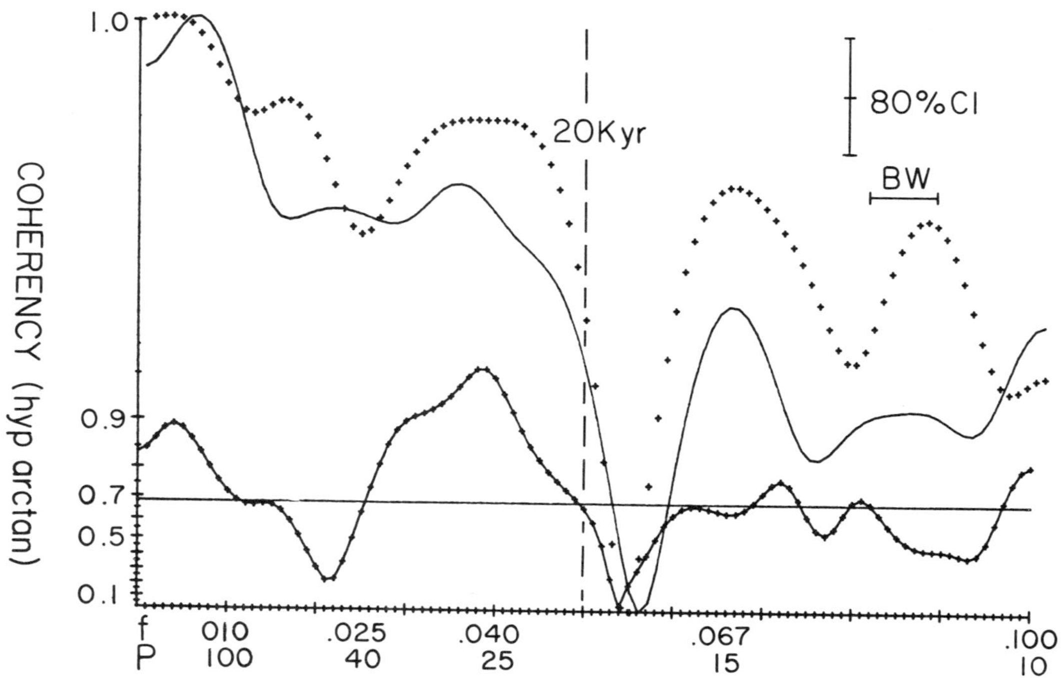

Figure 5 Variance *C. davisiana* abundance spectra from cores RC13-228 (solid-curved line) and RC13-229 (dotted-curved line) plotted on arbitrary log scale with indicated bandwidth (BW) and confidence interval (CI). Coherency spectrum (connected-dotted line) plotted on a hyperbolic arctangent scale provided with a 20% significance level (horizontal line). Frequencies (f) and periods (P) along x-axis are in cycles per thousand years and in thousands of years, respectively.

As a final experiment we compared the coherency at the dominant frequencies in the three oxygen isotope curves with the earth's orbital components. Since the insolation curve for 60°N for the month of July is a fair representation of the combined effects of the various components of the earth's orbit, we cross-correlated this curve (11) with the oxygen isotope data sets. The coherency between the oxygen isotope record in the core with the lower accumulation rate (RC13-229) and the insolation curve for 60°N at a frequency corresponding to that of

Table 4 Period (x 1000 years) and percentage of total variance of dominant frequency peaks in summer sea-surface temperature spectra.

RC13-229 (T=5000 years)	RC13-228 (T=5000 years)	RC13-228 (T=1250 years)
140 - (77%)	120 - (42%)	150 - (47%)
31 - (12%)	30 - (24%)	
19 - (7%)	23 - (20%)	23 - (26%)
	15 - (8%)	
11 - (3%)	12 - (4%)	
		9 - (3%)

Table 5 Coherency of oxygen isotope variations with obliquity and precession.

Core (T)	Coherency with Obliquity	Coherency with Precession
RC13-229 (5000 years)	0.859	0.665
RC13-228 (5000 years)	0.771	0.898
RC13-228 (1250 years)	0.813	0.876

obliquity is similar to coherency values at this same frequency acquired through cross-spectral analyses of the other two oxygen isotope data sets with insolation (Table 5). At a frequency corresponding to precession, however, the coherency between insolation and the isotopic record in core RC13-229 (the lower accumulation-rate record) is only just significant at the 20% significance level; and is much lower than the coherency values between insolation and the other two isotopic curves at this frequency (Table 5).

CONCLUSIONS

Although the statistical error in the calculation of these three variables may be responsible for a certain portion of the differences between the climatic signal as recorded in each core, we do not believe that it is the major cause. If this were the case, one would expect the summer sea-surface temperature record to exhibit the highest degree of dissimilarity since this variable has the largest percent of measurement error relative to its range of the three signals examined. Although the *C. davisiana* abundance record has the smallest percent of measurement error relative to its range, its signal is the least similar of the three sets of curves in the two cores.

Results of these various time and frequency domain analyses indicate that:

(1) A nearly identical oxygen isotope signal has been recorded in the sediments at these two sites despite the large difference in their accumulation rates (2.0 cm/kyr versus 3.7 cm/kyr) as evidenced by the high correlation coefficient (0.91) and similarity in the dominant frequency peaks in the data sets. At periods longer than about 15 000 years, the signals are significantly coherent and the spectra are essentially the same.

(2) The summer sea-surface temperature curves in the two data sets are not identical, with differences concentrated at periods shorter than about 25 000 years. At longer periods, the dominant frequencies are significantly coherent and the spectra are quite similar.

(3) The *C. davisiana* abundance curves in the two data sets are also not identical, with differences concentrated at periods, shorter than about 20 000 years. At longer periods, the dominant frequencies are significantly coherent and the spectra are similar.

(4) Not all climatic signals appear to be recorded in marine sediments with the same degree of resolution regardless of the accumulation rate at the record site. The recording reso-

lution depends not only on the accumulation rate but also on the variability of the specific climatic signal. If the climatic signal is dominated by medium to low frequency amplitude variations, then accumulation rates do not significantly alter the recording resolution of the particular signal. If, however, the signal is characterized by large-amplitude variations at relatively high frequencies, then the degree of recording resolution is affected by the accumulation rate of the sediment.

ACKNOWLEDGEMENTS

We thank N. Pisias and B. Molfino for their helpul suggestions at several stages during this project. This research was directly supported by National Science Foundation grant ATM80-19253 to Lamont-Doherty Geological Observatory.

REFERENCES

1. Hays, J.D., Imbrie, J., and Shackleton, N.J. : 1976, Science 194, pp. 1121-1132.
2. Pisias, N .G. : 1976, in : "Investigation of Late Quaternary Paleooceanography and Paleoclimatology", R.M. Cline and J.D. Hays (Eds), pp. 375-391, Geological Society of America, memoir 145.
3. Ruddiman, W.F. and McIntyre, A. : 1981, Science 212, pp. 617-627.
4. Prell, W.L. : 1982, Transactions, American Geophysical Union 63, pp. 996.
5. Leinen, M., Schramm, C., and Pisias, N. : 1982, Transactions, American Geophysical Union 63, p. 996.
6. Pisias, N.G. : 1983, Marine Geology 51, pp. 99-113.
7. Morley, J.J. : 1979, Quaternary Research 12, pp. 381-395.
8. Hays, J.D. and Shackleton, N.J. : 1976, Geology 4, pp. 649-652.
9. Morley, J.J. and Shackleton, N.J. : 1978, Geology 6, pp. 309-311.
10. Imbrie, J., Shackleton, N.J., Pisias, N.J., Morley, J.J., Prell, W.L., Martinson, D.G., Hays, J.D., McIntyre, A., and Mix, A. : 1984, in : "Milankovitch and Climate", A. Berger, J. Imbrie, J. Hays, G. Kukla and B. Saltzman (Eds), D. Reidel Publ. Company, Dordrecht, Holland. This volume.
11. Berger, A.L. : 1978, J. Atmos. Sci. 35(12), pp. 2362-2367.

EFFECTS OF BIOTURBATION ON CLIMATIC SPECTRA INFERRED FROM DEEP SEA CORES

H.N. Dalfes, S.H. Schneider, S.L. Thompson

National Center for Atmopsheric Research[1], P.O. Box 3000, Boulder, CO 80307, USA

ABSTRACT

A principal feature of variance spectra obtained from a variety of proxy climatic indicators has been a characteristic signature suggesting a "red noise" signal over periods ranging from about 100 000 years to less than 1 000 years. Superimposed on this red noise-like background are usually several peaks, which many investigators believe to represent significant climatic response at orbital frequencies. "Red" spectra have also been produced by stochastic climate models (2). To verify such models it is important to compare their spectra with observational spectra. However, we show that for most reasonable assumed sedimentation rates and sediment mixing lengths the effects of bioturbation reddens the spectrum at the high frequency end with a power gain factor that has a "-2 slope" asymptotically. This implies that any climatic inference made from the high-frequency end of an ocean core variance spectrum which does not correct for the effect of bioturbation is likely to be invalid. We show just how serious this distortion can be over a wide range of mixing and sedimentation parameters, and compute how spectra of Hays <u>et al.</u> (12) are modified by several different assumed mixing length and sedimentation rate cases.

INTRODUCTION

Explaining observed climatic spectra is one of the most important tasks for climate theory. The discrete signature (i.e. peaks) of a spectrum gives clues about possible forced or free oscillatory processes in the system. The continuum provides a

A. L. Berger et al. (eds.), Milankovitch and Climate, Part 1, 481–492.

test of our understanding of the interaction of climatic subsystems with drastically different characteristic time scales. One of the most popular attempts to explain the "redness" of the continuum of some observed climatic spectra, is the Brownian motion analogy proposed by Hasselmann and his co-workers (1,2). Their formalism leads to a variance spectrum asymptotically proportional to the inverse square of the frequency.

Deep sea sediment cores provide us with long time records of proxy climate indicators from which we can estimate climatic spectra. However, the original climatic/environmental information recorded in deep sea sediment layers goes through a chain of natural and man made transformations before being presented in the form of a climatic spectrum (see Fig. 1). Each of these transformations modifies the information content of the original time series. Since verification of our modelling efforts depends on the final product (climatic time series or spectra), it is crucially important to develop an understanding of the effects of the above mentioned transformation processes.

In this paper we will be investigating the effects of one biogenic process that transforms the climatic information recorded in sediment layers. It is well known that bottom dwelling organisms mix the uppermost layers of accumulated sediments. This process is called bioturbation. Studies based on radiocarbon ages (3) give mixed layer thickness estimates ranging from 48 cm to less than 4 cm. Sediment mixing due to bioturbation and other processes have been subject to various time domain modelling efforts (e.g. 3 and 4). Also, attempts (5) to "deconvolve" deep sea core profiles have been criticized (6) because such a technique cannot eliminate unambiguously the distortion due to bioturbation.

Here, we are addressing the problem in the frequency domain. Goreau (7) already gave a general formulation of the problem in the form of a recursive convolution equation in the time domain. He also provided an example application of his model for an observed spectrum. The analysis that we are giving here complements his work by illustrating the concepts with a simple model. We will describe a well known simple biogenic mixing model and derive its frequency domain properties. Later this model will be used to assess the importance of the effects of bioturbation on the continuous and discrete parts of climatic spectra.

A SIMPLE MODEL

To illustrate the concepts without turning to an unduly complex sediment mixing model, we adopt the well known

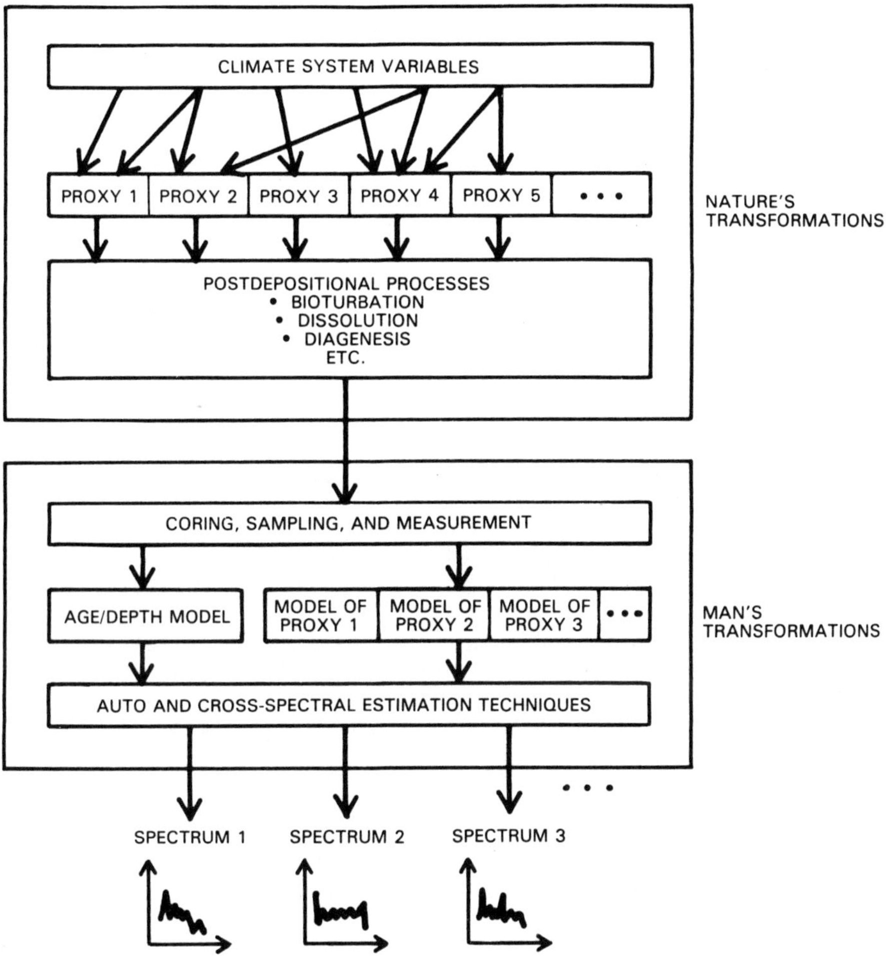

Figure 1 A schematic diagram of natural and man-made processes transforming spectra of climate variables into proxy spectra.

Berger-Heath mixing model (8). It is straightforward, simple model and has already been analyzed (4) and widely used in time domain studies. It assumes that the upper layers of sediments are well mixed instantaneously to a depth L from the surface. If I(x) is the actual concentration of the proxy scalar (i.e. the true climatic signal) incorporated at a depth x(t) in the core (where t is time) and M(x) is the measured value at x(t), then they are related by

$$\frac{dM}{dx} = \frac{1}{L}\,[I(x) - M(x)] \qquad [1]$$

or assuming a constant sediment accumulation rate r (i.e., x=rt),

$$\frac{dM}{dt} = \frac{1}{\tau}\,[I(t) - M(t)] \qquad [2]$$

where τ=L/r. The Fourier transformation of Eq.2 leads to a relation between variance spectra of bioturbed (S_M) and original (S_I) signals,

$$S_M(f) = G(f)\; S_I(f) \qquad [3]$$

where f is frequency and the variance gain factor G(f) is given by

$$G(f) = \frac{1}{1 + 4\,\pi^2 \tau^2 f^2} \qquad [4]$$

On Figure 2, we display the variance gain factor for a range of τ values. As it is also evident from Eq.4, at the high frequency end the gain factor asymptotes to a -2 log-log slope. In addition to frequency selective amplitude damping, bioturbation as modeled by Eq.2 introduces phase shifts. For Eq.1, the frequency dependence of this phase shift $\phi(f)$ is given by

$$\phi(f) = \tan^{-1} 2\,\pi f \tau \qquad [5]$$

and is plotted for a range of τ values on Figure 3. We have to also caution the reader that this phase shift is very much model dependent.

APPLICATIONS

Although tne above described model is a very simple one and is no substitute for more realistic modelling efforts, it can still give us a qualitative understanding of the impacts of biogenic mixing on the final climatic spectra and its interpretation.

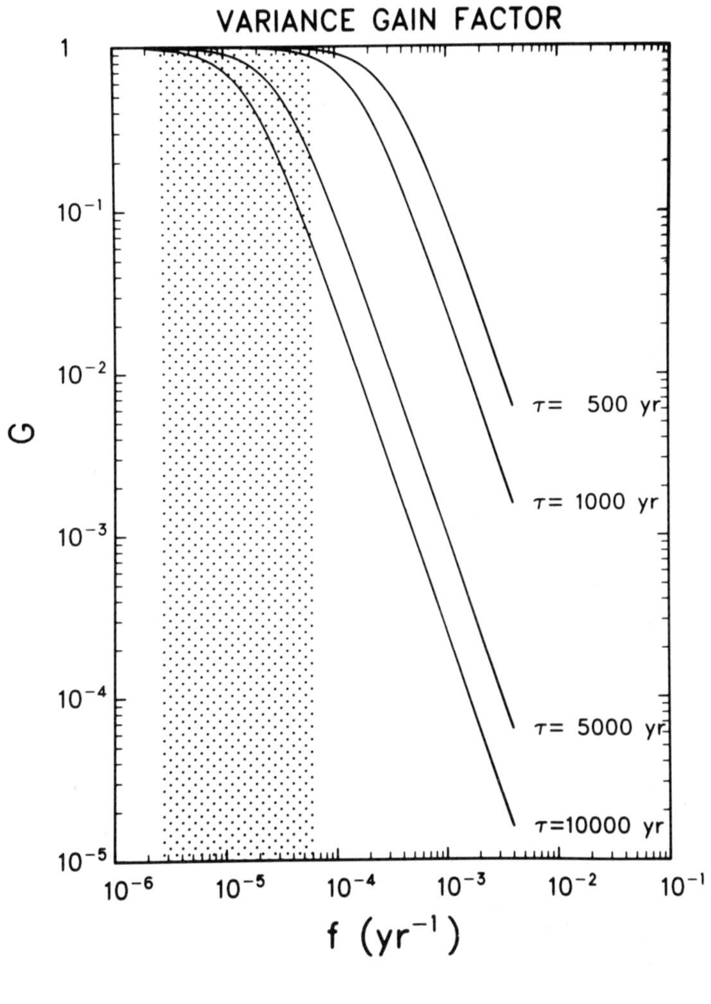

Figure 2 Variance gain factor (Eq.4) plotted against frequency for various τ parameter values. τ is the ratio of the mixed layer depth to the sedimentation rate. Shaded area depicts the frequency region of interest for orbital forcing studies.

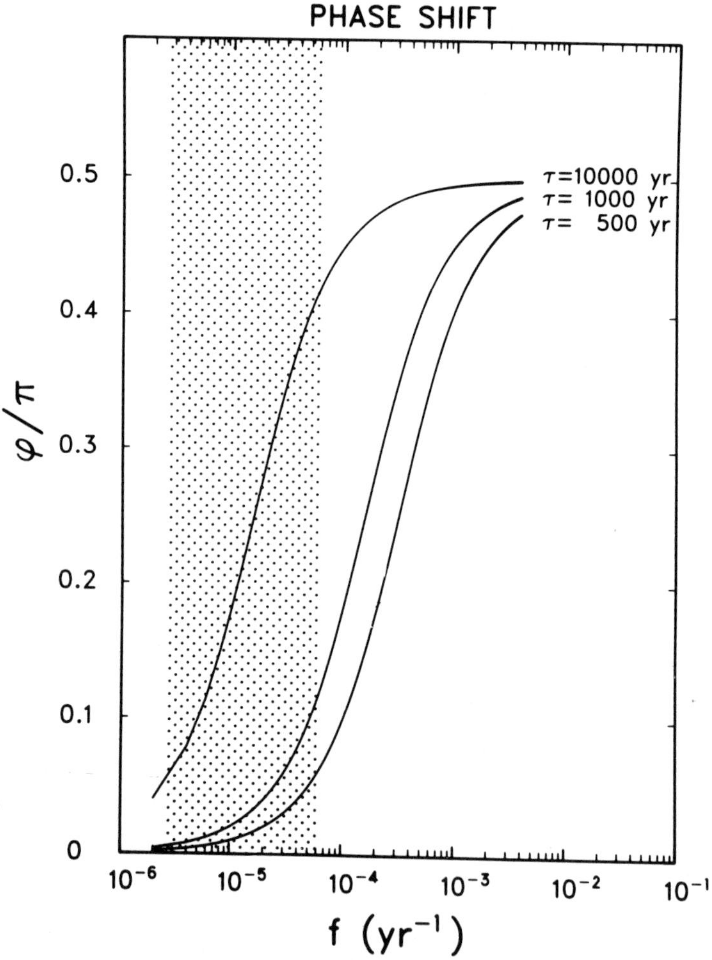

Figure 3 Bioturbation induced phase shift between the original signal and the recorded one based on the Berger-Heath model. The bioturbed signal leads the original signal.

Stochastic climate models based on a linear Langevin equation with additive forcing (1) predict a inverse square of the frequency type signature for the continuum of the climatic spectra. Several authors (9,10,11) attributed the character of the continuum of their spectra to such a "Brownian motion" mechanism. As it can be seen on Figure 2, bioturbation alone can generate a very similar feature. Therefore, one has to take into consideration possible effects due to mixing processes before hastily interpreting the climatic continuum of deep sea cores.

The discrete part of the climatic spectrum will also be influenced by bioturbation. Peaks of climatic spectra interpreted by many authors as responses of orbital forcings will lose some of their variance due to bioturbation damping. Also their relative phases will be altered. To illustrate these effects, we display on Figure 4 the effects of bioturbation, as described by our simple model, on signals with 100 kyr, 40 kyr and 20 kyr periodicities. For large τ values, relative magnitudes and phases of peaks at these frequencies will be appreciably modified.

We also applied a bioturbation "correction" to climatic spectra of Hays *et al.* (12), using a range of τ parameters. Resulting spectra along with the unmodified ones are displayed on Figures 5, 6 and 7. The correction effect can be drastic at the high frequency end, especially for high τ values.

CONCLUSIONS

It is well known that biogenic or other mixing processes can distort substantially the information contained in deep sea cores. We have shown how this distortion applies to the frequency domain as well as the time domain. For our assumed cases, bioturbation does not seem to change the location of discrete spectral peaks, but it does affect the fraction of variance accounted for by each of them. Moreover, and of concern to climate theorists, one should not trust the spectral signature of the continuum of any deep sea core spectra until bioturbation effects have been factored in. In particular, existing deep sea core spectra (and especially their high frequency end) should not be immediately interpreted as a confirmation of the "Brownian motion" model of the interaction among climatic subsystems possessing different characteristic time scales.

These rather cautionary conclusions are based on a very simple bioturbation model which provides us with no more than a first order estimate of possible distortions in core spectra. Nevertheless, it strongly suggests to us that all important assumptions used to translate deep sea core measurements into climatic spectra should be carefully re-examined to eliminate --

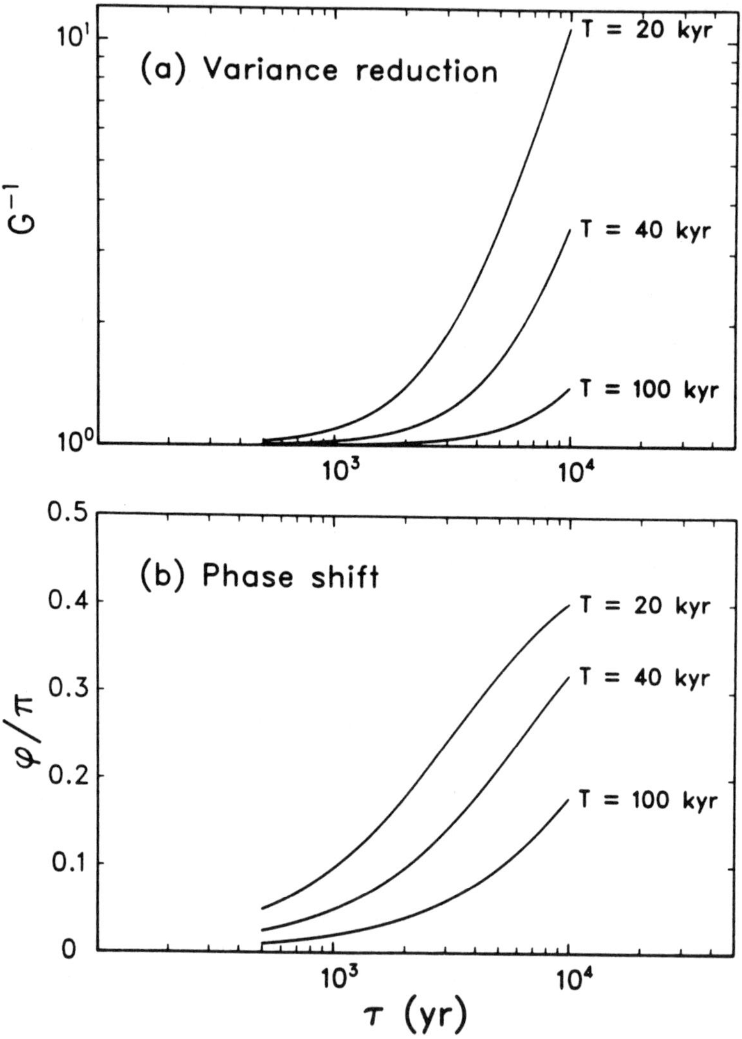

Figure 4 (a) Variance reduction due to bioturbation for three frequencies of importance for the orbital forcing problem; (b) Phase shift between the recorded and the original signals for the same three frequencies.

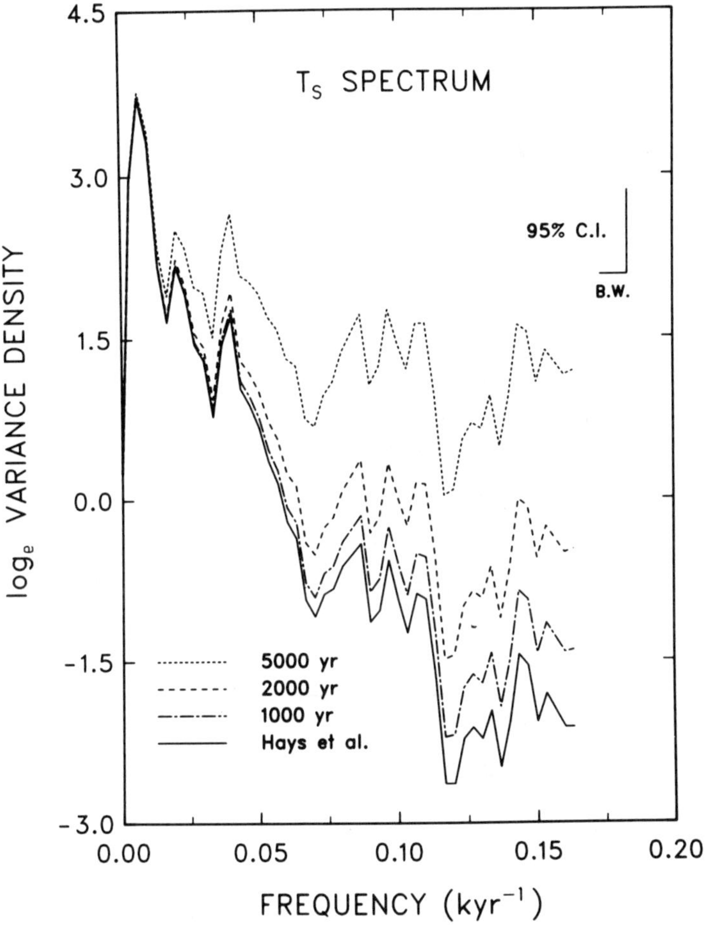

Figure 5 Hays et al. (12) surface temperature spectrum before and after application of bioturbation correction using a range of τ parameter values. Notice the drastic change in the slope of the continuum of the spectrum for a high τ value. The 95% confidence interval (C.I.) and bandwith (B.W.) of the original spectrum are also reproduced on this figure.

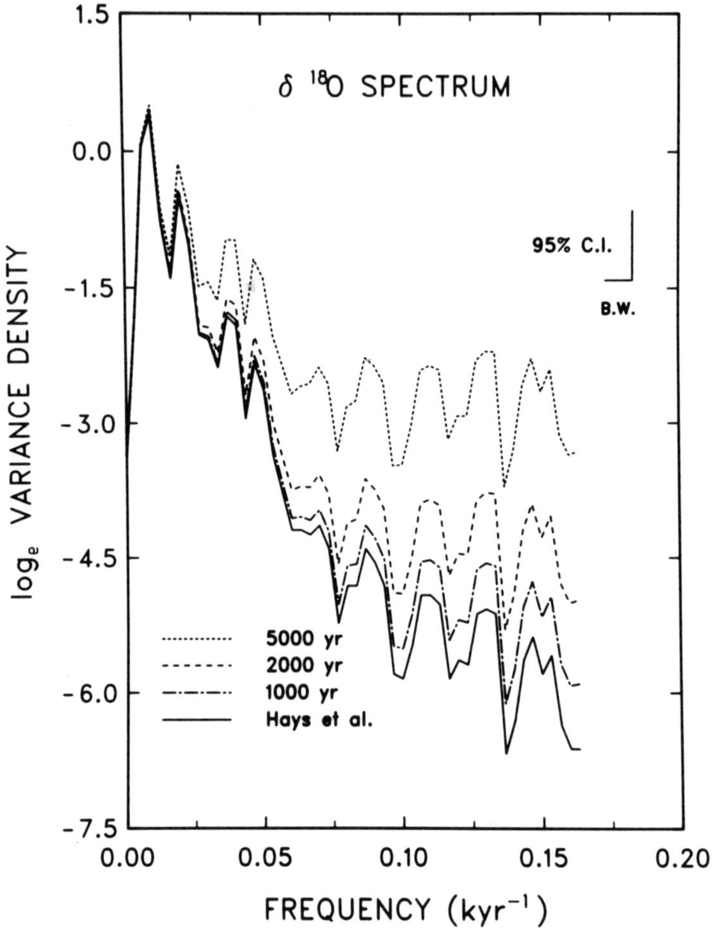

Figure 6 "Corrected" Hays et al. (12) δO^{18} spectrum.

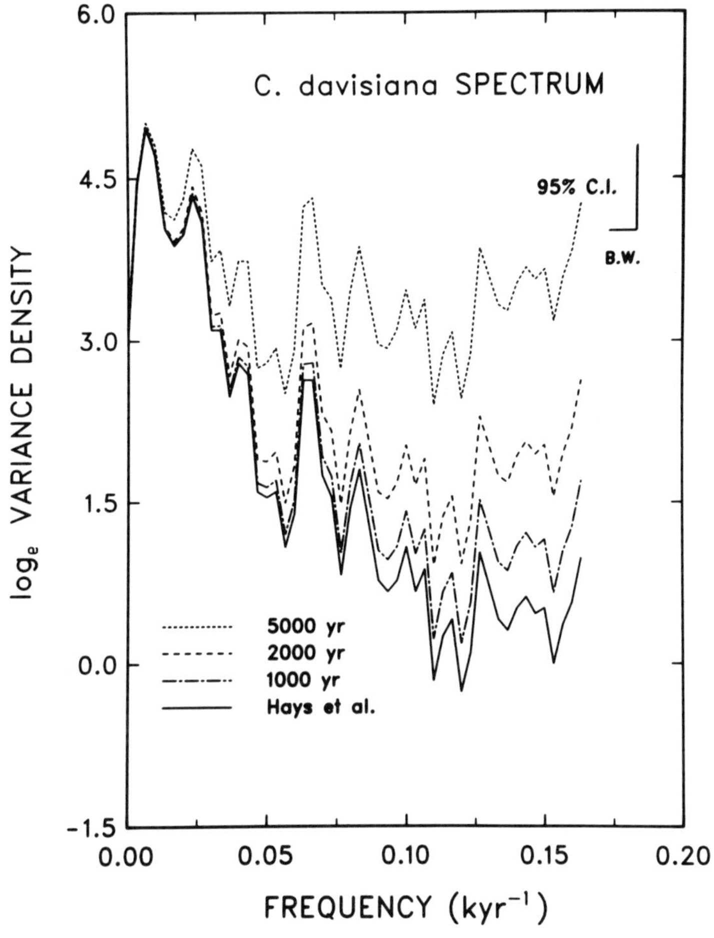

Figure 7 "Corrected" Hays *et al.* (12) *C. davisiana* spectrum.

or at least bound -- possible sources of distortion. For example, biases arising from questionable age/depth in core relationships should be assessed before far reaching conclusions are drawn about the nature of the climate system from spectral and time series analyses of deep sea cores.

REFERENCES

1. Hasselmann, K. : 1976, Tellus 28, pp. 473-485.
2. Lemke, P. : 1977, Tellus 29, pp. 385-392.
3. Peng, T.H., Broecker, W.S., Kipphut, G., and Shackleton, N.J. : 1977, in : "The fate of Fossil Fuel CO_2 in the Oceans", N.R. Andersen and A. Malahof (Eds), Plenum Press, New York, pp. 355-373.
4. Guinasso, N.L., and Schink, D.R. : 1975, J. Geophys. Res. 80, pp. 3022-3043.
5. Berger, W.H. : 1977, Nature 269, pp. 301-304.
6. Jones, G.A., and Ruddiman, W.F. : 1982, Quaternary Research 17, pp. 148-172.
7. Goreau, T.J. : 1980, Nature 287, pp. 620-622.
8. Berger, W.H., and Heath, G.R. : 1968, J. Mar. Res. 26, pp. 134-142.
9. Kominz, M.A., Heath, G.R., Ku, T.L., and Pisias, N.G. : 1979, Earth Planet. Sci. Lett. 45, pp. 394-410.
10. Pisias, N.G., and Moore, T.C. Jr. : 1981, Earth Planet. Sci. Lett. 52, pp. 450-458.
11. Schnitker, D. : 1982, Palaeogeography, -climatology, -ecology 40, pp. 213-234.
12. Hays, J.D., Imbrie, J., and Shackleton, N.J. : 1976, Science 194, pp. 1121-1131.

[1]The National Center for Atmospheric Research is sponsored by the National Science Foundation.

IMPACTS OF DEEP-SEA PROCESSES ON PALEOCLIMATIC SPECTRA

P. Pestiaux and A. Berger

Université Catholique de Louvain, Institut d'Astronomie et de Géophysique Georges Lemaître, Louvain-la-Neuve, Belgium

ABSTRACT

The three main deep-sea processes modifying the original paleoclimatic spectra are considered as a succession of three spectral transformations. They will be modelled to simulate their global effect on the original undisturbed paleoclimatic variability.

The two first transformations correspond to a reddening of the original paleoclimatic spectrum due to the long memory of the climate system and to vertical mixing (bioturbation). The total length of this memory has been estimated by an ARMA (p,q) stochastic model to range from 4 to 14 kyr.

A non-linear time dependent mixing model has then been designed to evaluate theoretical mixing functions, being given the diffusion coefficient and the sedimentation rate. The effect of the mixing has been evaluated using a cubic deconvolution, which allows demixing experiments with both experimental and theoretical mixing functions. This deconvolution method has been applied successfully to the first 170 kyr of the core V28-238, the restored paleoclimatic variability being of the order of that observed in high sedimentation rate deep-sea records.

Finally, a Fast Fourier Transform Stretching algorithm applied to the core V28-238 showed that the variations in the sedimentation rate, which can be identified as a dilatation-compression process of the paleoclimatic signal, broaden the width and decrease the amplitude of the spectral peaks.

A. L. Berger et al. (eds.), Milankovitch and Climate, Part 1, 493–510.

INTRODUCTION

The typical spectral shape of deep-sea climatic records can be considered as made of a few peaks, more or less broad, superimposed to a continuous spectral density rising towards the lower frequencies. This continuous spectral density can be explained either by integration of the random fluctuations (1), or by a deterministic transformation of the insolation input giving aperiodic solutions (2).

The typical spectral shape of the deep sea paleoclimatic record is, in fact, related to the following three physical processes :

(i) the memory of the long term components of the climate system ranging from 2 kyr to 10 kyr,
(ii) the vertical mixing due to bioturbation which partially blurs and smooths the climatic signal,
(iii) variations in sedimentation rates and/or strong modifications of the internal parameters of the climate system, leading to a non stationary climatic response. These variations are not only broadening the spectral peaks but can also introduce spurious peaks.

The memory part of the spectrum will be discussed briefly, insisting on the need for the identification of a stochastic model in order to evaluate the characteristic length of that memory.

The strong non linearity of the climate system implies that not only orbital frequencies (10^{-5} to 10^{-4} c.p.y.) are important, but also higher frequencies in the range from 10^{-4} to 10^{-2} c.p.y. It is therefore necessary to improve the resolution of the climatic signal and of the geological time scale, which requests a careful study of the bioturbation and of the sedimentation processes to be performed.

Bioturbation will be approached through theoretical and experimental mixing functions. A new deconvolution method by cubic splines has been calibrated and tested by mixing-demixing simulations on a high resolution core taken from the Indian ocean (3). The core V28-238 (4) has been deconvolved using a mixing function acting on the upper layer of the deep sea sediments.

The influence of a variable sedimentation rate is shown by

the analysis of the transformation of the original power spectrum due to compression or dilatation of the record, a spectral method being suggested in order to evaluate the spectral uncertainty coming from the variation in the sedimentation rate.

THE "RED NOISE" BACKGROUND SPECTRUM

The red noise shape of the power spectrum of a time series is related to "persistence" and reflects the memory of the system. In such a time series, each value is influenced by the preceeding ones, and the amplitude of the spectrum will tend to decrease from the longer to the shorter periodicities.

All deep sea climatic records exhibit a typical red noise spectrum indicating that these paleoclimatic data can be partially described statistically by low order autoregressive processes (5,6,7,8). Such a "persistence" effect can be associated with the long range memory of the climate system including the characteristic response-times of the deep ocean ($\sim$1 kyr) and of the ice sheets ($\sim$6-10 kyr). To evaluate quantitatively the length of this memory, it is necessary to identify stochastic models among the auto-regressive ones (AR) or among the wider class of autoregressive-moving average models (ARMA) described for example in Box and Jenkins (9). The time series $y(n)$ is said to be an ARMA process of order (p,q) if it is generated according to a linear causal relationship

$$y(n) + \sum_{k=1}^{p} a_k\, y(n-k) = \sum_{k=0}^{q} b_k\, w(n-k)$$

where the excitation sequence $w(n)$ is a zero mean white noise time series whose individual elements have variance one, p and q being the orders of the autoregressive and moving-average contributions. ARMA models have been identified on six oxygen isotope records (10) taken from the PACDATA bank (11). The appropriate orders of the models, p and q, have been selected according to a test of independence of the residuals. However the models order differs from core to core and does not correspond to the same memory (Table 1). The power spectra of these deep sea records drawn in a logarithmic scale exhibit also strong differences, the log power-log frequency slopes ranging from -1 to -3. These results are interpreted as a consequence of the differences either in the local response of the climate system or in the time scale inaccuracies coming from the variations in the sedimentation rate.

Table 1 Orders of the adjusted ARMA (p,q) stochastic models together with the statistical significance of the autocorrelation of the residues. Autocor test (5%) indicates whether or not the residuals are uncorrelated at the 5% significance level. N is the number of data, T is the sampling interval, p and q, the orders of the AR and MA contributions to the global ARMA process.

CORE	N	T	p	q	AUTOCOR TEST 5%
V28 23	489	2 kyr	7	3	YES
RC11 120	416	1 kyr	5	5	NO
RC14 37	161	3 kyr	4	1	YES
V19 28	476	1 kyr	12	4	NO
V28 239	663	3 kyr	3	3	YES
V19 240	424	1 kyr	4	5	YES

VERTICAL MIXING OF DEEP-SEA SEDIMENTS

Vertical mixing in deep-sea sediments, due to bioturbation, is a significant difficulty for the restoration of paleoclimatic signals. Benthic infauna burrow into the uppermost 5-30 cm of sediment (12,13). As a consequence this layer may record information spanning everywhere from 3 kyr to 15 kyr depending on the sedimentation rate. This mixing has two types of embarrassing consequences. First, the vertical exchange of sediment partially blurrs and smooths the climatic signal. The global variance and therefore the height of all the spectral peaks in a power spectrum diagram including the possible Milankovitch ones, are decreased (14). Furthermore, the amplitude of the shortest (highest frequency) climatic oscillations are reduced or suppressed by such a low pass filter which reinforces the typical red noise shape of the power spectrum. On the other hand, the bioturbation contributes to increase the stratigraphic uncertainties, offsets the timing of isotopic events and limits the study of the mechanism of glaciation (15).

Assuming that the deconvolution problem (i.e. the mathematical reconstruction of the unmixed record knowing the mixing function and the mixed record) is solved, the problem of the choice of an appropriate mixing function still remains. The only way to identify a mixing function experimentally is to detect some tracers with known initial distribution, for example the microtektites as shown by Glass (12,15) and by Ruddiman and Glover (13). Unfortunately such tracers are not worldwide (17) and this experimental mixing function is probably applicable only on parts of the analyzed deep-sea core. This is one of the reasons for building one-dimensional mixing models which allows the computation of a theoretical mixing function, by taking a Dirac initial concentration profile as input for this model. A non-linear version of the time-dependent advection-diffusion mixing model of Guinasso and Schink (18) has been integrated numerically by a modified Crowley method (19) which allows a wider class of experiments to be considered, including those with time-varying sedimentation rates (20). The mathematical formulation of the model is given by

$$\frac{\partial c(x,t)}{\partial t} = \frac{\partial}{\partial x}\left[k(x)\frac{\partial c(x,t)}{\partial x}\right] - v(t)\frac{\partial c(x,t)}{\partial x} \qquad [1]$$

where $c(x,t)$ is the concentration [cm^{-3}]
t the time [kyr]
$c(x)$ the diffusion coefficient [cm^{-2} kyr^{-1}]
$v(t)$ the sedimentation rate [cm kyr^{-1}]
x the depth increasing from the top to the bottom [cm]

This equation is subject to the spatial boundary conditions :

$$-k(0)\frac{\partial c(0,t)}{\partial x} + v(t)\,c(0,t) = 0 \qquad \text{for } x=0$$

$$-k(1)\frac{\partial c(1,t)}{\partial x} = 0 \qquad \text{for } x=1$$

and to the temporal boundary condition :

$$c(x,0) = f(x) \qquad \text{for } t=0$$

where $f(x)$ is the initial concentration in the interval $x=[0,1]$. If $f(x)$ is a δ-impulse function, the mixing function is nothing else than the modified initial concentration $c(x,t)$ after its migration through the mixing layer. The theoretical mixing function used in this paper has been found by taking a slow variation of the sedimentation rate, around a value of 2 cm kyr^{-1}, and a constant diffusion coefficient K equal to 3 cm^2 kyr^{-1}. It is illustrated in the upper part of Figure 3.

Having a representation of this mixing function, we will now try to reproduce the original signal from the recorded one. The mixed profile $O(x)$ may be represented by a convolution integral of the unmixed signal $i(x)$ with a mixing function $m(x)$ so that :

$$O(x) = \int_0^{\infty} i(s)\, m(x-s)\,ds \qquad [2]$$

Theoretically, the true value $i(x)$ can then be found by deconvolution providing the mixing function $m(x)$ is known.

Having such a theoretical or experimental mixing function, the deconvolution can be performed in two ways. The first one is to take the ratio of the Fourier transforms of the mixed record and the mixing function. Defining the one-sided Fourier Transform Y(f) of a function of the real variable, y(x), by

$$Y(f) = \int_0^\infty y(t)\, e^{-i2\pi fx} dx \qquad \text{noted } y(x) \rightharpoonup Y(f) \qquad [3]$$

and its Inverse Fourier Transform by

$$y(x) = \int_0^\infty Y(f)\, e^{i2\pi fx}\, df \quad \text{noted } y(x) \leftharpoondown Y(f) \;, \qquad [4]$$

the problem of deconvolution is theoretically simplified by the use of the convolution theorem. It demonstrates that a convolution integral is transformed into a simple product by the application of the Fourier Transform

$$o(x) = \int_0^\infty i(s)\, m(x-s) ds \rightleftharpoons O(f) = I(f).M(f) \qquad [5]$$

Unfortunately, this method is very sensitive to the noise level of the original data and fails in any case when the mixing function becomes close to zero (21).

The other method to reconstruct the unmixed record is to apply a deconvolution in the time domain. The cubic spline deconvolution applied in this case is less sensitive to the noise level, and is able to give realistic results for the study of the bioturbation problem (22). The cubic spline deconvolution decomposes both the output o(x) and the mixing function m(x) in cubic splines :

$$o(x) = \sum_{k=1}^{N-1} u_k(x) \quad \text{where } u_k(x) = u_{1k}x^3+u_{2k}x^2+u_{3k}x+u_{4k} \qquad [6]$$

and determines, in one step, the coefficients w_{1k}, w_{2k}, w_{3k} and w_{4k} corresponding to the cubic splines decomposition of the input i(x)

$$i(x) = \sum_{k=1}^{N-1} w_k(x) \quad \text{where } w_k(x) = w_{1k}x^3+w_{2k}x^2+w_{3k}x+w_{4k} \qquad [7]$$

The results presented illustrate the power of this method which has been applied to the mixing and demixing of the core MD77-191 (unpublished data from J.C. Duplessy), this core being supposed initially non perturbed by bioturbation since its sedimentation rate exceeds 20 cm kyr^{-1}. Figures 1, 2 and 3 show the mixing and demixing of this record using respectively two hypothetical triangular mixing functions of different mixing

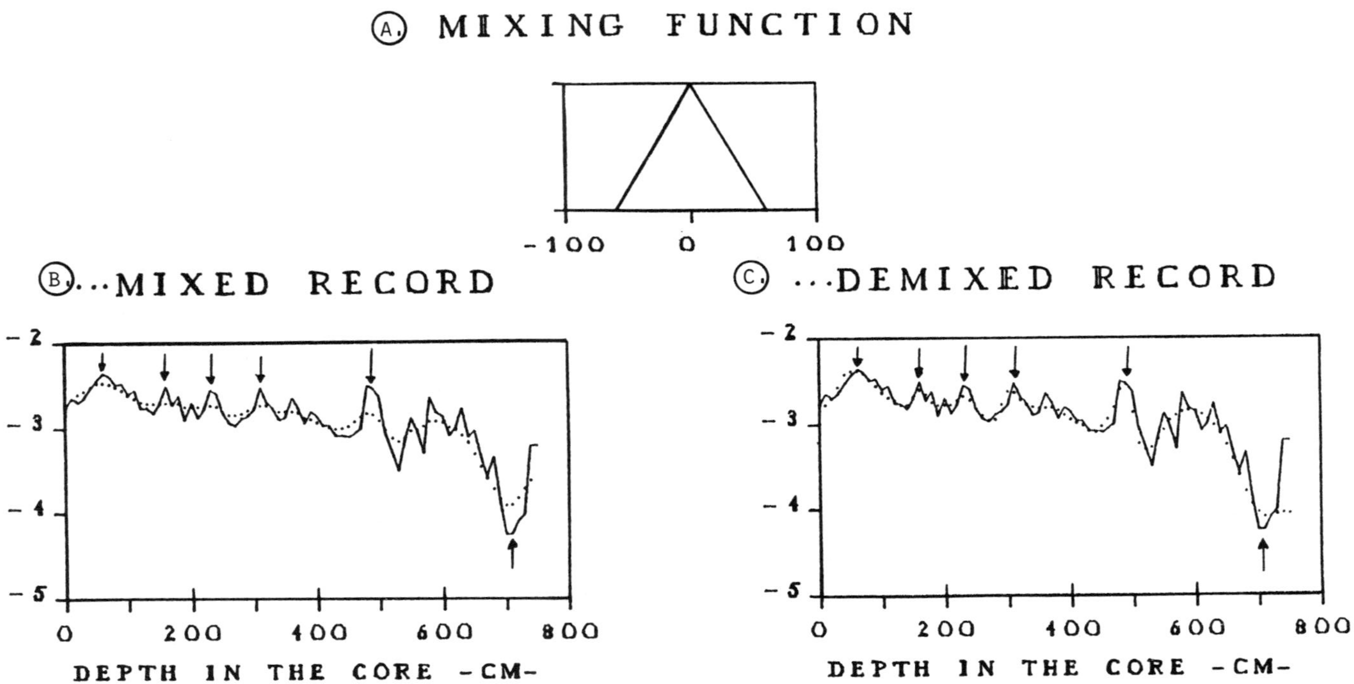

Figure 1 Mixing-Demixing simulation of the oxygen isotopic record of the core MD77191 with a triangular symmetric mixing function (Fig. 1a). The dotted line (...) represents the result of mixing (Fig. 1b) and demixing (Fig. 1c) superimposed to the true original record. The arrows indicate the strong suppressions and restorations of the variability.

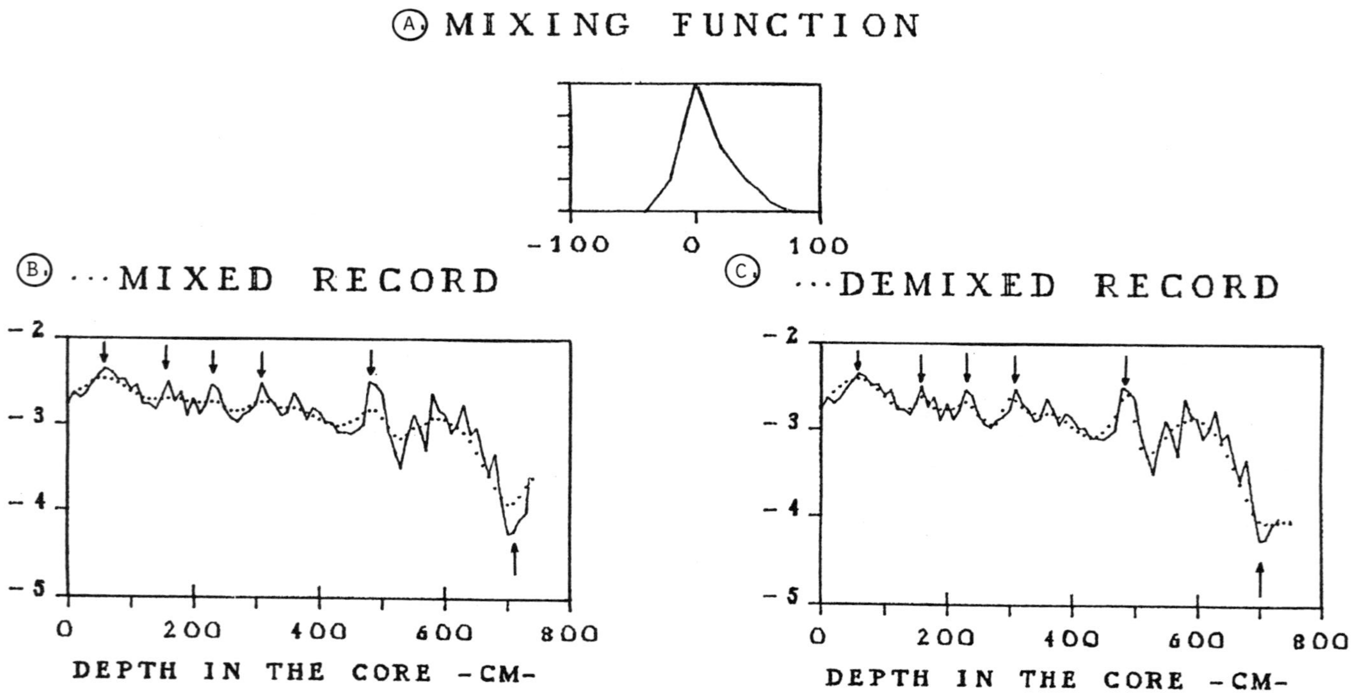

Figure 2 Mixing-Demixing simulation of the core MD77191 with the experimental asymmetric mixing function shown in Figure 2a.

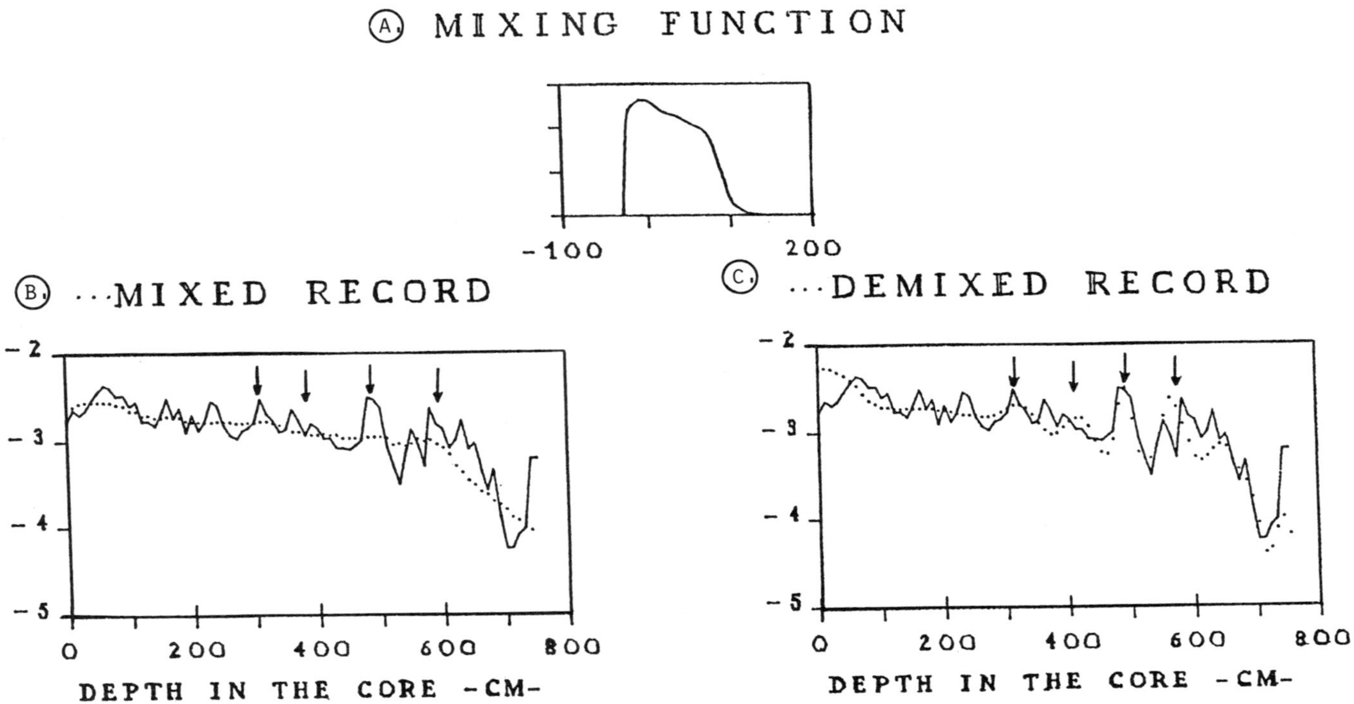

Figure 3 Mixing-Demixing simulation of the core MD77191 with the theoretical mixing function found by the advection-diffusion mixing model (Fig. 3a).

lengths, and the theoretical mixing function found from the mixing model described above. The mixing functions used act up to a depth of 100 cms. The mean sedimentation rate being 20 cm/kyr, it was assumed that the mixing depth would be around 5-10 cm in a low sedimentation rate (1 to 2 cm/kyr) deep sea core. The two first mixing functions have been chosen triangular by considering the shape of the experimental mixing functions derived from microtektites, the third one, a theoretical mixing function, being deduced from the mixing model. The triangular symmetric and asymmetric mixing functions have similar mixing and demixing properties. However, the theoretical mixing function seems able to restore more variability at depths between 400 and 800 centimetres.

Figure 4 is intended to prove that the method can be applied to longer records. The deep-sea core V28-238 (4) has indeed been successfully demixed by using a triangular mixing function acting on a mixing layer of 20 cm.

A comparison between the power spectra corresponding to the mixed and unmixed records of the first 170 kyr of the core V28-238 shows the gain in power corresponding to the high frequency variability restored by the method (Fig. 5).

VARIATIONS IN SEDIMENTATION RATES

Table 2 shows the variations of the sedimenation rate of a set of 13 deep sea cores (from J.C. Duplessy and N. Shackleton). These variations have been simply deduced by assuming a constant sedimentation rate between the last glacial maximum (18 kyr BP), the three isotopic substages 5a, 5c, 5e (82 kyr BP, 106 kyr BP, 125 kyr BP) and the Bruhnes-Matuyama magnetic bondary (730 kyr BP). It is obvious, from this table, that the variation in the sedimentation rate is a reality not only from core to core but also in a core.

Indeed, the main sources for sea sediment, in addition to the ocean itself, are rivers, glaciers, wind and volcanous. Furthermore, the sedimentation rates are also related to deep sea circulation, the highest sedimentation rates suggesting the existence of a stagnation zone where the fine-grained sediment is deposited (23). Although the relationship between bottom water currents and climate is not clear, it is a matter of fact that the sedimentation rate has a local character in space and time and is strongly influenced by the climate itself. One of the suggestions for trying to solve this problem of a variable sedimentation rate is therefore to adjust the parameters of a sedimentation rate model on a restricted-well-dated part of the deep-sea record. This calibrated model can then be applied to

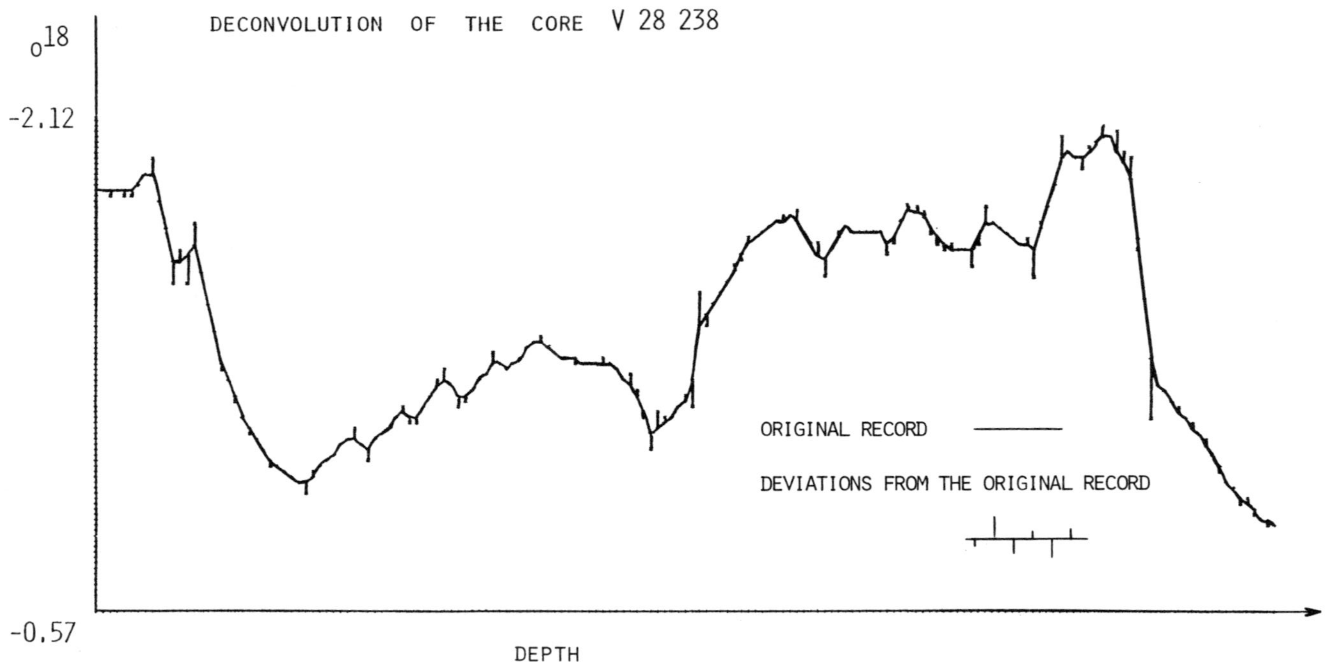

Figure 4 Cubic splines deconvolution (Demixing) of the first 170 kyr of the core V28-238. The deviations from the original record due to demixing are indicated by superimposed vertical bars.

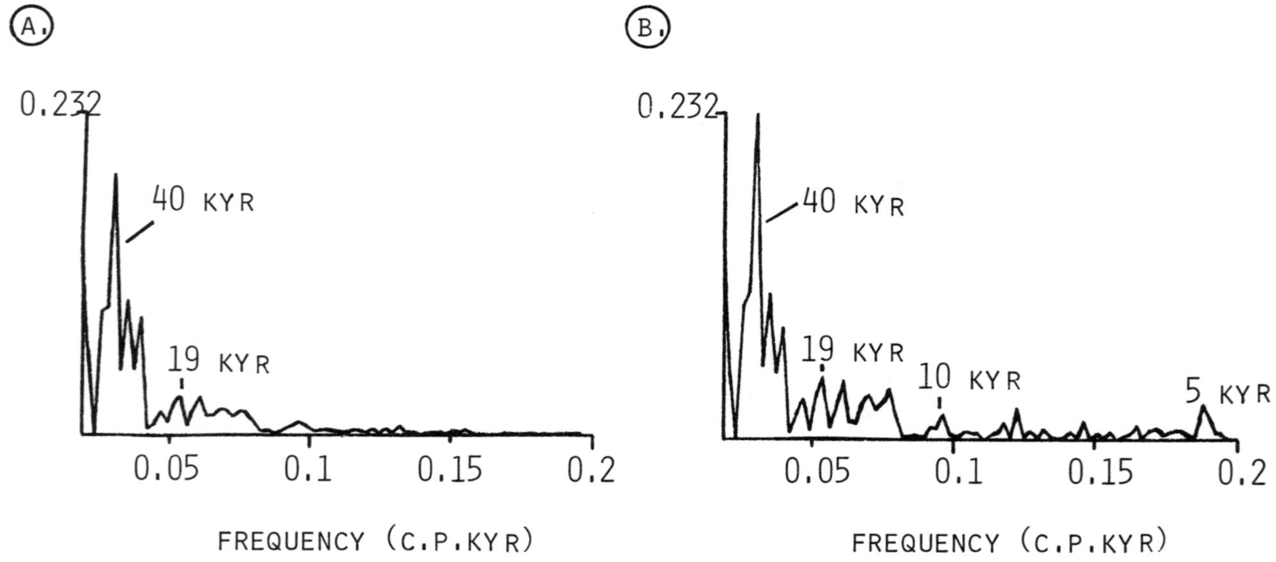

Figure 5 Power spectrum of the original record supposed mixed (Fig. 5a) compared to the one of the demixed record (Fig. 5b).

Table 2 Evaluation of the mean sedimentation rates characterizing a set of 14 deep sea cores taken from PACDATA bank.

Core	File	Sedimentation Rates (dates in kyr BP) 0-18	18-22	82-105	105-125	125-730
MD73004	D01	1.94	1.48	1.30	1.25	------
MD73025	D02	17.33	----	----	9.9	------
MD76135	D03	12.22	7.97	3.48	----	------
MD76131	D04	10.55	----	----	----	------
RC12344	D05	14.44	----	----	-----	------
MD77169	D06	7.22	9.06	4.34	4.0	------
V28238	S01	2.33	1.61	1.74	1.25	1.46
RC11120	S05	3.89	3.44	2.61	4.0	------
RC1437	S06	2.5	----	----	1.17	------
V1928	S08	10.56	4.22	1.73	3.0	------
V19929	S09	6.67	8.28	3.04	5.5	------
V28239	S11	1.61	----	1.32	1.0	1.013
V1940	S18	3.11	2.56	1.74	2.0	------

another part of the record where accurate datum levels are not available. This work is in progress but requires that, at least, one part of the record be accurately dated to get reliable results. Even if this self-regulation approach is based on a physical model of sedimentation, the necessary condition of applicability remains some kind of stationarity in the process of sedimentation, as it is usually assumed with traditional timing method.

In order to understand the effect on the spectrum resulting either from the artefact of the non detected variations in the sedimentation rate, or from the non stationarity of the climatic response, a spectral method based on Fast Fourier Transform has been suggested in order to allow a large number of successive compression dilatation of the original record to be taken into account. This compression/dilatation effect is in fact considered as being the result on the signal, of the physical processes described above and leading to a non stationarity in the spectral characteristics. The method has been derived from an obvious property of the Fourier Transform, the time scaling property which illustrates the fact that if the record y is stretched its Fourier Transform, Y will be compressed and vice versa :

$$y(at) \rightleftarrows Y\left(\frac{f}{a}\right) \quad , \qquad [8]$$

a being the scaling factor.

In order to illustrate the method, let's take a n data segment of a record; this part having to be stretched. Its Discrete Fourier Transform is given by

$$Y(f_j) = \sum_{k=0}^{n-1} y(t_k)\, e^{-i2\pi f_j t_k} \qquad [9]$$

where $f_j = \frac{j}{n\Delta t}$

$t_k = k\ t$

and $j,k = 0,n-1$

If that part of the record is stretched by a factor a, the resulting number of data for equivalent sampling Δt, will be m, the integer part of the ratio n/a. The problem is then reduced to a Fourier interpolation. Indeed, the Discrete Fourier Transform of n points is symmetrical with regard to the $\frac{n}{2}$ Transformed value, $Y(f_{n/2})$, corresponding to the Nyquist frequency. If m-n zero values are inserted in the middle part of the Fourier Transformed data, the number of discrete frequencies is increased without adding any high frequency variability. The

Inverse Fourier Transform of this m values gives a set of m values with a time interval $\Delta t'$ less than Δt in the case of interpolation. In order to introduce a stretching effect rather than an interpolation, it is sufficient to keep the sampling interval the same :

$$y(t_k) = \frac{1}{n} \sum_{j=0}^{m-1} Y(f_j') \; e^{+i2\pi f_j' t_k} \qquad [10]$$

where $f_j' = \frac{j}{\Delta t}$,

$t_k = k\Delta t$, and $j,k = 0, \ldots, m-1$.

If the sampling interval Δt is chosen sufficiently small to avoid non zero values of the Fourier Transformed data around the Nyquist frequency $f_{n/2}$, a similar approach can be used to simulate a compression of that segment by suppressing n-m zero values in the middle part of the Fourier Transformed data, i.e. around the Nyquist frequency. Defining the number of segments over which the sedimentation rate may have varied and the successive stretching and/or compression factors, the whole modified record and its associated power spectrum are produced by the use of the Fast Fourier Transform algorithm (24). This method has been applied to the core V28-238 (4) leading to the conclusion that the dilatation-compression process broaden the width and decrease the amplitude of the spectral peaks (Fig. 6).

CONCLUSIONS

The nature of deep sea paleoclimatic records implies that the paleoclimatic explanation of their spectral structure can only be found after having replaced these records in their deep sea context which depends on the instantaneous and local climatic characteristics. Obviously, the internal parameters of the climatic system (among which the ice and vegetation cover, the atmospheric and oceanic circulations and the precipitation amount) have changed at the paleoclimatic time scale, inducing changes in the depositional and postdepositional processes.

The resulting deep sea paleoclimatic record although not devoid of information, presents a strong red noise background with a few number of broad significant spectral peaks. The data analysis methods described in this paper, allow the study of the spectral characteristics of these records without making working assumptions too restrictive. In particular, the presence of astronomical spectral components, although weakened

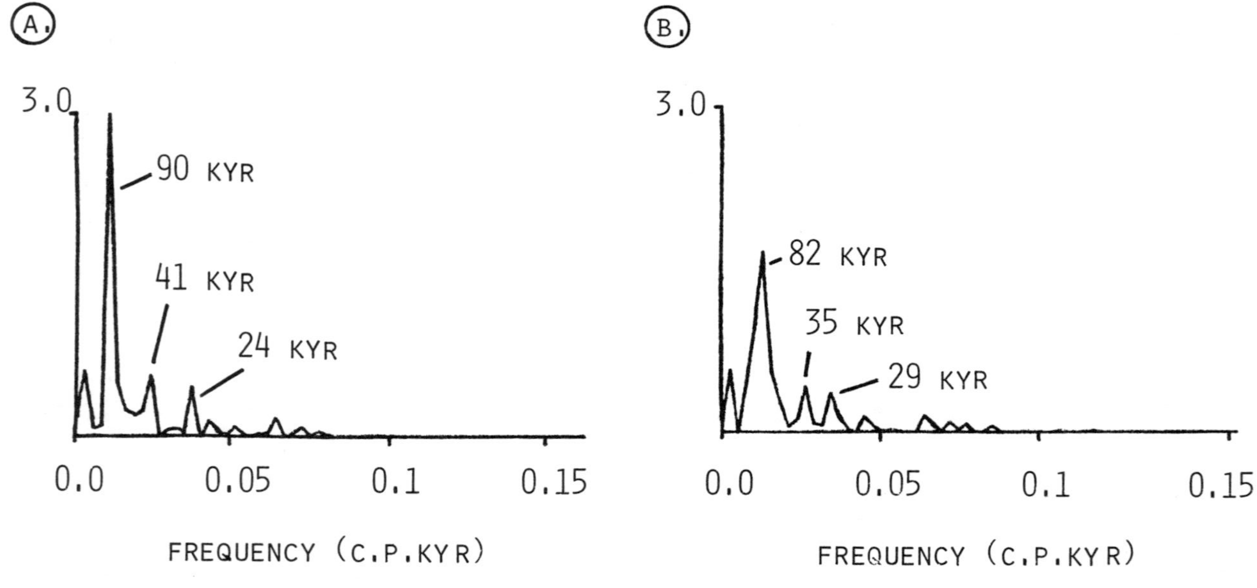

Figure 6 Power spectrum of the first 400 kyr of the core V28-238 (Fig. 6a) and of the same record compressed and dilated with a 10% uncertainty at the isotopic transitions.

and distorded by this disturbed environment, are indicative of a much higher paleoclimatic variability at these frequencies.

The problem of the variation in the sedimentation rates is the most critical and needs either refined experimental age control, or the elaboration of a tuning method based on an a priori time or frequency adjustment of the geological records. Such a tuning procedure relying on some kind of similarity in space and time, the weaker the tuning assumptions will be, the larger are the chances to avoid circularity.

REFERENCES

1. Hasselman, K. : 1976, Tellus 28, pp. 473-484.
2. Le Treut, H., and Ghil, M. : 1983, J. Geophys. Res. 88, n°C9, pp. 5167-5190.
3. Duplessy, J.Cl. : 1982, Nature 295, pp. 494-498.
4. Shackleton, N.J., and Opdyke, N.D. : 1973, J. Quat. Res. 3, pp. 39-55.
5. Petersen, E.L., and Larsen, S.E. : 1978, Tellus 30, pp. 193-200.
6. Kominz, M.A., Heath, G.R., Ku, T.L., and Pisias, N.G. : 1979, Earth Planet. Sci. Lett. 53, pp. 279-295.
7. Rooth, C.G.H., Emiliani, C., and Poor, H.W. : 1978, Earth Planet. Sci. Lett. 41, pp. 387-394.
8. Viecelli, J.A. : 1982, J. Geophys. Res. 87, n°C4, pp. 3099-3104.
9. Box, G.E.P., and Jenkins, G.M. : 1976, Time Series Analysis Forecasting and Control, rev.ed., Holden Day, San Francisco, Calif.
10. Shackleton, N.J. : 1977, Phil. Trans. R. Soc. London B280, pp. 169-182.
11. Berger, A., and Pestiaux, P. : 1982, An introduction to the IAG PACDATA Bank. Contribution n°28, Institute of Astronomy and Geophysics, Catholic University of Louvain-la-Neuve, Belgium.
12. Glass, B.P. : 1967, Nature 214, pp. 372-376.
13. Ruddiman, W.F., and Glover, L.K. : 1972, Geol. Soc. Amer. Bull. 83, pp. 2817-2836.
14. Goreau, T.J. : 1980, Nature 287, pp. 620-622.
15. Hutson, W.H. : 1980, Geology 8, pp. 127-130.
16. Glass, B.P., Baker, R.N., Störzer, D., and Wagner, G.A. : 1973, Earth and Planet Sci. Lett. 19, pp. 184-190.
17. Shaw, H.F., and Wasserburg, G.J. : 1982, Earth and Planet Sci. Lett. 60, pp. 155-177.
18. Guinasso, N.L., and Schink, N.D. : 1975, J. Geophys. Res. 80, pp. 3032-3043.
19. Crowley, W.P. : 1968, Mon. Wea. Rev. 99, pp. 1-11.

20. Pestiaux, P., and Gaspar, Ph. : 1984, Numerical simulations of abyssal sediments mixing. (in preparation)
21. Ablowitz, M.J., and Segur, H. : 1981, Solitons and the Inverse Scattering Transform SIAM Philadelphia.
22. Pestiaux, P. : 1982, A Spline based method for deep sea records deconvolution. Progress Report 1982/1, Institute of Astronomy and Geophysics, Catholic University of Louvain-la-Neuve, Belgium.
23. Ledbetter, M.T. : 1979, Marine Geology 33, pp. 71-89.
24. Cooley, J.W., and Tukey, J.W. : 1965, Math. Computation 19, pp. 297-301.